BUSINESS MATHEMA

BUSINESS MATHEMATICS AND STATISTICS

BY

S. LETCHFORD BSc(Econ) FIMA

CASSELL · LONDON
in association with Metropolitan College

CASSELL LTD.
35 Red Lion Square
London WC1R 4SG
Sydney, Toronto
An affiliate of Macmillan Publishing Co. Inc., New York

© 1974, 1977 CASSELL LTD.

Second edition 1977
Reprinted 1979, 1980, 1981 (with minor corrections)

ISBN 0 304 29760 7

Printed in Hong Kong
by Colorcraft Ltd

PREFACE TO THE SECOND EDITION

The subjects with which this book is concerned, Statistics and Business Mathematics, are closely related in two ways. Both are essential tools of management, whilst Statistics provides the analysis of uncertainty which plays a vital role in the decision-theory approach to production planning. "Business Mathematics" is here interpreted in the widest sense to include what is generally known as Management Mathematics, which may be described as Operational Research made easy.

The book is designed as a comprehensive introductory course for students whose professional studies include either Statistics or Management Mathematics. Since both these subjects figure very prominently in most contemporary professional examinations leading to qualifications in accountancy and management, an integrated approach of this kind should have a wide appeal.

Many of the calculations which form part of the Exercises are ideally suited for working with a pocket electronic calculator. However, there is considerable divergence in the practice of examining boards as to the extent to which such aids are permitted in an examination. The student is therefore advised not to rely exclusively on a calculator, but to be prepared to use other aids, such as logarithm tables and the slide rule, as well.

Every care has been taken to avoid difficult mathematical arguments, and the reader will find that a knowledge of mathematics to about GCE O-level standard is quite sufficient for an understanding of most of the text. Additional mathematical topics which may not previously have been encountered in O-level work, and which are relevant to the subject matter of this book, are explained in detail.

The growing importance of scientific techniques in management, which was noted in the preface to the first edition, has been confirmed by events, and it may be predicted that an even greater familiarity with statistical and quantitative techniques than has hitherto been the case will be expected in industry in the future. This tendency is reflected in the present edition by the inclusion of two new chapters on Time Discounting and Matrices, the former of which is of especial importance in an inflationary environment.

Acknowledgements are due to the School Examination Department of the University of London for kind permission to use Tables

1–3 of the Statistical Tables, which appear in the booklet *Mathematical Formulae including Statistical Formulae and Tables*. The table of Random Sampling Numbers (Table 5) is reproduced with permission of the Department of Statistics and Computer Science, University College London, from Tracts for Computers No. 24.

June 1976   S. LETCHFORD.

CONTENTS

CHAPTER 1
Statistical Data and its Uses

1. The Science of Statistics

Though the collection of statistical data for various practical purposes, such as the assessment of military potential and taxation, dates back to antiquity, the Science of Statistics is of recent growth. The seventeenth century in Europe saw a rapid development of interest in Natural Science and Mathematics which, already in the Renaissance, had achieved notable successes. It was inevitable that Man's increasing knowledge of nature should stimulate him to acquire an equally exact knowledge of himself and of human society. We therefore find that in England in the seventeenth century, economists and others recognised the need for more accurate information about the state of society. The value of such information is obvious, for it makes possible the formulation of more effective policies by government.

Adequate methods of collecting and classifying data are an important step in the development of Statistics, but they do not constitute the whole story. The data is needed for making predictions and investigating the relationship between cause and effect. One of the earliest attempts to use statistical data as a guide to what might happen in the future was that of the astronomer Edmund Halley who compiled life tables for the purpose of fixing insurance premiums. These tables were based on records of the number of persons alive at different ages in the Polish city of Breslau, and from them estimates were made of the likelihood that a person of a given age would be alive in a certain number of years time. This likelihood, or probability, is expressed as the ratio of the number of persons surviving to the later date to the number alive at the earlier and it is assumed, for the purposes of the life table, that the ratio will be true for the whole population as well as for the part from which it was derived. The simple assumption that this is the case is a crude form of statistical inference, and while it was accepted in the seventeenth century because no means of improving it existed, it would not be accepted today because it includes no statement of the reliability of the estimate.

Concurrently with the growing interest in the more scientific study of society, mathematicians were founding the new science of Probability. Their interest in this subject arose, at first, out of their preoccupation with games of chance, particularly those in which

1

gambling was involved. As an example of such a game, consider two players tossing a coin in turn, the winner being the player who first obtains a specified number of "heads". If both players have placed equal stakes on the outcome of the game, and the winner takes all, how are the stakes to be divided between the two players if the game is stopped before the winning number of heads is reached? This may be rather a frivolous problem, of no importance to anyone except the gamblers, but it led to the development of a very important branch of mathematics which engaged the attention of the leading mathematicians of the seventeenth and eighteenth centuries. It came to be seen that this new science of the mathematics of chance or probability had much wider and more serious applications than to games of chance. It enables, for example, estimates to be made of the reliability of information when used in a wider context than that from which it was obtained and has therefore become the foundation of Statistics and statistical inference. It also has important applications in the Natural Sciences which are not unconnected with its use in Statistics, though this, of course, lies beyond the scope of our present study.

2. Decision-making

In most cases in which statistical data is employed, the conclusions drawn from it go beyond the data. It is true that the data can be complete in varying degrees and, the greater its comprehensiveness, the more reliable any predictions or conclusions are which are based on it. But it is seldom true that the data relating to any question is wholly complete. For example, it is difficult to imagine data more complete than that derived from a Census of Population, because it is obtained about everyone alive at the time of the Census. But if an estimate is obtained from it of the proportion of males and females in the population, we shall hope that this estimate provides information, not only about the population from which it was obtained, but about future populations as well, i.e., populations about which we have, as yet, no data. It is no exaggeration to say that almost no useful conclusions derived from statistical data are completely reliable; but the application of statistical techniques enables one to set limits to this reliability which are expressed in terms of the likelihood of their being exceeded. This fact provides the clue to the importance of Statistics in assisting in reaching business decisions.

Decision-making implies the existence of a choice between two or more lines of action. In business, the policy adopted will be that which has the best showing on a cost–benefit basis. One way of reaching a decision is to make an informal guess, on the basis of past experience, about the cost–benefit aspects of a policy which has yet to be tried. But a more effective decision can frequently be reached by the use of statistical techniques. Suppose, for example, that a firm has available two different processes, using different machinery, for producing electric light bulbs. One of these is the existing process, and the producer wishes to obtain information which will enable him to decide whether it is worth while changing to the alternative method. The criterion for choosing between the two processes is, let us say, the length of life of an electric bulb. In order to obtain information on this matter, he can install test equipment for the alternative process and select a number of bulbs produced by it for testing. The tests will provide information about the length of time an average bulb may be expected to burn, which can be compared with the performance of an average bulb produced by the existing method. But the data about both processes is necessarily incomplete and there may be a good deal of chance fluctuation of performance about that of the average bulb and, indeed, that average itself, which is only an estimate from incomplete data, may not be representative of the true average performance. The statistician has methods of deciding all these questions and is able to determine whether there is a real difference in performance between the two types of bulb and, if so, what this difference is. He does this entirely on the basis of limited data, so that his conclusions are not certain, but on the other hand, he can ensure that they are as nearly certain as possible. Suppose, then, that the statistician guarantees a minimum difference between the performance of the two types of bulb and that the alternative method of production shows a better performance in terms of length of life, than the existing one. The producer must then decide whether it is worthwhile to change to the new method, taking account of the cost of changing to the new equipment, scrapping the old before it has ceased to be useful, and the higher price he can charge for the product because of its greater efficiency. It will be seen, therefore, that the statistician's contribution to decision-making is very often limited to the provision of only part of the data needed before a decision can be reached. There may, indeed, be other areas in which his activities are valuable in a particular context, for example, he may carry out market research work on the marketability of the new product. A final decision cannot, however, be reached merely on the knowledge that one thing is better, from some point of view, than another. There must, in addition, be an assessment of the monetary advantages which this superiority produces.

It would be wrong to suggest that there is any ultimate limit to the statistician's contribution to business decision-making. The decision to expand or contract an enterprise depends on its predicted rate of return which is based, to some extent, on past performance. An important factor affecting its estimate is the method of depreciation adopted. Different methods lead to different estimates of the rate of return, depending on a number of external factors, for example inflation, over which a firm has no control. In these circumstances, it is important to decide which method of depreciation will yield the most representative estimate, since vital decisions depend on its reliability. Statistical techniques can be usefully employed in reaching a conclusion on this question since it is possible to construct a statistical model which takes account of all the relevant variables, such as inflation which, with the aid of historical data, can be programmed for a computer. This program can be arranged to take account of uncertainty with regard to the length of life of assets, the rate of inflation, and so on, and produces, on the computer, the values of various statistical parameters which enable a correct choice to be made of the best method of depreciation. A good deal of interesting work has been done on this problem, though no final solution has yet been reached.

The most important management decisions relate usually to input and output, but there are many areas within a firm where decisions are made on matters relating only indirectly to the productive capacity of the firm. The question, for example, of improving facilities available to employees is an important one for Personnel Management. Study of accident rate and safety factors in the operation of machinery is another. Statistical techniques are often an indispensable means of obtaining information which enables such problems to be solved.

3. The Origins of Statistical Data

Faced with any problem for the determination of which statistical data is necessary, a firm relies on two possible sources. In the first place, since it is only one unit in a larger economic whole, there are numerous external factors on which its operation depends. A producer needs to know a great deal about the general condition of the economy, the level of wage rates and employment, general price trends, the price trends and level of production of the particular goods in which he is interested, and so on. Information about all these matters is made available by government departments and coordinated by the Central Statistical Office. It is important to notice that though such information is collected on a vast scale and with the expenditure of large sums of money, it is still limited in completeness, as already mentioned. This data has, nevertheless, a high degree of reliability since it is not usually presented in a crude form but is duly processed and corrected so as to be properly representative. It must be remembered that, even in the field of government statistics, a great deal of the information is based on estimates. As well as government sources of information, much data which is useful to industry is provided by private organisations. The *Financial Times*, for example, publishes indispensable data on share prices and the world's commodity markets. University departments carry out, and publish data from, social surveys which can be of considerable incidental value to the producer. In addition, data is published by UN, UNESCO and other international organisations on economic conditions overseas which is of great value to those interested in overseas investment and trade.

But, in addition, a firm has many problems to solve which are peculiar to itself and, to do this, it must collect its own data. Whilst, for example, government statistics may provide information about the trend of sales and prices in the general product-area which interests a producer, he will still need to know something of the way in which the market will react to his particular products which may be distinguished from similar products by certain specific differences such as trade names, type of packing, and so on. He will therefore need information about market possibilities for his own product, which he can obtain through his own market research activities or, more usually in the case of smaller firms, research carried out by market research agencies. In organising the production process, the individual producer is bound to rely almost entirely on statistical information collected within the firm. If the organisation is complex, the firm will usually have its own statistical department which will often be associated with an Operational Research Unit. The information obtained by these activities will form the basis of estimates used for policy-decisions. As already emphasised, such estimates will not be certainly accurate, but the degree of confidence which can be placed in them can be accurately determined by the appropriate statistical methods.

It will be seen that statistical data can be of two kinds: that which is used for the purpose for which it was collected, called *primary data*; and that which is used for some other purpose than that for which it was collected, called *secondary data*. In the Census of Population, for example, data is collected on Housing Conditions and, when used to formulate government policies on housing is primary data, since it is collected precisely for that purpose. It also, however, may provide useful information to the private sector of the building industry and, when so used, it is secondary data. This distinction is extremely important because, whereas primary data, provided it is properly collected, can be confidently used for its particular purpose, secondary data can be used only with qualifications. For example, an index of the trend of house prices for the United Kingdom would have to be cautiously interpreted by a builder living in Northumberland. In using secondary statistics, it is very important to be clear about the exact definitions of the categories to which they apply. More will be said about the need for precise definition in the classification of statistical data in the next chapter.

4. Descriptive Statistics and Statistical Inference

In any logical argument, conclusions are drawn from evidence, called the premisses of the argument, and the value of the conclusion depends both on whether the premisses are true and also on whether or not the argument is free from logical fallacies. This is true of all kinds of arguments, including those based on statistical data. It is usual to call the data of a statistical argument *descriptive statistics* and to allow this term to include the presentation of statistics in tabular or graphic forms which can be readily assimilated, particularly by the layman. From such data, it is often possible to draw provisional inferences without using statistical methods at all. Descriptive data is often presented in advertising material and government reports in order that inferences of this kind may be made. The proper presentation of statistical data is thus of great importance, since it suggests hypotheses which can subsequently be tested by statistical means. This presentation often brings out certain facts which need explaining. For example, coal production, in terms of output per man shift, rose between 1913 and 1938, in the United Kingdom and U.S.A. respectively, by 13% and 36%. Without using statistical methods, this is fairly obviously a significant difference, though it can be statistically tested and, in cases where the difference is less, such tests may be essential before any reliable inference can be drawn. Supposing, however, the fact established that there was a striking difference in increase of productivity in coal-mining in the period alluded to, it is next necessary to explain the difference in terms of greater mechanisation, improved organisation, and so on. The factors involved may be numerous and complex, so that however well the data is presented, no conclusion can be drawn without using statistical techniques.

The difference between descriptive statistics and statistical inference may be further illustrated by a hypothetical enquiry into absenteeism in a certain firm. The descriptive statistics here consist of the number of man-days lost through absenteeism in different age-groups. A glance at a table of this data, or a graphical presentation of it, may suggest that the younger age-groups are more prone to absenteeism in this particular firm than the older age-groups. This is an informal inference; but it can be tested statistically and it then becomes a statistical inference. It should be noted that, however "obvious" an inference from descriptive data may be, the statistician cannot be satisfied with its validity (i.e. whether it really follows logically from the evidence) until the data has been submitted to the proper statistical tests.

Consider, now, an example from an entirely different field. A group of students take an examination and it is required to find whether those who did well in the examination as a whole also did well in certain questions, whilst those who did badly in the examination also were rather unsuccessful in answering the same questions. We wish to ascertain, that is to say, the capacity of certain questions to discriminate between good and bad candidates. The descriptive data needed here is obvious: the marks of candidates for the whole examination need to be compared with their marks for individual questions. If the number of candidates or questions is large, it will be quite impossible to draw any reliable conclusion from the descriptive data alone, however well presented. This is so even if the data is summarised by means of single statistics, such as averages, since these can be misleading for reasons explained in later chapters. In this case, therefore, the only satisfactory procedure is to analyse the data by means of statistical techniques.

Numerous books have been written on the fallacies to which statistical arguments are liable (e.g., *How to lie with Statistics*, by Darrell Huff and *Use and Abuse of Statistics*, by W. J. Reichmann). Many of these fallacies arise in the way descriptive statistics are presented, inferences being drawn from them without the proper control of statistical methods. Of course, non-statistical arguments may be and often are fallacious and misleading as, for example, in political discussions. The literature on statistical fallacies suggests, however, that some of them are peculiar to statistics. Whilst this is certainly true, the fact should not be overlooked that certain fallacies which often occur in statistical arguments occur also in other fields: one important example is failure to define terms precisely. Government publications are usually accompanied by copious notes on the exact definitions of the various categories for which statistics are given so that the risk to the careful student of misinterpretation is minimised. There are also a number of separate official publications in which the methods of calculating various statistics (e.g. those relating to National Income) are explained. It may be added that the logic of certain statistical methods is, itself, not altogether un-controversial, though its discussion is the province of philosophers, and, in this book, we shall accept unquestioningly the logical validity of the methods used.

5. Accuracy and Approximation

Errors in published statistics arise from two main sources. First, even though the intention is to collect all the data bearing on a particular topic, the records from which it is obtained may be in-complete. For example, figures for the value of exports are obtained from records of documents lodged with H.M. Customs; but some exporters fail to register documents, which leads to an undervaluation of exports. Second, some statistics are estimated from incomplete or sample data or are obtained in some other way by the use of statisti-cal methods. For example, expenditure on travel between the UK and the Continent is obtained from sample data, whilst in 1939 an estimate was made of the size of the population of England and Wales between two Census dates which was based on the trend of the population during the preceding decades. In each of these cases, it would be misleading to give data to the nearest pound or the nearest person. Instead, the figures are given to the nearest £1,000,000 (often denoted by £ mn. or £ million) or the nearest 10,000 persons.

When calculating an estimate, a figure may be obtained through the pure arithmetical properties of the numbers involved, which appears to be accurate to the last unit or, perhaps, to several decimal places. To publish the figure to this calculated degree of approxima-tion would, however, introduce *spurious accuracy* into the data. It is important to remember that the estimate is only reliable within the limits allowed by the accuracy of the data from which it is ob-tained. The limits of this accuracy are frequently known and, since an estimate may be used to make further calculations, it is worth considering in some detail the rules for determining the degree of approximation of calculated results derived from approximate data. Some assistance in doing this is provided by the comparatively new branch of mathematics called *interval arithmetic* which derives its importance from the fact that many calculations by computer are based on data which is only approximate; and so it is important that the computer also calculates the limits allowed by the data within which the correct result must lie.

Most readers will be familiar with the idea of an equation and the use of equality signs. In dealing with approximations, it is inequality rather than equality which is important. The signs used in mathematics for denoting inequality are $<$ (read from left to right as "less than") and $>$ (read from left to right as "greater than"). For example the statement "2 is less than 4" can be written symbolically as $2 < 4$ or, alternatively, as $4 > 2$ ("4 is greater than 2"). These signs are called signs of *strict* inequality. The meaning of this terminology is made clearer by considering algebraic letters, which can represent any arithmtical numbers, instead of actual numbers. Thus $x < y$ states that x is less than y, and the inequality is satisfied by any pair of numbers x and y for which the inequality is true. It is strict inequality because it is satisfied only when x differs from y, even though the amount of the difference is infinitesimal. These signs for strict inequality may be contrasted with those for non-strict inequality denoted by $\leqslant$ ("is less than or equal to") and $\geqslant$ ("is greater than or equal to"). To illustrate the use of these signs, the non-strict inequality $x \leqslant y$ is satisfied by all pairs of numbers such that x is less than y together with all pairs of equal numbers, with a corresponding definition for $x \geqslant y$. These signs are convenient for expressing, in mathematical terms, the fact that a number A lies somewhere between the limits a and b, where $a < b$. This fact is denoted by the expression

$$a < A < b.$$

The fact can be alternatively expressed by saying that A lies in the *open* interval $[a, b]$, or simply $A = [a, b]$. The interval is "open" because strict inequality signs are used to define it which means that, although A cannot be less than or greater than a and b respectively, it still does not have any precisely defined end-values. If, on the other hand, non-strict inequality signs are used to define the interval as $a \leqslant A \leqslant b$, then A is said to lie in a *closed* interval because, in this case, the end-values of A are exactly defined, i.e. A can actually take the values a or b and still lie within the interval as thus defined. For many purposes in Statistics, it is sufficient to use strict inequality, which is the procedure that will be followed in the remainder of this section.

We are now in a position to introduce those rules of interval arithmetic which are important for our present purpose. Let A and B be two numbers defined on the intervals

$$A = [a, b] \quad \text{and} \quad B = [c, d]$$

where $a < b$ and $c < d$. That is to say, the intervals are

$$(a < A < b) = [a, b] \quad \text{and} \quad (c < B < d) = [c, d].$$

Then the definitions of the four operations of interval arithmetic, corresponding to those of ordinary arithmetic, are (assuming that a, b, c and d are all positive numbers):

(addition) $\quad\quad A + B = [a, b] + [c, d] = [a + c, b + d]$
(multiplication) $\quad A \times B = [a, b] \times [c, d] = [a \times c, b \times d]$
(subtraction) $\quad A - B = [a, b] - [c, d] = [a - d, b - c]$
(division) $\quad\quad A \div B = [a, b] \div [c, d] = [a/d, b/c]$.

(See, however, Ex. 1, No. 12.)

The justification of these definitions should be obvious if it is recalled that the result of any calculation must reflect the least and the greatest possible values within which the true result lies, consistent with the degree of approximation of the data. In addition, this is secured by adding the smallest possible values that A and B can have to give the lower limit of the result and the largest possible values to give the upper limit. When subtracting B from A, the procedure is different because, in order to find the lower limit of the difference, the largest possible value of B must be subtracted from the smallest possible value of A; whilst to find the higher limit of the difference, the smallest possible value of B must be subtracted from the largest possible value of A. There are parallel variations in procedure when finding the product or quotient of two numbers in interval arithmetic. The following examples illustrate some of these points.

EXAMPLE 1

Find the value of (a) $A \times B$ *and* (b) A/B, *where* $A = 120$ (*correct to 2 significant figures*) *and* $B = 12$ (*correct to 2 significant figures*).

The data tell us that the intervals for A and B are

$\quad\quad\quad\quad A = [115, 125] \quad \text{and } B = [11 \cdot 5, 12 \cdot 5]$
Hence $\quad\quad A \times B = [115 \times 11 \cdot 5, 125 \times 12 \cdot 5]$
$\quad\quad\quad\quad\quad = [1322 \cdot 5, 1562 \cdot 5]$
$\quad\quad\quad\quad A/B = [115/12 \cdot 5, 125/11 \cdot 5]$
$\quad\quad\quad\quad\quad = [9 \cdot 2, 10 \cdot 9]$

EXAMPLE 2

Evaluate $A \times (A - B)$ *where*
$\quad\quad A = 20 \pm 10\% \quad \text{and} \quad B = 12 \pm 5\%$.

The interval limits here are expressed as percentages of the central value, i.e., A lies in the interval $20 \pm 10\%$ of 20 or $A = [18, 22]$. Similarly, $B = [11\cdot4, 12\cdot6]$.

Evaluating $A - B$ first, since it is bracketed,

$$A - B = [18 - 12\cdot6, 22 - 11\cdot4]$$
$$= [5\cdot4, 10\cdot6]$$

So
$$A \times (A - B) = [18 \times 5\cdot4, 22 \times 10\cdot6]$$
$$= [97\cdot2, 233\cdot2]$$

For practice, the reader should evaluate the expression

$$A \times A - A \times B$$

where A and B have the same values as in Example 2. He will find that the result is not equal to $A \times (A - B)$. This shows that there are certain rules of ordinary arithmetic which do not apply to interval arithmetic. A few comments on this are given in section 6.

There is, in Statistics, an important distinction to be made between *absolute error* and *relative error*. This can be illustrated by reference to the product $A \times B$ in Example 1. Suppose that it is assumed that A and B actually do have the values 120 and 12 respectively. Then $A \times B = 1440$ and the greatest error which can result from making this assumption is $1562\cdot5 - 1440$ or 120 (approximately). This is the absolute error arising from the assumption that $A = 120$, $B = 12$ since it includes no reference to the actual size of the product. But clearly, an error of a given absolute magnitude will be more or less important according to whether the true result is small or large. Since it is often necessary in Statistics to compare the errors in very different magnitudes, it is desirable to have a measure of error which will reflect the relationship between absolute error and the true value of the magnitude. This is the purpose of a measure of relative error, which is defined as the ratio of absolute error to the true magnitude of the quantity being measured. *Ex hypothesi* we do not know the true magnitude and so, in order to calculate relative error, an estimate of the true magnitude is substituted for it. Relative error is usually expressed as a percentage. Thus in Example 1 (a),

$$\text{Relative error} = \tfrac{120}{1440} \times 100\% = 8\tfrac{1}{3}\%.$$

Since this measure of error is independent of the true magnitude of the quantity being measured, it can be compared with the relative errors of other quantities of different magnitudes.

The process of expressing a number approximately is known as *rounding* and in nearly all cases in which numbers are rounded, rounding errors occur. For example, the sum of ten numbers which have been rounded will almost certainly be different from the rounded sum of the numbers themselves. It is important, therefore, to have rules for rounding numbers which will not lead to an accumulation of rounding errors. If, for example, the rule for rounding numbers to the nearest integer were that in all cases the fractional part of the number should be ignored, then the sum of the rounded numbers would certainly be an underestimate of the true sum. An error of this kind is known as *biased error* or *cumulative error*. On the other hand, if the rule for rounding to the nearest integer is such that, about half the numbers will be too large and the other half too small, then the errors will tend to cancel out so that the sum of the rounded numbers is about what it should be. Errors arising when a rule of this kind is adopted are known as *compensating errors*.

6. Some Mathematical Notes

In expressing a whole number to so many *significant figures*, any zeros to the right of the first non-zero digit are not counted as significant figures. For example, the number 1261 expressed to 2 significant figures is 1300. The rule for correcting the first significant figure (2 in this case) is to add 1 to it if the digit to the right is 5 or more and to leave it unaltered if this digit is less than 5. For example, 1249 expressed to 2 significant figures is 1200. A similar rule applies to the rounding of decimal fractions. For example 0·00416 is 0·0042 expressed to 2 significant figures, the zeros between the decimal point and the first non-zero digit not counting as significant figures. However, if a number consists of both an integral and a fractional part, then any zeros on either side of the decimal point could count as significant figures. For example, 50·021 is expressed as 50·02 to 4 significant figures.

Mistakes often occur when multiplying or dividing both sides of an inequality by the same number. Thus if $x < y$ and a is a positive number greater than zero (i.e., $a > 0$) then it is also true that $ax < ay$ and $x/a < y/a$. But if a is a negative number (i.e., $a < 0$) then it is not true that $ax < ay$ or $x/a < y/a$. To obtain true inequalities when multiplying or dividing by a negative number, the inequality signs must be *reversed*. For example $4 < 7$; but $-2 \times 4 > -2 \times 7$ i.e., $-8 > -14$, and similarly $4/(-2) > 7/(-2)$ i.e., $-2 > -3·5$. The student should experiment with various numbers himself to verify this result.

Finally, something may be usefully said about the applicability of the rules of ordinary arithmetic to interval arithmetic. If A and B are numbers in ordinary arithmetic, then it is a rule that the product of the numbers is the same whichever of the two possible orders of multiplication is used, i.e., $A \times B = B \times A$. This rule applies also to interval arithmetic. For

$$A \times B = [a, b] \times [c, d]$$
$$= [ac, bd]$$
$$= [ca, db]$$
$$= [c, d] \times [a, b]$$
$$= B \times A.$$

But there are other rules of ordinary arithmetic which are not so applicable, an instance being given in Example 2 of the previous section. Thus, whereas in ordinary arithmetic

$$A \times (A - B) = A \times A - A \times B,$$

in interval arithmetic,

$$A \times (A - B) = [a^2 - ad, b^2 - bc]$$

and $\qquad A \times A - A \times B = [a^2 - bd, b^2 - ac]$

so that the two expressions are not equal. Another interesting difference is that though in ordinary arithmetic $A \times A = A^2$ so that, provided A is not zero, A^2 is always a positive number greater than zero (i.e., $A^2 > 0$), it is possible in interval arithmetic for the product $A \times A$ to have a lower limit which is negative. Thus let $A = [-5, 5]$. Then $A \times A = [-5 \times 5, 5 \times 5] = [-25, 25]$. But $A^2 = [0, 25]$. It will be seen, from this illustration, that the rules for multiplication and division of intervals need modification when some of the interval limits are negative numbers. This modification is not difficult to carry out if it is remembered that a number may take any value in its interval, so that in multiplying (say) two intervals, those limits are selected which give the upper and lower limits of the product.

EXERCISES 1

1. Explain the rôle of Statistics in business decision-making.

2. Give four examples of decision-making situations in which management might employ the services of a statistician.

3. Distinguish between a firm's external and internal sources of statistical data, giving examples of each kind.

4. What is the difference between primary and secondary data? Why is it important that statisticians should make a distinction between primary and secondary data?

5. Define the term *descriptive statistics*. What is its relationship to statistical inference?

6. Give an example of spurious accuracy in statistical data. What kind of fallacy could spurious accuracy produce?

7. If $A = [128, 130]$ and $B = [208, 210]$ then the product $A \times B$ can be given correct to
    (i) 1 significant figure,
    (ii) 2 significant figures, or
    (iii) 3 significant figures.
    (Select the appropriate answer.)

8. Verify that, if $A = [3, 5]$, $B = [2, 6]$, $C = [4, 5]$ then
$$(A - B) + C = (A + C) - B.$$
    Prove that this is true for all intervals.

9. If $a < b$, then which of the following statements are true?
    (i) $a - b < 0$, (ii) $b - a < 0$, (iii) $a/b < 1$, (iv) $a - c < b - c$.

10. Express the quotient A/B correct to the largest number of significant figures justified by the approximate data
$$A = [125, 140] \quad \text{and} \quad B = [6, 8].$$
    Explain why the same cannot be done when $B = [5, 7]$.

11. Show that, if A, B and C are all known to be positive although their exact values are unknown, then
$$A \times (B + C) = A \times B + A \times C.$$
    Verify that this relationship does not hold when
$$A = [2, 3], \quad B = [5, 6] \quad \text{and} \quad C = [-4, -2].$$

12. Show that the rules for finding $A + B$ and $A - B$ given in section 5 are still true when either A or B or both may be negative.

13. The headteacher of a small village school wishes to find out the number of children in the village. Each child in his school is asked, on a particular day, to write down the number of brothers and sisters he or she has. These are then totalled and added to the number of children in the school.
    The method will lead to errors. Give two reasons why the total might be too large, and two reasons why the total might be too small.

14. The side of a square is measured and found to be 4 cm long within ± 1 mm. Find (a) the absolute error and (b) the relative error arising from the assumption that the area of the square is exactly 16 square cm.

15. A manufacturer, in making an article, has the following expenses:

$$
\begin{array}{ll}
\text{Materials} & £2000 \pm 5\% \\
\text{Wages} & £4000 \pm £300
\end{array}
$$

He plans to sell the articles made as follows:

$$\begin{array}{ll} \text{No. of articles} & 1000 \pm 70 \\ \text{Price} & £8 \pm 6{\cdot}25\% \end{array}$$

Find (a) Maximum and minimum expenses;
     (b) Maximum and minimum receipts;
     (c) Maximum and minimum profits;
     (d) Maximum and minimum profit per article.

16. (a) Define absolute error, relative error, compensating error and biased error.

Income from Employment before Tax in a
Certain Country

	Currency units to nearest million
Wages	11,320
Salaries	7,510
Payments to Armed Forces, etc.	473
Employer's contributions to government welfare schemes	831
	20,134

(b) What is the maximum absolute error in the total income from employment before tax?

(c) A company employs 250 persons (rounded to the nearest 10) and has a weekly wage bill of 5000 currency units (rounded to the nearest 100). Give the greatest and least average weekly wage.

17. Three quantities x, y, and z are connected by the relationship

$$\frac{1}{x} = \frac{1}{y} - \frac{1}{z}.$$

If y and z are measured as $5{\cdot}0$ cm and $8{\cdot}0$ cm respectively, calculate the range of values within which x must lie.

CHAPTER 2

Presentation of Statistical Data

1. Classification

A great deal of statistical data is obtained from questionnaires which have been completed by individuals. Statistics is, in general however, an impersonal science and interested in the total picture of some subject of enquiry rather than the records of individuals. This means that, at an early stage of a statistical enquiry, it is necessary to collate data obtained from individual sources and to arrange it in a form which is readily intelligible. The purpose of this arrangement is twofold: first, it may be necessary in order to make the data intelligible to the layman; second, it is necessary in order that the statistician may carry out further calculations on the data. In most statistical enquiries, those carrying out the enquiry will have some preliminary knowledge of its subject matter and they will generally have a clear idea of its objectives. But it is obvious that the enquiry would never be made unless there were considerable ignorance or uncertainty about its outcome. The initial method of presenting data must therefore be designed to throw light on these doubtful areas and, in particular, to bring out the relationships between the various categories into which the data can be divided.

The first method of presentation with which we are concerned in this chapter is *tabulation*. Correct tabulation is largely an exercise in logic and clear thinking, and the fundamental problem is that of classification. There are two ways of defining a class of objects: either *extensively*, by enumerating its individual members; or *intensively*, by stating some defining property which all members of a class shall possess in order to qualify for membership. Very often, a class can be defined in either of these ways. For example, the class of M.P.s can be defined by means of a list of their names (extensive definition) or by means of the property: "having satisfied all the conditions necessary for election to parliament". At the time at which the list was made, these two definitions are equivalent, though this will clearly not be so if a general election takes place. The intensive definition probably has greater stability, because the number of members of parliament (635) is likely to be changed very seldom and only when there is some important constitutional reform. From a logical point of view, therefore, the intensive definition of a class is superior to the extensive method when both are available, because of its greater generality and permanence. However, logic is

16

an abstract science, and is concerned with what is always true, whereas statistical data refers, usually, to what is true at a particular period of time. Even so, the intensive definition of classes by a single property is the more satisfactory from the statistical point of view because of its impersonal nature. The statistician is more interested in the total number of M.Ps. than in their identities. Moreover though statistical data is not general in the sense that it is independent of a particular time and place, it is general in the sense that the statistician is interested in the numerical relationships of classes both at a particular time and for comparison with other times. The fact that a communist was elected in a bye-election by a constituency which previously returned a communist member is a more important fact to the statistician than that a different individual was elected.

The general method of defining a class by means of a single property or set of properties is that most widely adopted by statisticians. But though this is a convenient procedure, it raises certain logical problems which must be satisfactorily solved if statistical data is to convey an accurate impression of reality. When a class is defined by a list of its individual members, there is no doubt about who does or who does not belong to the class. But when properties are used to define a class, there may be some doubt about whether a particular individual belongs to a class or not. For this reason, definitions of classes often need to be very explicit and to state in some detail what is or is not to be included in the class. The class of "structurally separate dwellings", for example, is a good illustration of this point. Does it include caravans? Does "expenditure on food" include only food consumed at home or also food consumed in restaurants? Failure to be clear about these points when tabulating data will obviously lead to mis-allocation of individuals to classes and a consequent distortion of the statistical picture. Even when the statistician has succeeded in overcoming this difficulty, it is still necessary, when presenting the data, to clarify points of definition by means of footnotes so that it shall not be misinterpreted by the user.

A second logical problem of classification arises because the members of a class often have to be classified into sub-classes. The sub-classes of a class must be defined so that they are *mutually exclusive* and *collectively exhaustive*. Classes are mutually exclusive when a member of one cannot also be a member of another. The problem of meeting this requirement is quite different from that of precise definition. Classes may be precisely defined, in the sense that there is no doubt whether or not an individual belongs to a particular class, and still not be mutually exclusive. Suppose, for example, that a group of people were classified according to whether they were blue-eyed, fair-haired or neither blue-eyed nor fair-haired. It is clear that those who are neither blue-eyed nor fair-haired cannot fall into either of the other classes, so that this class is mutually exclusive of the other two. But some individuals may be both blue-eyed and fair-haired and these will consequently belong to the class of blue-eyed people and to the class of fair-haired people, so these two classes will not be mutually exclusive. From the statistical point of view, it will seem that the number of blue-eyed people together with the number of fair-haired people is greater than the total number of people possessing either of these characteristics. Consequently, this classification will lead to inconsistency in the data. To remedy this defect, the classes must be re-defined so that they are mutually exclusive. This will yield four classes:—

Blue-eyed individuals who are not fair-haired
Fair-haired individuals who are not blue-eyed
Blue-eyed and fair-haired individuals
Individuals who are neither fair-haired nor blue-eyed.

This classification has the advantage that it makes the data consistent; for the total of the number of members in each class is the same as the number of members of the whole group. It is also a collectively exhaustive classification, because every member of the whole group falls into one of the four classes. Classification into classes which are not mutually exclusive is known as the fallacy of cross-classification or cross-division and can clearly give a false impression of the composition of a group because it seems to show that more members of the group possess certain characteristics than really do.

It is desirable that any classification of statistical data should be collectively exhaustive, i.e., should use all the data, otherwise some of the data will be wasted and this may lead to a loss of information. Very often, in order to secure a collectively exhaustive classification, it may be necessary to define certain classes negatively in terms of non-possession of certain properties and this can often be very informative. For example, the employed population can be classified into wage earners and non-wage earners. The wage earners form a homogeneous class because they are all paid weekly (though some may receive income in other ways as well). The non-wage earners are a heterogeneous class, since there are different ways in which their income may be paid. Information about the numbers in this class may, however, still be informative to someone, for instance, the Inspector of Taxes. Moreover, changes in the composition of the population with respect to this classification may yield useful comparisons over time. Generally speaking, it can be said that a classifying property which leads to a homogeneous classification is more informative than one which leads to a heterogeneous classification; but the latter need not be wholly valueless and may sometimes be needed in order to classify the whole data. Sometimes, of course, it is unnecessary to resort to a negative defining property in order to produce a complete classification. A member of a human population must be either male or female and cannot be both; at least, in a factual sense there is no other possibility, though in a strict logical sense, such a possibility must always be allowed to exist. A classification of this kind clearly relies on an extensive knowledge of the whole population. Negative classification may be adopted for convenience or may be an indication of ignorance of a field in which more information could be usefully sought.

2. Variables and Attributes

The properties used for classifying a group of individuals may be either measurable or non-measurable. Examples of measurable characteristics are: height, income, I.Q., examination marks. These are called *variable* characteristics because they vary fairly continuously (in some cases almost completely so) from one individual to another. They are very good properties to use for classification because they allow precise definition; at least to within the degree of accuracy of the methods of measurement, which are often highly efficient. Examples of non-measurable characteristics are: sex, marital status, religious persuasion, hair-colour. These are termed *attributes* because they are distinguished by qualitative rather than by measurable differences between individuals. Attributes can yield precise definitions, particularly if they fall into definite legal categories, though legal definitions are, themselves, often a matter of controversy. Their use for classification often requires greater knowledge of the subject matter than do measurable characteristics in order to avoid cross-classification and to obtain homogeneous classifications.

Some of the problems of using attributes for classification have already been considered in the preceding section and we shall now discuss the use of variables for this purpose. Variables can themselves be classified into *discrete* and *continuous*. A discrete variable is one which can take only certain definite values. For example, examination marks are discrete variables, since only a whole number of marks is usually awarded for any subject and, expressed as percentages, marks may take any of the values 1, 2 up to 100, but no intermediate values. A continuous variable may take any value within a given range of values, an infinitesimal difference between adjacent values being possible. For example, the heights of most adult males in the UK lie within the range 5 ft. to 7 ft. and individual heights may differ by indiscernible amounts. Height is, therefore, a continuous variable.

Where a group to be classified by some measurable characteristic is large, the question whether the variable is discrete or continuous is an important one because it determines the way in which the range of values which the variable may take should be divided into sub-classes. Where the variable can take a great many values, but is discrete (as in the case of examination marks), or when the variable is continuous, it is necessary to divide the whole range of possible values into shorter intervals. But, when this is done, the discrete and continuous variables are treated differently as the following illustration shows:

MARK (%)	HEIGHT (in.)
1– 25	60 but less than 66
26– 50	66 ,, ,, ,, 72
51– 75	72 ,, ,, ,, 78
76–100	78 ,, ,, ,, 84

With discrete variables, there is no problem about marginal cases, so that the intervals can be defined by precise values at both ends; but it may often be difficult to determine whether a continuous variable is a little less or a little more than some arbitrarily chosen value, and in this case individuals should be classified by intervals which are open at one end and closed at the other. The intervals then form a continuous series, and no individual will be omitted or counted twice.

The values taken by some discrete variables may be too few to be classified by intervals; the appropriate method is then to determine each class by means of the actual values which individuals take. Data relating to the size of families in a particular town, for example, should be treated in this way:

SIZE OF FAMILIES IN THE TOWN OF X IN 1973

No. of children	0	1	2	3	4	5	>5	Total
No. of families	253	1921	2235	1528	326	128	73	6464

The table shows how many families have each of the stated number of children. It will be noted that the title includes a reference to the time and place to which the data apply, and this should always be stated unless it is immediately evident from the context. A few families have more than 5 children, but the number in each category above 5 is too small to justify separate classes, so they are grouped into the single class: >5 where the sign $>$ means "greater than". Instead of the symbol, the words "greater than" could also be used. Even when the classification is by intervals, it may be desirable to leave vague the lower and upper limits of the lowest and highest intervals respectively. Thus, in the height classification in the previous paragraph, two further intervals could be included: "less than 60" and "84 and over", though it is unlikely that many individuals will fall into either of these categories.

For practical purposes, the distinction between discrete and continuous variables is relative. If height can be measured accurately only to the nearest $1/10$ of an inch, then in an interval of 2 feet the variable can take only 240 different values. From a theoretical point of view, however, height is a truly continuous variable; and it is only the inadequacy of measuring instruments which introduces discontinuity. In a mathematical sense, the greater the number of subdivisions of which an interval is capable, the more nearly it approaches to continuity and thus, in later work in Statistics, it is possible to treat many variables as continuous which are really discrete, simply because the variable can take a very large number of values over the appropriate interval.

3. Tabulation

The tabulation of statistical data is essentially a one- or two-dimensional process, so that a table can be thought of as possessing two axes, a horizontal and a vertical. The information given in the table refers to a single group of individuals where "individual" may refer to a person, a unit of currency, a house or other physical good. In a one-way table, the group is classified in only one way. For example, the table in the preceding section is a one-way table in which families are classified according to the number of children belonging to them. In a two-way table, a group is classified from two points of view, each number in the body of the table showing the number of individuals belonging to both of two intersecting classes. An example of a two-way table is shown below.

The main purpose of this table is to show the increase in production of cotton piece goods in the period 1937–42 (about 3,000 mn. sq. yds.). Notice that much of the exported material will also be included in the figures for production, but this is a fairly obvious fact and there is little likelihood of misinterpretation, for "Production" clearly refers to *total* production.

CHAPTER 2

COTTON PIECE GOODS: PRINCIPAL PRODUCERS
(Million square yards)

	1937		1942	
	Production	Exports	Production	Exports
U.K.	3,806	1,921	1,850	485
U.S.A.	9,321	236	12,000	450
India	5,548(b)	120(a)	5,800(b)	940(a)
Brazil	900	7	1,400	250
Mexico	370	—	500	30
Canada	245	5	350	20
Other accessible countries, excluding Russia and the Continent	800	—	2,100	—
Total	20,990	2,289	24,000	2,175

(a) Exports by sea, excluding Burma.
(b) Including hand-loom production.

(Source: *Cotton Working Party Report, 1946.*)

As well as the raw statistical data, a table may also show certain derived statistics which have been obtained from the raw data by calculation. For example, the table above shows Totals, whilst in the following table the figures in the final column have been obtained by dividing those in the second by the figures in the third for each year shown.

Both of these tables are really a combination of two tables. The first consists of two two-way tables, one showing a classification of cotton piece goods into "Production, 1937" and "Production, 1942" against "Country"; the other showing "Exports, 1937" and "Exports, 1942" also against Country. The combined table is possible because the vertical classification (by Country) is the same in both cases. It would, of course, be possible to make an indefinite extension of this table horizontally. The second table is a combination of two one-way tables, one being a classification of the size of the electorate by election year, the other being a classification of the number of seats in the House of Commons, also at each election year. The supplementary information shown in both tables enables the significance of the raw data to be more readily appreciated.

HOUSE OF COMMONS: NUMBER OF SEATS AND ELECTORS PER SEAT

	Number of electors (Thousands)	Number of seats	Electors per seat (Thousands)
Election year			
1900	6,733	670	10·0
1906	7,267	670	10·8
1910 (Jan.)	7,706	670	11·5
1910 (Dec.)	7,721	670	11·5
1918[1]	21,392	707	30·3
1922[2]	20,874	615	33·9
1923	21,286	615	34·6
1924	21,732	615	35·3
1929	28,851	615	46·9
1931	29,953	615	48·7
1935	31,374	615	51·0
1945	33,240	640	51·9
1950	34,412	625	55·1
1951	34,919	625	55·9
1955	34,852	630	55·3
1959	35,398	630	56·2
1964	35,894	630	57·0
1966	35,957	630	57·1
1970	39,615	630	62·9

1. Including women voters (8,479 thousand) for the first time.
2. Excluding Eire from 1922.

(Source: *Vacher's Parliamentary Companion.*)

The following example illustrates the relationship between data in its original and tabulated forms.

EXAMPLE 1

"*The number of registered wholly unemployed excluding school-eavers on 13th January 1969 in Great Britain was 580,318. After adjustment for normal seasonal variations, the number in this group was about 506,000, representing 2·2 per cent. of employees, compared with about 520,000 in December.*

In addition, there were 3,695 unemployed school-leavers and 10,506 temporarily stopped workers registered, so the total registered unemployed was 594,519, representing 2·6 per cent. of employees. This was 42,829 more than in December when the percentage rate was 2·4.

Among those wholly unemployed in January, 248,799 (42·8 per cent.) had been registered for not more than 8 weeks compared with 218,498 (40·7 per cent.) in December; 106,712 (18·4 per cent.) had been registered for not more than 2 weeks, compared with 85,067 (15·8 per cent.) in December.

Between December and January the number temporarily stopped fell by 1,169 and the number of school-leavers unemployed rose by 1,200."

(Source: *Employment and Productivity Gazette.*)

Arrange this information in an appropriate tabular form.

The data is shown in the table opposite. It will be seen, that in order to obtain some of the figures, a few simple arithmetical calculations are necessary. The percentage figures in the original data might have been included, but doing so would have made the table less simple without adding to the information it conveys, particularly as the total number of employees can be calculated (to 2 significant figures) and inserted for comparison.

4. Diagrams

The understanding of tabulated statistical data presupposes an ability to appreciate the relationships between numerical magnitudes, which people possess in rather varying degrees. It is therefore useful to have alternative methods of presenting statistical data which can be easily comprehended by the intelligent but, perhaps, innumerate layman. Pictures and diagrams are very suitable for this purpose and, in the remainder of this chapter, several types of diagram will be discussed, each of which are suitable for particular purposes. It is very important to bear in mind that an effective presentation of data in diagrammatic form often requires a right choice of diagram.

Because its significance is readily appreciated by everyone, pictorially represented information is widely used by government departments and political parties for disseminating important information to the public. When the information is statistical, the pictures used are termed *pictograms.* Many examples of the use of pictograms are to be found in the popular press. The number of children attending primary school in a certain year might, for example, be represented by a row of children, each child being equivalent to 100,000 children. The last figure in the row need not

NUMBER OF REGISTERED UNEMPLOYED IN GT. BRITAIN, DEC. 1968–13 JAN. 1969

	Total no. of Employees	Wholly Unemployed†			Unemployed School Leavers	Temporarily Stopped	Total
		Total	Max. Period of Registration				
			8 Weeks	2 Weeks			
Dec. 1968	23 mn.	537,520 (520,000*)	218,498	85,067	2,495	11,675	551,690
Jan. 1969	23 mn.	580,318 (506,000*)	248,799	106,712	3,695	10,506	594,519

† Excluding school leavers.
* Seasonally adjusted.

(Source: *Employment and Productivity Gazette.*)

be a complete child, for it is possible to represent the data to the nearest 50,000 by allowing half a child to represent this number. A pictogram of this kind might consist of five rows of children corresponding to the number of children in primary school in five successive decades. Variations in the number of children in each row will make it possible to compare changes easily. A diagram of this kind could be accompanied by another showing the number of children of primary school age in the population at each decade and would thereby be made more informative.

When pictures are used to represent numbers of individual things (persons, cars, sums of money, etc.), there is not much likelihood that they will be seriously misleading because a two-dimensional

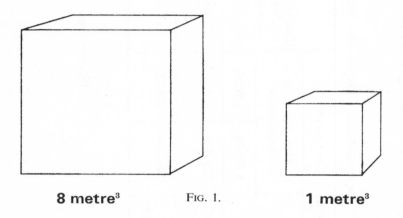

8 metre³   FIG. 1.   **1 metre³**

picture is quite adequate. The case is different when volumetric data is being represented, for example, that for the production of beer. A large barrel might represent a million barrels of beer, whilst a small barrel represents 125,000 barrels or $\frac{1}{8}$ of the quantity represented by a large barrel. But since a barrel is a three-dimensional object, the small barrel should not occupy $\frac{1}{8}$ of the *area* of a large barrel but be considerably larger than this. An area of 1 square metre will be $\frac{1}{8}$ of an area of 8 square metres represented on the same scale. But, as Fig. 1 shows, a volume of 1 cubic metre will occupy $\frac{1}{4}$ of the space occupied in a two-dimensional picture by a volume of 8 cubic metres on the same scale. If the difference between the sizes of the two cubes was intended to represent a change in some quantity over time, the change would look misleadingly large if the smaller cube were drawn $\frac{1}{8}$ of the size of the larger.

5. Pie Charts

Pie charts are useful for illustrating the proportional relationships between magnitudes when these are more significant than the actual magnitudes themselves. It is possibly more significant to know, in some contexts, that a man spends $\frac{1}{3}$ of his total income on food than to know the actual amount so spent. The proportion of a man's income which he spends on different items can therefore be shown appropriately by means of a pie chart. This is a circular diagram which is divided into sectors by drawing radii from the centre to the circumference. The areas of the sectors are made proportional to the magnitudes of the individual components of the total being represented. The usual method of drawing a pie chart begins by reducing the individual components to percentages. The area of each sector is determined by the angle between its bounding radii and this angle is found by taking the appropriate percentage of 360 degrees (the total number of degrees in a complete circle). For example, a component representing 25% of the total appears in the chart as a sector bounded by radii the angle between which is 25% of 360° or 1 right angle. The circle should be drawn large enough for the designation of each component to be written in on the diagram (Fig. 2). The following example illustrates.

EXAMPLE 2

Construct a pie chart from the table below to illustrate the composition of United Kingdom exports in 1967.

Exports of the United Kingdom, 1967
Analysis by area—£mn. per month

North America	Latin America	Western Europe	Sterling Area	Soviet Union and Eastern Europe	Rest of the World
68·9	13·9	159·2	127·2	14·0	35·6

(Source: *Monthly Digest of Statistics.*)

							Total
Value of exports £mn.	68·9	13·9	159·2	127·2	14·0	35·6	418·8
% of total	16·4	3·3	38·0	30·4	3·4	8·5	100
% of 360°	59	12	137	109	12	31	360

PIE CHART SHOWING THE DESTINATIONS
OF EXPORTS FROM THE UK IN 1967

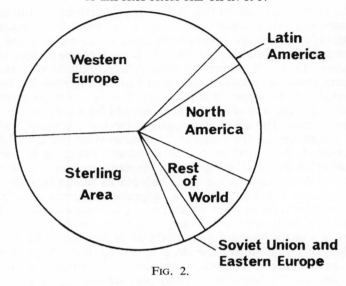

FIG. 2.

The composition of two totals can be compared by drawing two pie charts, one to represent each total. If the totals are of different magnitudes, it would obviously be misleading to draw the two circles the same size. The logical procedure is to make the areas proportional to the totals. Thus if these were £800 and £200, the areas of the circles would be in the ratio 800/200 or 4/1. Since the area of a circle is πr^2, where r is the radius of the circle, the ratio between the *squares* of the radii of the two circles must be in the ratio of the areas. Hence the radii of the circles will be in the ratio 2/1.

6. Histograms

It was seen in section 2 that it is often possible to classify the individual members of a group according to some measurable characteristic called a variable or, sometimes, a variate. This classification will show the number of individuals corresponding to each value, or range of values, of the variate. The data thus obtained can be presented in tabular form and can also be represented diagrammatically by means of a *histogram*. This is a diagram very like a graph, with two axes intersecting at right angles. It is a convention that the horizontal axis is used to represent the variable characteristic or variate, whilst the vertical axis represents the number of individuals corresponding to each value of the variable. Using these axes, a rectangle is drawn for each value or range of values of the variable so that its *area* is proportional to the number of individuals corresponding to that value. It must be emphasised that it is the area and not the height of a rectangle which is proportional to the number of individuals. Where, however, one is dealing with a variable which takes only single values or a discrete or continuous variable for which the ranges of values are equal intervals, the bases of the rectangles on the horizontal axis will be equal so that, in this case, the height of each rectangle (as well as the area) will also be proportional to the number of individuals in each class. Since this is the general rule it can be said, with little chance of misunderstanding, that the vertical axis represents a number of individuals. It is usual to call the number of individuals in each class the *frequency* of the value of the variable which defines that class. The frequency of that value is just the number of individuals possessing it out of the whole group; that is, the number of times that value occurs in the whole group.

To illustrate the construction of the diagram, consider, first, the data for the size of families in a certain town given in the table in section 2. In this case, the variable is the number of children per family, which can take only a limited number of single values. The frequency of these values is the number of families having a particular number of children.

SIZE OF FAMILIES IN THE TOWN OF X IN 1973

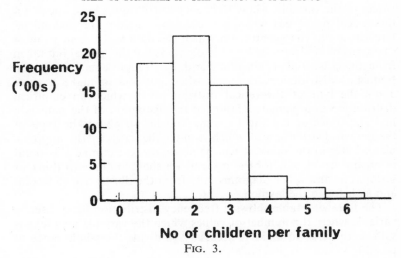

FIG. 3.

It is logical to draw the rectangles immediately adjacent to each other, since there are no values of the variate intermediate between the consecutive whole numbers of children. Equal intervals on the horizontal axis represent each value of the variate, so that the heights of the rectangles, as well as their areas, will be proportional to each class frequency. The total area of the rectangles is, of course, proportional to the total number of families, i.e., 6464. The centre of the base of each rectangle corresponds to the position of each of the whole numbers shown. It follows that the extremities of the base of each rectangle correspond to whole numbers $\pm\frac{1}{2}$ unit. For example, the base of the rectangle for the frequency of families with no children extends from $0 - \frac{1}{2}$ unit to $0 + \frac{1}{2}$ unit; that with families with 1 child from $1 - \frac{1}{2}$ unit to $1 + \frac{1}{2}$ unit and so on. Since there is no information about the number of different classes with more than 5 children, it is assumed that the 73 families in this category all have 6 children. This makes it possible to draw the base of the rectangle with a frequency of 73 equal to the bases of the other rectangles, which is useful for comparison (Fig. 3).

The histogram shows, at a glance, the relative sizes of each class corresponding to the different number of children per family and is possibly more informative to the layman than the original table from which it has been drawn. But as well as having an illustrative value, histograms have an important theoretical rôle in Statistics. They show the *frequency distribution* of the variable, that is, the way in which the numbers of individuals are shared between different values of the variable. Many frequency distributions have important theoretical properties which are used in Statistics for making inferences about the group from which the data was taken. In most cases, the data illustrated by a histogram is not theoretical but taken from an actual study of the real world, i.e., it represents an empirical frequency distribution. But it is often possible to make a guess about the type of theoretical distribution to which an empirical distribution approximates. Study of the histogram of the data is a first step towards coming to some conclusion about the type of theoretical distribution to which it might be expected to approximate. Later in the book, it will be necessary to examine this point in greater detail but, for the present, we shall continue to think of histograms and other diagrams only from the illustrative viewpoint and as helps to the layman.

The following table shows a frequency distribution for a discrete variable where the number of values which the variable may take is sufficiently large to make it necessary to divide the whole range of possible values into intervals:

I.Q. OF 100 CHILDREN AT A JUNIOR SCHOOL

I.Q. No. of children with given I.Q.	50–59	60–69	70–79	80–89	90–99
	1	2	8	18	23

I.Q. No. of children with given I.Q.	100–109	110–119	120–129	130–139
	21	15	9	3

The histogram (Fig. 4) is constructed in the same way as in the previous example except that the base of each rectangle now represents a range of values and not just a single value. The mid-point of the base of each rectangle now corresponds to the mid-point of an interval: $54\frac{1}{2}$, $64\frac{1}{2}$, $74\frac{1}{2}$, etc. Since no value of the variable occurs between the whole number end-points of each interval, it is still necessary to draw the vertical boundaries of each rectangle at $\frac{1}{2}$ unit less than the lower end-points and $\frac{1}{2}$ unit more than the upper end-points. The central rectangle is the fifth in the group, corresponding to the range 90–99; and the diagram clearly reveals that the distribution is not absolutely symmetrical about this centre, but that more individuals occur to the right of centre than to the left. Distributions of this kind are said to be *positively skewed*. If a larger number of

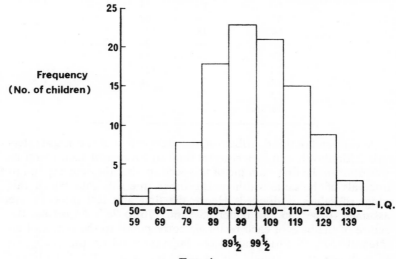

FIG. 4.

individuals occurs to the left of centre than to the right, the distribution is *negatively skewed*. Histograms bring out this kind of feature very clearly and thus give important information about the group being investigated. In this example, the diagram shows that, in *this particular school*, the children tend to be of slightly above average intelligence. Of course, one should not jump to the conclusion that this is true of all schools because, if the method of constructing the I.Q. test is correct, the results for all children should show that there are just as many above as below the centre of the distribution.

In a frequency distribution of a continuous variable such as the heights of human individuals, the vertical boundaries of the rectangles of the histogram correspond exactly to the end-points of the intervals into which the whole range of values is divided. This is precisely because the variable may take all values in the range, so that between any two values, however close, it is always possible to insert another value which may be that of some individual.

DISTRIBUTION OF THE HEIGHTS OF 1000 MEN

Height (in.)			No. of Men
	Under 58		2
58 and	,,	60	5
60 ,,	,,	62	14
62 ,,	,,	64	60
64 ,,	,,	66	187
66 ,,	,,	68	304
68 ,,	,,	70	263
70 ,,	,,	72	121
72 ,,	,,	74	36
74 ,,	,,	76	7
76 and over			1

At each end of this distribution, the exact extent of the height intervals is doubtful, and it is conventional to assume in such cases, as was done in the first example of this section, that they correspond to intervals of the same width as the other intervals into which this range of values is divided. Hence the first and last intervals are assumed to be "56 and under 58" and "76 to 78". As before, the centre of the base of each rectangle corresponds to the centre of an interval: 57″, 59″, 61″ and so on. Superimposed on the histogram (Fig. 5) is a set of straight lines joining the mid-points of the top of each rectangle. These lines form a figure called a *frequency polygon*. In a sense, a frequency polygon gives a more accurate picture of a continuous distribution than a set of rectangles; for a rectangle extending over an interval seems to suggest that there is the same number of individuals in each sub-interval which need not be the case. Moreover, one may reasonably expect that as the intervals are made narrower, the tops of the correspondingly narrower rectangles will tend to form a smooth curve similar to the edges of the frequency polygon. It should not be forgotten that the size of the intervals chosen to classify the group is arbitrarily chosen and that, in a sense, an interval of any size, however small, gives a slightly

DISTRIBUTION OF THE HEIGHTS OF 1000 MEN

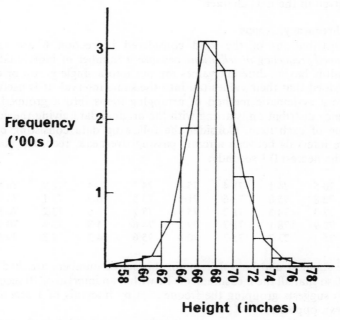

FIG. 5.

distorted picture of the distribution. For practical purposes, however, this inaccuracy is unimportant and can be minimised by a proper choice of interval.

When constructing a histogram of frequencies assigned to classes defined by intervals of the variable, the data should be carefully scrutinised to ensure whether or not the intervals are equal. For example, in Exercises 2, No. 13 the first nine classes are defined by equal intervals of 1 week, but the intervals by which succeeding classes are defined are variable in width. Hence if a rectangle of width 2 mm and height 10 cm represents a frequency of 50,000 within a class defined by an interval of width 1 week, the same frequency will be represented by a rectangle of height 2·5 cm when the width of the interval is 4 weeks, the width of the rectangle in this case being 8 mm.

It will be seen that a histogram has the great advantage of showing clearly the character of a frequency distribution. In particular, it shows how the individuals are arranged about its central portion. A detailed discussion of the importance of this for Statistical Method is given in the next chapter.

7. Frequency Groups

Distributions of the kind considered in section 6 are called *grouped frequency distributions* because a number of individuals all possibly having different values are put into a single group or class provided that their values fall into the same interval. It is useful to have a systematic method of arranging items into a grouped frequency distribution, starting with the original data giving the actual value of each item. Consider the following data consisting of 40 time intervals between aircraft passing overhead, recorded correct to the nearest 0·1 seconds:

70·5	74·1	71·4	75·6	74·2	76·4	72·9	74·5
72·8	75·8	73·6	71·9	73·5	76·9	73·1	74·9
77·3	74·3	71·2	75·9	78·7	77·6	73·2	70·8
72·9	78·1	71·7	79·3	74·6	74·8	72·8	70·9
75·3	73·7	75·7	70·8	75·6	74·2	72·2	79·6

The smallest and largest items in this set of numbers are 70·5 and 79·6 so that all the measurements lie within an interval of 10 seconds. This suggests grouping the frequencies by intervals of 1 second as shown opposite.

In grouping the frequencies, it is important to choose the size of the interval so that a minimum of about 10 classes is obtained. The reason for this should be clear from what was said at the end of the preceding section. If there are too few intervals, a distorted picture of the distribution will almost certainly be the result; and this is a drawback not only when presenting the results diagrammatically, but also when using the data to carry out statistical calculations. On

Interval between aircraft (secs.)	Tally mark	Frequency
70 but under 71	////	4
71 ,, ,, 72	////	4
72 ,, ,, 73	/////	5
73 ,, ,, 74	/////	5
74 ,, ,, 75	///// ///	8
75 ,, ,, 76	///// /	6
76 ,, ,, 77	//	2
77 ,, ,, 78	//	2
78 ,, ,, 79	//	2
79 to 80	//	2
		Total 40

the other hand, if there are too many intervals, the data becomes inconvenient to handle, so care should also be taken not to make the interval too small.

8. Bar Charts

Histograms are a useful way of presenting data classified according to variable. Pie charts, as has been seen, perform a similar function for a classification by attribute. Another effective way of presenting data classified by attribute is the *simple bar chart*. This has the advantage over the pie chart that it makes it easier to compare magnitudes, particularly those that are not very different. On the other hand, the pie chart shows more clearly than the bar chart how each component is related to the total. A simple bar chart illustrating the production of cotton piece goods in 1942 (see section 3) is shown in Fig. 6.

In this case the rectangles, unlike those in the histogram, are drawn with an interval between each. Each rectangle should be the same width so that its height (as well as area) is proportional to the class number. Where each component has a verbal description, this can be written above the appropriate rectangle. A simple bar chart is also useful, however, for showing the change of some quantity over time. In this case, the successive years (or months) to which each rectangle refers can be written below the horizontal axis.

More detailed information about classification by attribute is conveyed by a *component bar chart* in which the rectangles are divided into several sections, each of which is proportional to the magnitudes of component sub-classes. The following data for

PRODUCTION OF COTTON PIECE GOODS, 1942

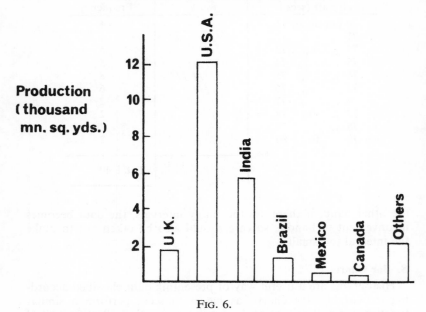

FIG. 6.

the changes which have taken place in the age distribution of the
population of Great Britain since 1851 can be illustrated by this
method.

Age distribution per 1000 persons			
Year	0–14	15–64	65 and over
1851	355	598	47
1891	351	601	48
1911	308	639	53
1939	214	697	89
1947	215	681	105
1957	229	653	118

(Source: Stern *Britain Yesterday and To-day*.)

Strictly speaking, Fig. 7 is a *percentage* component bar chart since
the heights of all the rectangles are the same, although the absolute
size of the population will clearly have varied in these years. How-

AGE DISTRIBUTION OF THE POPULATION OF
GREAT BRITAIN, 1851–1957

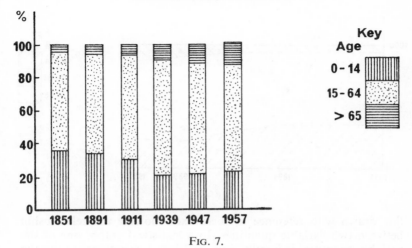

FIG. 7.

ever, the age structure of the population is significant and can be compared, whatever the actual size of the population may be, so that, from one point of view, the above chart conveys valuable information. A component bar chart showing the absolute size of the population and the numbers in each age group in each year could also be constructed if the data were available, in which case the rectangles would not be all of the same height. Comparative age structures would not be so clearly apparent on such a chart, particularly when the variation in the numbers in some age groups is small, though significant.

The same data might also be illustrated by a *strata chart*, which is a useful device for showing how data which varies over time changes its composition (Fig. 8).

The horizontal scale is divided into equal intervals, each representing the same time interval. Data will often be available for consecutive years; but in the example illustrated, there are a great many intervening years for which data is missing. In this case, the horizontal scale should still be preserved, but it is obvious that the sections of the chart corresponding to these years will be conjectural.

9. Graphs

As with most of the diagrams previously discussed, a graph requires two axes intersecting at right angles. The graph itself is a

AGE DISTRIBUTION PER 1000 OF THE POPULATION
OF GREAT BRITAIN, 1851–1957

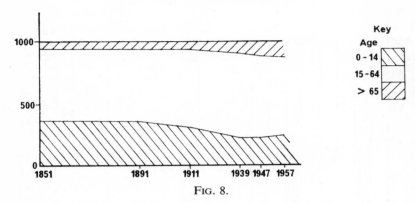

FIG. 8.

line drawn with reference to these axes showing the relationship
between two variable quantities. In a statistical graph, one of the
variable quantities is usually time, and it is conventional to use the
horizontal axis of the graph to represent this quantity. In the course
of this book, several different kinds of graph are discussed, so
attention will be confined here to important points relating to the
construction of statistical graphs. Since a graph of the kind now
under consideration is intended to convey statistical information in
a readily intelligible form, the criterion for constructing such a
graph must be that of conveying the maximum amount of information with the minimum loss of clarity. This means that usually
several graphs have to be drawn using the same set of axes in order
to bring out relevant comparisons. The graphs in Figs. 9 and 10
show two methods by which several pieces of information can be
presented using a single set of axes.

In Fig. 9 several graphs are drawn using only two axes. The graphs
are distinguished by clearly indicating, in words, the shares to which
they refer and also by using a different kind of line for each graph.
When there is little space on the graph for writing or when the
graphs nearly coincide, the meanings of the different lines can be
indicated by means of a key. In Fig. 10, two vertical axes are used
because "No. of Pneumatic Picks" and "Tonnage Cut" cannot be
measured in homogeneous units. Though the scales of the two
vertical axes represent different kinds of things, however, they are
so graduated that the two graphs are close enough together for
comparisons to be made. Even when the units of measurement of

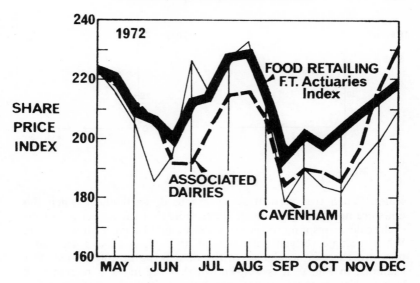

FIG. 9. Index of Food Retailing Share Prices, May–Dec. 1972.

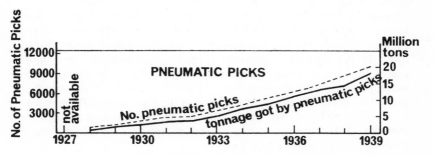

FIG. 10. Number of Pneumatic Picks employed in British Mines and
Tonnage of Coal Cut, 1927–39.

two variable quantities are both homogeneous, for example if both
are units of the same currency, two vertical axes should be used if
their orders of magnitude are considerably different; otherwise, if
the same vertical axis is used for both variables, their graphs will be
too far apart for any effective comparison to be possible.

A point of difference to notice between these two graphs is that
in Fig. 9 the base line corresponds to 160 on the vertical scale,
whilst in Fig. 10 the base line corresponds to zero on both vertical

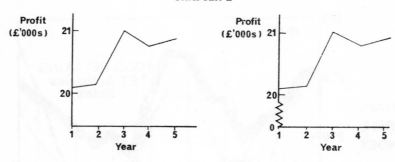

FIG. 11.

scales. When two vertical scales are used, particularly when the units are not homogeneous, it is desirable that the lowest points on each scale correspond to zero in order to avoid a misleading picture. When a single vertical scale is used, this is not always necessary, provided there is no chance of the data being misinterpreted. For example, in Fig. 9, it is well-known that the index is related to a base of 100, so that it is unlikely that the oscillations of the graph will be viewed as more spectacular than they really are. On the other hand, omission of the zero mark may produce an altogether erroneous picture of the data. In the diagram on the left (Fig. 11), for example, a firm appears to have enjoyed a spectacular increase in profit in Year 3, whereas this increase is less than £1000 or 5% of the total. In the right-hand diagram (Fig. 11), however, the base line represents zero, and the vertical scale is broken to avoid unnecessary waste of space over the inoperative part of the scale. Although the same data is presented in this graph as in the one on the left, the user is less likely to be misled, because the broken scale acts as a warning that he must consider the absolute magnitudes involved when assessing the significance of the data.

Time is an important variable in Statistics, and many investigations are concerned with the way some quantity changes historically. But statistical enquiries often seek to determine the relationships between variables of which time is not one. For example, it may be of interest to a firm to know how its output varies with the amount of labour employed, both variables being measured in suitable units (possibly physical units of product and man-hours). The interest here is in establishing whether there is a regular relationship between the two variables, or whether this relationship is altogether capricious. A graph can often bring out which of these two situations prevails, though it is sometimes very difficult to decide, in marginal cases, whether the relationship is regular or not. In such cases, even where the position is intuitively fairly obvious, the statistician prefers to apply statistical tests in order to decide the question. A great deal depends, from the decision-making point of view, upon knowing how sure one can be that a conclusion based on the data is true; and it is the purpose of statistical method to determine how certain we can be of our results in situations of this kind. It follows that, although graphs and diagrams can often be illuminating, their use constitutes only the first stage of a statistical investigation, the findings of which must be confirmed by applying the appropriate statistical methods to the results.

EXERCISES 2

1. Name two characteristics which can be used to classify the pupils of a secondary school into two mutually exclusive classes.

2. Why is it necessary to define classifying properties precisely? Give a precise definition of "salary earner".

3. Which of the following classifications are (a) mutually exclusive, (b) collectively exhaustive?
   (i) Of books in a library into fiction and non-fiction;
   (ii) Of books in a library into fiction, non-fiction, short stories and essays;
   (iii) of income into earned and unearned income;
   (iv) of animals into fish, reptiles and mammals.

4. Give two examples of each of the following: (a) discrete variable, (b) continuous variable and (c) attribute.

5. Mention four features of a good statistical table.

6. Arrange the following information in a convenient tabular form, and fill in any gaps in your table:
   The number of goods vehicles licensed in the United Kingdom increased by approximately $2\frac{1}{2}$ per cent. from 1,513,000 in 1964 to 1,551,000 in 1970. The number of goods vehicles of up to $1\frac{1}{2}$ tons (unladen weight) rose from 872,000 to 933,000 in this time, an increase of 61,000 or 7 per cent. The increase was most dramatic in the case of vehicles of over 8 tons, viz. 175 per cent., an increase of 35,000 on the 1964 figure of 20,000. There was

also a marked rise in the number of goods vehicles of 5 to 8 tons, from 70,000 in 1964 to 132,000 in 1970, an increase of 89 per cent. The number of goods vehicles of intermediate weight actually fell in the period in question. For $1\frac{1}{2}$ to 3 ton vehicles the fall was from 291,000 to 197,000 or 32 per cent, while the number of 3 to 5 ton vehicles went down by 26,000 from 260,000 in 1964 to 234,000 in 1970.

Source: *New Society*, April 1972.

7. Construct a blank table to show absenteeism among the employees of an industrial establishment according to the length of absence (viz. "under three days", "three days and under one week", "one week and under two weeks", "two weeks and over"), classifying the absentees by sex, by marital status (i.e. "single" or "married") and by age ("under 18 years", "18 years and under 50 years", and "50 years and over").

(NOTE: The table should be designed to apply to *one* month only. Totals and sub-totals may be included.)

8. Draw a blank table, with great attention to definition and clearness, in which can be shown the value of exports in 1972 from five countries—viz., the United Kingdom, Norway, Sweden, Denmark and the Netherlands—to each other. Include lines or columns in which suitable percentages can be written.

9. The numbers of the principal farm animals in Great Britain are (to a sufficient degree of accuracy) cattle 12 million, sheep 30 million, pigs 6 million. A Pie Chart is to be drawn to illustrate the proportions of the three kinds of animals. State the angle of the sector which represents pigs.

10. Pie Charts of different sizes are to be drawn to illustrate and compare the acreage under cereal crops in 1960 and 1970. What will be the radius of the 1970 chart if the radius of the 1960 chart is 10 cm.?

| | Acres (100s) | |
	1960	1970
Wheat	20	36
Barley	22	28
Oats	33	44

Draw these two charts.

11. Sketch, *to approximate scale only*, two different diagrams illustrating the following data:

Country	Area (thousands of square miles)
England	50
Scotland	30·5
Wales	8
Northern Ireland	5·5

State briefly any advantage or disadvantage in the chosen methods of representation.

12. The numbers of British subjects entering European countries in 1969 were as follows. (The numbers are given in thousands.)

France	4408
Belgium	2304
Holland	944
Scandinavia	428
Others	252

(Source: *Monthly Digest of Statistics.*)
Represent this information by a Pie Chart.

13. Construct histograms to illustrate the following unemployment figures.

Duration of unemployment in weeks	Males	Females
One or less	46,675	13,202
Over 1 and up to 2	37,606	9,229
,, 2 ,, ,, ,, 3	23,671	4,935
,, 3 ,, ,, ,, 4	22,107	3,941
,, 4 ,, ,, ,, 5	20,422	3,774
,, 5 ,, ,, ,, 6	19,320	3,612
,, 6 ,, ,, ,, 7	18,542	3,440
,, 7 ,, ,, ,, 8	15,237	3,086
,, 8 ,, ,, ,, 9	14,555	2,727
,, 9 ,, ,, ,, 13	47,046	9,186
,, 13 ,, ,, ,, 26	80,893	13,344
,, 26 ,, ,, ,, 39	40,144	4,986
,, 39 ,, ,, ,, 52	25,424	3,002
Over 52	82,534	8,308
Total	494,176	86,772

(Source: *Employment and Productivity Gazette.*

14. Construct histograms for the following data:

DISTRIBUTION OF INCOME

Range of After-tax Income £	Year 1	Year 2
50– 250	5,420	4,600
250– 500	8,130	7,650
500– 750	7,690	8,140
750–1,000	3,250	4,600
1,000–2,000	1,465	2,000
2,000–4,000	178	300
4,000–6,000	16	20
6,000 and over	1	2

Is there any evidence that the distribution of income has become more or less even between the two years?

15.

Type of Course	Number of classes within following class sizes	
	15 or less	more than 15
Full-time or sandwich	29,170	6,637
Block release	2,720	155
Part-time Day	28,518	471
Evening	17,858	304
Total	78,266	7,567

(Source: *National Advisory Council on Education for Industry and Commerce 1966.*)

Draw two bar-charts showing types of course expressed as a percentage of the total number of classes within each category of size.

16.

PRODUCTIVITY IN THE MOTOR INDUSTRY IN 1965

	Vehicles Produced per Employee in 1965	Sales per Employee in 1965 £
U.K.		
B.M.C.	7·1	4,383
Ford	10·9	6,377
Vauxhall	10·1	5,905
Leyland	3·1	3,922
Rootes	7·0	5,833
West Germany		
Volkswagen	13·6	6,760
Ford	13·8	7,338
Opel	12·0	6,255
Daimler Benz	2·9	5,563

Prepare a diagram to illustrate the differences in productivity. Which of the two measures of labour productivity do you consider to be the best, and how do you account for the differences in productivity indicated by the two measures?

17. Construct suitable diagrams to represent the data given below. A different form of representation should be used for each part.

(i) The following table shows the numbers, in thousands, of votes cast for Conservative, Labour, Liberal and Independent candidates in two areas, A and B, at a General Election.

Number of votes (thousands)

	Conservative	Labour	Liberal	Independent
Area A	121	112	15	8
Area B	148	204	32	16

How would your representation have differed if, for each political party, the percentage of the total vote cast in each area had been given instead of the number of votes?

(ii) The following table shows the consumption in million metric tons of coal equivalent, of solid and liquid fuel in Western Europe during the years 1963 to 1967.

Consumption (10^6 metric tons of coal equivalent)

	1963	1964	1965	1966	1967
Solid Fuel	557	539	515	485	459
Liquid Fuel	364	416	466	521	552

(Source—*U.N. Statistical Yearbook*)

18. An examination of a sample of 50 bolts taken from the output of a machine manufacturing steel bolts of nominal length 2·5 cm gave the following lengths in cm.

2·514	2·471	2·493	2·532	2·507
2·508	2·503	2·493	2·504	2·498
2·493	2·518	2·511	2·528	2·486
2·508	2·509	2·513	2·505	2·494
2·497	2·502	2·513	2·484	2·478
2·518	2·502	2·493	2·524	2·506
2·498	2·504	2·513	2·507	2·497
2·503	2·518	2·499	2·498	2·549
2·518	2·548	2·541	2·505	2·486
2·471	2·518	2·511	2·486	2·497

Group these data into a frequency distribution table, using a class interval of 0·01 cm and lowest class boundary of 2·47 cm. Represent these data by a histogram.

19.

	Unemployment % in Great Britain	Average hourly earnings (percentage change compared with the previous year)
1956	1·2	8·2
7	1·3	6·6
8	2·4	3·4
9	1·9	2·9
1960	1·5	7·3
1	1·6	6·9
2	2·2	4·4
3	2·1	3·6
4	1·5	8·1
5	1·4	9·5
6	1·9	6·5
7	2·4	5·0
8	2·4	6·9

Prepare a graph to illustrate the relationship between unemployment and the change in hourly earnings. Use the vertical scale to represent change in hourly earnings and the horizontal scale to represent % unemployment.

Use your graph to estimate the rate of increase in hourly earnings for a level of unemployment of 3%.

Draw another graph with time along the horizontal scale.

20.

QUARTERLY NUMBER OF HOUSES COMPLETED
(SEASONALLY ADJUSTED)

Quarter		Houses completed for Public Authorities (thousands)	Houses completed for Private Developers (thousands)
1967	1	49	47
	2	52	48
	3	52	50
	4	51	55
1968	1	48	59
	2	49	55
	3	48	54
	4	48	53
1969	1	45	48
	2	46	47
	3	48	44
	4	47	42
1970	1	47	43
	2	46	41
	3	46	43
	4	43	43
1971	1	45	46
	2	40	46
	3	37	48
	4	37	51

(Source: *Economic Trends*, March 1972.)

Using the same scales and axes draw graphs of the above series and comment briefly on them.

21. Name *two* types of graph or diagram which have not been mentioned in these Exercises. Using made-up data, give an example of each type such as one might expect to see in a publication for the general public, about the Tourist Industry.

22. The table below shows the quantity, in hundreds of litres, of wheat, barley and oats produced on a certain farm during the years 1971 to 1974.

Year	1971	1972	1973	1974
Wheat	34	43	43	45
Barley	18	14	16	13
Oats	27	24	27	34

(a) Construct a component bar chart to illustrate these data.

(b) For each year express the figure for each crop as a percentage of the annual total and hence construct a percentage bar chart.

(c) Comment briefly on the advantages and disadvantages of these methods of illustrating the data.

CHAPTER 3

Measures of Location

1. Properties of Frequency Distributions

The concept of a frequency distribution underlies the large majority of statistical calculations. It will be seen from the section on histograms in the preceding chapter that frequency distributions often differ considerably in character; but whilst mere inspection of this histogram can reveal something of the relation between frequency distributions of comparable data, it is necessary, from a statistical point of view, to have more precise ways of determining the properties of such distributions than that afforded by a diagrammatic presentation. One obvious property of a frequency distribution is the range of values which the variable takes. The histogram shows that a frequency distribution has two extreme limits, and that outside these limits the values of the variable occur with zero frequency. In comparing two distributions, therefore, it could be asked whether the values taken by the variable in each lie more or less between the same limits, or whether there is some striking difference. This is not, however, a very satisfactory basis of comparison, since in many distributions, the limits of the variable are not very clearly defined. It might well be that a few items in one distribution may have very low or very high values although the main part of the distribution is almost exactly the same as one not having these extreme values.

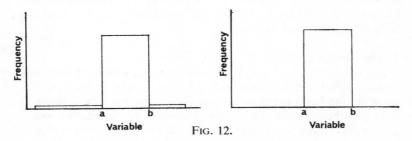

FIG. 12.

In both cases illustrated in Fig. 12, most of the frequencies fall in the interval [a, b] of the variable and, moreover, they are uniformly distributed in this interval. The end-points of the distribution on the left differ, however, from those on the right, though the frequencies are small outside the interval [a, b]. These two distributions have a

49

common property, namely their location on the horizontal axis, which is not indicated by comparing the range of values which the variable can take for the two distributions.

There are several measures of location which are satisfactory according to the purpose for which they are used. All of them have two features: they consist of a single value of the variable which is defined by the way it is calculated either directly or indirectly with reference to all the data. It should be immediately obvious that such measures are greatly superior to the range as a means of measuring location, because the end-points of a distribution are often quite independent of the frequencies which lie between them and the manner in which these frequencies are distributed. A measure of location, then, is defined in terms of a single value of the variable; and it will be seen that this value is only accidentally related to the mid-point or central value of the range, because this point depends only on the end-points of the distribution and is quite independent of its nature. Another advantage of having a single value to represent this important positional property of a distribution is that it provides information about the distribution in a form which is precise and concise. This enables one to make precise comparisons between distributions which are free from the errors to which intuitive comparisons, based on the appearance of diagrams, are liable. It often happens in Statistics that differences which are too small to be intuitively obvious turn out to be very significant when they are investigated mathematically. It will be seen later that there are other properties, apart from measures of location, which can be precisely defined in mathematical terms and which are also important for comparing distributions. The remainder of this chapter will, however, be concerned with the definition and calculation of the different measures of location.

2. The Arithmetic Mean

The word "average" has, in popular usage, a variety of meanings some of which are mathematical and some non-mathematical. For example, the "average man" is a concept which is very difficult to define mathematically. Obviously it means "representative man", but there are many respects in which a man may be representative of everyone and an average man is, presumably, one who is representative in all or nearly all respects, some of which may not be measurable. The idea of a cricket average or a goal average is, however, another popular sense of "average" which is mathematical. It is, in fact, the familiar arithmetic average or mean. A batsman's average score for the season is simply the total number of runs he makes divided by the number of times he is dismissed. For example, if a batsman has 5 innings in which he scores 23, 51, 0, 29 and 105 runs, and he is out 4 times, then his batting average is

$$\frac{23 + 51 + 0 + 29 + 105}{4} = 52 \text{ runs.}$$

Strictly speaking, this is the average number of runs per dismissal. One might also calculate the average number of runs per innings by dividing the total by 5 instead of 4, but such an average would clearly not be very meaningful. A batsman's average is usually interpreted as being indicative or representative of his overall performance and would be misleading unless it were calculated with reference to the number of times he was out.

The arithmetic mean is a representative statistic and, in this sense, it is an important measure of location. In calculating the run average above, it will be observed that each value of the variable (runs scored) occurs only once. In a frequency distribution, the frequency of each value, or range of values, of the variable is usually greater than 1. In order to find the average value of the variable for the distribution, the convenient procedure is to multiply each value of the variable by its corresponding frequency, find the sum of the products and divide this sum by the total frequency to give the average. The procedure is illustrated by the calculation of the average number of children per family from the data on page 20:

No. of children = X	No. of families = f	$f \times X$
0	253	0
1	1,921	1,921
2	2,235	4,470
3	1,528	4,584
4	326	1,304
5	128	640
6	73	438
	6,464	13,357

Arithmetic mean = 13,357/6464 = 2·1 (approx.)

The practice will be adopted of denoting the value of the variable in a frequency distribution by the letter X, whilst the frequencies of each value of X will be denoted by the letter f. In this example, X can take seven values (0, 1, 2, etc.) whilst one value of f (number of families) corresponds to each value of X. The product $f \times X$, usually written fX, is thus the total number of children belonging to families of a given size. The total number of children in families of all sizes is denoted by the symbol ΣfX where Σ is the Greek capital letter "sigma" and indicates that all terms like fX are to be added. The total frequency, i.e., the total number of families is denoted by Σf. So, in this example,

$$\Sigma fX = 13,357, \qquad \Sigma f = 6464$$

and   Arithmetic mean $= \Sigma fX/\Sigma f = 13,357/6464 = 2\cdot1$

The meaning of the sigma notation can be clarified by using the subscript i to indicate which frequency class is being considered. Thus X_i is the value of the variable with frequency f_i where $i = 1, 2, 3, 4, 5, 6, 7$; so that i stands for the ith class.

Thus $X_1 = 0, \qquad X_2 = 1, \qquad X_3 = 2$ etc.
and $f_1 = 253, \quad f_2 = 1921, \quad f_3 = 2235$ etc.
Then

$$\Sigma fX = \sum_{i=1}^{7} f_i X_i = 0 \times 253 + 1 \times 1921 + 2 \times 2235 + \text{etc.} = 13,357$$

$$\Sigma f = \sum_{i=1}^{7} f_i = 253 + 1921 + 2235 + \text{etc.} = 6464.$$

In this example, the average number of children per family is $2\cdot1$, which has a paradoxical appearance because it is inconceivable that any family should have $0\cdot1$ of a child. It is tempting to say that the average must be 2; but to yield to this temptation is to miss the whole point of using the arithmetic mean as a measure of location. The number $2\cdot1$ is not arbitrary for this distribution and is comparable with averages which have been calculated in the same way for other distributions. It locates a single value of the variable in the distribution which is, in a certain sense typical of it, having been calculated from the whole data. It is sometimes called a *population parameter* and measures precisely an important property of the distribution. There is no more reason why it should be an exact whole number than there is that an important physical constant, such as the acceleration due to gravity, measured in any system of units, should have an exact value. Also, in comparing distributions, fractional differences between their arithmetic means may be extremely important.

The calculation of the arithmetic mean of a grouped frequency distribution, such as that for the I.Q. of 100 children, page 31, is performed in exactly the same way as in the above example, except that, since the exact value of each individual in a frequency class is not stated, it is necessary to assume that the value for every individual is the central value of the interval which defines the class to which it belongs. Making this assumption will produce an average which almost certainly will differ from the true average calculated from the complete data; but this difference is in most cases too small to be important and, in any event, it can be estimated fairly accurately by statistical methods, though this refinement will not be discussed here. It should be noted that the assumption referred to is equivalent to the assumption that the mean value of any frequency class is the central value of the interval defining the class. If this is so for all classes, then the true mean will be obtained. It will be true, if the frequencies are uniformly distributed through each class, that is, if the distribution of frequencies over any interval is exactly represented by the corresponding rectangle of the histogram. Using the data from the example on page 31, the method of calculation is as follows:

I.Q. Interval	Mid-point of Interval $= X$	No. of children $= f$	$f \times X$
50– 59	54·5	1	54·5
60– 69	64·5	2	129·0
70– 79	74·5	8	596·0
80– 89	84·5	18	1521·0
90– 99	94·5	23	2173·5
100–109	104·5	21	2194·5
110–119	114·5	15	1717·5
120–129	124·5	9	1120·5
130–139	134·5	3	403·5
		100	9910·0

Arithmetic mean, $\bar{X} = \Sigma fX / \Sigma f = 9910/100$
$$= 99 \cdot 1.$$

The symbol $\bar{X}$ always denotes the arithmetic mean value of the variable X.

It will be observed that quite a lot of arithmetic is involved in finding some of the products fX in this example. When a calculating machine is available, this may not be a handicap; but certainly when calculating by hand, it is useful to have an alternative method of finding $\bar{X}$ which saves time and is less liable to error. This is achieved by "coding" the values of X so that they are all small numbers. To do this, one value of X is chosen, say 94·5, and subtracted from all the others. The calculation can be further simplified by dividing these differences by 10 (the number of scores in each interval). Then, instead of calculating fX, we calculate $f(X - 94·5)/10$. The arithmetic mean of these products is

$$\frac{\frac{1}{10}\Sigma f(X - 94·5)}{\Sigma f} = \frac{1}{10}\frac{\Sigma fX}{\Sigma f} - \frac{1}{10}\frac{\Sigma(f \times 94·5)}{\Sigma f}$$

$$= \frac{1}{10}\frac{\Sigma fX}{\Sigma f} - \frac{1}{10}\frac{94·5\,\Sigma f}{\Sigma f}$$

$$= \frac{\bar{X}}{10} - \frac{94·5}{10}.$$

So $$\bar{X} = 10 \times \frac{1}{10}\frac{\Sigma f(X - 94·5)}{\Sigma f} + 94·5.$$

The actual calculation is shown below.

I.Q. Interval	Mid-point of Interval $= X$	"Coded" Value of X $= (X - 94·5)/10$	No. of Children $= f$	$f(X - 94·5)/10$
50– 59	54·5	−4	1	−4
60– 69	64·5	−3	2	−6
70– 79	74·5	−2	8	−16
80– 89	84·5	−1	18	−18
90– 99	94·5	0	23	0
100–109	104·5	1	21	21
110–119	114·5	2	15	30
120–129	124·5	3	9	27
130–139	134·5	4	3	12
			100	90
				−44
				46

Arithmetic mean, $\bar{X} = 10 \times \frac{46}{100} + 94·5$
$= 4·6 + 94·5$
$= 99·1$ (as before).

This method of selecting an *assumed mean* in order to shorten calculations is widely used in statistical work and the student is advised to study this example carefully and apply the method wherever possible. Which value of X is selected as the assumed mean is a matter of convenience, and the student should verify that other values of X used for this purpose will give the same result. It is useful to choose an actual value of X since this ensures that one frequency will be multiplied by zero.

The foregoing method can also be used for finding the arithmetic mean of the frequency distribution of a continuous variable. The centre of each interval is found exactly as before by taking the mean of the extreme values of the interval. Since each interval contains an infinite number of possible values of the variable, the width of the interval is just the difference between its limits. For example "60 in. but less than 62 in." represents an interval of 2 in. In the case of the I.Q. scores, the intervals consisted of 10 scores, which is not equal to the difference between the limits of the intervals, viz., 9. This must be borne in mind when coding the values of the variable.

3. The Median

The median of a distribution is more obviously a measure of its location than the arithmetic mean. It is defined as the value of the variable such that 50% of the frequencies lie below and 50% above it. To find the median of a set of numbers, the numbers are first arranged in order of magnitude. If there is an odd number of numbers, then the median value is the central one when they have been so arranged. For example, the median of the numbers: 2, 7, 8, 15, 21 is 8. When the number of numbers is even, there is no central number, but there are two middle numbers and the median, in this case, is the average of these two middle numbers. For example, the median of the numbers: 5, 8, 9, 10, 14, 17 is $\frac{1}{2}(9 + 10) = 9\cdot5$.

In a grouped frequency distribution, the items are already arranged according to the order of magnitude of the variable. If the total frequency is n, then the median value is that of the $(n + 1)/2$th item whether n is odd or even. The fact that when n is even, there is no exactly corresponding item, is unimportant when finding the median of a frequency distribution. The median may be found graphically, or by calculation. In both cases, the method depends on first constructing a cumulative frequency table from the given data. The cumulative frequency table for the I.Q. of 100 children (page 31) is shown overleaf.

The median item of this distribution is the $(100 + 1)/2$th or $50\frac{1}{2}$th item. This falls in the interval 90–99 which contains 23 items of which the median item is the $(50\frac{1}{2} - 29)$th or $21\frac{1}{2}$th. The value of the variable corresponding to this item is readily found by simple

I.Q.	Cumulative Frequency
59 and below	1
69 ,, ,,	3
79 ,, ,,	11
89 ,, ,,	29
99 ,, ,,	52
109 ,, ,,	73
119 ,, ,,	88
129 ,, ,,	97
139 ,, ,,	100

proportion. Thus 23 items correspond to an interval of 10 scores; so $21\frac{1}{2}$ items correspond to an interval of

$$\frac{21\frac{1}{2}}{23} \times 10 = 9\cdot3 \text{ scores.}$$

Hence   median score $= 89 + 9\cdot3 = 98\cdot3$.

It is useful to have a formula for making this calculation. Let l_1 be the upper limit of the class immediately below that containing the median item and r_1 the frequency of items below l_1. Let l_2 be the upper limit of the class containing the median item and r_2 the frequency of items below l_2. Let $n = \Sigma f$ (total frequency).

Then   Median $= l_1 + \dfrac{\frac{1}{2}(n + 1) - r_1}{r_2 - r_1} \times (l_2 - l_1)$.

In the above example, $n = 100$, $l_1 = 89$, $r_1 = 29$, $l_2 = 99$, $r_2 = 52$.

To obtain the median graphically, the cumulative frequencies in the above table are plotted against the corresponding upper interval limits of the scores and the resulting set of points are joined by a smooth curve. The graph in Fig. 13 is called an *Ogive*. It is actually a "less than" Ogive since any point on the curve shows how many items there are with smaller values of the variable than that to which the point corresponds.

In the frequency distribution of a continuous variable, the upper and lower limits of adjacent intervals coincide, and it is obviously valid to use the formula above in order to calculate the median of such a distribution. If a typical interval in a continuous distribution is "a and less than b", then the cumulative frequencies will apply to ranges of the variable which are strictly less than a, less than b, and so on. This should be indicated in the cumulative frequency table by writing "less than a", "less than b" etc., opposite the appropriate cumulative frequencies.

As well as the median, it is often useful to calculate the values of the variable below and above which 25% of the frequencies lie.

OGIVE OF I.Q. SCORES

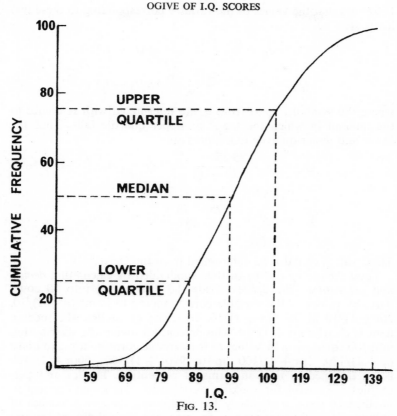

FIG. 13.

These two values are called the *lower* and *upper quartiles*, respectively, of the distribution. The upper and lower quartile values of the variable are usually denoted by Q_3 and Q_1. The median divides the interval between these two quartiles, and so is denoted by Q_2. If q_1, q_3 and q_2 are the lower and upper quartile and median items respectively, then the lower and upper quartile items should have the desirable property that

$$q_1 + q_3 = 2q_2$$
$$q_3 - q_1 = q_2$$

where
$$q_2 = (n + 1)/2.$$

Solving these equations, we find that

$$q_1 = (n + 1)/4 \quad \text{and} \quad q_3 = 3(n + 1)/4.$$

It follows that the values of the variable corresponding to these two items are

$$Q_1 = l_1 + \frac{\frac{1}{4}(n + 1) - r_1}{r_2 - r_1} \times (l_2 - l_1)$$

$$Q_3 = l_1 + \frac{\frac{3}{4}(n + 1) - r_1}{r_2 - r_1} \times (l_2 - l_1)$$

where the symbols, apart from n, are interpreted with reference to the interval in which the lower or upper quartile falls. Thus the lower and upper quartile I.Q. scores are:

$$Q_1 = 79 + \frac{25 \cdot 25 - 11}{29 - 11} \times (89 - 79)$$

$$= 86 \cdot 9$$

$$Q_3 = 109 + \frac{75 \cdot 75 - 73}{88 - 73} \times (119 - 109)$$

$$= 110 \cdot 8.$$

These values can also be determined from the Ogive.

Total frequency can be further subdivided by calculating *deciles* and *percentiles*. The deciles divide the distribution into 10 equal parts by values of the variable corresponding to items $(n + 1)/10$, $2(n + 1)/10$ up to $9(n + 1)/10$. In terms of deciles, the median item is clearly $5(n + 1)/10$. The percentiles divide the distribution into 100 equal parts by values of the variable corresponding to items $(n + 1)/100$, $2(n + 1)/100$ up to $99(n + 1)/100$; $50(n + 1)/100$ being the median item in terms of percentiles. Deciles and percentiles are useful for ranking examination marks and scores in intelligence tests, particularly for comparing the performances of individuals in different tests or for assessing the validity of the test itself.

4. The Mode

The mode of a frequency distribution is the value of the variable of greatest frequency. The modal frequency group is therefore the one containing the largest number of individuals and the value of the variable corresponding to this group is the value which is "in fashion" or, according to the French expression *à la mode*. For example, the modal number of children in the distribution shown by the histogram in Fig. 3 is 2, the rectangle corresponding to this number being the largest in the histogram. As a measure of location, the mode is rather unsatisfactory because it might occur anywhere in the distribution, though it is usually found somewhere in the middle. If it is very pronounced, i.e., contains a large proportion of the items in the distribution, it will have a considerable effect on the arithmetic mean, which will, in this case, tend to be located near it. So while in exceptional cases unsatisfactory, the mode is fairly representative in ordinary cases. Sometimes, indeed, a distribution may have more than one mode, the numbers in each modal group being very little different from each other. It may be expected therefore, that the mode is a satisfactory measure of location in a prominently uni-modal distribution.

In a frequency distribution which is grouped by intervals of the value of the variable, the modal value can be found either graphically from the histogram, or by calculation. As an illustration of the graphical method, consider the histogram for the distribution of I.Q. scores (p. 31) shown in Fig. 14.

I.Q. OF 100 CHILDREN AT A JUNIOR SCHOOL

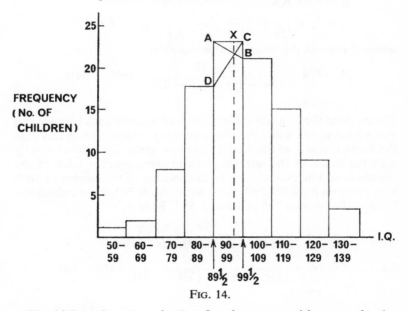

FIG. 14.

The highest frequency is that for the group with scores in the closed interval 90–99. The modal score is a single value lying in this interval, its exact value depending not only on the frequency in the modal group but also on the frequencies in the two groups adjacent to the modal group. The construction must allow for the fact that the mode is pulled towards the adjacent group having the higher frequency. This is effected by joining the corners A,C of the modal rectangle with the corners B,D of the adjacent rectangles. A perpendicular from the point of intersection of AB and CD to the horizontal axis intersects this axis at the modal value of the variable. In this example, the required value is $89\frac{1}{2} + 7 = 96\frac{1}{2}$.

If the modal value lies a distance AX above the lower limit of the modal group, it can be shown geometrically that

$$AX = \frac{AC.AD}{AD + BC}.$$

Let f_2 be the frequency in the modal group and f_1 and f_3 the frequencies in the lower and upper adjacent groups respectively. And let l_1, l_2 be the upper and lower limits of the adjacent groups.

Then $AC = l_2 - l_1$, $AD = f_2 - f_1$, $BC = f_2 - f_3$. It follows that the modal value is given by the formula:

$$Z = l_1 + AX$$
$$= l_1 + \frac{f_2 - f_1}{(f_2 - f_1) + (f_2 - f_3)} \times (l_2 - l_1)$$

where Z denotes the mode. In this example,

$$Z = 89\frac{1}{2} + \frac{23 - 18}{(23 - 18) + (23 - 21)} \times (99\frac{1}{2} - 89\frac{1}{2})$$
$$= 96\frac{1}{2}.$$

The mode of the frequency distribution of a continuous variable can also be calculated using the above formula, except that in this case the limits l_1 and l_2 of the modal frequency group correspond exactly with the limits of the interval given in the frequency table of the distribution. For example, in the distribution of the heights of 1000 men given on page 32, the highest frequency is 304, these individuals lying in the interval "66 and under 68". So here,

$$l_1 = 66 \quad \text{and} \quad l_2 = 68.$$

Also $\qquad f_1 = 187, \quad f_2 = 304, \quad f_3 = 263.$

So $\qquad Z = 66 + \dfrac{304 - 187}{(304 - 187) + (304 - 263)} \times (68 - 66)$
$$= 67{\cdot}5 \text{ in.}$$

5. Comparison of Mean, Median and Mode

The arithmetic mean or, as it is usually called simply, the mean, is the most useful measure of location in a wide variety of statistical calculations. It has been seen that it is directly derived from all the given data, that is, the value of every item in a distribution affects the value of the mean. Although it is widely used in everyday life, it is really a statistic of a highly theoretical nature, and this is the reason why it is often misleading when incautiously interpreted. It is often not obviously representative of the data from which it is derived, and no item in the data may, in fact, have the average value. It can happen that the mean is widely different from any item in the distribution. For example, the mean of the numbers: 1, 3, 6, 100 is 27·5 which is considerably different from any of the individual numbers and, therefore, hardly representative of any of them. Moreover, the value of the mean may look unrealistic when it is fractional but the objects about which the data is collected cannot have fractional values (e.g., men, live farm animals, etc.). These are, however, disadvantages of the mean which are only present when it is used for purposes for which it is not really intended. Sometimes, of course, it can be a representative value and, if accompanied by other information which shows this, can be useful for ordinary purposes. But its main utility lies in the part it plays in statistical calculations.

The median is derived indirectly from the whole data, but it does not have much reference to the actual values taken by individual items. All that is certainly known about it is that it divides the data into two equal parts such that the items in one part have values greater than the median, whilst in the other part the values of the items are less than the median. However, some of the items above and below the median may have values which are extremely different from it. In certain statistical tests, the median is essential. One advantage which it has over the mean is that it can often be found before all the data is collected, which saves time and money. For example, if one wishes to determine the median length of life of 49 cathode ray tubes which are all of the same design, one could switch them on and wait until 25 had failed, the life of the 25th being the median life. The value of the median may be all that it is necessary to know in such a case, in which event the test can be terminated and the remaining 24 tubes saved.

As a measure of location, the mode is not very much used in statistical calculations, though it is, of course, representative in a sense in which the mean often is not. For example, the modal group in the distribution of incomes in the United Kingdom (after tax) includes between 40% and 50% of all incomes and, in a case of this sort, it is informative to know what the mode is. Mean income, after tax, is considerably higher than the mode, and so is somewhat unrepresentative. Unlike the mean, the mode of an empirical distribution is not a precisely determined single magnitude, even though a precise formula can be used to estimate it. The case is different with a theoretical distribution which is defined by a mathematical equation; for then the mode may be given exactly and will have a bearing on the character of the distribution. An empirical distribubution moreover, may be bi-modal, for example the height distribution of all adult human beings in the UK, so that the modal value does not, in this case, provide a single measure of location, however imprecise.

It will be seen that the information value of the three measures of location, as distinct from their value in further statistical calculations, is enhanced if they are considered together. In many distributions which are encountered in practice, it is found that the mean, mode and median are connected by the same relationships. For example, the median usually lies between the mode and the mean, except when the three measures coincide. The three possibilities are illustrated by the frequency polygons shown in Fig. 15.

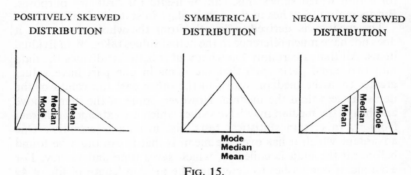

FIG. 15.

As might be expected, the mean, mode and median coincide when the distribution is symmetrical provided, of course, that the central value of the distribution is that for which the frequency is greatest, which in many symmetrical, or approximately symmetrical, distributions is the case. An approximate relationship between the three measures, which has been found in many instances to hold, is given by the formula:

$$3(\text{Mean} - \text{Median}) = \text{Mean} - \text{Mode}$$

or in symbols:

$$3(\bar{X} - Q_2) = \bar{X} - Z.$$

The reader may care to verify that, in the example of I.Q. scores, this relationship approximately holds. It must be emphasised that all the relationships just discussed are based on the investigation of empirical distributions. There is no necessary reason why they should be true, and it is possible to construct imaginary distributions for which they are false. The distinction between the properties of empirical and theoretical distributions is a vital one in Statistics, as will be seen in later chapters.

6. The Geometric Mean

A fourth measure of location which is often useful is the *geometric mean*. The geometric mean of a set of n numbers is the nth root of the product of the numbers. For example, the geometric mean of the numbers 2 and 8 is $\sqrt[2]{(2 \times 8)} = 4$. The geometric mean of the numbers: 3, 25 and 45 is $\sqrt[3]{(3 \times 25 \times 45)} = 15$. In general, if the variable X_i occurs with frequency f_i where there are m frequency groups, then the geometric mean of the distribution is:

$$\text{G.M.} = \sqrt[n]{(X_1{}^{f_1} \times X_2{}^{f_2} \times \ldots \times X_m{}^{f_m})}$$

where
$$n = \sum_{i=1}^{m} f_i.$$

The actual calculation of the geometric mean is best performed by logarithms, except when the numbers are very simple. It should be noted that it can be calculated only when the variable takes positive values greater than zero $(X_i > 0)$. In other cases it is meaningless. An interesting property of the geometric mean is that it is always less than the arithmetic mean, except when the values of all the items are the same. This indicates that the geometric mean is less influenced by very large items than the arithmetic mean. Related to this is another important property of the G.M., namely that if the number of items is large, then even a considerable change in the value of one of them has little effect. This property is utilised in calculating the mean of a set of index numbers which show day-to-day changes in a quantity such as the price of shares. The *Financial Times* Actuaries Index, illustrated in the graph of Chapter 2, Fig. 9, is an example of an average calculated in this way. The F.T. 500 Share Index, for example, is the G.M. of 500 share indices. Even if the price of one of these shares doubled in one day, the other shares being unaltered, the index would be increased only by a factor of $\sqrt[500]{2}$ which is very little different from unity. The G.M. thus has great stability when changes in only a few items in a distribution are taking place, and so it gives a more balanced picture of change than would the arithmetic mean, for example.

Before leaving the subject of measures of location, it should be mentioned that they are also sometimes called *measures of central tendency*, for obvious reasons.

7. Percentage Frequency

It is often convenient to convert frequencies in a frequency table to percentages. The relationship between actual and percentage frequency is illustrated by the following table:

Variable, X	1	2	3	4	Total
Frequency	98	126	219	57	500
% Frequency	19·6	25·2	43·8	11·4	100
Cu. % Frequency	19·6	44·8	88·6	100·0	—

The percentage frequencies in line 3 of the table are sometimes called *relative frequencies*, and from a mathematical point of view give the same information as the actual (or absolute) frequencies in line 2. For example, percentage frequencies can be used to calculate the mean value of X instead of the actual frequencies. Percentage frequencies are often much easier to handle mathematically than actual frequencies and hence are widely used in Statistics. Also, percentage frequencies for different frequency distributions can be compared, even though the total absolute frequencies differ. For example, two frequency distributions may have the same properties, in which case, the percentage frequencies for both will be the same, although the absolute frequencies differ. The fourth line of the table shows the cumulative percentage frequency for the distribution and can be used, if necessary, to construct the ogive. The histogram and cumulative frequency curve based on percentage frequencies are, of course, the same shape as the corresponding diagrams based on the original data. It is worth noting that if the percentage cumulative frequency curve is used to find the median and quartiles graphically then, since the total frequency is unknown, one cannot do better than say that the median corresponds to a cumulative frequency of 50%, whilst the upper and lower quartiles correspond to cumulative frequencies of 75% and 25% respectively. This is illustrated in the ogive (Fig. 16).

Relative frequencies are sometimes expressed as fractions between 0 and 1, so that their sum is 1 instead of 100. To obtain relative frequencies in this form, each percentage frequency is divided by 100 giving, for the above data: 0·196, 0·252, 0·438, 0·114. Since the sum of these numbers is 1, it immediately follows that the mean of the distribution is:

$$\overline{X} = 0·196 \times 1 + 0·252 \times 2 + 0·438 \times 3 + 0·114 \times 4 = 2·47.$$

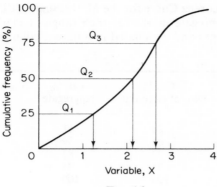

FIG. 16.

This may be compared with the mean calculated in the ordinary way.

$$\overline{X} = \frac{\sum fX}{\sum f} = \frac{98 \times 1 + 126 \times 2 + 219 \times 3 + 57 \times 4}{500} = 2\cdot47.$$

The calculation of cumulative percentage frequency is often necessary in order to compare the way a quantity is distributed (or shared) between the individual members of a group. For example, Income after tax is distributed in a certain way between members of the working population and it is instructive to know whether this distribution is more or less equal and also how the distribution is changing from one period to another. This information can be obtained by constructing a *Lorenz Curve* for the data. The following example illustrates.

MATHS. AND ENGLISH MARKS OF 50 CANDIDATES

Maths. Mark	No. of Candidates	Aggregate Marks	English Marks	No. of Candidates	Aggregate Marks
1– 20	14	198	1– 20	6	95
21– 40	17	512	21– 40	14	501
41– 60	15	790	41– 60	21	1137
61– 80	3	217	61– 80	6	423
81–100	1	85	81–100	3	265
	50	1802		50	2421

To construct a Lorenz Curve for the Maths. marks, the number of candidates and aggregate marks for each range of marks are converted to percentages and cumulated in adjacent columns, as in the following table:

No. of candidates %	Cu. % No. of candidates	Cu. % Aggregate	Aggregate marks %
28	28	11	11
34	62	39	28
30	92	83	44
6	98	95	12
2	100	100	5

LORENZ CURVES OF MATHS AND ENGLISH MARKS

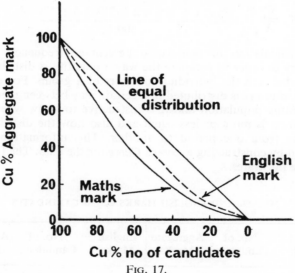

FIG. 17.

The axes of the graph (Fig. 17) are graduated so that the origin corresponds to zero on the vertical scale and 100 on the horizontal scale, which is graduated from left to right in descending order of magnitude. This is in order that each curve should begin and end on an axis of the graph. The inequality of a distribution is indicated by the area lying between the curve and the line of equal distribution. If all candidates obtain the same mark, then 50% of the candidates obtain 50 % of the marks and so all points of the Lorenz Curve will, in this case, lie on the line of equal distribution. In the present example, the Curve shows that 50 % of the candidates (those with the lowest marks) share between them only 26 % of the marks, so this is a rather unequal distribution: a few candidates have obtained the majority of the marks. A similar curve, constructed in the same way, for English marks, shows that this distribution is much more equal than that of the Maths. marks; for example, the lower 50% of the candidates obtained 36% of the marks, and the curve for English marks is, accordingly, closer to the line of equal distribution. Unless the value of the variable (marks in the present instance) is the same for all individuals, the Lorenz Curve must lie below the line of equal distribution, as a little reflection will show.

The Lorenz Curve is useful in social and economic studies for showing how equal or unequal is the distribution of such quantities as Income and Personal Wealth among the members of the community. The skewness of the distribution also gives some indication of this, of course. A symmetrical distribution results in a curve lying closer to the line of equal distribution than an asymmetrical one. Thus the distribution of the Maths. marks is more positively skewed than that of the English marks, which is more nearly symmetrical.

8. The Sigma Notation

Since the Σ notation, denoting summation, is used a great deal in Statistics and other branches of mathematics, a few additional notes on its meaning are now given. The symbol $\sum_{i=1}^{m} X_i$ is an instruction to find the sum of the m values of the variable X, namely:

$$X_1 + X_2 + X_3 + \ldots + X_m.$$

The dots in this expression are a shorthand method of indicating the missing terms, in this case running from X_4 to X_{m-1}. If k is a constant number, then

$$\sum_{i=1}^{m} kX_i = kX_1 + kX_2 + kX_3 + \ldots + kX_m$$
$$= k(X_1 + X_2 + X_3 + \ldots + X_m)$$
$$= k \sum_{i=1}^{m} X_i.$$

In other words, if each value of X is multiplied by the same number k, then k can be placed outside the summation sign. Suppose that, for all i, $X_i = 1$, then

$$\sum_{i=1}^{m} kX_i = k(1 + 1 + 1 + \text{to } m \text{ terms})$$
$$= k \times m.$$

When manipulating the summation notation, a term such as $\sum_{i=1}^{m} k$
is often obtained, and the above shows that

$$\sum_{i=1}^{m} k = mk.$$

The summation sign can also indicate the sum of $X_i{}^2$, $X_i{}^3$, etc. For example,

$$\sum_{i=1}^{m} X_i{}^2 = X_1{}^2 + X_2{}^2 + X_3{}^2 + \ldots + X_m{}^2.$$

Also, if f_i is the frequency of X_i, then

$$\sum_{i=1}^{m} f_i X_i{}^2 = f_1 X_1{}^2 + f_2 X_2{}^2 + f_3 X_3{}^2 + \ldots + f_m X_m{}^2.$$

It is often convenient to separate the sum of a bracketed expression into two sums. For example, if a and b are two constants, then

$$\sum_{i=1}^{m} (a + bX_i) = (a + bX_1) + \ldots + (a + bX_m)$$
$$= ma + b(X_1 + \ldots + X_m)$$
$$= \sum_{i=1}^{m} a + b \sum_{i=1}^{m} X_i.$$

The summation is said to be *distributive* over each term in the bracket. As a further example,

$$\sum_{i=1}^{m} (a - bX_i)^2 = \sum_{i=1}^{m} (a^2 - 2abX_i + b^2 X_i{}^2)$$
$$= \sum_{i=1}^{m} a^2 - 2ab \sum_{i=1}^{m} X_i + b^2 \sum_{i=1}^{m} X_i{}^2.$$

When the context of a problem indicates clearly what the limits of summation are, they are sometimes omitted for convenience. Thus, if it is obvious that there are m values of X to be added, this can be indicated by writing ΣX in place of $\sum_{i=1}^{m} X_i$; but, on the other hand, it can be a help to clear thinking if the limits are inserted and sometimes it may be indispensable to do so.

It is sometimes necessary to indicate the sum of the products of corresponding values of *two* variables, and the summation notation easily lends itself to this end. For example, if X and Y are two variables with corresponding pairs of values X_i and Y_i, then

$$\sum_{i=1}^{m} X_i Y_i = X_1 Y_1 + X_2 Y_2 + \ldots + X_m Y_m.$$

EXAMPLE 1

If $\bar{X}$ is the mean value of the variable X, show that $\Sigma (X - \bar{X}) = 0$.

Let the m values of X be denoted by X_i ($i = 1, 2, \ldots, m$).

Then
$$\sum_{i=1}^{m} (X_i - \bar{X}) = \sum_{i=1}^{m} X_i - \sum_{i=1}^{m} \bar{X}$$

$$= \sum_{i=1}^{m} X_i - m\bar{X}$$

$$= \sum_{i=1}^{m} X_i - \sum_{i=1}^{m} X_i$$

$$= 0 \quad \text{(as required).}$$

This, of course, follows from the definition of the mean $\bar{X}$ as

$$\bar{X} = \sum_{i=1}^{m} X_i / m,$$

it being understood in this example that the frequency of each value of X is just 1.

EXERCISES 3

1. Find the mean of the n consecutive integers $1, 2, 3, \ldots, n$.

2. Find the median of 10, 17, 5, 18, 2, 17, 19, 13.

3. The sales of a company in 1970 and 1971 were £120,000 and £132,000 respectively. What will be the sales in 1972 if there is the same percentage increase?

4. Sketch frequency polygons, one of which is bi-modal and the other extremely asymmetrical.

5. The mean wages of 100, 150 and 250 men employed by three different firms are £19, £23 and £18 per week respectively. Calculate the mean wage per week of all the men.

6. Estimate the mode of the following distribution:

Length (cm)	0–	5–	10–	15–	20 & over
Frequency	8	12	6	3	1

7. A motorist notes that, according to the clock and the distance-measuring instrument in his car, he has taken 1 hour to travel 50 km. He concludes that his average speed was 50 km/h. If each of his instruments is accurate to 1% only, between what limits does his true average speed lie?

8. Observations of a continuous variable, which can take positive values only, are classified into four classes whose central values are $\frac{1}{2}$, $1\frac{1}{2}$, 3 and 7. What are the sizes of the corresponding class intervals?

9. The following table shows the milk yield, in litres, of 100 cows in one year. Estimate the upper and lower quartiles and the median.

Milk yield	1500–	2000–	2500–	3000–	3500–	4000–5000
No. of cows	14	25	34	20	5	2

10. The average wage of four men is £17 per week. What is the average wage of a further six men if the average wage of all ten men is £20 per week?

11. The heights of 25 boys are measured to the nearest centimetre and are then grouped as follows:

Height (in cm)	151–155	156–160	161–165	166–170	171–175
Frequency	4	8	7	5	1

Which of the following statements may be true and which must be false?
(a) The modal class contains 7 members. (b) The median height is 158 cm. (c) The median height is 161 cm. (d) The total range of heights is 20 cm.

Answer: May be true   a   b   c   d
Must be false   a   b   c   d

12. The table below shows the distribution of the marks of 648 candidates in a G.C.E. mathematics examination.

Mark:	10	20	30	40	50
No. of candidates who scored less than this mark:	8	34	104	190	310

Mark:	60	70	80	90	100
No. of candidates who scored less than this mark:	450	543	615	638	648

Draw a cumulative frequency graph to show these data, representing marks on the horizontal axis and number of candidates on the vertical axis. Use the graph to estimate: (i) how many candidates scored less than 75 marks, (ii) the pass mark, if 60% of the 648 candidates passed, (iii) how many candidates failed to pass by only one mark.

13. Weekly earnings of full-time men clerks in U.K. in 1970 based on data from Family Expenditure Survey 1970.

Range of Weekly Earnings	Number of Men
under £14	5
£14 but under £16	19
£16 ,, ,, £18	22
£18 ,, ,, £20	25
£20 ,, ,, £22	42
£22 ,, ,, £24	35
£24 ,, ,, £26	31
£26 ,, ,, £28	19
£28 ,, ,, £30	25
£30 ,, ,, £35	47
£35 ,, ,, £40	29
£40 ,, ,, £45	10
£45 and over	10

For the above data construct an ogive and hence find median, upper quartile, lower quartile and the highest decile.

Check your result for the median by means of a calculation.

Find the mode of this distribution, either graphically or by calculation.

Calculate the mean earnings and show the positions of the mean, median and mode on a histogram of the data. What conclusions does this enable you to draw about the distribution of earnings?

14. From the data given below, draw an ogive, and from it estimate:
    (a) the median and upper and lower quartiles.
    (b) the percentage of the population in the age ranges 10–19, 20–29 and 30–39.

Check the answers to (a) by calculation.

The data represent a standardised percentage age distribution for established towns.

AGE	% OF TOTAL
0– 4	8·2
5–14	12·9
15–24	14·1
25–34	15·3
35–44	15·7
45–54	13·0
55–64	10·3
65–69	4·1
70 and over	6·4
	100·0

15. Find the geometric mean of the numbers: (a) 6, 8, 36 and (b) 7, 11, 55.

16. The Population of England and Wales increased from 9 mn. in 1801 to 49 mn. in 1971. Assuming that the numbers increased by the same percentage each decade, find this percentage.

17. Distribution of Income after tax in 1958:

Range of income after Tax £	No. of Incomes (thousands)	Income after tax (£ mn.)
50– 250	5420	1240
250– 500	8130	3108
500– 750	7690	4746
750–1000	3250	2740
1000–2000	1465	1835
2000–4000	178	472
4000–6000	16	73
6000 and over	0·9	6

Draw a Lorenz Curve to illustrate this data.

Explain how to estimate aggregate Income after tax for each range of income if this data were unavailable.

What alternative diagrammatic method could be used to illustrate this data, and what precautions would be necessary in using it?

18. Calculate the values of: (a) $\sum_{i=1}^{9} X_i$ and (b) $\sum_{i=1}^{9} iX_i$ assuming, in both cases, that $X_i = i$. [For example, $X_1 = 1$, $X_2 = 2$, etc.]

19. Find the value of $\sum_{i=1}^{5} X_i$ where $X_i = 2i - 1$. Hence find the mean of these five values of X.

20. Show that $\Sigma (X_i - \bar{X})^2 = \Sigma X_i^2 - n\bar{X}^2$ where $\bar{X}$ is the mean of the n values of X over which the summation is taken. Verify that this relation is true when $n = 4$ and $X_1 = 7$, $X_2 = 9$, $X_3 = 15$, $X_4 = 17$.

21. Show that $\Sigma (X_i - \bar{X})(Y_i - \bar{Y}) = \Sigma X_i Y_i - n\bar{X}\bar{Y}$ where X and Y are variables which take n pairs of values X_i, Y_i and $\bar{X}$, $\bar{Y}$ are the means of the n values of X and Y respectively.
    Verify that the relationship is true when $n = 5$ and

$$X_1 = 2, \quad X_2 = 5, \quad X_3 = 6, \quad X_4 = 6, \quad X_5 = 11$$
$$Y_1 = 1, \quad Y_2 = 4, \quad Y_3 = 5, \quad Y_4 = 6, \quad Y_5 = 9.$$

22. If A is an assumed mean of the n values of the variable X, show that

$$\bar{X} = A + \frac{\Sigma (X - A)}{n}.$$

23. Calculate the mean of the age distribution in No. 14. Take the mid-point of the highest age group as 75.

24. Sixty motor cars were subjected to a mileage test. Each was supplied with a measured gallon of fuel and driven round a circular track until the fuel was consumed. The number of miles covered by the cars was as follows:

18·6	38·6	9·5	31·9	36·8	30·1
20·0	38·3	38·0	22·5	23·8	34·7
32·5	25·3	40·6	29·6	26·3	34·9
26·9	28·1	28·9	32·3	32·9	31·6
34·1	32·7	30·6	29·3	49·5	29·4
29·1	36·0	37·5	33·7	23·1	52·6
33·4	25·9	38·5	33·0	27·1	27·9
26·2	35·2	27·5	39·1	30·6	29·0
34·6	27·8	58·3	25·3	24·9	34·0
23·8	33·1	28·0	34·2	33·8	21·8

(a) Arrange these figures into a grouped frequency distribution table using a mileage interval of ten, i.e. "less than 10", "10 and less than 20", and so on. Calculate the mean of the distribution. (b) Cumulate the frequencies and, graphically or otherwise, find the median. Comment on the skewness of the distribution.

CHAPTER 4

Measures of Dispersion

1. Dispersion

It has been seen that the arithmetic mean is the most representative measure of location of all the items in a frequency distribution considered collectively; although it may be very unrepresentative of some, or perhaps most, items considered individually. The mode and median are more representative of parts of the data than the mean, but less representative of the whole data, though there may be little or no difference in certain cases, for instance if a distribution is symmetrical. It should, however, be obvious that additional information about a distribution will increase the information value of the measure of location. Two frequency distributions may both have

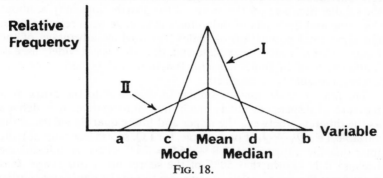

FIG. 18.

the same mean, mode and median and yet be very different in character because of the way in which the frequencies of different values of the variable are related to these measures. The frequency polygons in Fig. 18 for two different distributions should clarify the point.

Thus both distributions are symmetrical, having the same mean, mode and median. But the items in distribution I all have values which are close to the mean compared to those of the items in distribution II. In a sense, therefore, the mean of the first distribution is more representative than that of the second; though the mean value itself gives no indication of this, since it is the same in both cases. The *dispersion* of the data about the mean for distribution II is greater than that for I, and it is clearly desirable to have some measure of this dispersion.

2. Range and Inter-quartile Range

The most obvious measure of dispersion, as appears from the diagram (Fig. 18), is the range of values which the variable takes. The *range* is defined as the difference between the least and greatest values of the variable. In a grouped frequency distribution, this is simply the difference between the upper limit of the last frequency group and the lower limit of the first. The range for distribution I is $d-c$ and for II is $b-a$. For the distribution of I.Q. scores on page 31 it is $139-50 = 89$. A disadvantage of the range, which may occur to some readers after the discussion at the beginning of Chapter 3, is that having a few extreme items may be the only respect in which two otherwise similar distributions differ. This can happen, for example, when the heights of two sets of adult males, the numbers being different in each set, are grouped in two frequency distributions. The set with the larger number of individuals is more likely to contain a few individuals with extreme height measurements than the set with the smaller number; yet the means of the distributions may be about the same and both sets of individuals may have been selected from the same total population of males. An obvious advantage of the range is that it is easy to calculate and, though it is not widely used in Statistics, it often fulfils a useful function in Engineering for controlling the quality of products.

The *inter-quartile range* is similar in character to the range as a measure of dispersion, but is much more informative. It is defined as the difference between the upper and lower quartile values of the variable, i.e., $Q_3 - Q_1$. For example, for I.Q. scores (see page 58), the inter-quartile range is $110 \cdot 8 - 86 \cdot 9 = 23 \cdot 9$. This is informative because it is known that 50% of the scores lie in this range. It is convenient for most statistical purposes to use the *semi-inter-quartile range* (or *quartile deviation*) instead of the quartile range, and this is defined as

$$Q = \tfrac{1}{2}(Q_3 - Q_1).$$

In a symmetrical distribution, it is obvious that 50% of the distribution lies in the interval $Q_2 \pm Q$, where Q_2 is the median. If the distribution is asymmetrical, Q_1 and Q_3 do not coincide with the limits of this interval, and this fact provides one means, among others, of measuring skewness.

3. Mean Deviation

The mean deviation of a set of numbers is defined as the sum of the differences of the numbers from their mean, each of the differences being taken as positive, divided by the number of the numbers. Some of the values of a variable lie above their mean and some below and it was shown in Chapter 3, Example 1 that the *algebraic* sum $\Sigma(X - \bar{X})$ is zero. In order to find the total deviation of the items from their mean, it is therefore necessary to take the differences $X - \bar{X}$ as positive when X is less than $\bar{X}(X < \bar{X})$. To indicate that this difference is positive, it is written as $|X - \bar{X}|$; this is sometimes called the *absolute* value of the difference to distinguish it from the algebraic value which may be either positive or negative, depending on whether X is above or below the mean. For example, the algebraic value of $2 - 3$ is -1 whilst the absolute value of this difference is $|2 - 3| = 1$. If $\bar{X}$ is less than X then, of course, the absolute and algebraic differences are equal; for example $3 - 2 = |3 - 2| = 1$. The mean deviation of the variable X is therefore defined by the formula: $\qquad$ M.D. $= \Sigma |X - \bar{X}|/n$

where n is the number of values of the variable, the frequency of each value being just 1. For a grouped frequency distribution in which f is the frequency of each class, this formula becomes:

$$\text{M.D.} = \Sigma f|X - \bar{X}|/\Sigma f.$$

The following illustrates the calculation of mean deviation for the data for I.Q. scores on page 53, for which $\bar{X} = 99 \cdot 1$.

I.Q. Mid-point of Interval $= X$	Deviation from Mean taken as Positive $= |X - \bar{X}|$	No. of Children $= f$	$f \times |X - \bar{X}|$
54·5	44·6	1	44·6
64·5	34·6	2	69·2
74·5	24·6	8	196·8
84·5	14·6	18	262·8
94·5	4·6	23	105·8
104·5	5·4	21	113·4
114·5	15·4	15	231·0
124·5	25·4	9	228·6
134·5	35·4	3	106·2
		100	1358·4

Total deviation from mean $= 1358 \cdot 4$

$$\begin{aligned} \text{M.D.} &= \Sigma f|X - \bar{X}|/\Sigma f \\ &= 1358 \cdot 4/100 \\ &= 13 \cdot 6 \text{ (approx.)} \end{aligned}$$

Mean deviation is useful as a descriptive measure of dispersion and can also be used to compare the dispersions of two distributions. An important defect is that it gives equal weight to extreme items and items whose deviation from the mean is small; so that the existence of several extreme items, which may well modify the character of the distribution, is not adequately reflected. Moreover, the mean deviations of two distributions cannot be combined in any simple mathematical way if the two distributions have different means. As will be seen later, it is often useful to combine distributions in this way in order to obtain a better picture of some area of study, in which case, mean deviation must be calculated for the combined distributions *ab initio*, which is inconvenient. For some important theoretical distributions, there is an easily ascertainable relationship between mean deviation and standard deviation, which is the measure next to be considered; and so for statistical purposes, mean deviation is often superfluous as well as being difficult to handle mathematically.

4. Standard Deviation

It was suggested in the preceding section that a desirable property of a measure of dispersion is that it should give due emphasis to extreme items in a distribution. This can be achieved by considering the *squares* of the deviations of a set of numbers from their mean. For example, the deviations from the mean of the numbers 2, 7, 9 (mean 6) are 4, 1, 3 respectively. 2 is much farther from the mean than either 7 or 9, but its deviation from the mean is only 4 times that of the deviation of 7 from the mean. If the squares of the deviations are now considered, viz., 16, 1, 9, it is seen that the squared deviation of 2 is 16 times the squared deviation of 7 from the mean. The sum of the squared deviations of these numbers from their mean, viz., $16 + 1 + 9 = 26$, is therefore very much affected by the presence of extreme values. The mean of this sum, 26/3, is called the *variance* of the set of numbers and is denoted by σ^2 where σ is the small Greek letter sigma, or sometimes by Var.(X). To obtain a measure of dispersion from the variance which shall be of the same order as the mean, which is linear (i.e., of unit power), the square root of the variance is chosen. This value is called the *standard deviation* of the set of numbers and is denoted by σ or, sometimes, S.D. (X). Thus, for the set of numbers just considered, the standard deviation is

$$\sigma = \sqrt{(26/3)} = 2\cdot94 \text{ (approx.)}$$

The reason for using the square root of the variance, rather than the variance itself, as a measure of dispersion is that this measure must be additive to the mean and so must be in the same units as the mean. For example, if the variable represents length expressed in centimetres, then the units of the mean are centimetres. But the variance, in this case, will be expressed in square centimetres and so is not additive to the mean; whereas the standard deviation, since it is the square root of the variance, will be in centimetres and can be added to or subtracted from the mean. The importance of this property of S.D. lies in the fact that it is often of interest to know whether a given value of the variable lies within an interval from the mean expressed in terms of the standard deviation.

The formula for the standard deviation of a grouped frequency distribution is:

$$\sigma = \sqrt{\{\Sigma f(X - \bar{X})^2 / \Sigma f\}}$$

The following illustrates the calculation of the S.D. of I.Q. scores ($\bar{X} = 99 \cdot 1$).

I.Q. Mid-point of Interval = X	Deviation from Mean = $(X - \bar{X})$	No. of Children = f	$f(X - \bar{X})$	$f(X - \bar{X})^2$
54·5	−44·6	1	−44·6	1989·16
64·5	−34·6	2	−69·2	2394·32
74·5	−24·6	8	−196·8	4841·28
84·5	−14·6	18	−262·8	3836·88
94·5	− 4·6	23	−105·8	486·68
104·5	5·4	21	113·4	612·36
114·5	15·4	15	231·0	3557·40
124·5	25·4	9	228·6	5806·44
134·5	35·4	3	106·2	3759·48
		100	0	27284·00

Total sum of squared deviations = $\Sigma f(X - \bar{X})^2 = 27284$

Var. $(X) = \Sigma f(X - \bar{X})^2 / \Sigma f = 27284/100$

Standard deviation, $\sigma = \sqrt{(272 \cdot 84)} = 16 \cdot 52$.

The square root may be evaluated by means of four-figure logarithm tables. Alternatively, a slide rule will often give a sufficient degree of accuracy.

It will be observed, in the above table, that the deviations are not expressed as absolute magnitudes as in the calculation of mean deviation. This is because the square of any number, whether negative or positive, is always a positive number, so that $(X - \bar{X})^2 \geqslant 0$ for all values of X. The advantage of expressing $X - \bar{X}$ as a "signed" magnitude is that the term $\Sigma f(X - \bar{X})$ is zero, and this provides a check on the calculations for the fourth column of the table. However, it will be seen that, using actual values of X to find the standard deviation may entail some quite heavy arithmetic, and it is useful to have an alternative procedure, using "coded" values of X, similar to that used when calculating the mean (page 54). Thus let x be the "coded" value of X such that $x = (X - 94.5)/10$. Then the calculation proceeds as follows:

I.Q. Mid-point of Interval $= X$	"Coded" value of X $= x$	No. of Children $= f$	fx	fx^2
54·5	−4	1	− 4	16
64·5	−3	2	− 6	18
74·5	−2	8	−16	32
84·5	−1	18	−18	18
94·5	0	23	0	0
104·5	1	21	21	21
114·5	2	15	30	60
124·5	3	9	27	81
134·5	4	3	12	48
		100	90	294
			−44	
			46	

From this table, the variance of x can be found. Thus:

$$\bar{x} = \Sigma fx / \Sigma f = 46/100 = 0.46$$

$$\text{Var. } (x) = \Sigma f(x - \bar{x})^2 / \Sigma f$$

$$= \frac{\Sigma fx^2}{\Sigma f} - (\bar{x})^2$$

$$= \frac{294}{100} - (0.46)^2$$

$$= 2.7284$$

Now in obtaining the "coded" value of X, an assumed mean, 94·5, is deducted from each value of X and the differences divided by 10. The squares of these differences are therefore divided by 100, so that it may be expected that Var. (X) is 100 times Var. (x).

Hence   Var. $(X) = 100 \times 2\cdot7284 = 272\cdot84$

$$\text{and S.D. } (X) = \sigma = \sqrt{(272\cdot84)}$$
$$= 16\cdot52 \text{ (as before).}$$

To obtain a general formula for calculating S.D. (X) by this method, let $x = (X - A)/h$ where A is a convenient assumed mean and h is the difference between the upper and lower limits of each class interval. Then

$$\text{S.D. } (X) = h\sqrt{\left(\frac{\Sigma fx^2}{\Sigma f} - (\bar{x})^2\right)}.$$

In some problems, it is convenient to choose $A = 0$ and $h = 1$, in which case, the above formula becomes

$$\text{S.D. } (X) = \sqrt{\left(\frac{\Sigma fX^2}{\Sigma f} - (\bar{X})^2\right)}.$$

Because it gives more prominence to extreme items, standard deviation is always larger than mean deviation, except when both are zero or all deviations are numerically equal.

5. Coefficient of Variation

The four measures of dispersion just discussed indicate the *variability* of the data. A high value of standard deviation, for example, indicates that the data is very variable, or well spread out about the mean. However, the magnitudes of these measures are relative to the size of the mean: the variability of data with a given variability and high mean may not be so important as that of data with a lower mean and the same variability. For example, if the mean lives of cathode ray tubes and electric light bulbs is 3000 hours and 1000 hours respectively, and these lives have the same variability, then this is not so important in the case of the cathode ray tubes as in that of the bulbs. It is therefore desirable to have a relative measure of the variability of data which takes account of its average value. The most widely used of these is the *coefficient of variation*, which is defined as the standard deviation divided by the mean and is usually expressed as a percentage. Thus,

$$\text{Coefficient of Variation} = \frac{\sigma}{\bar{X}} \times 100\%.$$

An alternative relative measure, which is less in use, is the mean deviation divided by the mean, also expressed as a percentage, i.e.,

$$\frac{\text{M.D.}}{\bar{X}} \times 100\%.$$

It will be shown in the next section that the standard deviation of a set of numbers is unaltered if the same value is subtracted from each of the numbers or, in other words, if the origin of the numbers is changed. It is therefore essential, when calculating the coefficient of variation, to use the actual value of the mean and not the mean of the transformed set of numbers which is obtained when such a transformation is used to facilitate the calculation of S.D.

Another advantage of the coefficient of variation over standard deviation as a means of comparing the variability of two sets of data is that it is not expressed in any units but is a pure number or ratio. It can therefore be used to compare the distributions of variables whose units differ. For example, the variability of weekly output might be compared with that of weekly absenteeism, the former being measured in physical units of output, the latter in man-hours.

6. Some Properties of Standard Deviation

It will be obvious from the existence of alternative methods of calculating standard deviation that it has some very convenient mathematical properties.

(1) If the same value is subtracted from each of a set of numbers, the standard deviation of the transformed set is equal to that of the original set.

For if the mean of the variable X is $\bar{X}$, then the mean of $X - A$ is $\bar{X} - A$.

Hence
$$\begin{aligned}
\text{Var. } (X - A) &= \Sigma \{(X - A) - (\bar{X} - A)\}^2/n \\
&= \Sigma (X - \bar{X})^2/n \\
&= \text{Var. } (X).
\end{aligned}$$

(2) If each of a set of numbers is multiplied by the same number H then the standard deviation of the transformed set is H times that of the original set.

For if the mean of X is $\bar{X}$, then the mean of HX is $H\bar{X}$.

So
$$\begin{aligned}
\text{Var. } (HX) &= \Sigma (HX - H\bar{X})^2/n \\
&= \Sigma H^2(X - \bar{X})^2/n \\
&= H^2 \text{Var. } (X).
\end{aligned}$$

Together, these two properties enable one to calculate the standard deviation of a set of numbers from their "coded" values.

Thus putting $1/h = H$,

$$\text{Var.}\left(\frac{X-A}{h}\right) = \text{Var.}\,[H(X-A)]$$

$$= H^2\,\text{Var.}\,(X-A) \qquad \text{(by property (2))}$$

$$= H^2\,\text{Var.}\,(X). \qquad \text{(by property (1))}$$

So $\quad \text{Var.}\,(X) = \dfrac{1}{H^2}\,\text{Var.}\left(\dfrac{X-A}{h}\right)$

$$= h^2\,\text{Var.}\left(\frac{X-A}{h}\right)$$

and $\qquad \sigma = h\sqrt{\left\{\text{Var.}\left(\dfrac{X-A}{h}\right)\right\}}$

$$= h\,\text{S.D.}\,(x) \qquad \text{(where } x = (X-A)/h\text{)}.$$

EXAMPLE 1

$x_1, x_2, x_3, \ldots\ldots, x_n$ *are n values of a variable having a mean value* m_x *and a variance* $s_x{}^2$. *These values are transformed using the relation* $y = ax + b$, *where* $a > 0$, *to the n values* $y_1, y_2, y_3, \ldots\ldots, y_n$. *Give the mean value* m_y *and the variance* $s_y{}^2$ *of these n values of y in terms of* m_x, s_x, a *and b.*

Some experimental results became 17, 72, 32, 27, 42, 77, 87, 47, 62, 57 as the result of such a transformation. If the original mean and variance were 9 and 19 respectively find the transformation that was used.

What value of x became 42 under the transformation?

$$m_y = \sum_{i=1}^{n} y_i/n$$

$$= \sum_{i=1}^{n} (ax_i + b)/n$$

$$= \frac{a\sum_{i=1}^{n} x_i}{n} + \frac{\sum_{i=1}^{n} b}{n}.$$

$$= am_x + \frac{nb}{n}$$

$$= am_x + b.$$

$$s_y{}^2 = \sum_{i=1}^{n} (y_i - m_y)^2/n$$

$$= \sum_{i=1}^{n} \{(ax_i + b) - (am_x + b)\}^2/n$$

$$= a^2 \sum_{i=1}^{n} (x_i - m_x)^2/n$$

$$= a^2 s_x^2.$$

In order to find the transformation used for the experimental results, it is necessary to find the mean and variance of the transformed data.

y	$y - m_y$	$(y - m_y)^2$
17	-35	1225
72	20	400
32	-20	400
27	-25	625
42	-10	100
77	25	625
87	35	1225
47	-5	25
62	10	100
57	5	25
520	0	4750

$$m_y = 520/10 = 52; \qquad s_y^2 = 4750/10 = 475.$$

It is given that $m_x = 9$ and $s_x^2 = 19$.

So from the first part of the problem,

$$52 = 9a + b \quad \text{and} \quad 475 = 19a^2.$$

Hence $a^2 = 475/19 = 25$, so $a = 5$.
$$b = 52 - 9 \times 5 = 7.$$

The required transformation is thus $y = 5x + 7$.

If $y = 42$, then $x = (42 - 7)/5 = 7$.

The kind of transformation used in this example can often be applied to standardise a set of measurements having a given mean and standard deviation into a set of numbers with, say, mean 50 and standard deviation 5. Often, in Statistics, the data is transformed so that its mean is zero and standard deviation 1. For example, if the mean of the frequency distribution of a continuous variable X is

$\bar{X}$ and the standard deviation is σ then the distribution of the variable

$$x = (X - \bar{X})/\sigma$$

has mean zero and standard deviation 1. The importance of such transformations is that, although the mean and standard deviation of the distribution are changed, other important properties of the distribution are unaltered. For example, the quartile values of the original distribution become the quartile values of the new distribution under the transformation, so that it is possible to determine between what limits of the new distribution 50% of the values lie when the limits of the original distribution enclosing these frequencies are known. Consider, for example, the transformation illustrated in Fig. 19.

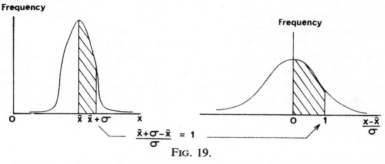

FIG. 19.

For both distributions, the frequencies are the same, so that the areas under the frequency polygons, which are drawn here as smooth curves, are equal. In the left-hand diagram, the shaded area is proportional to the frequency of the items lying in the interval $[\bar{X}, \bar{X} + \sigma]$. The corresponding interval in the right-hand diagram is [0, 1], the shaded area of this diagram being equal to that on the left. Under this kind of transformation, therefore, areal properties are preserved or remain invariant. This fact is used to tabulate the areas of the graph of a frequency distribution which are enclosed within various intervals measured from the mean or some other convenient origin. Now frequency distributions of actual data with different means and standard deviations can often be transformed, by the above method, so that they correspond to a standard frequency distribution with mean zero and standard deviation 1. By tabulating the areas lying between different values of the variable and some convenient origin for this standard distribution, the frequencies for corresponding intervals of distributions which can be transformed into the standard distribution can be obtained. Unless transformations of this kind were possible, the use of statistical tables would be out of the question, because a different table would be needed for each distribution.

Another general property of statistical tables is that the frequencies, shown in them are relative frequencies. It is always possible, however, to obtain actual frequencies from the table by multiplying relative frequency by the total frequency of the distribution in question. It will be observed that the distributions depicted above are symmetrical about the mean. The distribution on the right is known as the *Standard Normal distribution* and many actual distributions can be approximately transformed to it. It is sometimes denoted by $N(0, 1)$, showing that it has mean zero and standard deviation 1. This discussion can be summarised, therefore, by saying that all distributions of the form $N(\bar{X}, \sigma)$ can be transformed into the same standard distribution $N(0, 1)$ in a way which leaves areas enclosed between corresponding intervals of the variable unchanged.

A further property of standard deviation is that its square (the variance) is less than the mean squared deviations measured from any value of the variable other than the mean. The mean of the squares of the deviations measured from the median, for example, is greater than the variance unless, of course, the distribution is symmetrical.

7. Measures of Skewness

It has already been shown that the existence of skewness in a distribution is often revealed by its histogram. If the distribution is only slightly skew, then this may be difficult to detect from the diagram. Further information about skewness can, of course, be obtained by noting the relationship between the mean, mode and median of the distribution. If the mean is to the right of the mode there is positive skewness, and if to the left negative skewness; the median lying between the mode and the mean in both cases. But the actual differences between the three measures of location is only an absolute indication of the amount of skewness, its importance depending on the amount of dispersion. A given difference between the mean and mode is significant of a smaller amount of skewness the greater the dispersion of the data. So as, with variability, a relative measure of skewness is needed.

There are several such measures, the simplest of which depends on the relationship between the mean, mode and standard deviation and which is given by the formula:

$$\text{sk.} = \frac{\text{Mean} - \text{Mode}}{\text{Standard deviation}} = \frac{\bar{X} - Z}{\sigma}.$$

This is sometimes called Karl Pearson's formula.

Another measure of skewness, based on the relationship between the quartiles, is given by the formula:

$$\text{sk.} = \frac{\text{Upper quartile} + \text{Lower quartile} - 2 \text{ Median}}{\text{Upper quartile} - \text{Lower quartile}}$$

$$= \frac{Q_3 + Q_1 - 2Q_2}{Q_3 - Q_1}.$$

The reasons why both these formulae are measures of skewness should be fairly obvious. In the particular case of a symmetrical distribution, both measures are zero, for then $\bar{X} = Z$ and $Q_2 = \frac{1}{2}(Q_3 + Q_1)$. The second formula is generally known as Bowley's formula after Professor A. L. Bowley. It is fairly obvious that this measure of skewness has a value between $+1$ and -1. Pearson's coefficient gives a value about three times that obtained by Bowley's formula and varies, in fact, between $+3$ and -3.

EXERCISES 4

1. Calculate the mean deviation of
$$2 \quad 3 \quad 7 \quad 8 \quad 10$$

2. Calculate the variance of
$$102 \quad 104 \quad 106 \quad 108 \quad 110$$

3. The marks in an examination had a mean of 30 and a S.D. of 8. It was decided to adjust them in order that the adjusted S.D. should be 20. If an original mark of 42 corresponds to an adjusted mark of 78, what is the mean of the adjusted marks?

4. Calculate the mean deviation of the following set of numbers:
$$7 \quad 11 \quad 6 \quad 14 \quad 1 \quad 9$$

5. A small company is about to start production on an item of clothing. The company is initially limited to producing items of one particular size (owing to the cost of installing machinery, etc.). If you were in charge of production which population average size—the mean, mode or median—would you be most interested in estimating?

6. An area of heathland was divided into 144 squares of equal size

and the number of plants of a particular species in each square
was recorded. The tabulated results are shown below. Find the
mean and the standard deviation of the number of plants per
square.

No. of plants	0	1	2	3	4	5
No. of squares	70	44	19	10	0	1

7. The marks obtained by five candidates in a test were 18, 22, 24,
   25 and 36. These marks are to be adjusted so that the mean is
   50 and the S.D. 20. Find the adjusted mark corresponding to
   the original mark of 22.

8. The lifetimes of 210 television tubes gave the following distribution.

Lifetime (thousands of hours)	1·00–	1·50–	2·00–	2·50–	3·00–
No. of tubes	2	8	22	43	66

Lifetime (thousands of hours)	3·50–	4·00–	4·50–	5·00–5·50
No. of tubes	42	18	6	3

Find the mean lifetime of the tubes and the standard deviation
of the distribution. Calculate the coefficient of variation.

   Calculate the semi-inter-quartile range and Pearson's measure
of skewness.

9. Calculate the skewness of the distribution given below, using
   Bowley's formula.

Class	Frequency
0–	4
10–	14
20–	28
30–	22
40–	16
50–70	16

10. Val spent five days of his summer holidays bean-picking for a
    local farmer. His daily earnings were equivalent to the following
    numbers of new pennies:
                    60, 70, 82, 74, 84.
    Calculate
       (a) the mean daily earnings,
       (b) the mean deviation of daily earnings from the mean,
       (c) the standard deviation of daily earnings.

    Suggest, and find, another measure of dispersion which might
    appropriately be applied to this data.

11. All the children in a number of families were together at a party. Each child was asked to state the number of children in his (or her) family. Two children said one child, four children said two children, and twelve children said three.

    (a) How many families were at the party?

    (b) Calculate the arithmetic mean of the number of children per family.

12. Calculate (a) the arithmetic mean (b) the mean deviation from the mean (c) the standard deviation, for the following set of marks: 30, 34, 43, 47, 54, 59, 62, 67, 68, 76.

    How many of these marks are within the range:

    Mean $\pm$ standard deviation?

13. When the information collected during a statistical investigation is being analysed two of the important features are the *central tendency* and the *spread or dispersion* of the results.

    Give three different measures that could be used for each of these characteristics, indicating briefly situations in which it would be advantageous or disadvantageous to use each of the measures for the *central tendency*.

    Describe the advantages and disadvantages of any one of the measures specified for the *spread or dispersion* of the results.

14. The heights, in metres, of ten men are 1·50, 1·57, 1·59, 1·63, 1·68, 1·85, 1·82, 1·84, 1·72, 1·90 measured correct to the nearest 0·01 m.

    Calculate the arithmetic mean, the mean deviation from the arithmetic mean and the standard deviation of these heights.

    Explain the meaning of the phrase "a height of 1·68 m correct to the nearest 0·01 m".

15. A set of values of a variable Y are as follows: 4·03, 4·07, 4·04, 4·09, 4·12, 4·10, 4·02, 4·08, 4·06 and 4·04.

    (a) Express each of the values of Y in the form $\frac{1}{100} X + 4$.

    (b) Calculate the arithmetic mean and the variance of the set of values of X and hence deduce the arithmetic mean and variance of Y.

    (c) A linear transformation is now applied to the original values of Y so that the new set of values has an arithmetic mean of 9·172 and a variance of $6·176 \times 10^{-4}$. Determine the equation representing this transformation.

16. For the following results of an I.Q. test estimate

    (a) the mean;

    (b) the standard deviation;

(c) the inter-quartile range.
(d) the coefficient of variation.

Mark	70	74	78	82	86	90	94	98
Number of pupils	4	9	16	28	45	66	85	72

Mark	102	106	110	114	118	122	126
Number of pupils	54	38	27	18	11	5	2

17. The following data gives the monthly expenditure on advertising in 1969 of the branches of Cosmetics Ltd:

COSMETICS LTD MONTHLY ADVERTISING EXPENDITURE IN 1969

£	Number of branches
800 and less than 1000	50
1000 ,, ,, ,, 1200	200
1200 ,, ,, ,, 1400	350
1400 ,, ,, ,, 1600	150
1600 ,, ,, ,, 1800	100
1800 ,, ,, ,, 2000	75
2000 ,, ,, ,, 2200	50
2200 ,, ,, ,, 2400	25

(a) From the above data calculate the median monthly expenditure, and explain what it indicates about the branches' advertising expenditure in 1969.
(b) Calculate the semi-inter-quartile range from the data and explain the purpose of this calculation.

18. The distribution shown below is the output of the factories of Quality Clothing Ltd, for the month of May 1972. You are required to:

(a) calculate the standard deviation from these figures, and
(b) contrast the mean deviation and the standard deviation as measures of dispersion and indicate briefly what the standard deviation calculated in (a) means for the monthly output of Quality Clothing Ltd.

QUALITY CLOTHING LTD

Monthly Output Men's Suits (000's)	Number of Factories
23 and under 28	10
28 ,, ,, 33	20
33 ,, ,, 38	20
38 ,, ,, 43	24
43 ,, ,, 48	20
48 ,, ,, 53	16
53 ,, ,, 58	8
58 ,, ,, 63	2

19. Recorded below are the goals scored by 60 teams on a particular Saturday.

```
0  5  2  3  2  2  0  1  1  0
1  1  1  0  1  0  1  1  1  2
1  0  2  3  0  1  1  1  3  2
0  1  2  0  1  5  1  1  3  1
2  1  1  3  1  3  0  2  1  2
1  2  0  2  0  1  1  0  0  1
```

(a) Tabulate these scores in a frequency table. Use the table to calculate the mean number of goals scored, the standard deviation and the mean deviation from the mean.

(b) A further 32 teams played on the same Saturday as the first 60 teams. The mean number of goals scored by all 92 teams was 1·25. Of the further 32 teams, calculate the number scoring two goals given that the remainder scored 27 goals between them.

CHAPTER 5

Probability and Probability Distributions

1. Probability and Sampling

The preceding chapters have been concerned mainly with descriptive statistics, i.e., the collection and presentation of data, and, apart from an informal consideration of what conclusions might be reached about the subject matter of the data, no systematic attempt has yet been made to reach conclusions having scientific validity. So far, no mention has been made of whether the data collected summarises the whole subject matter of the enquiry or just a part of it; although it was suggested that, in practice, the data is very seldom complete. There are good reasons why, even if complete data could be obtained, it would be undesirable to collect it. A manufacturer of cathode ray tubes, for example, might wish to know the average length of life of the tubes which he has in stock; but it is not possible to burn every tube until it fails in order to obtain this information. The sensible procedure is to select a small number of tubes for test and, from the average life of these, to estimate the average life of the whole stock. This procedure is called *sampling*. The tubes selected for testing form the *sample*, whilst the whole stock constitutes the *population* from which the sample is drawn. A procedure of this kind is adopted in nearly all statistical enquiries. The question arises: to what extent can one be reasonably sure that sample estimates are representative of the population? The possibility of answering this question depends on the fact that, provided samples are properly selected, those samples which are most representative of the population are, on the whole, most likely to be selected. So that, although it is possible to choose a sample, under these conditions, which would be highly misleading, one is unlikely to do so; moreover, it is usually possible to determine how unlikely such a possibility is.

It is clear, then, that underlying the procedure of obtaining information by taking samples, is the idea of measuring degrees of likelihood. Now likelihood is, to some extent, a subjective concept depending on a personal estimation that such and such will be the case. Sometimes it is impossible to get beyond the element of personal judgement, for example when judging the outcome of a horse-race. But for statistical purposes an attempt must be made to base the measurement of likelihood on a secure objective foundation. When this is done, it is usual to think in terms of *probabilities* rather than likelihoods; a probability being a numerical measure of a likelihood.

In this chapter, consideration is given to some of the definitions and leading ideas of the theory of probability whilst, in the next, the application of these ideas to sampling will be discussed.

2. Sample Spaces

The results of our actions are never completely certain, though many are almost so, otherwise an organised life would be impossible. It would be very disconcerting if one could never be almost certain that a letter would reach its destination safely or that one's cheques would be honoured provided one had a sufficient credit balance. Nevertheless, to every action, there is always more than one *outcome*, though some outcomes may be just "theoretical" possibilities. There are, however, a large number of actions the outcomes of which are by no means certain. When a coin is tossed, for example, there are two possible outcomes, namely that it falls heads or falls tails, and one cannot be certain which of these two will actually happen. If the coin is balanced, or unbiased, then the two possibilities are equally likely or *equiprobable*. The probability that the coin falls heads is defined as the ratio of the number of ways this can happen to the total number of ways the coin can fall, viz. 1/2. In general, if an event can happen in a ways and fail to happen in b ways, then the total number of ways in which it can happen or fail to happen is $a + b$, so that the probability that the event happens is $a/(a + b)$, it being assumed that all the outcomes are equally probable.

When an action is performed, the outcomes of which are more or less probable, one is said to make a *trial*. Any outcome of a trial is termed an *event*, an event with a single element being known as a *simple event*. Thus, in tossing a coin one is making a trial with two possible outcomes, heads or tails, each of which is a simple event. An event with more than one element is called a *compound event*; for example, if a coin is tossed twice, the result of the first toss together with that of the second consists of two elements or simple events and is thus a compound event. In order to evaluate the probability of an event, simple or compound, following on some trial, it is evidently necessary to have some means of enumerating all possible, equiprobable, outcomes of the trial and then finding the number of these outcomes which are favourable to the event in question. All the possible outcomes of a trial constitute the *sample space* of the trial. For outcomes consisting of not more than three simple events in conjunction, a sample space can be represented geometrically as a one-, two- or three-dimensional diagram, each point of which is an outcome, all points being equiprobable. For a simple event, the sample space consists of a number of points on a straight line. For

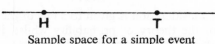

H   T
Sample space for a simple event
FIG. 20.

example, the diagram (Fig. 20) represents the sample space for a single toss of a *true* coin, and consists of two points corresponding to each of the two possible outcomes ("head" or "tail"). The probability of the simple event "head" is the ratio of the number of points of the sample space favourable to this outcome to the total number of points in the space, i.e., 1/2.

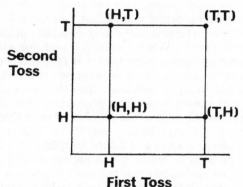

First Toss
Sample space for a compound event
FIG. 21.

If an unbiased or true coin is tossed twice, the sample space of the trial has four points corresponding to the four equally likely outcomes: "head" first, "head" second; "head" first, "tail" second etc. Each outcome in this case is a compound event, the order in which the constituent elements of the event occur being important. This is indicated in the diagram (Fig. 21) by labelling each point in the diagram by an *ordered pair* of letters, the first showing the result of the first toss (horizontal axis), the second the result of the second toss (vertical axis). For example, the point representing "head" first, "tail" second is denoted by the ordered pair of letters (H, T). Where the results of both tosses are the same (both "heads" or both "tails") the order is, of course, immaterial; but this is not true for all points in the space, so care must be taken about the order in which the results occur. Thus although (H, T) and (T, H) both have the same number of heads and tails, they represent two distinct events. There are thus two events favourable to obtaining a head and a tail with two tosses of a single coin out of four possible outcomes, so that the probability of this outcome is 2/4 or 1/2. Since two heads can occur in only one way, the probability of this event is 1/4. In this example, the order in question is a temporal order referring to successive tosses of the same coin; but the type of order can be changed by making the trial consist of simultaneous tosses of two coins. In this case, the horizontal axis of the diagram represents the first coin and the vertical axis the second coin; but order is equally important in both cases.

The points of a sample space represent outcomes or events which are mutually exclusive and collectively exhaustive. Thus, if the sample space of a trial consists of n points, the probability of any one outcome represented by one point in the sample space is $1/n$. The probability of one or other of the events occurring is $n \times 1/n = 1$, i.e., one of the events is certain to occur as the result of a trial since the sample space exhausts all the possibilities. It is certain, for example, that when a coin is tossed once, either a "head" or a "tail" will occur. The probability that an event not in the sample space will occur is zero, i.e., such an event is impossible as a result of the trial. Thus the definition of the probability measure which has been adopted implies that any probability has the following properties:

If p_i is the probability of outcome i of a trial, then
(1) p_i can take any value from 0 to 1: $0 \leqslant p_i \leqslant 1$;
(2) $p_i = 0$ when outcome i is not in the sample space (impossibility);
(3) $\Sigma p_i = 1$ when the outcomes i exhaust all the points in the sample space and are mutually exclusive (certainty).

Two events are said to be *mutually exclusive* if they cannot happen together or, in other words, if the probability of their occurring together is zero. For example, the probability that a coin will fall both "head" and "tail" is zero, so that these two events are mutually exclusive.

Two events are said to be *independent* in a probability sense if the occurrence of one of them does not affect the probability of the occurrence of the other. For example, if a coin is tossed twice and a head occurs first time, then the probability of a head on the second toss is still 1/2. The events "head" first, "head" second are independent. The idea of independence can be clarified by considering an example in which events are not independent in a probability sense.

Suppose that from a box containing four counters numbered 1 to 4 a counter is selected in such a way that each counter has an equal chance of selection and that the counter so selected is placed on one square of a board divided into 2 blue squares, 1 green and 1 red

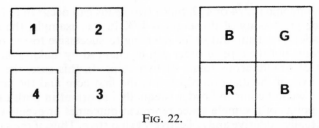

FIG. 22.

square in such a way that each square is equally likely to be selected (Fig. 22). The placing might, for example, be done by a robot that was uninfluenced by a preference for one colour over another. The sample space for the outcome of one trial can be listed as follows:

(B, 1)	(G, 1)	(B, 1)	(R, 1)
(B, 2)	(G, 2)	(B, 2)	(R, 2)
(B, 3)	(G, 3)	(B, 3)	(R, 3)
(B, 4)	(G, 4)	(B, 4)	(R, 4)

The sample space consists of 16 points, so that the probability that the green square is covered by the counter numbered 4 is 1/16. The probability that a blue square is covered by the counter 4 is, of course twice this (or 1/8) because there are two blue squares. Now suppose that at the first trial the green square is covered by the counter 4. At a second trial, the probability that the green square will be covered by counter 2, assuming that the robot chooses only squares which have not been already covered, is zero. If, however, some other square had been covered by the counter 4 at the first trial, the probability of covering green with counter 2 at the second trial is obviously not zero. Hence, in this case, the outcome of the second trial is not independent of that of the first.

The selection of an object from a collection of objects in such a way that each object has an equal chance of being chosen is termed a *random* selection. Thus, in the above example, a trial consisted of randomly selecting a counter from the box and placing it at random on one of the four coloured squares.

It will be clear, from the examples just discussed, that whilst a simple or compound event consists of just one point of a sample space, an outcome may consist of several points. For example, in two tosses of a single coin, the outcome "head" and "tail" consists of two points of the sample space. To make this point clear, consider what happens when two exactly similar unbiased six-sided dice are thrown. Let the score on the first dice be X and that on the second Y and consider the outcome X differs from Y by 4, i.e.,

$|X - Y| = 4$. The sample space for all possible outcomes from the trial is shown in Fig. 23.

The sample space consists of $6 \times 6 = 36$ points corresponding to all the possible combinations of scores on the two dice. The number of events favourable to the outcome $|X - Y| = 4$ is four. Hence the probability of this outcome is 4/36 or 1/9. It is sometimes convenient

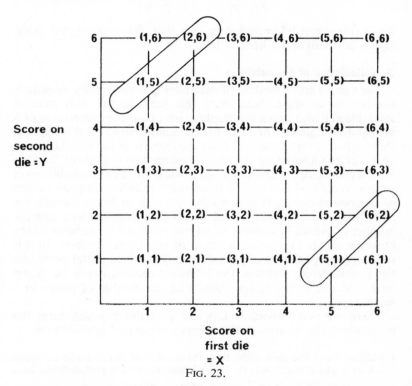

FIG. 23.

to denote the probability of an outcome O by $P(O)$. Thus, in the example just discussed,

$$P(|X - Y| = 4) = 1/9.$$

So far only sample spaces have been considered which can be represented geometrically in one or two dimensions. An outcome consisting of 3 simple events, i.e., a compound event with three elements, gives rise to a three-dimensional sample space. It is rather inconvenient to draw a three-dimensional diagram, particularly if the number of possible outcomes is large and it is much simpler to list the sample space. For example, if three fair coins are tossed, the sample space of outcomes consists of 8 points which can be listed as follows:

$$(H, H, H) \quad (H, T, H)$$
$$(H, H, T) \quad (T, H, H)$$
$$(H, T, T) \quad (T, H, T)$$
$$(T, T, T) \quad (T, T, H)$$

From this it can be immediately seen that, for example, the probability of 2 tails and 1 head is 3/8.

3. Calculation of Probabilities

The sample space method of determining a probability essentially consists in counting. Sometimes this may be the only method available and also, when any doubt exists about the correctness of a probability, it always helps to list the sample space. But obviously, this method is very laborious when the number of points is large and also is often unnecessary. An alternative method consists of calculating the probabilities. This can be done when the initial probabilities of simple events are known and it is desired to calculate the probabilities of compound events. It is also often possible to find a formula for calculating the total number of points in a sample space and the number of points favourable to an outcome, the probability of the outcome being, of course, the ratio of these two numbers. In this section, the calculation of probabilities from given initial probabilities is considered, whilst in the following section, it will be shown how to derive formulae for calculating the number of points in a sample space.

There are two important Laws of Probability which form the basis of calculating probabilities from given initial probabilities.

I Addition Law: The probability that one or other of two mutually exclusive events A and B happens is the sum of their respective probabilities. I.e.,

$$P(A \text{ or } B) = P(A) + P(B).$$

Example

When an unbiased six-sided dice is thrown once, the probability that the score is X is $P(X = x) = 1/6$, where $x = 1, 2, 3, 4, 5, 6$. Since only one face of the dice can appear at one trial, the probability that $X = 1$ or 3 is

$$P(X = 1 \text{ or } X = 3) = P(X = 1) + P(X = 3)$$
$$= \tfrac{1}{6} + \tfrac{1}{6}$$
$$= \tfrac{1}{3}.$$

Also, since one side must appear, it follows that

$$\sum_{x=1}^{6} P(X = x) = 6 \times \tfrac{1}{6} = 1.$$

II Multiplication Law: The probability that two independent events A and B occur together is the product of their respective probabilities. I.e.,

$$P(A \text{ and } B) = P(A)P(B).$$

Example

When two unbiased coins are tossed, the probability of head on the first and tail on the second is

$$\begin{aligned} P(H, T) &= P(H)P(T) \\ &= \tfrac{1}{2} \times \tfrac{1}{2} \\ &= \tfrac{1}{4}. \end{aligned}$$

Since the events (H, T) and (T, H) are mutually exclusive, it follows from Laws I and II together that the probability of a head and a tail in either order is

$$\begin{aligned} P\{(H, T) \text{ or } (T, H)\} &= \tfrac{1}{2} \times \tfrac{1}{2} + \tfrac{1}{2} \times \tfrac{1}{2} \\ &= \tfrac{1}{4} + \tfrac{1}{4} \\ &= \tfrac{1}{2}. \end{aligned}$$

The probability of the simultaneous occurrence of two or more events is sometimes called their *joint probability*.

In order to find the probability that one or other of two events occurs when the events are *not* mutually exclusive but are independent, Law I must be modified as follows:

Ia. The probability that one or other of two non-mutually exclusive but independent events occurs is the sum of their respective probabilities minus their joint probability. I.e.,

$$P(A \text{ or } B) = P(A) + P(B) - P(A)P(B).$$

Since the events are not mutually exclusive, they may both occur together, so that at least one of the points in the sample space will be counted twice in the sum $P(A) + P(B)$; so that it is necessary to deduct from this sum the probability of these points, i.e., either $P(A, B) = P(A)P(B)$ or $P(B, A) = P(B)P(A)$ must be deducted.

The probability of the joint occurrence of two events which are *not* independent is not equal to the simple product of their respective probabilities since the occurrence of one of the events alters the probability of the occurrence of the other. Hence Law II must be modified to suit this case.

IIa. The probability that two non-independent events A and B occur together is the product of the probability that one of the events occurs and the conditional probability that the other occurs given that the first has occurred. I.e.,

$$P(A, B) = P(A)P(B|A) = P(B)P(A|B).$$

Here $P(B|A)$ denotes the probability of the occurrence of B when A is known to have occurred and is termed the *conditional probability* of B given A. $P(A|B)$ is, of course, the conditional probability of A given B, and these two conditional probabilities are not equal unless $P(A) = P(B)$.

Example

A box contains 10 electric light bulbs, two of which are defective and the remainder sound. Let A be the event: choosing a defective bulb; and B the event: choosing a sound bulb. Then the probability of randomly selecting a defective bulb is

$$P(A) = 2/10 \text{ or } 1/5.$$

The probability of selecting a sound bulb when the first bulb selected was defective and was not replaced in the box is the conditional probability

$$P(B|A) = \frac{8}{10-1} = \frac{8}{9}.$$

Hence, by IIa, the probability of selecting a defective bulb first and a sound bulb second is

$$\begin{aligned} P(A, B) &= P(A)P(B|A) \\ &= \tfrac{1}{5} \times \tfrac{8}{9} \\ &= 8/45. \end{aligned}$$

Alternatively, the probability of selecting a sound bulb first and a defective bulb second is

$$\begin{aligned} P(B, A) &= P(B)P(A|B) \\ &= \frac{8}{10} \times \frac{2}{10-1} \\ &= 8/45. \end{aligned}$$

Note that, in this case, $P(B|A) = 8/9$ and $P(A|B) = 2/9$, so that the two conditional probabilities are not equal.

EXAMPLE 1

Two fair dice each have faces labelled 1 to 6 in the normal way. One die has the faces 1 and 2 coloured red, the second has faces 1, 2, 3 and 4 coloured red, whilst all other faces are white.

Calculate the probability of the following events

(a) *the sum of the scores is even,*

(b) *both faces are red.*

Show that these events are independent.

(a) Let $X = 2n$ and $X = 2n + 1$ be the events that the scores on the first dice are even and odd, respectively. Then $P(X = 2n) = \frac{1}{2}$ and $P(X = 2n + 1) = \frac{1}{2}$. Similarly, let $Y = 2m$ and $Y = 2m + 1$ be the events that the scores on the second dice are even and odd, respectively. Then $P(Y = 2m) = \frac{1}{2}$ and $P(Y = 2m + 1) = \frac{1}{2}$. An even sum occurs when the scores on each dice are both even or both odd. Hence the probability that this sum is even is

$P\{(X = 2n,\ Y = 2m) \text{ or } (X = 2n + 1,\ Y = 2m + 1)\}$
$= P(X = 2n,\ Y = 2m) + P(X = 2n + 1,\ Y = 2m + 1)$ (by I)
$= \frac{1}{2} \times \frac{1}{2} + \frac{1}{2} \times \frac{1}{2}$ (by II)
$= 1/2.$

(b) Let $P(R_1)$ and $P(R_2)$ be the probabilities that the faces of the first and second dice respectively are red.

Then $P(R_1) = \frac{2}{6} = \frac{1}{3}$ and $P(R_2) = \frac{4}{6} = \frac{2}{3}$. Hence the probability that both faces are red is

$$P(R_1,\ R_2) = \frac{1}{3} \times \frac{2}{3} \qquad \text{(by II)}$$
$$= 2/9.$$

Let E and R be the events that the sum of the scores is even and both faces are red respectively. Then these two events are independent if the conditional probability of E given R is equal to the probability of E, i.e., if

$$P(E|R) = P(E).$$

Now if both faces are red, $P(X = 2n) = P(X = 2n + 1) = \frac{1}{2}$ and $P(Y = 2m) = P(Y = 2m + 1) = \frac{2}{4} = \frac{1}{2}$.

Hence $P(E|R) = \frac{1}{2} \times \frac{1}{2} + \frac{1}{2} \times \frac{1}{2} = \frac{1}{2}$, and since $P(E) = \frac{1}{2}$, from (a), it follows that E and R are independent.

EXAMPLE 2

Sid and Tom are twins and are due to run in the heats of the 100 metres sprint. Only the winners of each heat run in the final. Assuming that the probability of Sid winning any heat in which he runs is $\frac{1}{4}$, whilst for Tom it is $\frac{1}{5}$, calculate the probability that

(a) *Sid and Tom both run in the final, assuming that they run in different heats,*

(b) *at least one of the twins runs in the final, assuming that they run in different heats,*

(c) *neither of them runs in the final, assuming that they run in the same heat.*

(a) Let $P(S)$ and $P(T)$ be the probabilities that Sid and Tom win their heats respectively, so that

$$P(S) = \tfrac{1}{4} \text{ and } P(T) = \tfrac{1}{5}.$$

Then, if they run in different heats, the probability that both win their heats and so run in the final is

$$\begin{aligned} P(S, T) &= P(S)P(T) \qquad\qquad \text{(by II)} \\ &= \tfrac{1}{4} \times \tfrac{1}{5} \\ &= 1/20. \end{aligned}$$

(Note that since S and T both represent a win, the order in which they occur is immaterial.)

(b) The probability that S or T wins his heat is, by Ia (since the events are not mutually exclusive),

$$\begin{aligned} P(S \text{ or } T) &= P(S) + P(T) - P(S)P(T) \\ &= \tfrac{1}{4} + \tfrac{1}{5} - \tfrac{1}{20} \\ &= 2/5. \end{aligned}$$

(c) If both run in the same heat, then only one can run in the final. It follows that S and T are now mutually exclusive events, so that the probability that either twin runs in the final is, by I,

$$\begin{aligned} P(S \text{ or } T) &= \tfrac{1}{4} + \tfrac{1}{5} \\ &= 9/20. \end{aligned}$$

Since it is certain that just one twin or neither of them will run in the final, the probability that neither runs in the final

$$\begin{aligned} &= 1 - \tfrac{9}{20} \\ &= 11/20. \end{aligned}$$

Events which are both mutually exclusive and collectively exhaustive are said to be *complementary*. This means that at a single trial one, but only one, of the events must certainly occur. Thus in Example 2 (c) the events "either twin runs in the final" and "neither twin runs in the final" are complementary events. Denoting these events, respectively, by A and A' (not-A), it follows that

$$P(A) + P(A') = 1.$$

Hence if one probability, $P(A)$, is known, the other is easily obtained from the relation

$$P(A') = 1 - P(A).$$

4. Permutations and Combinations

It is often easy enough to compute the total number of points in a sample space. Thus if each point in the sample space represents a compound event (A, B) and A consists of m simple events and B of n simple events and these two sets of simple events are *independent*, then the total number of points in the sample space is simply $m \times n$. It is important that the events of a sample space should all be equally likely, otherwise a sample point will not necessarily represent a random selection of simple events, and it will not then be possible to obtain probabilities simply by counting points in the sample space.

When the sets of events constituting the points of a sample space are not independent, this simple method of computing the number of points is not available. For example, consider three cards each bearing one of the letters a, b, c. A card drawn at random can be drawn in three ways. But once it has been drawn, there remain only two ways in which a second card can be drawn, whilst at the third drawing there is not even a choice. Hence the result of a drawing is not independent of the results of preceding drawings. It could, of course, be made independent by replacing a card after it had been drawn, so that it could be drawn again at the succeeding drawing. In this case, the number of points in the sample space would be $3 \times 3 \times 3$ or $3^3 = 27$, all equiprobable. But in the case first considered, the number of equiprobable points will be much less than this. This number can be found by considering that the first card can be drawn in 3 ways; for each of these ways the second card can be drawn in 2 ways; and for each way in which the second card is drawn, there remains 1 way in which the third card can be drawn. Hence the total number of equiprobable outcomes of such a trial is $3 \times 2 \times 1 = 6$. The method of calculation used here is illustrated schematically by the "tree" diagram in Fig. 24.

The sample space consists of the number of different arrangements of the letters a, b, c, the elements of the space being:

(a, b, c)   (b, a, c)   (c, a, b)
(a, c, b)   (b, c, a)   (c, b, a)

Each arrangement is called a *permutation* of the letters a, b, c. The method of calculating the number of permutations of 3 different objects can be generalised to calculate the number of permutations of any number, say n, of different objects. Thus the number of ways in which n different objects can be arranged is

$$n(n-1)(n-2) \ . \ . \ . \ . \ . \ (2)(1),$$

where the dots represent the missing consecutive whole numbers

First Selection   Second Selection   Third Selection

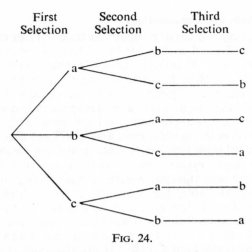

FIG. 24.

from 3 to $(n - 3)$. This product is usually written as $n!$ and called *factorial n*. Thus, if $n = 5$, $n! = 5 \times 4 \times 3 \times 2 \times 1 = 120$. This is the number of ways in which 5 different objects can be arranged. Suppose that these 5 objects are the letters a, b, c, d, e. Then the number of different permutations of these letters containing a in the first position is clearly $4! = 4 \times 3 \times 2 \times 1 = 24$. Hence, if a random selection of one permutation is made from the total of 120 permutations in the sample space, the probability that the permutation selected has a in the first position is $4!/5! = 1/5$. By similar reasoning, the number of ways in which a can occur in the first position and b in the last position is equal to the number of permutations of the remaining 3 letters, namely $3! = 3 \times 2 \times 1 = 6$. Hence the probability of selecting a permutation with a in the first position and b in the last position is $3!/5! = 1/20$.

Now suppose that a trial consists of selecting some but not all objects from a set of n different objects, without replacing the objects as they are selected. If the number of objects to be selected is $r < n$, then the total number of ways in which the selection can be made is

$$n(n - 1)(n - 2)\ldots\ldots(n - r + 2)(n - r + 1) = n!/(n - r)!$$

This expression is obtained in exactly the same way as that for the number of ways of selecting all n objects, except that selection stops when the rth selection has been made. In terms of the tree diagram, selection stops at the rth stage of the tree when there are $(n - r + 1)$ objects still remaining, so that the rth selection can be made in $(n - r + 1)$ ways. A *combination* of r objects from n different objects is a set of r of these n objects independently of the order in which they are selected. The total number of different combinations of r objects from n different objects is usually denoted by $C(n, r)$ or $\binom{n}{r}$. So the number of ways of selecting r objects when the order of selection is taken into account is

$$r! \times C(n, r) = \frac{n!}{(n-r)!}.$$

It follows that the total number of combinations of r objects is

$$C(n, r) = \frac{n!}{(n-r)!\, r!}.$$

For example, the number of different combinations of 3 letters from the 5 letters a, b, c, d, e is

$$C(5, 3) = \frac{5!}{(5-3)!\, 3!}$$
$$= \frac{5 \times 4 \times 3 \times 2 \times 1}{2 \times 1 \times 3 \times 2 \times 1}$$
$$= 10.$$

The reader should satisfy himself that the selections are:

(abc), (abd), (abe), (acd), (ace),
(ade), (ebc), (ebd), (ecd), (dbc).

The total number of ways of selecting these 10 combinations, taking account of the order of selection, is $3! \times 10 = 60$.

EXAMPLE 3

(i) *A student is asked to do three questions from an exercise containing eight questions. How many different selections are possible?*

(ii) *A student, asked to do three particular questions from an exercise containing eight questions, ignores these instructions and answers four questions selected at random.*

Find the probability that he has answered

(a) *all the three questions set,*
(b) *exactly two of the three questions set,*
assuming that all combinations were equally likely to be selected.

(i) No. of ways of choosing 3 questions $= C(8, 3) = \dfrac{8!}{5!\,3!}$

$$= \dfrac{8 \times 7 \times 6}{3 \times 2 \times 1}$$

$$= 56.$$

(ii) No. of ways of choosing 4 questions $= C(8, 4) = \dfrac{8!}{4!\,4!}$

$$= \dfrac{8 \times 7 \times 6 \times 5}{4 \times 3 \times 2 \times 1}$$

$$= 70$$

No. of the selections of 4 questions which include the 3 questions set is the same as the number of ways of choosing 1 of the 5 remaining questions, namely

$$C(5, 1) = \dfrac{5!}{4!\,1!} = 5$$

Hence probability of answering all three questions set $= 5/70$ or $1/14$.

No. of selections of 4 questions which include 2 of the questions set $= C(3, 2) \times C(5, 2)$

$$= \dfrac{3!}{1!\,2!} \times \dfrac{5!}{3!\,2!} = 30.$$

Hence probability of answering exactly 2 of the 3 questions set $= 30/70$ or $3/7$.

5. Binomial Probabilities

A *binomial trial* is a trial which has exactly two mutually exclusive outcomes. Examples are: tossing a coin, the outcome of which is a head or a tail; selecting an electric light bulb from a collection of bulbs each of which is either sound or defective, the outcome of which is either a sound or defective bulb. The trials are independent if the probabilities of the outcomes are the same for all trials. For example, when a coin is tossed several times, the probability of a head on each occasion is the same, being independent of the outcomes of preceding tosses. The probability of selecting a defective light bulb is the same from trial to trial if the bulb selected is replaced after each trial.

It is often convenient to denote the outcomes of a binomial trial by the numerals 0 and 1. These can be regarded as the values which can be taken by a variable X. Thus for a binomial trial,

$$P(X = 0) + P(X = 1) = 1$$
$$\text{and } P(X = 0, X = 1) = 0.$$

These relationships follow from the fact that the outcomes are mutually exclusive and collectively exhaustive, so that one is certain to occur, but not both. In other words, $X = 0$ and $X = 1$ are complementary events.

The number of outcomes from a set of n binomial trials is 2^n. For example when $n = 3$, the outcomes are:

$$(0, 0, 0) \quad (1, 0, 0) \quad (1, 1, 0) \quad (1, 1, 1)$$
$$(0, 0, 1) \quad (0, 1, 1) \quad (0, 1, 0) \quad (1, 0, 1)$$

If the trials are independent, the probability of any outcome from a set of n trials is the product of the probabilities of the n outcomes resulting at each trial. For example,

$$P(0, 1, 0) = P(X = 0, X = 1, X = 0)$$
$$= P(X = 0) \, P(X = 1) \, P(X = 0).$$

It is clear that the probabilities of the outcomes from n trials will be the same if and only if $P(X = 0) = P(X = 1) = 1/2$. But sets of outcomes in which 0 and 1 occur the same number of times, for example: $(0, 0, 1)$, $(0, 1, 0)$, $(1, 0, 0)$; do have the same probability for all values of $P(X = 0)$ or $P(X = 1)$. It will be seen that the three outcomes just considered are permutations of 3 things, 2 of which are the same. It is useful to have a formula for calculating the number of permutations of n things, r of which are of one kind and $(n - r)$ of another kind. Now the number of permutations of n different things is $n!$, as has already been shown. If r of these different objects are replaced by r similar objects, then every permutation which was formerly distinguishable only by a permutation of the r different objects becomes indistinguishable when the r objects are the same. Hence the number of different permutations is now $n!/r!$. By the same reasoning, if the remaining $(n - r)$ different objects are replaced by $(n - r)$ objects all alike, then the number of distinct permutations is

$$\binom{n}{r} = \frac{n!}{(n - r)! \, r!}.$$

It will be seen that this is the same as the number of different combinations of r objects which can be selected from n different objects.

It follows that, in n binomial trials, the number of outcomes in which there are r 0's and $(n - r)$ 1's is $\binom{n}{r}$. Suppose that $P(X=0)=p$ and $P(X = 1) = q (= 1 - p)$, then the probability of r 0's and $(n - r)$ 1's in any order is

$$\binom{n}{r} q^{n-r} p^r.$$

Now let X be the number of 0's obtained in n binomial trials. It will be seen that X can take any of the $n + 1$ values from 0 to n, so that

$$P(X = r) = \binom{n}{r} q^{n-r} p^r.$$

For example, in 3 tosses of a fair coin, the probability of 2 heads (in any order) is

$$P(X = 2) = \frac{3!}{1! \, 2!} \left(\frac{1}{2}\right)^1 \left(\frac{1}{2}\right)^2 = 3/8.$$

This can be verified by referring to the list of possible outcomes. Thus there are 8 possible outcomes, 3 of which are favourable to the event $X = 2$, namely (0, 1, 1), (1, 1, 0) and (1, 0, 1).

The expression above for $P(X = r)$ is an example of a *probability function*, of which there are many types. A probability function is often denoted by $P(X)$. Since each value of the variable X of such a function is mutually exclusive of the other values, it follows that

$$\sum_{r=0}^{n} P(X = r) = 1.$$

The $(n + 1)$ values of the binomial probability function are the terms of the expansion of the binomial expression $(q + p)^n$, where $q + p = 1$. Thus

$$\sum_{r=0}^{n} P(X = r) = (q + p)^n$$

$$= \binom{n}{0} q^n + \binom{n}{1} q^{n-1} p + \binom{n}{2} q^{n-2} p^2$$

$$+ \dots + \binom{n}{n-1} q p^{n-1} + \binom{n}{n} p^n$$

$$= 1.$$

The terms $\binom{n}{r}$ are the *coefficients* of the expansion, where

$$\binom{n}{r} = \frac{n!}{(n-r)! \, r!}.$$

The coefficients of the first and last terms of the expansion are $\binom{n}{0} = \binom{n}{n} = 1$. This must clearly be so since these terms give the probability of n 1's and n 0's respectively and there is only one way in which n things which are all the same can be arranged. This means that

$$\frac{n!}{n!\,0!} = \frac{n!}{0!\,n!} = 1 \text{ so that the symbol } 0! = 1.$$

EXAMPLE 4

Four items are randomly selected from a frequency distribution, the total frequency of which is large. What is the probability that the selection consists of 1 item greater than the median and 3 items less than the median.

Probability of an item greater than the median $= \frac{1}{2}$
„   „   „   „   less   „   „   „ $= \frac{1}{2}$

Let X be the number of items among the four selected which are greater than the median.

Then the required probability is

$$P(X = 1) = \binom{4}{1}\left(\frac{1}{2}\right)^3\left(\frac{1}{2}\right)$$

$$= \frac{4!}{3!\,1!} \times \frac{1}{16}$$

$$= 1/4.$$

This result is easily verified by listing the outcomes. Thus the number of possible outcomes is $2^4 = 16$ and, among these, the favourable outcomes are (0, 1, 1, 1), (1, 0, 1, 1), (1, 1, 0, 1) and (1, 1, 1, 0). The fact that the total frequency of the distribution is large means that, even if the items are not replaced after selection, each selection is virtually independent, so that the probability of selecting an item greater than the median is still $\frac{1}{2}$, even though an item has been already selected.

EXAMPLE 5

Each of four bags contains three coloured discs, two red and one green. A disc is drawn at random from each bag.
Find the probability that

(a) *four red discs are chosen,*
(b) *two red discs and two green discs are chosen.*

Since each selection is independent of the rest, and there are two mutually exclusive outcomes, this constitutes a series of independent binomial trails. If R and G represent the events of drawing a red and a green counter respectively from a bag, then

$$P(R) = \tfrac{2}{3} \text{ and } P(G) = \tfrac{1}{3}.$$

If X represents the number of red discs chosen, then the required probabilities are:

(a)
$$P(X = 4) = \frac{4!}{0!\,4!}\left(\frac{2}{3}\right)^4$$
$$= 16/81.$$

(b)
$$P(X = 2) = \frac{4!}{2!\,2!}\left(\frac{1}{3}\right)^2\left(\frac{2}{3}\right)^2$$
$$= 6 \times \frac{4}{81}$$
$$= 8/27.$$

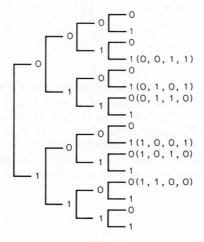

FIG. 25.

The different outcomes (taking account of order) of a series of binomial trials can be obtained systematically by means of a tree diagram such as that shown in Fig. 25. For four trials ($n = 4$), the **number of branches of the tree at the final stage is 16 or 2^4, and it is** clear that, if the tree has n stages, the number of branches at the final stage will be 2^n. It is easily ascertained from the tree that the number of outcomes in which there are two 0's and two 1's (for example) is six and one can also obtain the different orders in which these constituents occur.

It has already been seen that $C(n, r)$, the number of ways in which r successes can occur in n binomial trials, can be calculated by means of a formula. Provided that n is not too large, the values of $C(n, r)$, for different values of n and r, can also be generated by means of a device known as *Pascal's triangle* (shown below).

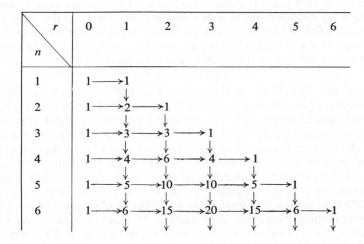

The coefficient for the nth row and rth column of the table is found by adding the two coefficients in the rth and $(r - 1)$th columns of the $(n - 1)$th row, that is,

$$C(n, r) = C(n - 1, r - 1) + C(n - 1, r).$$

For example,

$$C(6, 2) = C(5, 1) + C(5, 2)$$
$$= 5 + 10$$
$$= 15.$$

This can easily be verified by calculation, for

$$C(6, 2) = \frac{6!}{4!\,2!}$$

$$= \frac{6 \times 5}{2 \times 1}$$

$$= 15.$$

6. Probability and Frequency Distributions

If an item is selected at random from a frequency distribution, the probability that the item selected belongs to a given frequency class is proportional to the frequency of the items in that class. If the total frequency is Σf and the frequency in class i is f_i, then the probability of selecting an item at random from class i is $f_i/\Sigma f$. It will be seen, therefore, that there is a close relationship between probability and frequency distributions. If X is a discrete variable, then the value of the probability function for a particular value of the variable X_i, namely $P(X_i)$, is the probability of randomly selecting an item from the class i defined by the value of the variable X_i. So

$$P(X_i) = f_i/\Sigma f.$$

It follows that $P(X_i)$ is a relative frequency expressed, not as a percentage (see Chapter 3, section 7), but as a number having a value in the closed interval $[0, 1]$. For example a probability of $0{\cdot}02$ is equal to a percentage frequency of $100 \times 0{\cdot}02$ or 2%. $P(X_i)$ is proportional to the relative frequency of class i if and only if the selection is a random one, i.e., if and only if each item in the distribution has an equal chance of being selected. For this reason, X_i as it occurs in the probability function is called a *random variable*. Since $P(X_i)$ is a relative frequency, it is possible to use it to calculate the mean of the corresponding frequency distribution. If there are m frequency classes, then there are m corresponding values of $P(X_i)$, namely $P(X_1)$, $P(X_2)$, up to $P(X_m)$. Hence

$$\sum_{i=1}^{m} X_i\,P(X_i) = \sum_{i=1}^{m} f_i X_i/\Sigma f = \bar{X}.$$

This means that when the frequency function is known, the mean value of the random variable can be calculated. This mean value is known as the *expected value* of the variable.

In order to illustrate the connection between a probability function and a frequency distribution, consider the binomial probability function

$$P(X = r) = \binom{n}{r} q^{n-r} p^r.$$

Suppose a fair coin is tossed six times, and let r be the number of heads obtained in these 6 tosses. Then $n = 6$ and r can take any value from 0 to 6, whilst $p = q = \frac{1}{2}$. The probabilities of each value of r are then

$$P(X = 0) = \binom{6}{0}\left(\frac{1}{2}\right)^6 = \frac{1}{64}, \quad P(X = 1) = \binom{6}{1}\left(\frac{1}{2}\right)^5\left(\frac{1}{2}\right) = \frac{6}{64},$$

$$P(X = 2) = \binom{6}{2}\left(\frac{1}{2}\right)^4\left(\frac{1}{2}\right)^2 = \frac{15}{64}, \text{ etc.}$$

The distribution of these probabilities is shown in the following table.

r	0	1	2	3	4	5	6	Total
$P(X = r)$	$\frac{1}{64}$	$\frac{6}{64}$	$\frac{15}{64}$	$\frac{20}{64}$	$\frac{15}{64}$	$\frac{6}{64}$	$\frac{1}{64}$	1
$64 \times P(X = r)$	1	6	15	20	15	6	1	64

If the experiment of tossing the coin 6 times is repeated 64 times, then the expected frequencies of the number of times 0, 1, 2 up to 6 heads is obtained are found by multiplying each value of the probability function by 64. These frequencies are shown in the third row of the table. Thus the second row shows relative frequencies, whilst the third row shows the corresponding actual frequencies when the total frequency (i.e., number of experiments) is 64. Actual frequencies when the number of experiments is some other number, say 1000, are derived in exactly the same way.

It must be emphasised that the frequencies shown above are the *expected* frequencies which will result from an ideal set of experiments with a fair coin. In an actual series of experiments, the frequencies of the number of heads obtained will almost certainly differ from the expected frequencies though, provided the coin used is fair, or very nearly so, these frequencies should not differ by much from the expected frequencies. The results of such experiments show that the relative differences between actual and expected frequencies tends to diminish as the number of experiments is increased, provided that all the experiments are random. This is an example of the operation of the *Law of Large Numbers*, which can be stated in the form: *In a series of random experiments, observed relative frequencies approximate more closely to expected relative frequencies as the number of experiments is indefinitely increased.* This law is popularly known as the Law of Averages and plays an important part in the daily lives of everyone. In effect, the Law of Large Numbers means that when experiments are performed, there is always some random variation of actual results about the expected results; but this random variation becomes less and less important as more experiments are performed. Hence, on the average, our expectations tend to be realised provided there are no non-random factors affecting the results of our actions or experiments. A firm, for example, which is neither expanding nor contracting its business may expect that its profits will remain, on the average, the same from year to year, though they may be somewhat less than the average in some years and rather more than the average in others. These variations are due to random causes which are operating all the time and which tend to cancel out in the long-run.

EXAMPLE 6

Calculate the expected value of x in the following probability distribution.

x	2	3	4	5	6	7	8	9
probability	0·03	0·08	0·24	0·29	0·18	0·10	0·06	0·02

The expected value of x is just its mean value and so is the sum of the products of each value of the variable and their respective probabilities.

Thus $\bar{x} = 0{\cdot}06 + 0{\cdot}24 + 0{\cdot}96 + 1{\cdot}45 + 1{\cdot}08 + 0{\cdot}7 + 0{\cdot}48 + 0{\cdot}18$
$= 5{\cdot}15.$

The expected value of a variable x is often denoted by the symbol $E(x)$ which is defined as

$$E(x) = \Sigma x P(x) = \bar{x},$$

where $P(x)$ gives the probability distribution of x, so that $\Sigma P(x) = 1$, and summation is over all the values which x can take. The idea of an expected value is not confined to the arithmetic mean of a variable x but may also indicate the arithmetic mean of an algebraic expression in which x occurs, for example, the square of x, that is x^2. Thus

$$E(x^2) = \Sigma x^2 P(x)$$

is the mean or expected value of x^2. In Example 6,

$$E(x^2) = 2^2 \times 0{\cdot}03 + 3^2 \times 0{\cdot}08 + \ldots + 9^2 \times 0{\cdot}02$$
$$= 28{\cdot}77$$

Similarly, the variance of a set of numbers is the expected or average value of the squared deviations about the mean of the numbers, that is

$$E\{(x - \bar{x})^2\} = \Sigma(x - \bar{x})^2 \, P(x) = \text{Var. } (x).$$

In Example 6 the variance is therefore

$$\begin{aligned}
\text{Var. } (x) &= (2 - 5{\cdot}15)^2 \times 0{\cdot}03 + (3 - 5{\cdot}15)^2 \\
&\qquad \times 0{\cdot}08 + \ldots + (9 - 5{\cdot}15)^2 \times 0{\cdot}02 \\
&= 2{\cdot}25
\end{aligned}$$

Alternatively, the variance of x is given by

$$\begin{aligned}
\text{Var. } (x) &= E(x^2) - \{E(x)\}^2 \\
&= 28{\cdot}77 - 5{\cdot}15^2 \\
&= 2{\cdot}25
\end{aligned}$$

The expected value of a variable is not necessarily the value one would expect to obtain on the majority of occasions on which a random selection is made. This is obviously true when the variable can take only integral values and the expected value is not a whole number. In this case, the expected value of the variable is a value which it never takes. It is, however, *expected* in the sense that it is expected to be the average of a large number of random selections.

7. Probability Distributions

Probability distributions may be obtained either from the results of actual experiments or be defined theoretically by some mathematical expression. The former type are called empirical distributions whilst the latter are known as theoretical distributions. In practice it is found that many empirical probability distributions approximate to one of a limited number of kinds of theoretical distribution. Theoretical distributions are important in Statistics because their values for different values of the variable can be readily calculated and tabulated. If an actual distribution is known to approximate to a theoretical distribution, it is possible to test various hypotheses about it, using the tabulated values of the theoretical distribution. From such a table of values it is possible, for example, to determine how many items of an actual distribution may be expected to lie either above or below a stated value of the variable. If the variable is discrete, then each value of the variable has a probability which is either finite or zero; but when the variable is continuous, the probability of a particular value is always either zero or infinitesimally small. It is therefore convenient, when tabulating a probability distribution to tabulate the probability that an item has a value less than a stated value of the variable rather than the probability that it has that value, though sometimes the latter probability is tabulated as well.

If a random variable can take any value in the range $a \leqslant X \leqslant b$ with a non-zero probability, whilst the probability that a value of X lies outside this range is zero, then the probability that the value of the variable lies in the interval $[a, X]$ is given by

$$F(X) = \sum_{X=a}^{X} P(X).$$

Hence $F(X)$ is the probability that X has a value less than or equal to X. $F(X)$ is called the *probability distribution function*, or sometimes just the distribution function. It gives the cumulative relative frequency of the variable X. For example, in the experiment with the coin in the preceding section, the probability that X is less than or equal to 4 is simply the sum of the probabilities that $X = 0, 1, 2, 3, 4$; so in this case, the corresponding distribution function has the value

$$F(4) = \sum_{r=0}^{4} P(X = r)$$
$$= \tfrac{1}{64} + \tfrac{6}{64} + \tfrac{15}{64} + \tfrac{20}{64} + \tfrac{15}{64}$$
$$= 57/64.$$

It is thus possible to tabulate the function $F(X)$, corresponding to the binomial probability function, for different values of n and p. However, it is found that, when n is very large, the binomial probability function approximates to a continuous theoretical distribution called the Normal probability function. Tables of values for the distribution function $F(X)$ corresponding to this probability distribution give the probability that X is less than a stated value, whatever the size of n, provided n is large. This is very convenient because a single table of values can be used instead of a large number of different tables. Many other distributions apart from the binomial distribution are found to approximate to a Normal distribution. For example, if several measurements are made of the same length, the values obtained seldom agree exactly, but tend to be symmetrically distributed about the mean of the measurements. In the same way, the heights of a population of adult males tend to be symmetrically distributed about the mean height of the population. Both these variables are Normally distributed and a table of values of the Normal distribution can be used to test hypotheses about the set of measurements or the heights of males. The kind of hypothesis one usually wishes to test is whether the means of a random selection of such measurements or heights can be taken as the actual length measured or as the actual mean height of the population of males.

The values shown in Table 1 at the end of the book are those of the Standard Normal distribution $N(0, 1)$ having mean zero and standard deviation 1. The curve of the distribution is shown in Fig. 26.

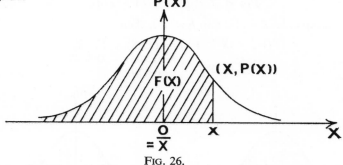

FIG. 26.

The theoretical nature of the distribution is shown by the fact that the curve extends in both directions to minus infinity $(-\infty)$ and to plus infinity $(+\infty)$ which means that no value of X is absolutely impossible. But of course, in an actual distribution this is not so, since the variable always has some finite least and greatest value. However, this difference between an actual and the theoretical distribution is unimportant, since the theoretical probability that a value of X lies outside the limits $X = [-3, 3]$ is very small.

The probability that X is less than a stated value is equal to the area under the Normal curve lying to the left of the perpendicular to the horizontal axis at X (the shaded area shown in Fig. 26). The probability that an item has a value of X less than the mean $\bar{X} = 0$ is, of course $\frac{1}{2}$ or 0·5 since the distribution is symmetrical. It is therefore necessary to tabulate only for values of X lying above the mean. Thus the table shows that 0·9332 of the distribution lies to the left of $X = 1·5$, so 0·9332 is the probability that an item randomly selected has a value less than 1·5. Since the total area under the Normal curve, being the sum of the probabilities that X takes any value, is 1, it follows that in order to find the probability that a randomly selected item is less than $-1·5$, it is only necessary to subtract 0·9332 from 1. So $P(X < -1·5) = 1 - 0·9332 = 0·0668$ or 6·68%. The probability that X lies in the interval $[-1·5, 1·5]$ is thus $1 - 2(1 - 0·9332) = 2 \times 0·9332 - 1$ or 0·8664, so that 86·64% of the distribution lies in this interval.

The probability that X lies in the interval $[a, b]$ where a and b are both positive numbers, and therefore both lie above the mean, is equal to the singly shaded area in the left hand diagram (Fig. 27). The whole of the shaded area of the diagram is the probability that X is less than b, that is, $F(b)$, whilst the doubly shaded area is equal to the probability that X is less than a, that is $F(a)$. So

$$P(a < X < b) = F(b) - F(a).$$

For example, let $a = 1\cdot2$ and $b = 1\cdot8$, then

$$\begin{aligned}P(1\cdot2 < X < 1\cdot8) &= F(1\cdot8) - F(1\cdot2)\\ &= 0\cdot9641 - 0\cdot8849\\ &= 0\cdot0792.\end{aligned}$$

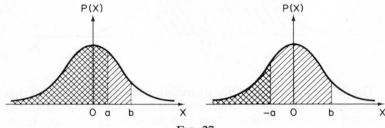

FIG. 27.

To find the probability that X lies in the interval $[-a, b]$, where the boundaries of the interval are on opposite sides of the mean (right-hand diagram in Fig 27), it is still the case that the required probability is equal to $F(b) - F(-a)$. But Table 1 only gives the value of $F(a)$. However, because the distribution is symmetrical, it follows that

$$F(-a) = 1 - F(a).$$

So

$$\begin{aligned}P(-a < X < b) &= F(b) - \{1 - F(a)\}\\ &= F(b) + F(a) - 1.\end{aligned}$$

Thus let $a = -1\cdot3$ and $b = 0\cdot8$, then

$$\begin{aligned}P(-1\cdot3 < X < 0\cdot8) &= 0\cdot7881 + 0\cdot9032 - 1\\ &= 0\cdot6913.\end{aligned}$$

If $a = b$ then, of course,

$$\begin{aligned}P(-a < X < b) &= P(-b < X < b)\\ &= 2F(b) - 1.\end{aligned}$$

Some published tables of the Normal distribution give the probability $P(0 < X < b)$ that X lies between zero and some positive value b. When using these tables, the probability $F(b)$ that X is less than b will obviously be obtained by adding $0\cdot5$ to the value tabulated against b, that is,

$$F(b) = P(0 < X < b) + 0\cdot5.$$

These tables are in some respects simpler to use than Table 1 since the probability that X lies in a given interval can be obtained more directly when the lower limit of the interval is negative. Thus

$$P(-a < X < b) = F(b) + F(a) - 1$$
$$= P(0 < X < b) + P(0 < X < a).$$

8. A Note on Terminology

Many writers define the term "simple event" so that it includes what, in this chapter, has been called a simple event or a compound event. In this sense, a simple event is just any point in a sample space of any dimension. The terminology adopted in this chapter helps to explain how a sample space of any dimension can be constructed, and once this has been grasped the terminology becomes unimportant. The term "Event", in an unqualified sense, may consist of a single event, or a collection of events all of which are favourable to the occurrence of the "Event" in question.

A sample space is called by various names by different writers. Among the alternatives are: *outcome space* and *possibility space*. The term sample space is convenient because each point in such a space represents a random sample, with a probability of selection equal to that of any other random sample which is represented by a point in the sample space. This enables one to obtain clear ideas about the meaning of "random sample", the need for which will be apparent in the next chapter.

EXERCISES 5

1. Assume that a child is equally likely to be a boy or a girl. A family contains 3 children. State the probability that: (i) they are all boys, (ii) they are all girls, (iii) the family contains both boys and girls.

2. Assume that the probability that a baby will be a boy is $0\cdot6$. Calculate the probabilities that the first two children in the family will be: (i) boys, (ii) of the same sex.

3. State the probability that a throw of an unbiased die will result in a score of 3 or more.

4. There were 10 wet days in June last year. If the name of an individual is selected at random from a directory, write down the probability that his or her birthday last year was on a wet June day. Assume all birthdays are equally likely.

5. A card is selected at random from an ordinary pack of 52 playing cards. State the probability (i) that the card is a club, (ii) that the card is either a club or an ace (or both).

6. You have four coins in your pocket: a sixpence and three new pennies. You take out three coins. What is the probability that you have only a new penny left in your pocket?

7. Two unbiased dice, each numbered 1 to 6, are thrown simultaneously. Which of the following statements are true and which are false?

   (a) Throwing two sixes is less probable than throwing two fours.
   (b) The probability that both dice show the same score is $1/6$.
   (c) The most likely total score is 6.

8. A jar contains 24 marbles, some red and some blue. If a marble is drawn at random from the jar the probability is $\frac{1}{4}$ that it is red. How many of the marbles are blue?

9. A bag contains 30 discs: 10 red, 10 green, 10 yellow.

   (i) If three are drawn out in succession and not replaced, what is the probability of drawing two reds and 1 yellow in that order?
   (ii) If each disc is replaced after drawing what would the answer be now?

10. Two events A and B are not independent. Write down an expression for $P(A \text{ or } B)$ in terms of the probability of A, the probability of B and the joint probability of A and B.

    Two cards are selected from an ordinary pack of playing cards and are not replaced after selection. Find the probability that the first is an ace or the second a ten or the first and second are ace and ten respectively.

11. Which of the following pairs of events are independent?

    (a) A head at two successive tosses of a coin.
    (b) A king at two successive selections from a pack of playing cards without replacement.
    (c) The completion of two lines for the same set of matches in a football pool coupon.

    (d) Two successive wet days.

12. Draw a tree diagram to find the number of permutations of the four letters a, b, c, d. What is this number?

13. Evaluate $n!$ when n equals (a) 5, (b) 7, (c) 3!.

14. An urn consists of 60 red marbles and 40 white marbles. Two sets of 9 marbles each are drawn with replacement from the urn and their colours are noted. What is the probability that the two sets differ by eight or more red marbles?

15. A bag contains four green balls and one red ball, which are identical apart from colour. A *trial* consists of making a random selection of a ball from the bag, noting its colour and then returning it to the bag. A *success* consists of drawing the red ball.

    (a) Calculate the probability of exactly two successes in five trials.

    (b) Calculate the probability of at least two successes in five trials.

16. (i) Four boxes with lids are distinguishable from each other only by their colours which are red, green, yellow and blue respectively. The boxes stand in a given order on a table and their lids are all removed and then replaced in a random order.

    Find the number of different orders by colour in which the lids can be replaced.

    Calculate the probabilities that (a) *exactly* two of the lids are on the correct boxes, and (b) *at least* two of the lids are on the correct boxes.

    (ii) Find the number of different ways in which all the letters of the word *PARALLEL* can be arranged. Calculate the probability that one of these arrangements, selected at random, begins with an *R* or an *E*.

    (The number of arrangements of n things of which r are of one kind, s of another kind and the remainder all different is $\dfrac{n!}{r!\,s!}$.)

17. Draw a tree diagram to illustrate the possible outcomes of tossing a coin 4 times. How many outcomes are there? If the coin is not fair, so that the probability of a head at each toss is $\frac{5}{8}$, find the probability that in four tosses of the coin three heads are obtained.

18. (i) Two men, Dave and Bill, decide to play a series of games of pure chance in which the probability of Bill winning in each game is 0·2 and of Dave winning in each game is 0·8. The series

is to consist of at most four games but will stop before this as soon as Bill wins a game.

Bill scores 200 points if he wins the first game, 100 points if he wins at the second game, 50 points if he wins at the third game and 25 points if he wins at the fourth game.

Calculate the expected value of Bill's score.

(ii) The same two men agree to play another series in which the probability of Dave winning is 0·6 and of Bill winning is 0·4. They decide to play a *best-of-five* match, i.e. the first person to win three games wins the match. Given that Dave wins the first two games calculate the probability that Bill now wins the match.

19. From prolonged observation on weekdays, during the day, at the ticket office of a main line terminus the probabilities of finding 0, 1, 2, 3, 4, 5 people waiting were stated to be 0·08, 0·17, 0·31, 0·28, 0·14 and 0·02 respectively.

Calculate (a) the expected value, and (b) the variance of the number of people waiting.

20. A party of nine people consists of five men and four women, and a group of four people is to be chosen at random from this party.

   (a) In how many ways can a group of four be chosen that contains at least three women? Hence calculate the probability that the four selected will contain at least three women.

   (b) If Mr. and Mrs. *A* are included in the original party of nine, what is the probability that the selected group of four will not include both Mr. and Mrs. *A*?

21. Twenty-five items are arranged in order of magnitude and it is found that there is only one median item. Four items are now selected at random without being replaced after selection. What is the probability that one of the items lies above the median and the other three below it?

22. If an item is selected from a standard Normal distribution $N(0, 1)$, what is the probability that it is (a) greater than 1, (b) greater than 2, (c) less than -1.

23. Find the probability that an item selected at random from a standard Normal distribution lies in the interval $X = [0, 1·65]$. If 3 independent selections are made from this distribution, calculate the probability that 2 of them lie in the interval $X = [0, 1·65]$.

24. Show that $\sum_{r=0}^{n} \binom{n}{r} = 2^n$.

25. Three independent selections are made from a frequency distribution. Calculate the probability that two of the selections lie above the upper quartile.

26. The outcomes of a binomial trial are "failure", denoted by $X = 0$, and "success", denoted by $X = 1$. If the expected number of successes in n independent trials is a, find $\bar{X}$ and interpret the meaning of $\bar{X}$. Show that the variance of X is $\bar{X}(1 - \bar{X})$.

27. Write down the coefficients of the 4th and 10th terms of the expansion of $(q + p)^{12}$.

28. Use the probability distribution on page 113 to find the expected number of heads in 6 tosses of a fair coin.

29. (a) Use Pascal's triangle to obtain the number of outcomes of each kind which may occur in ten binomial trials.
    (b) If the numbers obtained in (a) are the expected frequencies of 0, 1, 2, up to 10 successes obtained in a series of experiments each consisting of ten independent binomial trials, what can you say about the probability of a success at any trial? Calculate the mean and standard deviation of this distribution.

30. Given the following probability distribution:

x	1	3	5	7	9
probability	0·03	0·15	0·26	0·39	0·17

find the expected values of: (a) x, (b) $x - 1·5$, (c) $\frac{1}{2}x^2$ and (d) $\sqrt{x}$.

31. What is the probability that an item selected at random from a standard Normal distribution lies in the interval: (a) $[-0·5, 0·5]$, (b) $[0·9, 1·5]$, (c) $[-1·8, 1·2]$ and (d) $[-2, -1]$?
    What is the probability that the item lies *outside* the interval: (e) $[1·23, 1·92]$ and (f) $[-0·21, 1·51]$?

CHAPTER 6

Sampling and Significance Tests

1. Sample Means

A population of N items, each with a measurable characteristic X, gives rise to N values of the characteristic, some of which may, of course, be repeated values. Thus let the N items have the values:

$$X_1, X_2, X_3, \ldots, X_N.$$

A random selection of n items from these N values is called a *random sample of size n*. The values of the items in the sample are denoted by the small letter x, thus:

$$x_1, x_2, x_3, \ldots, x_n.$$

There are great advantages in assuming that the selection of each item in the sample is independent, so that each item has an equal chance of selection $(1/N)$ every time a selection is made. This means that the same item may occur more than once in a random sample. When N, the number of items in the population, is small, this can only be effected by replacing each item after it has been selected and before the next random selection is made. However, when N is large, replacement is unnecessary, because the values of X can then be expected to lie very close together, so that when one item is selected and not replaced it is still possible to select another item which is very close to it in value.

The number of independent random samples of size n from a population of size N is N^n, which is the numb r of equiprobable points in the sample space, because the first item in the sample can be selected in N ways, the second in N ways, and so on. If the N values of X are all different, then all the points in the sample space represent different samples taking into account the order of selection, whilst if some of the values of X are the same, some of the samples will also be the same. Since every population item has an equal chance of selection, the expected value of any item selected is the population mean, denoted by the Greek letter μ (pronounced mu). Hence the expected value of a sample mean is also μ; and so the mean of the means of all possible samples is the population mean. A sample mean is denoted by $\bar{x}$.

Next consider the expected squared deviation of any item in a sample from the population mean. This will be equal to the population variance, denoted by σ^2. Since each of the n items is independently selected, they all have the same expected squared deviation from the population mean, so that the sum of expected squared deviations of these n items is $n\sigma^2$. In order to obtain the expected squared deviation of a sample mean from the population mean, it is necessary to divide each item in the sample by the number of items in the sample, namely n; so that the squared deviations of items in the sample from the population mean are divided by n^2. Hence the expected squared deviation of a sample mean from the population mean is $n\sigma^2/n^2 = \sigma^2/n$. This is the variance of the sample means, so that the standard deviation of the sample means is the square root of this, namely $\sigma/\sqrt{n}$. Hence we have two important results about random sample means:

(1) The mean of all random sample means is the population mean μ.
(2) The standard deviation of the means of all random samples of size n is $\sigma/\sqrt{n}$.

These results are illustrated and verified by considering the following example.

Population: 1 3 6 6 ($N = 4$, $\mu = 4$, $\sigma = 3/\sqrt{2}$.)

Sample Space ($n = 2$)				Sample Means			
(1, 1)	(3, 1)	(6, 1)	(6, 1)	1	2	3·5	3·5
(1, 3)	(3, 3)	(6, 3)	(6, 3)	2	3	4·5	4·5
(1, 6)	(3, 6)	(6, 6)	(6, 6)	3·5	4·5	6	6
(1, 6)	(3, 6)	(6, 6)	(6, 6)	3·5	4·5	6	6

The sample means have the following frequency distribution:

$\bar{x}$	1	2	3	3·5	4·5	6	Total
frequency: f	1	2	1	4	4	4	16

It is easily verified, in the usual way, that the mean of this distribution is

$$\Sigma f\bar{x}/\Sigma f = 64/16 = 4 = \mu;$$

whilst the standard deviation is

$$\sqrt{\left(\frac{\Sigma f\bar{x}^2}{\Sigma f} - \mu^2\right)} = \sqrt{\left(\frac{292}{16} - 16\right)} = \frac{3}{2}.$$

Now in this example $\sigma/\sqrt{n} = \sigma/\sqrt{2}$

$$= \frac{3}{\sqrt{2} \times \sqrt{2}}$$

$$= \frac{3}{2}.$$

Hence, for this particular example, it has been verified that

$$\text{S.D.}(\bar{x}) = \sigma/\sqrt{n}.$$

The results (1) and (2) are, in fact true of any distribution of random sample means, whatever the sample size n. In the population chosen for this illustration, two values are the same (viz. 6), so that two of the four items in the population have the same value. To satisfy himself that the above results are true in other cases, the student should carry out the same procedure for a population in which none of the items has the same value.

The above frequency distribution of $\bar{x}$ has an interesting and useful property which is found in many distributions of random sample means, namely that there are an equal number of items on either side of the mean of the distribution. Hence the mean coincides with the median which shows that, although the distribution has no pronounced mode, it is approximately symmetrical. This tendency of sample means to be symmetrically distributed increases as the sample size n is increased, provided, of course that the population size N is sufficiently large in relation to n to allow a large number of points in the sample space. When N is large and n is greater than 50, it is found that the distribution of sample means approximates to a Normal distribution. If the population itself is Normally distributed, then the sample means will be Normally distributed whatever the sample size; though as few populations are exactly Normally distributed, 50 is a safe lower limit to use if it is desired to obtain a Normal distribution of sample means. This property has important consequences for testing hypotheses about the population mean based on random sampling, as will be shown in the next section.

2. Distribution of the Means of Large Samples

The standard deviation of sample means, $\sigma/\sqrt{n}$, is known as the *standard error of the mean*. Since it is a standard deviation, it gives some indication of the concentration of the sample means about their mean μ, and therefore of the variability that may be expected in the sample means resulting from random sampling. Moreover, when n is large, the sample means are Normally distributed, so that it is possible to transform their distribution into a Standard Normal distribution with mean 0 and standard deviation 1, so that it can then be determined, by reference to the tables of the Normal distribution, exactly what percentage of the sample means lies within a given number of standard errors from their mean. Thus (see Chapter 4, section 6):

If the sample means $\bar{x}$ are Normally distributed with mean μ and standard deviation $\sigma/\sqrt{n}$, then the variable $X = (\bar{x} - \mu)/(\sigma/\sqrt{n})$ has a Standard Normal distribution.

In this transformation, X is measured in standard error units, so that it is possible to determine the probability that a given sample mean lies within so many standard errors from the population mean.

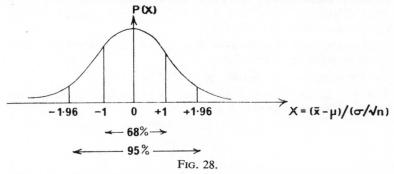

FIG. 28.

Thus 68% (approximately) of the sample means lie in the interval $\mu \pm \sigma/\sqrt{n}$, whilst almost exactly 95% of the sample means lie in the interval $\mu \pm 1.96\sigma/\sqrt{n}$. The latter limits are especially important in sampling theory. Since the distribution is symmetrical, it follows that 2·5% of the sample means lie above 1·96 standard errors and 2·5% lie below — 1·96 standard errors from the mean. Hence there is a probability of only 0·05 that a random sample has a mean which lies outside these limits (Fig. 28).

In order to test whether a sample has been drawn from a population with a given mean, the *Null Hypothesis* is made that this is the case. The object of the test is then to determine whether the Null Hypothesis is to be accepted or rejected. If the sample mean differs by more than 1·96 standard errors from the hypothetical population mean, then the hypothesis that it came from a population with such a mean is rejected at the 5% *level of significance*.

This test is called a *significance test*, the 5% level of significance being the first critical level of the test. Very often, if a Null Hypothesis passes a test at the 5% level, it is accepted; but in cases where it is necessary to be very sure that the hypothesis is false before it is rejected, a second critical level of 1% is used. Now 99% of a Normal distribution lies within ±2·58 standard errors from the mean, so that the probability is only 0·01 or 1% that a sample mean will lie above or below these limits, provided that it came from a population with the given mean.

EXAMPLE 1

The expected lifetime of electric light bulbs was 1500 hours with standard deviation 90 hours. To test a new batch a sample of 100 showed a mean lifetime of 1480 hours. Test the hypothesis that the mean lifetime of the electric light bulbs has not changed, using a significance level of (a) 0·05, (b) 0·01.

Here, the Null Hypothesis is that the old and new batches have the same mean, $\mu = 1500$ hours.

For the sample, $n = 100$, $\bar{x} = 1480$ hours.

The population standard deviation $\sigma = 90$ hours. Hence the Standard Normal variable

$$X = \left| \frac{1480 - 1500}{90/\sqrt{100}} \right|$$

$$= \frac{20 \times 10}{90}$$

$$= 2 \cdot 2.$$

Since this value of X (2·2 standard errors) is greater than 1·96, the probability is less than 0·05 that the test could have produced a mean as low as 1480 solely as a result of random variation, and so the hypothesis that there is no difference in the means is rejected at the 5% level. However, the value of X is not so great as 2·58, so that at the 1% level, random variation might have produced this result and the hypothesis cannot be rejected at this level.

The random variability of sample means is called *random error* or *sampling error*. Whenever samples are taken, some deviation of sample means from the population mean is to be expected due to sampling error. The purpose of a significance test is to determine whether such deviations are too great to be explicable in terms of sampling error alone. If they are too great, then the implication is that there is some non-random factor causing the deviation.

3. Estimation and Confidence Limits

Samples are very often drawn from a population with the object of determining its mean. In this case, it must be assumed that nothing is known of the population apart from the fact that the sample was drawn from it by some suitable random method. Not only is the mean unknown, but also the standard deviation σ of the population. In order to estimate the population mean from the sample mean, the standard error of the sample mean must be known, and so an estimate must also be made of the population standard deviation. For this purpose, the standard deviation of the sample can be used, provided that the sample size is sufficiently large (say, greater than 50). Thus the population variance can be estimated from the formula:

$$\text{Var.} \ (x) = s^2 = \Sigma \ (x - \bar{x})^2/n$$

where x is a sample value, $\bar{x}$ the sample mean and n the sample size. The estimated population standard deviation is then

$$\hat{\sigma} = s = \sqrt{(\Sigma \ (x - \bar{x})^2/n)},$$

where the "cap" sign over σ indicates that the formula is an estimate of the population parameter σ. It follows that the estimated standard error of the mean is

$$\hat{\sigma}/\sqrt{n} = s/\sqrt{n}.$$

This is called a *point estimate* of the standard error, because it consists of a single, unique value. The sample mean $\bar{x}$ provides a point estimate of the population mean, but is very seldom used, since it does not indicate how accurate the estimate is. To remedy this defect, it is replaced by an *interval estimate*, the limits of which are known to be exceeded, due to random errors, with a specified probability. The limits chosen are those which have only a 0·05 chance of being exceeded by chance and are known as the 95% *confidence limits*. The 95% confidence limits for an estimate of a population mean μ can be found as follows:

Since $X = (\bar{x} - \mu)/(s/\sqrt{n})$ is a Standard Normal variable, it follows that X lies in the interval $[-1\cdot96, 1\cdot96]$ with 95% probability, i.e.,

$$-1\cdot96 < \frac{\bar{x} - \mu}{(s/\sqrt{n})} < +1\cdot96 \text{ with probability } 0\cdot95$$

Rearranging this inequality:

$$-1\cdot96(s/\sqrt{n}) < \bar{x} - \mu < +1\cdot96(s/\sqrt{n})$$
$$-1\cdot96(s/\sqrt{n}) - \bar{x} < -\mu < 1\cdot96(s/\sqrt{n}) - \bar{x}$$
$$\bar{x} + 1\cdot96(s/\sqrt{n}) > \mu > \bar{x} - 1\cdot96(s/\sqrt{n}).$$

It follows that μ lies in the interval $\bar{x} \pm 1\cdot96(s/\sqrt{n})$ with probability 0·95, the limits of the interval being the 95% confidence limits. If a large number of samples are taken then, of course, the sample means will differ from one sample to another and so will the 95% confidence intervals. However, only 5% of these intervals will not contain the population mean. It is in this sense that one can say that there is a 0·95 chance that the 95% confidence interval obtained from a particular sample contains the population mean.

EXAMPLE 2

A sample of 100 units of a component is tested with the following results:

Life in hours	Under 85	85–89	90–94	95–99	100–104	105–109	110 and over
No. of components	3	10	17	39	18	9	4

On the basis of this sample, calculate 95% confidence limits for the mean life of the component. Would you advise a prospective purchaser to place a substantial order if he required a minimum life of 90 hours from this component?

From the data, $n = 100$, $\bar{x} = 97\cdot1$ hours and estimated population standard deviation is $s = 6\cdot6$ hours.

Standard error of mean $= 6\cdot6/\sqrt{100} = 0\cdot66$. The required 95% confidence limits are thus

$$97\cdot1 \pm 1\cdot96 \times 0\cdot66$$

i.e., $97\cdot1 \pm 1\cdot3$

so that the population mean lies between 95·8 hours and 98·4 hours with 95% confidence.

Assuming that the lives of components are Normally distributed with mean and standard deviation 98·4 and 6·6 hours respectively, it is nearly certain that at least 10% will have lives less than 90 hours, which is a rather high proportion.

It is not difficult to see that the standard deviation of sample means decreases as the sample size increases so that, if the parent population is normally distributed the items in the population will be much more dispersed about its mean than will the sample means. With increased sample size, the concentration of the sample means about the population mean increases, a tendency known as the *Central Limit Theorem* (see Fig. 29). It follows that there is a high probability that the mean of a large sample will differ by very little

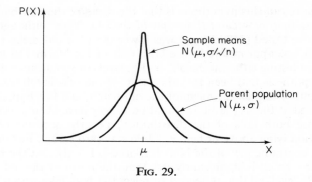

FIG. 29.

from the population mean. This fact can be used to increase the precision of any estimate of the population mean. Thus in Example 2, with a sample of 100 components, the population mean could be estimated to within $1\cdot3/97\cdot1$ or $1\cdot3\%$ with 95% probability. To increase the precision of the estimate to 1% a larger sample size would be needed. If the required sample size is n, then it must satisfy the condition that

$$1\cdot96 \times \frac{6\cdot6}{\sqrt{n}} = 1\% \text{ of } 97\cdot1 = 0\cdot971$$

It follows that

$$n = \frac{(1\cdot96 \times 6\cdot6)^2}{(0\cdot971)^2} = 177.$$

The precision desirable in a particular case will naturally depend on circumstances. A monetary advantage may derive from an accurate estimate, but this must be balanced against the cost of taking a large sample especially as this may be time-consuming.

In many cases, the formula $s = \sqrt{\{\Sigma\,(x - \bar{x})^2/(n - 1)\}}$ gives a better estimate of population standard deviation than the formula for s given previously. This formula is used mainly when the sample size is small and will make very little difference to the result when n is large, since the relative difference between n and $(n - 1)$ will then be very small. This formula is, however, very important when sample size is small, which is very often the case. The discussion of small samples is, however, postponed to a later chapter.

4. One- and Two-Tailed Tests

In Example 1, section 2, the Null Hypothesis tested was that old and new batches of electric light bulbs have the same mean life. The contradictory of this hypothesis is that the mean of the new batch is *either* less than *or* greater than that of the old. Thus, although the mean to be tested (1480 hours) was lower than the old mean (1500 hours), it was appropriate to use both tails of the Normal distribution when testing either at the 5% or 1% levels of significance. If the Null Hypothesis had been that the mean of the new batch was not significantly *less than* the mean of the old batch, and this hypothesis were tested at the 5% level, it would no longer have been appropriate to use both tails of the distribution, i.e., the sections of the distribution lying above or below ± 1.96 standard errors. For in this case the contradictory of the Null Hypothesis is only that the mean of the new batch is significantly less than the mean of the old and, at the 5% level, all that is needed to reject the Null Hypothesis is to show that the new mean could be as low as it is by chance with a probability of only 0.05. Now 5% of the distribution lies below -1.64 standard errors from the mean and it is this limit which is the correct one to use when testing the new hypothesis at the 5% level. Similarly, to test this hypothesis at the 1% level, the limit to use is at -2.33 standard errors below the mean, for 1% of the distribution lies below this limit. As a matter of fact, this does not affect the result of Example 1, since $X = 2.2$ is still too small to be significant at the 1% level, even when a one-tailed test is used.

It will be seen that the decision whether to use a one- or two-tailed test depends on the way in which the Null Hypothesis is formulated. If the hypothesis states that there is no significant difference between a sample and a population mean, without any further qualification, then a two-tailed test is the appropriate one to use. If, on the other hand, the hypothesis states that the sample mean does not differ from the population mean in some specified direction, then a one-tailed test is the right one to use. Of course, if a Null Hypothesis is rejected by a two-tailed test, the more restricted hypothesis will also be rejected by a one-tailed test at the same level of significance.

The question whether to use a one- or two-tailed test shows how necessary it is to formulate the Null Hypothesis clearly and precisely. In almost all tests of significance, it is not only the Null Hypothesis H_0 which is being tested but also the contradictory hypothesis H_1. Rejecting H_0 means accepting H_1 and conversely. For example, if the Null Hypothesis is $H_0 : \bar{x} = \mu$, then the hypothesis against which H_0 is tested is $H_1 : \bar{x} \neq \mu$, in which case a two-tailed test is obviously the one to use. Similarly, if the two alternative hypotheses are $H_0 : \bar{x} \ngtr \mu$, $H_1 : \bar{x} > \mu$, then only the right tail of the distribution will be used in the test, because if $\bar{x}$ lies above the appropriate limit in the right tail, this is sufficient to reject H_0 as thus formulated.

Cases arise in which the use of a one-tailed test is obviously indicated. For example, the number of defective items in a sample cannot be less than zero, and in any case, one is usually not interested in any number less than a certain minimum. So if the number of defective items in a sample is normally distributed, the left tail of the distribution will be irrelevant; the only interest will be in whether the number of defectives in a sample is *greater than* a given number. Hence the null hypothesis will be, not that the number of defectives in the population is either greater or less than a specified number, but simply that it is less than that number. This hypothesis is refuted at the 5% level if the number of defectives in the sample exceeds a critical number which, if the null hypothesis is true, is exceeded by chance only on 5% of the occasions on which samples are taken.

5. Standard Error of a Proportion

The selection of one item at random from a population which can be classified according to two mutually exclusive and collectively exhaustive attributes constitutes a binomial trial (see Chapter 5, section 5). If the population is large, it is possible to make a number of independent selections from the population without replacement, the result being a sample of size n when the number of items selected is n. If the proportion of items in the population possessing attribute S is $P(S) = p$, then p is the probability of randomly selecting an item with that attribute in one independent selection, whilst $q = 1 - p$ is the probability of not selecting the item with attribute S. Suppose that X takes the value 1 when an item with attribute S is drawn and 0 when the item drawn does not possess attribute S. Then the probability distribution of X is:

X	0	1	Total
Probability	q	p	1

The population mean and standard deviation are thus:

$$\mu = \frac{0 \times q + 1 \times p}{q + p} = p$$

$$\sigma^2 = \frac{q(0 - p)^2 + p(1 - p)^2}{q + p}$$

$$= qp^2 + pq^2$$
$$= qp(p + q)$$
$$= pq$$

so $$\sigma = \sqrt{(pq)}.$$

Let $\bar{x}$ be the proportion of items in a sample of size n which possess attribute S. Then by results (1) and (2) in section 1, the mean of the sample proportions is p and their standard deviation is $\sqrt{(pq/n)}$. Moreover, if n is large and p neither too large nor too small (i.e., not too close to the limits $p = 1$ or $p = 0$), then, by the property in section 2, the variable

$$X = (\bar{x} - p)/\sqrt{(pq/n)}$$

has a Standard Normal distribution. It is accordingly possible to test hypotheses about the proportion of items in a population possessing an attribute, based on tests applied to the sampling proportion of the attribute in exactly the same way as hypotheses about the population mean are tested.

EXAMPLE 3

A coin is tossed 100 *times, the number of heads obtained being* 59. *Test the hypothesis that the coin is fair.*

The Null Hypothesis is that $p = \frac{1}{2}$, so that the expected population standard deviation is $\sqrt{(\frac{1}{2} \times \frac{1}{2})} = \frac{1}{2}$.

$$\text{Sample proportion, } \bar{x} = \frac{59}{100} = 0.59$$

$$\text{Standard error of proportion} = \frac{1}{2}/\sqrt{100} = \frac{1}{20}.$$

Hence the Standard Normal variable

$$X = \frac{0.59 - 0.5}{1/20}$$
$$= 20 \times 0.09$$
$$= 1.8.$$

This value of X is less than 1.96 and so is too small to be significant at the 5% level of a two-tailed test. The Null Hypothesis that the coin is fair is therefore not rejected.

EXAMPLE 4

A random sample of coffee-drinkers of size 400 *showed that* 37% *consumed regularly a certain brand of coffee. Find the* 95% *confidence limits for the proportion of coffee-drinkers regularly consuming that brand.*

Here $\bar{x} = 0.37$ and $(1 - \bar{x}) = 0.63$.

Since the population standard deviation is unknown, it must be estimated from the sample.

Thus $\hat{\sigma} = \sqrt{(0.37 \times 0.63)}$.

Standard error of proportion $= \sqrt{(0.37 \times 0.63)}/\sqrt{400}$.

With 95% confidence, the population proportion can be expected to lie in the interval

$$0.37 \pm 1.96 \times \sqrt{(0.37 \times 0.63)}/20$$

i.e., 0.37 ± 0.047

or   between 32.3%   and   41.7%.

It is often more convenient to test hypotheses about the proportion of items possessing a given attribute in a population rather than the actual numbers. When the population is infinite as is the case when a coin is tossed or when an indefinite number of independent binomial trials is possible, then there is no alternative but to use a test based on the proportion. If, however, only a finite number of items in the population possess the attribute in question, then it is possible to adapt the test used in Example 3 to the number possessing the attribute rather than the proportion. If the population proportion is p, then the *expected* number of items possessing the attribute in a sample of size n is np, whilst the number in the sample actually possessing the attribute is $n\bar{x}$. Now the Standard Normal variable X will have the same value whether testing a proportion or the corresponding number. Hence for the number of items possessing an attribute,

$$X = n(\bar{x} - p)/n\sqrt{(pq/n)}$$
$$= (n\bar{x} - np)/\sqrt{(npq)}.$$

It follows that the sample numbers of items having an attribute in samples of size n have mean np and standard deviation (or standard error) $\sqrt{(npq)}$.

To test hypotheses about a binomial population based on samples of small size, one possibility is to use the binomial probabilities themselves rather than the Normal approximations to them. For example, when a coin is tossed 6 times, the probability of either 0 or 6 heads is $\frac{1}{64} + \frac{1}{64} = 0.03$. Hence, if the result of the tosses is 6 heads, the Null Hypothesis that the coin is fair would be rejected at the 5% level. When n is large, but p is very close either to 0 or 1, so that the sample proportions are not Normally distributed, it can be shown that these proportions have another distribution called the Poisson distribution, which can be used to calculate the probability that a given sample proportion came from a population with a specified population proportion. Consideration of this case is deferred to a later chapter.

6. Random Sampling

In the preceding discussion it has been assumed that a random sample of size n has somehow been obtained. It will be recalled that a sample is random if each item in the population has an equal chance of selection every time a selection is made. This condition is often very difficult to satisfy in practice, particularly when the population is large, which must be the case to obtain random samples without replacement. Even when it is ideally possible to obtain a random sample, each item of which has an equal chance of selection from a population, the result may be misleading. This point can be illustrated by considering the construction and purpose of a table of random sampling numbers (Table 5).

A table of random sampling numbers consists of repetitions of each of the ten digits 0 to 9, arranged in rows and columns in such a way that, when read along a row or down a column, the digits occur in random order. This means that the chance of a particular digit occurring in any specified position in a row or column is always 1/10, independently of the values of the digits occurring in its neighbourhood. In a block of 100 digits, say, the expected proportion of zeros is thus 1/10 or 0·1, whilst the standard deviation of the proportions of zeros occurring in all possible blocks of 100 digits is $\sqrt{(0·1 \times 0·9/100)} = 0·03$. These proportions are Normally distributed, so that the probability of finding a block of 100 with 22 zeros or more is the probability that a Standard Normal variable is greater than

$$X = \frac{0·22 - 0·1}{0·03} = 4.$$

From Table 1, the probability that X is greater than 4 is

$$1 - 0·99997 = 0·00003 \quad \text{or} \quad 0·003\%;$$

so that 1 block of 100 digits in 33,000 blocks can be expected to contain at least 22 zeros. If such a block occurred in an actual table of random sampling numbers, it would be most misleading as a sample from a population in which each of the digits occurred with equal frequency. Since random sampling numbers are generally used at some stage in selecting a random sample, the actual sample selected by using this abnormal block of 100 digits would also be misleading, because the item corresponding to the digit zero would be over-represented in the sample. The case considered here is an extreme one, and a less excessive repetition of a single digit could seriously invalidate the tables in which it occurred. For this reason, tables of random sampling numbers need to be carefully censored so that blocks in which digits are over-represented do not occur.

Random samples are sometimes selected by what is known as *intuitive sampling*. This consists in the investigator's selecting what, according to his own judgement, is a random sample. For example, an interviewer engaged in collecting material for a survey of preferences for certain radio programmes exhibited by the population of an urban area is stationed in a busy shopping centre and interviews what appears to her to be approximately every 25th passer-by. The objection to this method of obtaining a random sample is that it is liable to subjective bias. The appearance of certain people, because they look perhaps uncooperative, may deter her from interviewing them even though they fit in with her general numerical pattern of selection (i.e., every 25th person). Or suppose a sample of 100 to be taken for inspection from a batch of 1000 components, and that the inspector selects the sample by choosing 100 "here and there" from the batch. If he is a conscientious inspector, he may be unconsciously inclined to select those components which appear to be below the acceptable standard, assuming that this can be detected by simple observation. This is another example of intuitive sampling which may result in unconscious selective bias. Experiments have been performed in which human subjects write down sets of digits in what they believe to be random order; but statistical tests show that the subjects often exhibit an unconscious tendency to prefer some digit or digits more than the others.

The use of random sampling numbers to avoid the subjective bias to which intuitive sampling is liable is therefore to be highly recommended, because the method by which such numbers are generated, usually by electronic means, is free from unconscious bias on the part of the person compiling them; and so they provide an objective standard of randomness. To illustrate how they can be used, suppose that a small random sample of 10 components is to be selected from a batch of 100 components. Each component in the batch is labelled with a two-digit number from 00 to 99. The first 10 numbers in the first double column of Table 5 are then written down, namely: 23, 05, 14, 38, 97, 11, 43, 93, 49, 36. If a number is repeated in this list, the repetitions are usually discarded and the number of numbers brought up to the required number (10) by choosing the two-digit numbers immediately following the last number chosen. Although, strictly speaking, random sampling requires replacement of the items selected so that they could be re-selected, this is not so important if the sample size is small in relation to the population size. One advantage of not using repeated sampling numbers in these circumstances is that the likelihood of an unrepresentative or misleading sample is reduced. The components bearing the 10 random numbers thus obtained are next selected as the random sample and, since human judgement has been excluded, the sample so obtained should be free from bias, the only error being that due to sampling error to which the random sampling numbers are as liable as any other set of things which has been randomly selected.

7. The Sampling Frame

Before any random sample can be obtained, it is essential to define precisely the limits of the population being investigated. This may require a preliminary knowledge of the subject-matter of the investigation. For example, if the consumption of a certain product which is known to be very little used among certain sections of the population, is being investigated, then those sections can be excluded from the enquiry. The results obtained in this case will apply only to the population as thus defined. It is a common logical fallacy, when generalising results, to go beyond the evidence and to assume that what has been established for one group is necessarily true for apparently similar groups as well.

Once the population has been specified, it is necessary, at least ideally, to have a list of the names of every item in the population. This list is called the *sampling frame*. That for inanimate objects such as machine components may simply be a set of numbers whilst, for human subjects, it will consist of their names. A commonly used sampling frame is the Electoral Register. Some method of randomly selecting names from the sampling frame then gives the required random sample. In practice, it is seldom possible to use a complete sampling frame because of the prohibitive cost involved in collecting a widely scattered sample. Many sampling frames should ideally consist of every member of a country's population, and members of the resulting sample might, accordingly, be widely scattered about the country and often be difficult to locate. It is only a Government department which can afford to use a sampling frame as comprehensive as this. On the other hand, if a limited sampling frame is used which is thought to be representative, this opinion may turn out to be mistaken, resulting in a biased sample. A magazine enquiry addressed to readers of the magazine concerning their political opinions may give a misleading picture of the political opinions of the country as a whole. On the other hand, a limited sampling frame may give useful results. Thus if a scientific journal asks its readers to answer a questionnaire respecting their views on some scientific topic, for example whether more public money should be spent on research in that field, then the result of the enquiry could well be representative of scientific opinion generally, even though not all scientists read the journal regularly.

8. Simple and Stratified Sampling

In *simple sampling* every item in the population has the same chance of selection, and a sample selected in this way could, theoretically, come predominantly from one section of the population as was seen in the case of random sampling numbers. This is no drawback if the population is homogeneous, so that one section of it almost exactly resembles any other. However, considerable preliminary knowledge of the subject-matter may be necessary in order to be certain that this is true. From a statistical point of view, groups are homogeneous if they have roughly the same mean and variance. Suppose, for example, that a field is divided into 100 plots in which samples of four different varieties of wheat are to be tested for yield. Provided that all portions of the field resemble one another in soil fertility, amount of irrigation, exposure to sunshine and any other important relevant factors, then it can be expected that any variation in the yield of one variety of wheat sown on different plots will be due only to random causes. In this case, it is adequate to allocate the four varieties to different plots by a process of simple random selection so that, theoretically at least, most of one variety of wheat might be sown on adjacent plots without affecting the validity of the experiment.

Suppose now that it is desired to determine how prone a certain industry is to absenteeism, the industry being composed of both small and large firms. The procedure of simple sampling of firms could involve taking a random sample of all firms in such a way that only the smaller firms, which may be more numerous, are represented in the sample. But it might easily be the case that the size of a firm has an important effect on absenteeism in which case a sample which excluded larger firms altogether would be misleading because the population of firms was not homogeneous with reference to this particular enquiry. In this case, a better method of obtaining a representative random sample is to classify firms according to size, using the number of employees in a firm as a criterion for this purpose. The numbers selected from each size group can then be made proportional to the number of firms in the group from which the appropriate number will then be randomly selected. This procedure is called *stratified sampling*, and ensures that each homogeneous segment of the population is properly represented in the sample.

Stratified sampling is used a good deal in agricultural and other experiments where the data is not homogeneous. It is sometimes called "blocking" or "replication", each stratum from which the sample is selected being a block or replicate. The statistical methods often used to analyse sample data obtained in this way lie outside the scope of this book. However many of the results obtained from a stratified sample can be tested by elementary statistical methods.

9. Multi-stage and Quota Sampling

When the funds available for an enquiry are limited, the two sampling methods outlined in the preceding section have two undesirable qualities. Since the whole sampling frame is used in both, the items in the sample may be scattered over a wide territorial area and, if the data is obtained by means of a personal interview, which is often the most reliable method, it will be expensive to collect. Moreover, the items in the sample are predetermined by a random selective process such as the use of random sampling numbers, and the particular items enumerated in the sample are therefore the ones which should be contacted if bias is to be avoided; but it could easily happen that some of these items are difficult to locate. For example, if it is necessary to interview a specified individual in a household and him only, several calls may be necessary before he is found at home. It must be stressed that these deficiencies of simple and stratified sampling are economic; from the statistical point of view, they are best in the sense that they give the most reliable and accurate results. Since private enterprise frequently requires the use of compromise in order to save money, however, some modification of the ideal methods of sampling is often used, particularly if it is not absolutely essential to obtain results of the highest accuracy. Two such methods are in general use: *multi-stage* or *cluster sampling* and *quota sampling*.

The object of cluster sampling is to concentrate interviews into a few areas by dividing the whole population into groups according to geographical location. From the total number of groups, a random sample of groups is drawn and from each group in this sample a random sample of individuals is selected, the sample size being proportional to the number of individuals in each group. For example, if an urban area can be divided into 100 regions each containing 100 households and the object is to obtain a random sample of 50 households, then 5 regions could be selected at random and from these selected regions 10 households out of 100 could be randomly selected for interview. The work of interviewers is accordingly concentrated in 5 regions instead of being spread over the whole urban area and, provided the regions are homogeneous, the sample obtained should not be misleading. Moreover, it should be truly random, since each individual household in the area has, at the beginning of the enquiry, an equal chance of selection. This process is the first stage in multi-stage sampling, which can be employed when the geographical area is very large. For example, if the enquiry extended over the whole country, a random sample of counties might be made at the first stage. The counties selected are then divided into regions and a sample of these regions made, taking care to ensure that rural and urban areas are properly represented. This constitutes the second stage of the process. A random sample of individuals could then be selected from the sample of areas, provided that these areas are small enough to produce the required concentration of interviewing work. If this is not the case, then the sample may be taken to a third stage. It is obvious, however, that the further the process of subdivision is taken, the greater the likelihood of bias being introduced into the final sample due to the lack of homogeneity in the groups at different stages.

Quota sampling is a form of stratified sampling in which the selection of individuals within strata is not random but is left to the interviewer. For example, a population may be classified according to sex, age group and social status, within each of which classes a certain specified number of individuals are to be interviewed. The objectives of the quota sample are attained when the required number of interviews have been carried out. Thus if an interviewer has to interview 50 adults of each sex in a certain area, it is left to her to select whichever 50 households she pleases, to interview, if possible, any one man and woman from each and, if the required number of 50 men and 50 women is not reached among these households, to continue calling at houses until the requisite number of interviews have been carried out. The weakness of this method, as with all forms of intuitive sampling, is that it is liable to subjective bias on the part of the interviewer. This can be mitigated by previous training of interviewers, though tests have shown that such training eliminates personal bias to a far smaller extent than might be expected.

Another method of sampling which is based on the whole sample frame is known as *quasi-random* or *systematic sampling*. This involves selecting names from the sample frame at equally spaced intervals, so that, if there are 10,000 individuals in the sample frame, a sample of 100 is obtained by selecting every 100th individual. If the list is arranged systematically in, say, alphabetical order, there is no reason why this should not, in many cases, produce a random sample;

but it is possible to imagine bias being introduced even in this case
if, for example, the names of foreign immigrants began with unusual initial letters which could be under-represented in the sample.
Moreover, if a second sample is taken close in time to the first by
the same method, so that little change has occurred in the sample
frame, many of the individuals in the first sample may be selected
for the second, which is clearly undesirable.

Apart from considerations of cost, the method of sampling
adopted will depend on the way the data is to be collected, for
example, whether by personal interview or postal enquiry. The
special problems relating to the best selection of a method of collecting data in relation to a particular enquiry are considered in
Chapter 10.

EXERCISES 6

1. Construct the sample spaces for each of the following populations, and find the means and standard errors of the corresponding sample means.

   (a) 3   9   11   13   Sample size: 2
   (b) 3   3   9   9   Sample size: 3
   (c) 1   5   7   13   19   Sample size: 2
   (d) 2   7   9   Sample size: 3

2. A variable is Normally distributed with mean 3 and standard
   deviation 1. If an item is randomly selected from the distribution,
   find the probability that it has a value (a) greater than 4, (b) less
   than 2, (c) between 2 and 4.

3. X has a Standard Normal distribution $N(0, 1)$. Which of the
   following statements are true?

   (a) The probability that X lies in the interval $+3$ to -3 is
       0·998.
   (b) The probability that X is greater than 1·75 is 0·9599.
   (c) The probability that X is less than 1 or greater than 2·53
       is 0·847.
   (d) X is more likely to be greater than 2 than less than 1·9.

4. X is Normally distributed with mean 2 and standard deviation
   1·5. Two sample values of X are randomly selected. Calculate
   the probability

   (a) that both values are less than 1·5,

    (b) that one value is less than 1·5 and one value greater than 1·5.

5. 100 items are randomly selected from a population with mean 2·6 and standard deviation 1·69. Find the probability that the sample mean

    (a) is greater than 2·73,
    (b) is less than 2,
    (c) differs from the population mean by more than 0·2.

6. Suggest a reason why the standard deviation (or standard error) of the mean of a random sample of two or more items is always less than the population standard deviation, except when all the items in the population have the same value.

7. A random sample of 50 items has mean 12·9. Is it likely to have come from a population with mean 15 and standard deviation 9?

8. What is meant by a confidence interval? What is the relation between the 5% level of a significance test and a 95% confidence interval?

9. A sample of size 100 has mean 5 and standard deviation 3. Calculate the 95% confidence limits for the population mean.

10. A coin is tossed 250 times, the number of heads obtained being 136. Test, at the 5% level of significance,

    (a) the hypothesis that the coin is fair,
    (b) that it is biased in favour of heads.

11. A telepathy experiment consists in calling over 500 cards which are comprised of equal numbers of four different cards.

    (a) Find the probability of getting a card right by pure guessing.
    (b) Find the expected number of cards right on the assumption of pure guessing.
    (c) Test the Null Hypothesis that pure guesswork was the only factor operating when the number of correct cards is 150. Formulate the Null Hypothesis which is being tested when a one-tailed test is used in this case.

12. (a) Illustrate graphically the relationship between the standard deviation and the areas under the normal curve of distribution.
(b) Assuming that the hub thickness of a particular type of gear is normally distributed around a mean thickness of 2·00 inches, with a standard deviation of 0·04 inches, say

(i) approximately how many gears will have a thickness between 1·96 and 2·04 inches in a production run of 5000 gears;

(ii) in a random selection of one gear from this production run of 5000, with what degree of confidence could it be predicted that its thickness would be between 1·92 and 2·08 inches?

13. The mean weight of a consignment of 500 sacks of sugar is 151 lb. and the standard deviation 15 lb. Assuming that the weights are normally distributed, find how many sacks weigh:

(a) between 120 and 155 lb.,
(b) more than 185 lb., and
(c) less than 128 lb.

14. (a) What is a sampling distribution of the means?

(b) For a random sample of the annual salaries of 50 salesmen drawn from a population of 1000 salesmen the mean salary was £1500 and the standard deviation £320.

Calculate the standard error of the mean and explain the use of this measure.

15. The average annual earnings of a group of 10,000 unskilled engineering workers employed by firms in north-east England in 1971 was £1000 and the standard deviation £200.

Assuming that the earnings were normally distributed, find how many workers earned:

(a) less than £1000
(b) more than £600 but less than £800
(c) more than £1000 but less than £1200
(d) above £1200.

16. (a) What is the standard error of a proportion?

(b) In a sample of 500 beer drinkers 50 were women. Estimate the population proportion at the 95% confidence level, and explain your answer.

17. In a sample of 60, 35 are found to possess attribute A. How sure can we be that the population from which the sample is drawn is not equally divided between those with attribute A and those without attribute A.

18. A cutting machine produces rods which are acceptable if their lengths are between 90 cm and 90·6 cm. Of all the rods produced 5% are rejected as too short and 8% are rejected as too long. Assuming that the lengths of the rods are normally distributed,

show that the mean and standard deviation of this distribution are respectively 90·3 cm and 0·197 cm, correct to three significant figures.

If the minimum acceptable length is reduced to 89·9 cm find the percentage of the rods that would now be rejected as too short.

19. The heights of boys in a certain school are normally distributed. 10% are over 1·8 metres and 20% are below 1·6 metres.

    Use Table 1 to form simultaneous equations for the mean height μ metres and the standard deviation σ metres.

    Find μ and σ.

    Hence find the interquartile range.

20. Give a rough sketch of a Normal probability curve.

    (i) Explain what is meant by the term *unit or standardised normal variable*.

    (ii) Find, using tables, the proportions of the total area under this curve that are within one, two and three standard deviations respectively of the arithmetic mean.

    (iii) 200 results are obtained from an experiment and their mean and standard deviation are found to be 5·3 and 0·6 respectively. Assuming that the results are normally distributed calculate, using tables, how many of them may be expected to be (a) greater than 5·5, (b) between 4·8 and 4·9.

21. A coin is tossed 10 times. Find, using the binomial probabilities, the probability that less than 2 or more than 8 heads are obtained, assuming that the coin is fair. If the number of heads actually obtained was 8, would you reject the Null Hypothesis that the coin is fair?

22. A dice is thrown 100 times and 25 sixes are obtained. Test the hypothesis that the dice is fair (a) at the 5% level, (b) at the 1% level.

23. A population is known to have mean 5 and standard deviation 2. A sample of size n is selected from this population and found to have mean 5·1. What is the smallest value of n consistent with the hypothesis, at the 5% level, that the sample was not random?

24. A company wishes to conduct a sample survey into the percentage of employees who prefer a new type of protective clothing. Recent experience suggests that about 60% of employees probably prefer the new type, but this figure is open to doubt. The sample percentage is required to be within 3% of the true percentage at the 95% confidence level.

On the basis of this information, calculate the size of sample required for the survey in the following circumstances:

(a) if 60% is accepted as being approximately the correct proportion,

(b) if 60% is rejected as being totally unreliable.

25. A coin is tossed n times and the proportion of heads obtained is 0·52. What must the value of n be in order to be 95% certain that the probability of a head lies in the interval $0·52 \pm 0·01$?

26. Calculate the mean and standard deviation of the 10 consecutive digits from 0 to 9.

    400 digits are written down in apparently random order and are found to have a mean of 4·2. Test the hypothesis that they represent a random selection from the digits 0 to 9.

27. 150 two-figure numbers are selected from a table of random sampling numbers by reading down successive double columns of the table. What is the probability that *exactly* one-fifth of the numbers so selected are less than 20? What is the probability that less than one-tenth of the numbers so selected are less than 20?

28. What is the principal object of sampling? Distinguish between random sampling and stratified sampling.

29. State and explain two possible sources of error in making a survey which involves calling at a number of houses in order to interview the occupants.

30. Explain the distinction between random sampling and quota sampling. In practical sampling situations in marketing, is it ever justifiable to use quota sampling?

31. Explain what is meant by (a) the sampling frame and (b) random sampling errors.

32. Without sampling techniques the statistician's work would be severely restricted. Discuss this statement and describe two commonly used methods of sampling.

CHAPTER 7

Correlation and Regression

1. Correlation

Two quantities are said to be correlated if there is some relationship between them, so that a change in one of the quantities is accompanied by a predictable change in the other. The two quantities are uncorrelated if they are unrelated or independent. For example, when two fair six-sided dice are thrown once, the scores on the two dice are independent of each other and so these scores are uncorrelated. The *sum* of the scores on the two dice is not however independent of the score on one of them, so that the sum of the scores and the score on one of the dice are quantities which are correlated. The term *independence* is used here in the probability sense defined on page 95. Thus if X and Y are the scores on the two dice, then these scores are independent because the conditional probability $P(Y|X) = \frac{1}{6} = P(Y)$. However, if $Z = X + Y$, then $P(Z|X)$ is not equal to $P(Z)$. For example, if $Z = 2$ and $X = 1$, then $P(Z|X) = \frac{1}{6}$; but $P(Z) = \frac{1}{36}$ since there is only 1 way of obtaining a sum of 2 out of 36 ways in which the two dice can fall when the score on each of them is unspecified.

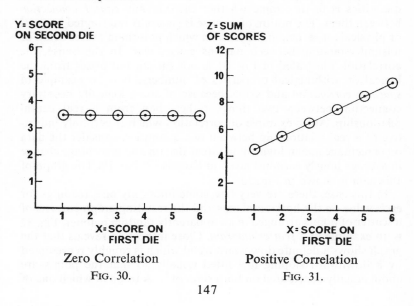

Zero Correlation
Fig. 30.

Positive Correlation
Fig. 31.

The type of correlation discussed in this chapter is that known as *linear correlation*. Two variables are said to be linearly correlated if the graph of the values of one of the variables corresponding to specified values of the other is a straight line which is not parallel to either of the two axes of the graph. The graphs of the two cases considered in the first paragraph illustrate this (Figs. 30 and 31).

To obtain these graphs, it is assumed that for each value of X (the score on the first die), the second die is thrown a very large number of times. Since this die is fair, it can be expected that to each value of X there are six values of Y repeated approximately the same number of times. Instead of showing these six points in Fig. 30, the mean of the six values of Y (3·5), is plotted instead. Since Y has the same mean value for each value of X, the corresponding graph of these independent scores is a straight line parallel to the horizontal axis. This illustrates the fact that there is zero correlation between X and Y, for Y does not change when X changes in any predictable way. In the graph, Fig. 31, there are also six values of Z corresponding to each value of X and the points are obtained by adding the mean of the scores Y (3·5) to each value of X, so that $Z = X + 3·5$. The graph is thus a straight line which slopes upwards from left to right and is an example of positive correlation. This means that as X increases, the total score on the two dice also increases *on the average*.

The primary object of investigating the correlation between two quantities is to determine whether there is any *causal connection* between them. The notion of a cause is generally interpreted in a real or physical sense, i.e., in the sense in which poisoning causes death or misunderstanding between nations causes war. In this sense, the correlation illustrated in Fig. 31 is not causal, but arises from the logical or arithmetical properties of numbers. It is an example of *spurious correlation* and arises because of some logically necessary connection between two things rather than from a real causal relationship. As an example of correlation which is certainly indicative of a real relationship between two quantities, consider the data on percentage unemployment in Great Britain and percentage change in average hourly earnings given in Exercise 2, No. 19. The graph of this data is shown in Fig. 32.

In this case, there are very few, sometimes only one, readings for each value on the horizontal axis and the resulting graph consists of a scatter of points arranged in an apparently random manner. Fig. 32 is an example of a *scatter diagram*. Close inspection reveals that the graph shows a definite downward trend which is roughly represented by a downward sloping line fitted visually so that the points are about equally distributed on both sides of it. A trend in which one of

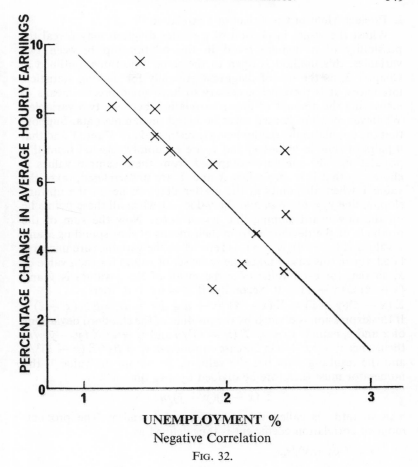

UNEMPLOYMENT %

Negative Correlation

FIG. 32.

the quantities decreases as the other increases indicates *negative correlation* between the quantities. The data for this particular example shows that, during the period considered, average hourly earnings were increasing from year to year, but at different rates; and the trend shows that the rate of increase tended to be high when unemployment was low and low at higher rates of unemployment. A knowledge of the economics of a competitive labour market makes this picture altogether plausible, and one may assume that this trend is evidence of a real underlying causal connection between levels of unemployment and earnings.

2. Product-Moment Coefficient of Correlation

Whilst the visual inspection of a scatter diagram may reveal the possibility of a definite trend in the relationship between two variables, this method is open to the same objections, outlined in Chapter 3, as the use of diagrams generally for making statistical inferences. It is therefore necessary to have some precise means of measuring the amount of linear correlation between two variables. Whatever measure is used must be based on sample data. Suppose that the population variables being investigated are X and Y and that n pairs of sample values x_i and y_i are randomly selected from this population. The measure computed from these sample values is chosen so that it is zero when X and Y are uncorrelated, takes the value 1 when all points in the scatter diagram lie on the upward sloping line $y = bx + a$, and the value -1 when all these points lie on the downward sloping line $y = a - bx$. Now the sum of the products of the deviations from their means of corresponding x and y values $\Sigma (x_i - \bar{x})(y_i - \bar{y})$, is zero when the variables are uncorrelated, for in this case y takes the same set of values for each value of x, so that for each value of x the mean of the y values is $\bar{y}$ and $(x - \bar{x}) \Sigma (y - \bar{y}) = 0$. Secondly, if $y = bx + a$, then
$$\Sigma (x - \bar{x})(y - \bar{y}) = \Sigma (x - \bar{x})(bx + a - b\bar{x} + a) = b \Sigma (x - \bar{x})^2.$$
If this expression is divided by the product of the standard deviations of x and y, namely $s_x = \sqrt{\Sigma (x - \bar{x})^2/n}$ and $s_y = \sqrt{\Sigma (y - \bar{y})^2/n}$, then, since $y = bx + a$ in the case considered, $s_y = b\sqrt{\Sigma (x - \bar{x})^2/n}$ and the resulting ratio has the value n. To obtain the value 1, the numerator must therefore be divided by n to obtain
$$\Sigma (x - \bar{x})(y - \bar{y})/n.$$

This quantity is called the *covariance* of x and y. The product-moment correlation coefficient is thus defined as
$$r = \text{Cov.}(xy)/s_x s_y$$
$$= \frac{\Sigma (x - \bar{x})(y - \bar{y})}{n} \bigg/ \left\{ \sqrt{\frac{\Sigma (x - \bar{x})^2}{n}} \sqrt{\frac{\Sigma (y - \bar{y})^2}{n}} \right\}$$
$$= \frac{\Sigma (x - \bar{x})(y - \bar{y})}{\sqrt{\{\Sigma (x - \bar{x})^2 \Sigma (y - \bar{y})^2\}}}.$$

It is easy to show that when $y = a - bx$, that is when all the points in the scatter diagram lie on a downward sloping straight line, then r as defined above takes the value -1.

For computational purposes, this formula is often inconvenient, for the same reason as the formula $\Sigma (x - \bar{x})^2/n$ is sometimes inconvenient for calculating the variance of x. An alternative formula for r, which is equivalent to that above, can be obtained as follows.

$$\Sigma (x - \bar{x})(y - \bar{y}) = \Sigma (xy - \bar{x}y - x\bar{y} + \bar{x}\bar{y})$$
$$= \Sigma xy - \bar{x} \Sigma y - \bar{y} \Sigma x + \Sigma \bar{x}\bar{y}$$
$$= \Sigma xy - n\bar{x}\bar{y} - n\bar{x}\bar{y} + n\bar{x}\bar{y}$$
$$= \Sigma xy - n\bar{x}\bar{y}$$
$$= \Sigma xy - (\Sigma x \Sigma y/n).$$

By putting $x = y$ and $\bar{x} = \bar{y}$ in this relationship, it follows that

$$\Sigma (x - \bar{x})^2 = \Sigma x^2 - \frac{(\Sigma x)^2}{n} \text{ and } \Sigma (y - \bar{y})^2 = \Sigma y^2 - \frac{(\Sigma y)^2}{n}.$$

Hence an alternative formula for r is

$$r = \frac{\Sigma xy - (\Sigma x \Sigma y/n)}{\sqrt{\left\{\left(\Sigma x^2 - \frac{(\Sigma x)^2}{n}\right)\left(\Sigma y^2 - \frac{(\Sigma y)^2}{n}\right)\right\}}}$$

As thus defined, r has the important mathematical property that it always lies in the interval $-1 \leqslant r \leqslant 1$. It takes the value $r = -1$ when there is perfect negative correlation between x and y, which happens when the pairs of x and y values can be represented by points on a graph which all lie on a downward sloping straight line. The value $r = 1$ indicates perfect positive correlation, i.e., when all points of the graph lie on an upward sloping straight line. When there is no correlation between x and y ($r = 0$), the means of the y values corresponding to each value of x lie on a straight line which is parallel to the horizontal axis, showing that a change in x is, on the average, unaccompanied by a change in y so that, in this case, x and y are independent. This is the situation illustrated in Fig. 30. Since the value of r is computed from randomly selected sample data, it is not to be expected that r will take any of the above three critical values exactly. But if the population values X and Y are either uncorrelated or perfectly correlated, then the value of r will lie close to one of these three values, any deviations from them being accounted for by sampling errors which will decrease as the number of pairs of values sampled is increased. It must be emphasised that r is a measure of *linear* correlation, so that if X and Y are correlated, but the law relating them is non–linear, the value of r could still be close to zero.

EXAMPLE 1

The following data for ten towns show (i) *the proportion of households owning a car and* (ii) *the index of social class* (*based upon occupation distribution of householders*).

Town	% with Cars	Social Class Index
A	51	106
B	48	104
C	43	100
D	36	96
E	30	90
F	24	86
G	22	84
H	16	74
I	12	64
J	10	66

Calculate the coefficient of correlation.

Method 1

Social Class Index $= x$	$(x - \bar{x})$	% with Cars $= y$	$(y - \bar{y})$	$(x - \bar{x})^2$	$(y - \bar{y})^2$	$(x - \bar{x})(y - \bar{y})$
106	19	51	21·8	361	475·24	414·2
104	17	48	18·8	289	353·44	319·6
100	13	43	13·8	169	190·44	179·4
96	9	36	6·8	81	46·24	61·2
90	3	30	0·8	9	0·64	2·4
86	− 1	24	− 5·2	1	27·04	5·2
84	− 3	22	− 7·2	9	51·84	21·6
74	−13	16	−13·2	169	174·24	171·6
64	−23	12	−17·2	529	295·84	395·6
66	−21	10	−19·2	441	368·64	403·2
870	0	292	0	2058	1983·60	1974·0

$$r = \frac{\Sigma(x - \bar{x})(y - \bar{y})}{\sqrt{\{\Sigma(x - \bar{x})^2 \ \Sigma(y - \bar{y})^2\}}}$$

$$= 1974/\sqrt{(2058 \times 1983·6)}$$
$$= 1974/2020$$
$$= 0·98.$$

Method 2

Social Class Index = x	x^2	% with Cars = y	y^2	xy
106	11236	51	2601	5406
104	10816	48	2304	4992
100	10000	43	1849	4300
96	9216	36	1296	3456
90	8100	30	900	2700
86	7396	24	576	2064
84	7056	22	484	1848
74	5476	16	256	1184
64	4096	12	144	768
66	4356	10	100	660
870	77748	292	10510	27378

$$r = \frac{\Sigma\, xy - (\Sigma\, x\, \Sigma\, y/n)}{\sqrt{\left\{\left(\Sigma\, x^2 - \frac{(\Sigma\, x)^2}{n}\right)\left(\Sigma\, y^2 - \frac{(\Sigma\, y)^2}{n}\right)\right\}}}$$

$$= \frac{27378 - (870 \times 292/10)}{\sqrt{\left\{\left(77748 - \frac{(870)^2}{10}\right)\left(10510 - \frac{(292)^2}{10}\right)\right\}}}$$

$$= 1974/2020$$

$$= 0.98.$$

Method 3 consists of subtracting an assumed mean from each of the variables, obtaining two "coded" series of numbers $X - a$ and $Y - b$, where a and b are conveniently chosen assumed means and X and Y are a pair of values in the original series. If the pairs of numbers $(X - a, Y - b)$ are plotted on a scatter diagram, they will be related in the same way as the original number pairs (X, Y); the only difference between the two sets of points is in their relation to the origin of the graph. Hence if there is a certain correlation between the number pairs (X, Y) there will be exactly the same correlation between the number pairs $(X - a, Y - b)$ and so the value of the correlation coefficient using the "coded" values will be exactly the same as for the original series in "uncoded" form. The "coded" values may, as in the present case, be easier to handle than the original values, and so this method is often useful when calculations are made manually. Method 2, on the other hand, is usually more suitable when mechanical aids to calculation are available. It is worth observing, however, that Methods 2 and 3 are, in one sense, identical, namely that in each assumed means are used, those in Method 2 being both equal to zero whereas those in Method 3 are chosen to lie more conveniently somewhere about the mid-values of the two series.

Method 3

Social Class Index—86 = x	x^2	% with Cars—30 = y	y^2	xy
20	400	21	441	420
18	324	18	324	324
14	196	13	169	182
10	100	6	36	60
4	16	0	0	0
0	0	−6	36	0
−2	4	−8	64	16
−12	144	−14	196	168
−22	484	−18	324	396
−20	400	−20	400	400
10	2068	−8	1990	1966

$$r = \frac{\Sigma xy - (\Sigma x \Sigma y / n)}{\sqrt{\left\{ \left(\Sigma x^2 - \frac{(\Sigma x)^2}{n} \right) \left(\Sigma y^2 - \frac{(\Sigma y)^2}{n} \right) \right\}}}$$

$$= \frac{1966 - (10 \times -8/10)}{\sqrt{\left\{ \left(2068 - \frac{(10)^2}{10} \right) \left(1990 - \frac{(8)^2}{10} \right) \right\}}}$$

$$= 1974/2020$$

$$= 0.98$$

3. Regression

If two population variables X and Y are related linearly, then the points on a graph representing corresponding pairs of (X, Y) values lie on, or approximately on, a straight line which has an equation of the form $Y = \beta X + \alpha$. In this equation, X is called the *independent* variable and Y the *dependent* variable. These terms have an obvious meaning when there is a real, physical relationship between X and Y such that a change in X can be said to cause a change in Y. When there is spurious correlation between X and Y, then it is really quite arbitrary which of the two variables is regarded as the independent and which the dependent one.

Once it has been established that there is linear correlation between two variables, it is useful to compute the values of β and α in the regression equation using sample data. It will be seen that the value of the correlation coefficient, whilst indicating the degree of linear correlation, tells one nothing about the amount of the change in Y when X changes by a given quantity. This can be determined only by estimating the value of β in the regression equation. Moreover, it is also necessary to know what value Y takes when X is zero. In order to obtain the best possible fit of the regression line to the sample pairs of values (x, y), the method of computation used should result in an equation whose graph passes as close as possible to the mean values of y for each value of x. Very often, there is only one value of y for each value of x, and then this requirement reduces to a line passing as close to all the points in the graph as possible. The method usually chosen to obtain this end is called the *method of least squares*. It can be shown that the sum of the squared deviations of a set of values from their mean is less than the sum of squared deviations of these values from any other origin. It follows that, by making the sum of the squared deviations of the y values from the regression line as small as possible, this line will pass as nearly as possible to all the means of the y values.

Suppose that the estimated values of β and α are b and a respectively, so that the regression equation for the sample data is $y = bx + a$. The least squares criterion requires that the values of b and a should be chosen to minimise the sum of squared deviations $\Sigma \, (y_i - \overline{bx_i + a})^2$. It can be shown by calculus methods (see Chapter 11, section 6) that the values of b and a which are sought satisfy the simultaneous equations:

$$\Sigma \, y_i - b \, \Sigma \, x_i - na = 0$$
$$\Sigma \, x_i y_i - b \, \Sigma \, x_i{}^2 - a \, \Sigma \, x_i = 0$$

where n is the number of pairs of (x, y) values in the sample. The formulae for b and a obtained from these equations are:

$$b = \frac{\Sigma \, xy - (\Sigma \, x \, \Sigma \, y/n)}{\Sigma \, x^2 - (\Sigma \, x)^2/n}$$

$$a = \bar{y} - b\bar{x}.$$

b is known as the *regression coefficient* and it will be seen that the formula from which it is computed is closely related to that for the product-moment correlation coefficient. Thus

$$b = \frac{s_y}{s_x}.r$$

where s_x and s_y are the standard deviations of x and y and r is the correlation coefficient defined in section 2. The formula for computing a can be re-arranged as $\bar{y} = b\bar{x} + a$, showing that the regression line passes through the means of the x and y values, namely $\bar{x}$ and $\bar{y}$.

Using the figures calculated in Example 1, Method 2, the value of b for the regression of y on x is

$$b = \frac{27378 - (870 \times 292/10)}{77748 - \frac{(870)^2}{10}}$$

$$= 1974/2058$$
$$= 0\cdot96.$$

Since $\bar{x} = 870/10 = 87$ and $\bar{y} = 292/10 = 29\cdot2$, it follows that

$$a = 29\cdot2 - 0\cdot96 \times 87$$
$$= -54\cdot3.$$

Hence the estimated regression equation for the population is

$$\hat{Y} = 0\cdot96\,X - 54\cdot3.$$

This is the equation for the regression of Y on X, in which X is the independent variable. In Example 1, this is a sensible choice to make, since it is reasonable to assume that the percentage of the population with cars is causally dependent on social class index and not conversely. It is theoretically possible, however, to compute also the equation for the regression of X on Y, namely

$$\hat{X} = b_1 Y + a_1$$

where
$$b_1 = \frac{\Sigma\, xy - (\Sigma\, x\, \Sigma\, y/n)}{\Sigma\, y^2 - (\Sigma\, y)^2/n} = \frac{s_x}{s_y}.r$$

$$a_1 = \bar{x} - b_1\bar{y}.$$

The student should verify using these formulae that, for Example 1, $b_1 = 0\cdot99$, $a_1 = 58\cdot0$. The regression equation for X on Y is thus

$$\hat{X} = 0\cdot99\,Y + 58\cdot0.$$

These two lines are shown in the scatter diagram (Fig. 33) for the data of Example 1. The figures obtained in Methods 1 and 3 will also give the same value of the regression coefficient in each case.

The two regression lines almost coincide in the diagram, which indicates that the amount of linear correlation is very high. In fact,

SCATTER DIAGRAM OF DATA IN EXAMPLE 1

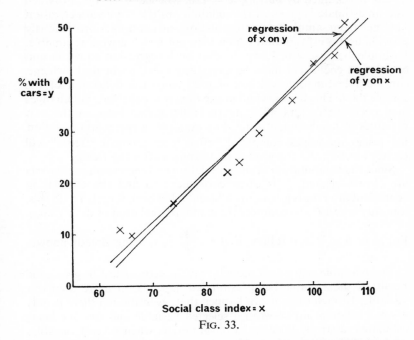

FIG. 33.

$r = 0.98$. When $r = \pm 1$, the two regression lines exactly coincide, indicating perfect correlation, either negative or positive. When there is no linear correlation between the two variables ($r = 0$), the two regression lines are perpendicular to one another and parallel to the horizontal or vertical axis. The formulae for computing a and a_1 show that both lines intersect at a point representing the mean values of x and y.

The regression equation $\hat{Y} = bX + a$ provides an estimate of Y for a given value of X. When the value of X chosen lies within the range of sample values of X, the corresponding estimate of Y, namely $\hat{Y}$, is said to have been obtained by *interpolation*. When X lies outside the range of sample values, the estimated value of Y is obtained by *extrapolation*. For example, an interpolated value of Y is obtained in Example 1 by putting $X = 80$, whence

$$\hat{Y} = 0.96 \times 80 - 54.3 = 22.5;$$

so it may be expected that in a town with social class index 80, 22.5% of households own cars. Similarly, an extrapolated value of

Y can be obtained by putting $X = 120$, whence $\hat{Y} = 60 \cdot 9$. Provided that an estimate is given of the reliability of the regression equation obtained from sample data, interpolation and extrapolation obviously provide useful information which may not be otherwise obtainable. It should be observed, however, that both regression equation and correlation coefficient must be cautiously used, particularly when a considerable time-interval has elapsed since the collection of the sample data. This data is valid at the time it is collected, but changes may occur in factors affecting the relationshlp between the two variables at a subsequent time. For example, a regression equation for prices on wages computed before a government "freeze" will clearly not be valid for prediction purposes after the freeze.

Since the computation of the correlation and regression coefficients are closely related, it is often convenient to find the correlation coefficient after the regression coefficient b has been found. To do this, it is only necessary to compute the standard deviation of the y values.

For since $b = \dfrac{s_y}{s_x} . r$, it follows that $r = \dfrac{s_x}{s_y} . b$, s_x being already known.

Two-variable regression models may sometimes fail to give good results if the variable being estimated depends on more than one variable. In such cases it can happen that, even though there is only a weak relationship between a selected variable and the one being estimated, a strong linear relationship exists when several variables are included in the analysis. This situation arises when the additional variables are correlated with each other, a complication which is taken care of by *multiple regression techniques*.

4. Other Methods of Computation

If the sample values of the independent variable x (say) are equally spaced, then calculations for the regression equation can be considerably simplified by "coding" the x values so that the sum of the "coded" values is zero. If this is done, the regression coefficient b of the regression of y on x is equal to the regression coefficient of y on the "coded" values of x. For let $u = x - A$ where A is a number chosen so that $\Sigma u = 0$, the obvious choice being $A = \bar{x}$. Then if $y = bx + a$, it follows that $y = b(u + A) + a = bu + (bA + a)$; so that b is also the regression coefficient of y on u.

EXAMPLE 2

Compute the regression equation of y on x and correlation co-efficient for the following data.

x:	2	4	6	8	10
y:	3	5	7	11	13

Since $\bar{x} = 6$, it follows that by letting $u = x - 6$, $\Sigma u = 0$. Using these "coded" values of x, the calculations are as follows.

$\begin{array}{c} x - 6 \\ = u \end{array}$	y	u^2	y^2	uy
−4	3	16	9	−12
−2	5	4	25	−10
0	7	0	49	0
2	11	4	121	22
4	13	16	169	52
0	39	40	373	52

$$b = \frac{\Sigma\, uy - (\Sigma\, u\, \Sigma\, y/n)}{\Sigma\, u^2 - (\Sigma\, u)^2/n}$$

$\quad = \Sigma\, uy / \Sigma\, u^2 \qquad\qquad$ (since $\Sigma\, u = 0$)

$\quad = 52/40$

$\quad = 1\cdot3$

So $\quad y = 1\cdot3u + \bar{y} \qquad\qquad$ (since $y = \bar{y}$ when $u = \bar{u} = 0$)

$\quad = 1\cdot3(x - 6) + (39/5)$

$\quad = 1\cdot3x - 7\cdot8 + 7\cdot8$

$\quad = 1\cdot3x$

The correlation coefficient

$$r = \frac{s_x}{s_y}.b$$

$$= \sqrt{\left(\frac{40}{373 - \dfrac{39^2}{5}}\right)} \times 1\cdot3 \qquad \text{(since } s_x = s_u)$$

$$= 0\cdot99$$

The value of r here is sufficiently large, despite the small sample size, to indicate strong positive correlation in the data.

5. Bivariate Frequency Distributions

When sample data is collected in order to investigate correlation, it is often convenient to construct a grouped frequency distribution of each of the variables which indicates the frequency with which items take specified values of x and y. This information is set out in a bivariate frequency table from which a correlation coefficient between the variables is easy to compute.

EXAMPLE 3

The table below shows how many times each of 50 machines, of varying ages, broke down in a given period of time:

(a) *Calculate the coefficient of correlation between the age of the machines and the number of times they broke down in a given period.*

(b) *What conclusions would you draw from the results of your calculation?*

Age of machine in Years	Number of Machines with				
	No Failure	One Failure	Two Failures	Three Failures	Four or More Failures
less than 2	5	2	2	1	—
2 and less than 4	2	1	2	4	3
4 and less than 6	3	1	1	1	4
6 and less than 8	—	2	3	1	2
8 and less than 10	1	—	2	2	1
10 or more	—	—	1	—	3

Let x represent the mid-points of class intervals of the age of machines and y the number of failures per machine

x \ y	1	3	5	7	9	11	f	fy	fy^2
0	5	2	3		1		11	0	0
1	2	1	1	2			6	6	6
2	2	2	1	3	2	1	11	22	44
3	1	4	1	1	2		9	27	81
4		3	4	2	1	3	13	52	208
f	10	12	10	8	6	4	50	107	339
fx	10	36	50	56	54	44	250		
fx^2	10	108	250	392	486	484	1730		

There are $6 \times 5 = 30$ possible values of the product xy, but since some of the frequencies in the table are zero, fxy will sometimes be zero. The easiest way to obtain all the non-zero values of fxy is to construct the second table shown below.

The sample size here (50) is large enough to justify the conclusion that r differs significantly from zero, so that there is evidence of some linear correlation between the age of a machine and the number of times it has failed. To be confident of this conclusion, it is necessary to use a significance test to test the hypothesis that r is different from zero, so that its value (0·37) does not result simply from sampling errors. Suitable significance tests for r will be considered in Chapter 13.

x \ y	1	3	5	7	9	11	fxy
0							0
1	2	3	5	14			24
2	4	12	10	42	36	22	126
3	3	36	15	21	54		129
4		36	80	56	36	132	340
fxy	9	87	110	133	126	154	619

$$r = \frac{\Sigma fxy - (\Sigma fx\, \Sigma fy/\Sigma f)}{\sqrt{\left\{\left(\Sigma fx^2 - \frac{(\Sigma fx)^2}{\Sigma f}\right)\left(\Sigma fy^2 - \frac{(\Sigma fy)^2}{\Sigma f}\right)\right\}}}$$

$$= \frac{619 - (250 \times 107/50)}{\sqrt{\left\{\left(1730 - \frac{250^2}{50}\right)\left(339 - \frac{107^2}{50}\right)\right\}}}$$

$$= 84/230$$

$$= 0{\cdot}37$$

6. Rank Correlation

The product-moment correlation coefficient is calculated from the actual values of x and y in the sample data. But there are occasions when the relative orders of magnitude of these pairs of values is more instructive than the values themselves. For example, if a number of candidates are interviewed for an appointment by three selectors who independently award each candidate a certain number of points, it may be of interest to enquire whether the scoring of the three judges is inter-consistent. Now one of the judges, say, might award marks in a way which would produce a rather low correlation coefficient with the marks of the other judges. On the other hand, the order of merit in which this judge's marks arranged the candidates could agree very closely with that of the other two judges, notwithstanding the small value of the product-moment correlation coefficient. It is accordingly useful to have some means of assessing the relationship between the *ranks* of two variables instead of between their actual values. This is provided by a *rank correlation coefficient*. The coefficient considered here is *Spearman's* coefficient of rank correlation, which is computed from the formula:

$$r_{\text{rank}} = 1 - \frac{6\,\Sigma\, d^2}{n(n^2 - 1)},$$

where d is the difference between the ranks of x and y for each pair of (x, y) values, and n is the number of pairs of values in the sample.

Like the product-moment correlation coefficient, r_{rank} can take any value from -1 to $+1$, these two extreme values indicating perfect negative and positive correlation between the ranks, whilst the value 0 indicates zero correlation. Here again, the correlation measured is linear correlation though, since the x and y ranks take the same values from 1 to n, there is really no other sort of correlation to consider in this case.

EXAMPLE 4

An experiment was conducted on 8 children to determine how a child's reading ability varied with his ability to write. The points awarded were as follows.

Child	A	B	C	D	E	F	G	H
Writing	7	8	4	0	2	6	9	5
Reading	8	9	4	2	3	7	6	5

Calculate the coefficient of rank correlation.

Child:	A	B	C	D	E	F	G	H	
Writing (rank):	3	2	6	8	7	4	1	5	
Reading (rank):	2	1	6	8	7	3	4	5	
d:	1	1	0	0	0	1	−3	0	$(\Sigma d = 0)$
d^2:	1	1	0	0	0	1	9	0	$(\Sigma d^2 = 12)$

$$r_{\text{rank}} = 1 - \frac{6 \times 12}{8(8^2 - 1)}$$

$$= 1 - \frac{72}{504}$$

$$= 0 \cdot 86.$$

The magnitude of r_{rank} in this case appears to justify the conclusion that there is a strong, positive linear correlation between the Writing and Reading ranks. More definite information about the significance of this value can be obtained from Table 3 at the end of the book. This table is constructed by considering all the possible ways in which the two rankings may be combined. When $n = 8$, there are 8! such ways and each combination gives rise to a certain value of Σd^2. By finding the frequency of each value of Σd^2 resulting from a random combination of the rankings, it is possible to calculate the probability that values less than or greater than specified values of Σd^2 occurred solely as the result of sampling errors. Thus when $n = 8$, the probability that Σd^2 is less than 12 or greater than 156 is 0·0054 or about $\frac{1}{2}\%$. In Example 4, the value of Σd^2 was 12 and so one can safely conclude, certainly at the 1% level of significance, that such a low value did not occur by chance as the result of sampling errors.

If either of the variables takes repeated values, some of the ranks will be the same, in which case it is necessary to adjust the ranking of the "tied" items so that they have the same rank whilst the sum of the ranks is what it would be if there were no tied items.

Item:	A	B	C	D	E
X (rank):	1	2	2	3	4
Y (rank):	1	1	3	3	2

Thus, in the illustration above, the X ranking of the tied items B and C lies between 2 and 3 and so B and C are both given the rank $2\frac{1}{2}$. Similarly, the Y ranking of A and B is adjusted so that each has the ranking $1\frac{1}{2}$, whilst C and D have the rank $4\frac{1}{2}$. The adjusted ranks are shown in the following table:

Item:	A	B	C	D	E	
X (rank):	1	$2\frac{1}{2}$	$2\frac{1}{2}$	4	5	
Y (rank):	$1\frac{1}{2}$	$1\frac{1}{2}$	$4\frac{1}{2}$	$4\frac{1}{2}$	3	
d:	$-\frac{1}{2}$	1	-2	$-\frac{1}{2}$	2	$(\Sigma d = 0)$.
d^2:	$\frac{1}{4}$	1	4	$\frac{1}{4}$	4	$(\Sigma d^2 = 9 \cdot 5)$.

It will be seen that the kind of data to which a rank correlation coefficient is particularly suited is that in which neither of the variables represent a characteristic which can be precisely measured by an objective standard. Even when there is some agreed standard of marking between judges, a margin of subjective difference between marks awarded for the same performance by different judges is always possible. These subjective differences will tend to be less pronounced among the ranks of marks than between the marks themselves and so a rank correlation measure is more independent of subjective bias in such cases than the product-moment coefficient. It has, moreover, the advantage over the product-moment coefficient that, at least for small samples, it is easier to calculate; and it is therefore sometimes used to provide a quick estimate of the product-moment coefficient. It is very often found, in fact, that these two measures of correlation do agree in value quite closely.

EXERCISES 7

1. Find the product-moment coefficient of correlation for each of the following series:

(a)	x:	2	7	3	5	
	y:	4	9	6	7	
(b)	x:	7	9	14	15	17
	y:	3	6	10	9	12
(c)	x:	2	5	8	11	15
	y:	2	23	62	119	223

2. Plot scatter diagrams for each of the series in Question 1 and fit a trend line to each visually.

3. Explain the distinction between *spurious* correlation and *real* correlation.

4. It is found that the numbers of television and car licences taken out each year are correlated. Is this evidence of a real causal connection between ownership of cars and television sets? What light does your answer throw on the limitations of the correlation coefficient as a measure of relationship?

5. Compute regression equations of y on x for each of the following series:

(a)	x:	3	5	6	10	
	y:	3	6	10	12	
(b)	x:	1	2	3	4	5
	y:	6	13	20	23	31
(c)	x:	10	18	25	27	30
	y:	102	363	627	730	903

State, in each case, whether you consider the use of a linear regression equation justifiable for making predictions.

6. Compute the regression equation of y on x and x on y for the series:

x:	1	2	3	4	5	6	7	8
y:	1	3	5	4	8	8	9	7

Use the transformation $u = x - 4.5$ in your calculations.

7. Describe the construction of a scatter diagram and a line of best fit. Illustrate by means of scatter diagrams the following three types of relationship between two variables:
   (a) strong positive relationship
   (b) weak negative relationship
   (c) absence of relationship.

8. From the data estimate the effect on cinema attendances of an increase of 500,000 television licences in 1971.

166 CHAPTER 7

Number of cinema admissions (mill.)	1960	1961	1962	1963	1964	1965
	501	449	395	357	343	327
Television licences (mill.)	10·5	11·3	11·8	12·4	12·9	13·3

Number of cinema admissions (mill.)	1966	1967	1968	1969	1970
	289	265	237	215	193
Television licences (mill.)	13·6	14·3	15·1	15·5	15·9

9. Values of two characteristics, P and Q, are as follows

P	1	2	3	4	5	6	7	8
Q	1·4	1·8	2·9	4·5	5·2	5·3	7·2	7·9

Plot a scatter diagram for this information and comment briefly on its features.

10. Calculate the regression equation of y on x and the product-moment correlation coefficient for the following series:

x:	3	5	9	11	12
y:	8	6	4	0	−3

11. The table below gives the results of a job evaluation carried out at your factory:

Earnings £ per Week	Number of Workers with Skill Rating of						
	200–299	300–399	400–499	500–599	600–699	700 and over	Total
12·00–13·99		1	2				3
14·00–15·99	3	5	1				9
16·00–17·99	2	10	3	1			16
18·00–19·99		2	6	2			10
20·00–21·99		4	12	3	1		20
22·00–23·99		1	8	7	4		20
24·00–25·99		1	1	5	1	1	9
26·00–27·99			2	3	2	3	10
28·00–29·99					2		2
30·00 and over						1	1
Total	5	24	35	21	10	5	100

Show, by calculating a correlation coefficient, whether there is any relationship between earnings and skill rating.

12. Two supervisors, Mr. A and Mr. B are considering the performance of individual employees within a group. Each supervisor has to rank the employees according to his opinion of their abilities.

(a) Find the coefficient of rank correlation for the following data.

RANKINGS OF 10 EMPLOYEES BY TWO SUPERVISORS

Employee	Ranking by Supervisor X	Ranking by Supervisor Y
A	2	3
B	1	2
C	3	1
D	4	4
E	6	6
F	5	7
G	8	5
H	7	9
I	10	10
J	9	8

(b) Explain what this coefficient shows.

13. (i) What is meant by *correlation?* Draw sketches to illustrate the difference between positive and negative correlation.

(ii) Two girls, Pat and Mary, were asked to taste ten different types of sweet which were in jars labelled A, B, C, D, E, F, G, H, I, J respectively. They were then each invited, in turn, to arrange the jars in the order of their preference, placing the jar containing the sweet they liked best first.

Pat arranged the jars in the order C, F, B, D, G, H, E, J, A, I. Mary then rearranged them into the order B, D, C, F, E, A, G, H, I, J.

State a formula for the coefficient of rank correlation. Use this formula to calculate the coefficient of rank correlation for these results.

If the results had shown complete agreement what would have been the value of the coefficient of rank correlation?

14. A manufacturer decided to run a competition as part of a sales promotion drive. The competition consisted of placing seven characteristics, labelled A, B, C, D, E, F, G in order of preference.

The adjudicator placed them in the order C, G, E, A, B, F, D whereas a competitor's entry read A, G, C, B, D, F, E.

Calculate the coefficient of rank correlation for these two orders.

15. The following table shows the "goals for" and "goals against" recorded at the end of a season by the top seven teams of a hockey league.

Position	Goals for	Goals against
1	53	31
2	62	30
3	53	33
4	59	44
5	45	38
6	44	34
7	43	34

Calculate coefficients of rank correlation between position and (i) goals for, (ii) goals against, (iii) goal average [i.e. goals for/ goals against], in order to decide which of these three is most closely related to position.

16. Two judges rank the four finalists in a beauty competition. What value of $\Sigma\, d^2$, where d denotes the difference in rank, gives a rank correlation of zero?

17. Two competition judges, A and B, rank four ice-skaters in order of merit. Given that $\Sigma\, d^2 = 10$,
    (i) calculate the value of the rank correlation coefficient,
    (ii) complete the set of ranks for judge B.

Judge	Ranks			
A	1	2	3	4
B	3			

18. What does a regression coefficient measure?

19. In a "Mock" examination, the marks of six candidates in the two Mathematics papers were as follows:

	A	B	C	D	E	F
Paper X	37	34	32	41	55	53
Paper Y	40	33	33	25	41	38

Calculate
  (i) Spearman's rank correlation coefficient,
  (ii) the product-moment correlation coefficient for the two sets of marks.

Without further calculation, state which of the two papers was the more difficult and which produced the greater spread of candidates. Give reasons for your answers.

20. From the following data calculate (a) the correlation coefficient between industrial output and exports, and (b) the regression equation of exports (Y) upon production (X).

Year	Index of Industrial Production (X)	Exports Index (Y)
1964	86	78
1965	89	80
1966	91	83
1967	93	84
1968	97	91
1969	100	94
1970	100	100
1971	101	105
1972	103	112
1973	110	123

21. Explain the difference between regression and correlation.

22. In a study of the operating efficiency of a chemical plant the following data were collected relating the output of the plant to one of the inputs.

Output Y	Input X	
45	17	
39	11	
30	8	$\Sigma X = 100$
42	13	$\Sigma Y = 330$
18	5	$\Sigma X^2 = 1,130$
26	7	$\Sigma Y^2 = 11,708$
32	9	$\Sigma XY = 3,612$
43	14	
35	10	
20	6	

(a) Calculate the correlation coefficient between output and input and interpret it.

(b) Calculate the coefficients in the regression equation

$$Y = a + bX.$$

(c) Plot the data and the regression line on a graph and discuss the suitability of this line as a description of the operating features of the plant.

CHAPTER 8

Index Numbers and Time Series

1. Price and Quantity Relatives

Index numbers have two main purposes. They may be used to provide a scale of measurement of some characteristic which is defined in terms of a number of measurements; an example is the Social class index of Example 1, Chapter 7. The object of such a scale is to enable comparisons to be made of the degree to which the characteristic is exemplified by different individuals. The scale is arranged so that one individual, usually a typical one, has the index 100, whilst the indices of the other individuals are expressed as a percentage of this typical index. The second, and more important purpose of index numbers when considering economic changes, is to make it possible to compare variations in a magnitude or set of magnitudes at different periods of time. This function of an index number is closely related to the first, and requires the choice of some base date at which the index number has the value 100, the index numbers at other dates being expressed as percentages of this base value. Many economic magnitudes change over time and these changes are capable of being measured by means of index numbers. Examples are: output of a firm, industry or country; unemployment; wages and prices. In certain contexts, it is of interest to know the actual magnitudes, for example, the actual number of unemployed, actual output measured in suitable units or average wages in pounds and pence. In some cases, there is no meaningful average in terms of ordinary quantity or money units, the average of all prices in money units, for example; and the use of an index number for measuring such magnitudes is really obligatory. But even in other cases, particularly when studying the relationships between two or more varying quantities, an index number may have great utility.

The two most important magnitudes for the measurement of which index numbers are needed are *price* and *quantity* (or *volume*). A simple price or quantity index which expresses a single price or quantity at one time as a percentage of that price or quantity at another time is called a *price relative* or a *quantity relative*. To illustrate the method of calculation, suppose that p_0 and p_1 are the prices of a certain commodity in Year 0 and Year 1 respectively. If both prices are expressed as a percentage of the price in Year 0, then the corresponding price indices are

$$\text{Year } 0 = \frac{p_0}{p_0} \times 100 = 100, \quad \text{Year } 1 = \frac{p_1}{p_0} \times 100.$$

Year 0 is called the *base year* of the index number series. The difference between the index numbers for the two years is the percentage by which prices have risen from Year 0 to Year 1. The following table shows the price relatives for four commodities in two selected years.

PRICES OF COMMODITIES PURCHASED BY AN AVERAGE FAMILY

Commodity	Year 0 p_0	Year 1 p_1	Price Relative Year 1	Year 3 p_3	Price Relative Year 3
A	£0·12	£0·13	108	£0·17	142
B	0·75	0·75	100	1·35	180
C	0·80	0·90	113	1·25	156
D	1·00	1·25	125	1·85	185

The table immediately shows the great advantage of using index numbers to record changes in the magnitudes of different things. For example, the prices of commodities A and D are very different, but it is easily apparent from the price relatives that the price of D has risen in three years considerably more than that of A in relation to their respective prices in Year 0.

In some calculations with index numbers, price relatives and actual prices can be used interchangeably. For example, if the base year is changed to Year 1, then the corresponding price relative for Year 3 is

$$\text{either } \frac{0\cdot17}{0\cdot13} \times 100 = 131 \quad \text{or} \quad \frac{142}{108} \times 100 = 131.$$

Similarly, the corresponding price relative for Year 0 when Year 1 = 100 is

$$\text{either } \frac{0\cdot12}{0\cdot13} \times 100 = 97 \quad \text{or} \quad \frac{100}{108} \times 100 = 97.$$

A quantity relative is precisely similar in conception to a price relative. For example, if q_0 and q_1 are quantities of electricity, measured in kilowatt-hours, consumed by a firm in Years 0 and 1 respectively, then the quantity relative for Year 1 on Year 0 = 100 is $(q_1/q_0) \times 100$.

2. Weighted Averages

A price relative is an index number showing changes in a single price at different times. It is usually of interest to find an index number representing changes in a *set* of prices rather than just one price. One possibility is to use the ratio between the average of the prices in a given year to the average of the prices of the same set of commodities in the base year, expressed as a percentage. Alternatively, the simple average of the price relatives for the given year may be used. For the data given in the table in section 1, the resulting index number for Year 1 will be

(a) using actual prices,

$$(\bar{p}_1/\bar{p}_0) \times 100 = \frac{\Sigma \, p_1/4}{\Sigma \, p_0/4} \times 100 = \frac{\Sigma \, p_1}{\Sigma \, p_0} \times 100$$

$$= \frac{0 \cdot 13 + 0 \cdot 75 + 0 \cdot 90 + 1 \cdot 25}{0 \cdot 12 + 0 \cdot 75 + 0 \cdot 80 + 1 \cdot 00} \times 100$$

$$= 113.$$

(b) using price relatives,

$$\frac{\Sigma \, (p_1/p_0)}{4} \times 100 = \frac{108 + 100 + 113 + 125}{4}.$$

$$= 112.$$

There is a slight discrepancy in the result given by the two methods, but this is unimportant provided that the same method is used consistently for calculating all the index numbers in a particular series.

Whilst, however, a simple average of price relatives is adequate for representing average price change when all the items in the index have the same importance, it will be very misleading when the importance of some items is greater than that of others. If the price of an item which is unimportant changes by a large amount then, from a practical point of view, the change will not be felt so much as will a smaller change in the price of an item of much more importance. Hence it is desirable that an index number which is intended to record changes in a set of prices should reflect the relative importance of each of the items whose prices are included in the index. This is effected by calculating a *weighted* instead of a simple average of either actual prices or price relatives. The weights are chosen so that they are proportional to quantities which measure the importance of the items and often have the arithmetical property that their sum is a round number such as 1 or 1000. The weights may relate to the relative importance of the items in the base year or to any other convenient year. When they refer to the base year, the index number is termed a *base weighted index number*.

To illustrate the method of calculating such an index, suppose that the base year weights for the data in section 1 are:

Commodity:	A	B	C	D	Total
Weights w_0:	0·4	0·1	0·3	0·2	1

(a) using actual prices,

Index for Year 1 on Year 0 = 100

$$= \frac{\Sigma\, w_0 p_1}{\Sigma\, w_0 p_0} \times 100$$

$$= \frac{0·4 \times 0·13 + 0·1 \times 0·75 + 0·3 \times 0·90 + 0·2 \times 1·25}{0·4 \times 0·12 + 0·1 \times 0·75 + 0·3 \times 0·80 + 0·2 \times 1·00} \times 100$$

$$= 115 \quad \text{(to nearest integer)}$$

(b) using price relatives,

Index for Year 1 on Year 0 = 100

$$= \frac{\Sigma\, w_0 (p_1/p_0)}{\Sigma\, w_0} \times 100$$

$$= \frac{0·4 \times 108 + 0·1 \times 100 + 0·3 \times 113 + 0·2 \times 125}{1}$$

$$= 112 \quad \text{(to nearest integer)}.$$

The index calculated from actual prices is known as an *aggregative index*. The two methods of calculation give different results here because of the way in which the weights are chosen. If price or quantity relatives are weighted with expenditure on each commodity in a given year, however, the resulting index is equivalent to an aggregative price or quantity index weighted by the quantities or prices in that year. The expenditure on a commodity in the base year is clearly given by the product $q_0 p_0$ which can accordingly be used to obtain a base weighted index number.

Suppose that q_0, q_n and p_0, p_n are the quantities and prices of a commodity in the base and current years respectively, then the price and quantity indices for the current year (Year n) on Year 0 = 100 are:

Price Index:

(a) Aggregative (using quantities as weights)

$$\frac{\Sigma\, q_0 p_n}{\Sigma\, q_0 p_0} \times 100$$

Quantity Index:

(a) Aggregative (using prices as weights)

$$\frac{\Sigma\, p_0 q_n}{\Sigma\, p_0 q_0} \times 100$$

(b) Using price relatives and expenditure weighting

$$\frac{\Sigma (q_0 p_0)(p_n/p_0)}{\Sigma\, q_0 p_0} \times 100$$

$$= \frac{\Sigma\, q_0 p_n}{\Sigma\, q_0 p_0} \times 100$$

(b) Using quantity relatives and expenditure weighting

$$\frac{\Sigma\, (q_0 p_0)(q_n/q_0)}{\Sigma\, p_0 q_0} \times 100$$

$$= \frac{\Sigma\, p_0 q_n}{\Sigma\, p_0 q_0} \times 100$$

It will be seen that the weights chosen here lead to the same result by both methods. Effectively, the price index is weighted by the quantities of each commodity at the base date and is known as the *Laspeyre Price Index*. The Laspeyre Quantity Index shown on the right is weighted by the price of each commodity at the base date.

After some time has elapsed since the base date, the expenditure weighting pattern of the Laspeyre Index may provide a somewhat irrelevant comparison between current and base year prices or quantities. To overcome this difficulty, the weighting pattern may be revised each year and used to calculate a *current weighted* or *Paasche Index* which is derived in an analogous manner to the Laspeyre Index. The formulae for the Paasche Index are:

Price Index: $\dfrac{\Sigma\, q_n p_n}{\Sigma\, q_n p_0} \times 100$ **Quantity Index:** $\dfrac{\Sigma\, p_n q_n}{\Sigma\, p_n q_0} \times 100$

Though this is a current weighted index, the base year is still Year 0 in the sense that in that year the index is 100. The index for Year n shows the extent of price or quantity changes since Year 0 on the assumption that the expenditure (i.e. weighting) pattern was the same in Year 0 as it is in Year n. From a practical point of view, this is often a more relevant comparison than one which relies on base weights, particularly when there has been a considerable change in spending habits between the two years compared.

EXAMPLE 1

Five feed components are to be used in the construction of an animal feed stuff index number. From the figures tabulated overleaf, calculate:

(*i*) *A Laspeyre Price Index;*

(*ii*) *A Paasche Quantity Index, taking* 1964 $=$ 100 *in each case.*

(i) Laspeyre's Price Index $= \dfrac{\Sigma\, q_0 p_6}{\Sigma\, q_0 p_0} \times 100$

$= \dfrac{390900}{376750} \times 100$

$= 104$ (to nearest integer)

Component	1964		1970	
	Price/Ton £ p_0	Consumption (tons) q_0	Price/Ton £ p_6	Consumption (tons) q_6
A	40	3,000	41	2,750
B	39	2,750	53	1,500
C	38	2,050	35	2,350
D	37	500	30	750
E	36	1,475	24	2,850

$$\text{(ii) Paasche's Quantity Index} = \frac{\Sigma p_6 q_6}{\Sigma p_6 q_0} \times 100$$

$$= \frac{365400}{390900} \times 100$$

$$= 93 \quad \text{(to nearest integer)}$$

The index numbers just described are known as *fixed base* index numbers, comparisons of index numbers in a series all being made with the same base year. However, the base of an index number may be changed from time to time, and it is useful if the method of calculating the index ensures that the numbers when calculated on a new base should bear the same relationship to each other as those in the original series. For instance, if the index for Year 0 is 100 and that for Year n is 200, this represents an increase of 100%; so that if Year n becomes the base year, the method of calculating the index should result in the index for Year 0 becoming 50 in the new series. If $I_{n,0}$ is the index for Year n on Year $0 = 100$ and $I_{0,n}$ the index for Year 0 on Year $n = 100$, then the relationship between the two index numbers when the base is changed from 0 to n is unchanged if

$$\frac{I_{0,n}}{100} \times \frac{I_{n,0}}{100} = 1.$$

For example, when

$$I_{0,n} = 50 \quad \text{and} \quad I_{n,0} = 200, \quad \frac{50}{100} \times \frac{200}{100} = 1$$

and this condition is satisfied. This test is known as the *time reversal test*, which is satisfied by neither Laspeyre's nor Paasche's Indices.

Thus for the Laspeyre (base weighted) price index

$$I_{n,0} = \frac{\Sigma q_0 p_n}{\Sigma q_0 p_0} \times 100$$

and

$$I_{0,n} = \frac{\Sigma q_n p_0}{\Sigma q_n p_n} \times 100$$

But the product of these two index numbers divided by 10,000 does not equal 1. On the other hand, an aggregative index with fixed weights does pass the time reversal test.

3. Chain Base Index Numbers

In the construction of some practical index numbers, such as the index of retail prices, the weights are changed annually and, in order to ensure that relevant comparisons are made between one year and another, the index for each year is based on the level of prices (or quantities) in the previous year, using current year weights. An index of this kind is known as a *chain base index*, the formula for which is:

$$\frac{\Sigma q_n p_n}{\Sigma q_n p_{n-1}} \times 100$$

where the q_n are the current year weights.

For example, a chain base index of prices might appear as follows:

Index for Year 2 (on Year 1 = 100) = 112
Index for Year 3 (on Year 2 = 100) = 118
Index for Year 4 (on Year 3 = 100) = 115
and so on.

In this form it is possible to compare one year's prices only with those of the previous year. It is not immediately obvious, for example, by how much prices have risen from Year 1 to Year 4. This is easily remedied by giving the index for Year 1 the value 100 and then recalculating the indices for subsequent years on this base (without changing the weights originally used). Thus the recalculated series on Year 1 = 100 is:

Year 1 = 100

Year 2 = 112

$$\text{Year } 3 = \frac{112 \times 118}{100} = 132$$

$$\text{Year } 4 = \frac{132 \times 115}{100} = 152$$

The base date may be changed from time to time, though this does not affect the fundamental principle of chaining used to calculate the index. The base date of the index of retail prices, for example, was changed in January 1956, January 1962 and January 1974. At these dates the index stood as follows:

1956 on 1956 = 100	1962 on 1956 = 100	1974 on 1962 = 100
100	118	192

In such cases, the index at various dates can be recalculated so that it refers to some earlier base date. For example, the index for 1974 on 1956 = 100 is

$$\frac{118 \times 192}{100} = 227.$$

The principle advantage of the chain base method is that it enables more accurate comparisons to be made in the short-run compared to the fixed base method. The weighting of many index numbers is revised at fairly short intervals and this may involve a change, not only in the existing pattern of weights, but also in the composition of the items in the index entailing the replacement of old by new items. In the long-run, however, comparisons using a chain base may be seriously misleading and due care must be exercised in making them.

4. Time Series

For most statistical purposes, index numbers are used to record changes in the magnitude of a quantity at successive points of time. The Index of Industrial Production is a series of this kind.

INDEX OF INDUSTRIAL PRODUCTION (1963 = 100)

Year	1965	1966	1967	1968	1969	1970
Index No.	112	113	114	120	123	124

A *time series* is a series of values, such as those above, which vary with time. The graph of a time series may reveal a trend in the

INDEX OF INDUSTRIAL PRODUCTION FOR THE U.K. 1965–1970

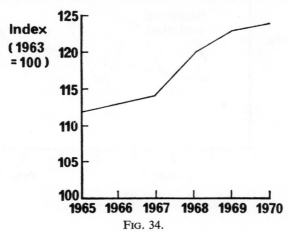

FIG. 34.

values. That for the Index of industrial production, for example, shows an upward trend in production for the years 1965–70 with rather a sharp increase from 1967 to 1968 (Fig. 34). This index is, in fact, a monthly index, and a graph of the monthly figures would not reveal the trend quite so clearly as that of the yearly average of the monthly figures, since the monthly index shows considerable fluctuation about the trend. The trend of a time series is extremely valuable because it provides a means of forecasting future movements in the series; however, disturbances in the original data often obscure the trend and it must therefore be adjusted before being used for this purpose. There are three kinds of irregularity in a time series which necessitate this adjustment: (a) the existence of seasonal variation, (b) the presence of long-term cyclical fluctuations, (c) disturbances due to intermittent influences. Seasonal variations are usually the most important factor obscuring the trend and are, fortunately, the easiest to remove. They consist of regular oscillations about the trend at intervals of a week, month, quarter, or sometimes longer. A series in which there is quarterly seasonal variation is illustrated in Fig. 35. Long-term cyclical fluctuations are due to under-lying economic causes which usually depend on world conditions, a familiar example being the trade cycle occupying approximately seven years. Because the exact causes of such disturbances are difficult to determine, it is often not possible to adjust data satisfactorily to eliminate them, particularly because the period of the cycle tends to be indefinite.

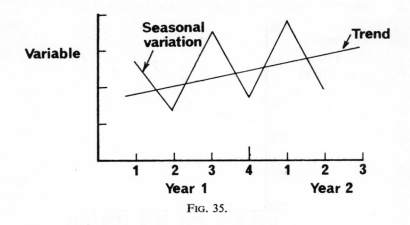

FIG. 35.

Disturbances due to unpredictable causes such as natural catas-
trophes, unusual weather conditions and so forth, occur inter-
mittently and at random and can therefore usually be treated as
random variations in sample data.

Time series are not confined only to index numbers, but may consist of quantities measured in money units, numbers of persons or
physical units of a commodity, or output. The trend need not be
linear or, indeed, follow any easily ascertained law at all; but it is
clearly very desirable that it should be possible to compute at least
an approximation to the trend in order that predictions may be
made.

5. Moving Averages

Seasonal variations often occur at definite intervals. For example,
sales of ice cream are higher in summer than in winter, whilst unemployment tends to be higher in winter than in the summer months.
In these and many other cases, a complete set of seasonal variations
occurs at yearly intervals and in order to find the trend of a time
series in which such variations are present it is appropriate to compute a *four-quarterly moving average*. This consists of a series of
averages computed from the figures in each of four consecutive
quarters, each average being based on the figures of the last three
quarters of the preceding average and the quarter following these
three.

SALES OF ELECTRIC BLANKETS (10,000'S)

Year	Quarters			
	1	2	3	4
1968	20	26	43	57
1969	15	21	43	68
1970	15	32	45	73

It is convenient to set out the calculations in tabular form as follows.

(1) Period	(2) Original Data	(3) Sums in Fours	(4) Sum of (3) in Pairs, Centred	(5) Trend (4) ÷ 8	(6) Variation from Trend (2)–(5)
1968: 1	20				
2	26				
3	43		287	35·9	+ 7·1
4	57	146	277	34·6	+22·4
1969: 1	15	141	272	34·0	−19·0
2	21	136	283	35·4	−14·4
3	43	136	294	36·8	+ 6·2
4	68	147	305	38·1	+29·9
1970: 1	15	147	318	39·8	−24·8
2	32	158	325	40·6	− 8·6
3	45	160			
4	73	165			

It would be possible to find the trend by dividing each of the sums in column (3) by 4, but the resulting average will then correspond to a point between two quarters instead of an actual quarter. In order to compute the variation from the trend the moving average must correspond exactly to a quarter and, to effect this, column (4), which consists of the sums of consecutive pairs of numbers in column (3), is computed and the sums centred on the appropriate quarter in column (1). Thus the first number, 287, in column (4) is the sum of the data for the four quarters of 1968 and that of Quarters 2–4 of 1968 and Quarter 1 of 1969. The centre of these two sets of quarterly intervals, to which the average, 35·9, in column (5) clearly belongs, is Quarter 3 of 1968.

1968: 1	20		
2	26	26	2
3	43 centre ⟶ 43		3
4	57	57	4
		15	1969: 1

SALES OF ELECTRIC BLANKETS 1968–1970

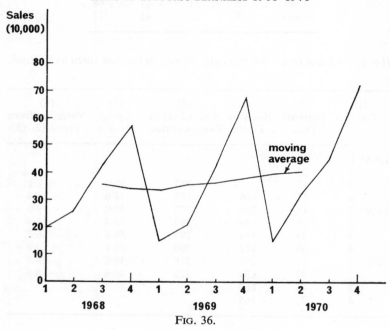

FIG. 36.

As Fig. 36 shows, the moving average reveals whatever trend there may be, although it may often happen that the additional information provided by a moving average has to be cautiously interpreted. The trend in the sales of electric blankets seems to be an upward one; but this result might have been produced by a variety of factors, the chief being either a series of bad winters or a rise in living standards.

6. Seasonal Adjustments

Whilst seasonal fluctuations are readily identified, they may be combined with irregular or random disturbances. In order to remove such random influences from the data, it is corrected for seasonal variations by calculating the average departure of the actual data from the trend over several years. Since random influences may operate in opposite directions in succeeding years, this method of averaging variations from the trend should do something to eliminate them. These average variations are calculated from the data of column (6) in the table of section 5. It will, of course, be a mere

SEASONAL VARIATIONS

Year	Quarter 1	2	3	4	
1968			7·1	22·4	
1969	−19·0	−14·4	6·2	29·9	
1970	−24·8	− 8·6			
Total	−43·8	−23·0	13·3	52·3	
Average	−21·9	−11·5	6·7	26·1	(sum = −0·6)
Adjusted Average	(+0·2) −21·7	(+0·1) −11·4	(+0·1) 6·8	(+0·2) 26·3	(sum = 0)

accident if the sum of the variations in column (6) is zero, and so the average quarterly variations will need adjusting so that their sum is zero. This is effected by subtracting one-quarter of the sum of the actual averages (if this sum is positive) from each of them. If the sum of the averages is negative, then one-quarter of this sum, taken as positive, must be added to each average. In order to obtain a result to one decimal place, this may entail correcting the differences also to one decimal place, the larger differences being subtracted from (or added to) the averages with larger absolute magnitudes. To bring the original data on to the trend line, the averages are *subtracted* from each quarter's figures, bearing in mind, of course, that subtracting a negative quantity is equivalent to adding its absolute magnitude. The seasonally corrected data for the sale of electric blankets is shown below.

The amount of seasonal variation is relevant both for forecasting and for assessing the current situation. For example, the trend in unemployment may be downward, whilst the number of unemployed in December, when there is a good deal of seasonal unemployment,

SALES OF ELECTRIC BLANKETS (10,000's).
SEASONALLY ADJUSTED.

Year	Quarters			
	1	2	3	4
1968	41·7	37·4	36·2	30·7
1969	36·7	32·4	36·2	41·7
1970	36·7	43·4	38·2	46·7

will almost certainly be above the trend value. However, provided that this number is lower than the average seasonal variation for that month, it is still consistent with a downward trend.

7. Deflating Time Series

Movements in the general level of prices, as well as seasonal variations, often obscure a trend in a time series. An increase in the absolute magnitude of a company's profits in a period of inflation, for example, may be entirely due to an increase in the price of its products compared to that of its input. In this case, the real rate of profit may well have declined, so that in order to ascertain the true state of affairs, profit figures must be adjusted to allow for the

Year	Indices of Basic Wage Rates (Jan. 1956 = 100)	Indices of Retail Prices (Jan. 1956 = 100)	Estimated Index of Real Wages (Jan. 1956 = 100)
1957	110·7	105·8	105
1958	113·4	109·0	104
1959	116·8	109·6	106
1960	119·9	110·7	108
1961	125·0	114·5	109
1962	129·3	117·5	110

general raising of price levels. One method of doing this is to calculate an index of profits at current prices which is then *deflated* by dividing by the current index of retail prices to obtain an index of real profits. If profits have been rising more slowly than the retail price index, then the actual rate of profit will appear to have been decreasing. A similar method is used to deflate the index of money wages in order to obtain an index of real wages.

BASIC WAGE RATES AND REAL WAGES (1957–1962)

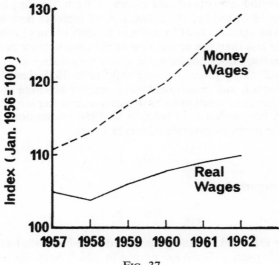

FIG. 37.

As Fig. 37 shows, when the series for money wages is deflated to obtain a series of real wage rates, the increase which has taken place in these rates does not appear quite so spectacular. The different gradients of the two graphs show that basic money wage rates increased faster from 1957 to 1962 than real wages. There is no meaningful sense, of course, in which money rates were above real rates in this period, although the graph of money rates lies above that of real rates. The graphs enable one to compare only the absolute rates of increase of the two series. However, the fact that the index of real wages is *numerically* less than that of money wages affects the interpretation of these two rates of increase, because an increase of 1 point in the lower index is more significant than an equal increase in the higher index.

8. Logarithmic Graphs

When comparing two time series, it is often instructive to determine the proportional rather than the actual rate of increase in the numbers comprising the series. The rate of increase of a variable is measured *per unit time*. For example, the production of motor cars in the United Kingdom increased from 708 (th.) in 1956 to 861 (th.) in 1957 so that the rate of increase in the actual number of cars produced is here (861 — 708) th. per year or 153 (th.) per year. In the same period, exports of cars increased from 336 (th.) in 1956 to 426 (th.) in 1957, so that the actual rate of increase here is 90 (th.) per year. The actual rate of increase in exports of cars in this period is therefore less than the actual rate of increase in their production. This comparison does not however give a very significant picture of the changes taking place, because exports in 1956 were far lower than production and consequently the smaller absolute increase of exports is larger in relation to 1956 exports than the larger absolute increase in production is in relation to 1956 production. For production, the proportional rate of increase was

$$\frac{153}{708} \times 100 = 21 \cdot 6\%;$$

whilst for exports it was

$$\frac{90}{336} \times 100 = 26 \cdot 8\%.$$

So far in this book, all the graphs used have been what are termed *natural scale graphs*. These are graphs in which both the horizontal and vertical axes are graduated so that equal distances on them represent equal increments in the variables. For example, on a natural scale, an increase from 100 to 200 is represented by the same distance on the scale as an increase from 1000 to 1100. It is clear that when natural scales are used, the gradients of the resulting graphs will be an indication of the actual rate of increase per unit time rather than the proportional rate of increase. In order to show the proportional rate of increase of a variable graphically, the *logarithm* of the variable (usually the dependent variable) is measured along one of the axes of the graph rather than its actual magnitude. The other axis of the graph is usually a natural scale along which the actual magnitudes of the other variable (usually the independent variable) are measured. Such a graph is known as a *semi-logarithmic graph*, one of the axes being a logarithmic scale whilst the other is a natural scale. The distinguishing feature of a semi-logarithmic graph is that a variable which is increasing at a constant proportional rate is represented by a straight line on the graph; although on the natural scale graph, the same variable will be represented by a curve which is not straight, but concave upwards, showing that the actual rate of increase of the variable is increasing.

This property of semi-logarithmic graphs depends on the fact that the logarithm of the product of two numbers is the sum of their logarithms. Thus the logarithm of $a \times a$ is $\log a + \log a$ or $2 \log a$. Suppose that a quantity Y doubles each year so that in Year 0 its value is A, in Year 1 it is $2A$, in Year 2 it is $2^2 A$ whilst in Year t it is $2^t A$. If $Y = 2^t A$, then $\log Y = \log(2^t A) = t \log 2 + \log A$, where A is a constant, being the value of Y in Year 0. It follows that the graph of $\log Y$ against t, measured on a natural scale, will be a straight line. The proportional rate of increase of Y each year is

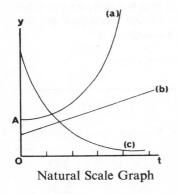

Natural Scale Graph

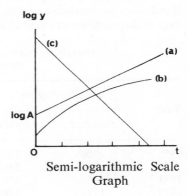

Semi-logarithmic Scale Graph

Fig. 38.

always the same, i.e., 100%; but the actual rate of increase is always increasing because 100% of Y is large when Y is large and small when it is small. The situation is illustrated in Fig. 38. In the natural scale graph, the curve (a) represents the equation $Y = 2^t A$ and shows that as t increases, Y increases at an increasing rate. The corresponding curve (a) in the semi-logarithmic scale graph represents the equation $\log Y = t \log 2 + \log A$ and is thus a straight line since both $\log 2$ and $\log A$ are constants. If Y is a variable which has a constant actual rate of increase (shown by the straight line (b) on the natural scale graph), then the corresponding curve (b) on the semi-logarithmic graph will show a diminishing proportional rate of increase, indicated by the fact that the gradient of curve (b) decreases as t increases. The curve (c) in the natural scale graph represents a quantity Y which is halved each year, i.e., $Y = (\frac{1}{2})^t A$ and the corresponding semi-logarithmic curve (c) is accordingly a straight line which slopes downwards, showing a constant proportional *decrease* in *Y*.

A semi-logarithmic graph can be constructed either by finding the logarithm of each number in the series and measuring these logarithms along the vertical axis of the graph so that equal distances represent equal increments in the *logarithm*; or, alternatively, the numbers may be plotted directly onto specially ruled semi-logarithmic graph paper. The advantage of the former method is that if the numbers are all close together in magnitude, the relation between them can be brought out clearly by choosing a large scale to represent the logarithms. Specially prepared graph paper, on the other hand, does not provide a choice of scale, though this is no disadvantage if the numbers are well spaced out in magnitude.

UNITED KINGDOM—MOTOR CARS, 1956–64
(thousands)

Year	Production		Export	
	Number	Logarithm	Number	Logarithm
1956	708	2·85	336	2·53
1957	861	2·94	426	2·63
1958	1052	3·02	487	2·69
1959	1190	3·08	569	2·76
1960	1353	3·13	570	2·76
1961	1004	3·00	371	2·57
1962	1249	3·10	545	2·74
1963	1608	3·21	616	2·79
1964	1868	3·27	679	2·83

In the table above, logarithms are given correct to two decimal places, since this represents about the greatest accuracy possible in measuring logarithms along the verticle scale. The graph in Fig. 39 shows both the logarithmic scale, which would be used when not plotting on specially prepared graph paper, and the actual figures for use when the figures are plotted directly. Inspection of the logarithmic scale shows that an equal increment in the logarithm is represented by equal distances on all parts of the scale. For example, the distance from 2·00 to 2·30 is the same as that from 3·00 to 3·30 on the logarithmic scale. On the other hand, the distance representing an increment of 500 in the actual figures is much greater from 100 to 600 than from 500 to 1000.

UNITED KINGDOM: PRODUCTION AND EXPORT OF MOTOR CARS, 1956–64

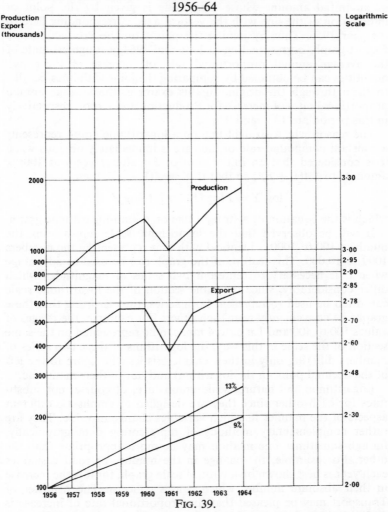

FIG. 39.

An interesting and useful property of the graph is that a straight line through its origin (100 in the present instance) shows the amount after successive years of a sum of money invested at a compound rate of interest of $100r\%$. Thus, at 9%, £100 will amount after 1 year to £109, after 2 years to £119 and after 8 years to £199; and these points all lie on a straight line through the origin. All lines parallel to this on the graph also represent the same rate of increase of an initial amount whose magnitude is given by the point of intersection of the line with the vertical axis, corresponding here to the year 1956. Thus by joining the points on the Production and Export graphs corresponding to 1956 and 1964, a rough estimate of the average annual proportional rate of increase of these two quantities can be obtained by comparing the joins with lines parallel to them through the origin. In this example, the average annual proportional rates of increase for Production and Export respectively in this period are 13% and 9%.

The reason why a straight line on a logarithmic graph represents a constant compound rate of increase is immediately obvious when it is considered that an initial sum of £A after t years at $100r\%$ amounts to £$A(1 + r)^t$; so that if $Y = A(1 + r)^t$, then

$$\log Y = t \log (1 + r) + \log A$$

which is the equation of a straight line on a semi-logarithmic graph.

It will be observed that the logarithmic scale representing the numbers 100 to 1000 is identical with that representing the numbers 1000 to 10,000. This feature of the graph can be used to advantage when it is necessary to represent two series of magnitudes which differ considerably, since the same section of the logarithmic scale can often be used to represent both series, thus ensuring that these graphs lie conveniently near each other. For example, the ranges of values 100 to 400 and 1 mn. to 4 mn. can be represented on the same section of the scale in this way, the logarithms of these two series of numbers differing only in their characteristics (the figure to the left of the decimal point in the logarithm) and not in their mantissae.

Logarithmic and natural scale graphs are, of course, not substitutes for each other since they are designed to emphasise different aspects of the manner in which variables change in value. They are rather complementary methods of representing data graphically, though sometimes one method may be more appropriate than the other. For example, the change in the number of road casualties each year is best shown on a natural scale graph, for it is the increase in their absolute number which causes concern. The Minister of Transport may be pleased that the proportional rate of increase is declining each year; but this decline may be associated with an increase in the absolute rate of increase, which is not so consoling to the general public.

The distance between any pair of numbers on a logarithmic scale is equal to that between any other pair, the ratio between the members of which are equal to that between those of the first pair. For example $500/100 = 1000/200$ and the distances on the logarithmic scale between 100 and 500 and 200 and 1000 are accordingly equal. For this reason, logarithmic scale graphs are also known as *ratio scale graphs*.

9. Linear Regression Equations

When time series data is used for forecasting, it is often useful to compute a linear regression equation for the data by the method explained in Chapter 7. A rough estimate of the future movement of a time series can, of course, be obtained visually once a trend line has been established by the method of moving averages. But it may be essential to produce a more precise estimate than is possible by visual means and, moreover, one for which confidence limits can be given.

Before a regression equation can be computed, it is important that the data should be seasonally corrected; since otherwise there will be considerable scatter about the regression line and a consequently high value for the standard error of any prediction. The most satisfactory procedure in most cases is to use the yearly average of the seasonally corrected data. The method of computation is illustrated here by calculating the regression equation for the Index of Retail Prices given in section 7. To facilitate calculations, the data is given to the nearest whole number.

Year $= x$	Index of Retail Prices $= y$	$x - 1959\frac{1}{2}$ $= u$	$y - 111$ $= v$	u^2	uv
1957	106	$-2\cdot5$	-5	$6\cdot25$	$12\cdot5$
1958	109	$-1\cdot5$	-2	$2\cdot25$	$3\cdot0$
1959	110	$-0\cdot5$	-1	$0\cdot25$	$0\cdot5$
1960	111	$0\cdot5$	0	$0\cdot25$	0
1961	115	$1\cdot5$	4	$2\cdot25$	$6\cdot0$
1962	118	$2\cdot5$	7	$6\cdot25$	$17\cdot5$
		0	3	$17\cdot50$	$39\cdot5$

The regression coefficient b satisfies the equation

$$(v - \bar{v}) = b(u - \bar{u}).$$

So
$$b = \frac{\Sigma\, uv - (\Sigma\, u\, \Sigma\, v/6)}{\Sigma\, u^2 - \dfrac{(\Sigma\, u)^2}{6}}$$

$$= \Sigma \, uv/\Sigma \, u^2 \qquad \text{(since } \Sigma \, u = 0\text{)}$$
$$= 39 \cdot 5/17 \cdot 5$$
$$= 2 \cdot 26.$$

Since $v = y - 111$ and $\bar{v} = 3/6 = 0 \cdot 5$, it follows that the equation for the regression of y on u is

$$y - 111 - 0 \cdot 5 = 2 \cdot 26u$$

or $\qquad\qquad\qquad\qquad y = 2 \cdot 26u + 111 \cdot 5.$

An estimate of the Index of Retail Prices for 1965 on Jan. 1956=100 is found from this equation by putting $u = 1965 - 1959\frac{1}{2} = 5 \cdot 5$.

Whence $\qquad\qquad\qquad y = 2 \cdot 26 \times 5 \cdot 5 + 111 \cdot 5$
$$= 124 \cdot 0.$$

The official index for 1965 on Jan. 1962 = 100 is 112·1. Hence the index for 1965 on Jan. 1956 = 100 is

$$\frac{117 \cdot 5 \times 112 \cdot 1}{100} = 132.$$

The discrepancy between the predicted and actual values is due partly to the fact that the regression is not wholly linear, but more

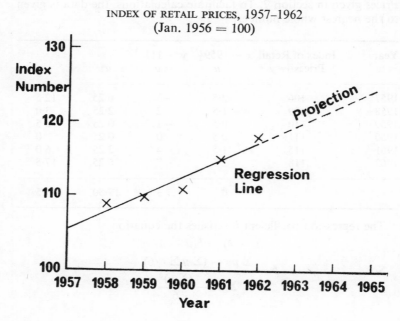

INDEX OF RETAIL PRICES, 1957–1962
(Jan. 1956 = 100)

FIG. 40.

importantly to the periodic revision of the weighting pattern of the index (Fig. 40).

This example illustrates the need for caution in making predictions from past data either by calculation or visually. The validity of any prediction assumes that the period to which extrapolation is made is similar in all important respects to that for which the data is collected and also that the method of calculating the data is the same.

10 Z-Charts

The Z-chart is a widely used method of showing sales or output data in a form in which it is possible to compare current performance, which is subject to seasonal variation, with the long-term trend of sales or output. This is effected by using data for sales (say) from the previous as well as the current year in order to obtain a moving annual total from which seasonal fluctuations are eliminated. The graph of the moving annual total therefore indicates the trend in annual sales or production, whilst the graph of monthly production or sales shows what seasonal variations are present. A cumulative total for the current year's data is also computed in order to show the position at any date in the current year. The following example illustrates the method of constructing a Z-chart (Fig. 41).

EXAMPLE 2

On p. 194 are monthly production figures, in '000 units, of an industrial company.

SALES (' 000 units per month)

Month	1967	1968	1968 Cumulative Total	1968 Moving Annual Total
Jan.	400	420	420	5020
Feb.	410	430	850	5040
Mar.	360	410	1260	5090
April	400	380	1640	5070
May	420	410	2050	5060
June	450	470	2520	5080
July	430	450	2970	5100
Aug.	380	400	3370	5120
Sept.	410	460	3830	5170
Oct.	450	490	4320	5210
Nov.	460	510	4830	5260
Dec.	430	480	5310	5310
	5000	5310		

MONTHLY PRODUCTION OF THE "XL" COMPANY, 1967/1968
(' 000, Units)

	Jan.	Feb.	Mar.	April	May	June
1967	400	410	360	400	420	450
1968	420	430	410	380	410	470
	July	Aug.	Sept.	Oct.	Nov.	Dec.
1967	430	380	410	450	460	430
1968	450	400	460	490	510	480

Calculate and plot a Z chart for the year 1968.

MONTHLY PRODUCTION OF THE "XL" COMPANY,
1967/1968

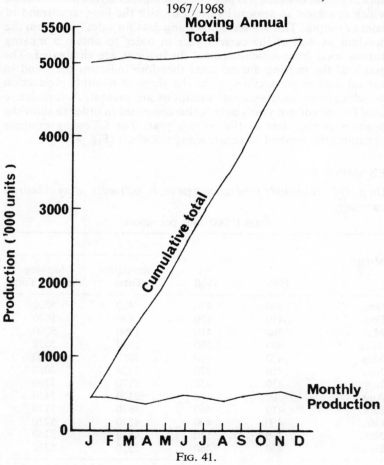

FIG. 41.

11. Exponential Smoothing

The moving average discussed in section 5 is an unweighted average; effectively, the value of each observation is given equal weighting. Extrapolation from a trend computed in this way takes no account of the known differences between forecast and observed values, although it is clear that this difference is an indicator of influences disturbing the trend which will have an effect on its future behaviour. The information provided by the difference between observed and forecast values is utilised in a technique known as *exponential smoothing*, which is an adaptive forecasting system by which the forecast for a given period is modified by the error in the forecast for the preceding period. The data required for making a new forecast for the next period is the forecast which was made for the present period, the observed value for the present period, and the value of a smoothing constant α, such that $0 \leqslant \alpha \leqslant 1$. Then

New forecast = old forecast + α(actual observation − old forecast).

Over several periods, the new forecast is thus related to a chain of old forecasts calculated in the same manner and giving less weight to observed values, the farther they are removed in time from the present new forecast. If F_0 is the new forecast and A_1 is the observed value for the present period, A_2 that of the immediately preceding period, A_3 the observed value for the period preceding that, and so on, then it can be shown that

$$F_0 = \alpha\{A_1 + (1 - \alpha)A_2 + (1 - \alpha)^2 A_3 + \ldots + (1 - \alpha)^{r-1}A_r\} + (1 - \alpha)^r F_r,$$

where the new forecast r periods ago was F_r.

A useful rule for finding α is given by the formula

$$\alpha = \frac{2}{n + 1},$$

where n is the number of periods in the equivalent moving average. For example, for a 4-quarterly moving average over 1 year ($n = 4$), $\alpha = 0.4$. The larger the value of n, of course, and the smaller the value of α, the greater will be the smoothing effect.

EXAMPLE 3

Calculate an exponentially weighted moving average, with $\alpha = 0.2$, from the following data:

Period Reference	Actual Demand	Old Forecast
1	16	16
2	20	
3	15	
4	19	
5	17	
6	21	
7	25	

With $\alpha = 0.2$ (i.e. 1/5),

New forecast = old forecast (b)
$$+ \; \alpha(\text{actual demand } (a) - \text{old forecast } (b))$$
$$= b + \frac{a - b}{5}.$$

Period	Actual Demand (a)	Old Forecast (b)	$\dfrac{a - b}{5}$	New Forecast
1	16·00	16·00	0	16·00
2	20·00	16·00	0·80	16·80
3	15·00	16·80	−0·36	16·44
4	19·00	16·44	0·51	16·95
5	17·00	16·95	0·01	16·96
6	21·00	16·96	0·81	17·77
7	25·00	17·77	1·45	19·22

To calculate a reliable trend, using an ordinary moving average requires a large number of prior observations. In this respect, an exponentially weighted moving average has the advantage that, since a relatively few observations are required, a smaller amount of data need be stored. This makes it particularly useful in computer systems of stock control where a large variety of items are carried in stock.

The larger the number of periods included in a moving average (i.e. the larger the value of n), the less likely is the moving average to be affected by random variations. On the other hand, the moving average will be less sensitive to trend when n is large. A high value of n thus gives high *stability* with respect to random variations but low *sensitivity* to changes which are due to real trends in the series.

A small value of n is less effective in eliminating random variations but more sensitive in showing up changes in the trend. The same remarks, of course, apply to the value of α used in exponential smoothing; a high value of α means less stability but more sensitivity. This is illustrated by the following data in which values of α of 0·5, 0·25 and 0·2 are used to obtain the new forecast.

| | | New Forecast | | |
Period	Actual Demand	$\alpha = 0.5$	$\alpha = 0.25$	$\alpha = 0.2$
1	15	15	15	15
2	19	17	16	15·8
3	18	17·5	16·5	16·24
4	25	21·25	18·63	17·99
5	20	20·63	18·97	18·39
6	29	24·81	21·48	20·52
7	31	27·91	23·86	22·61
8	26	26·95	24·39	23·29
9	34	30·48	26·80	25·43
10	40	35·24	30·10	28·35

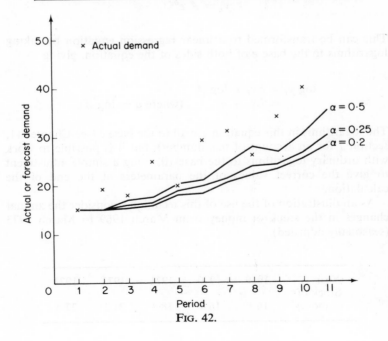

FIG. 42.

The graph (Fig. 42) shows that raising the value of α brings the new forecast closer to the observed values, but introduces greater fluctuations. In practice, a balance must be struck between sensitivity and stability in deciding how many observations are to be taken within a given time period, say one year, and it must also be borne in mind that the greater the number of observations which are made, the more costly will the exercise be.

12. Non-linear Regression

It is, of course, inappropriate to use a linear regression equation for predictive purposes when the data is related by a non-linear law. This difficulty may sometimes be circumvented if the non-linear law can be transformed so that the data is related in a linear fashion. Thus the graph of a time series may not be even approximately a straight line when plotted on a natural scale graph, but could be so when plotted on a semi-logarithmic graph. If this is the case, it shows that the data is related by an exponential law and the regression equation will be basically of the form

$$y_i = A \ e^{bx_i}.$$

This can be transformed to a linear regression equation by taking logarithms to the base e of both sides of the equation, giving

$$\log y_i = bx_i + \log A$$
$$= bx_i + a \qquad \text{(where } a = \log A\text{)}.$$

The logarithms in this equation are all to the base e (see Chapter 11, section 7 for an account of this number), but it is possible to work with ordinary logarithms to the base 10, using a simple adjustment to give the correct values of the parameters at the end of the calculation.

As an illustration of the use of this technique, consider the annual changes in the stock of money from March 1969 to March 1973 (seasonally adjusted).

Year	1969	1970	1971	1972	1973
Stock of money	16·1	16·4	18·4	21·2	27·4

Year = X	Stock of money = Y	$(X-1971)$ = x	log Y = y	x^2	y^2	xy
1969	16·1	−2	1·2068	4	1·4564	−2·4136
1970	16·4	−1	1·2148	1	1·4757	−1·2148
1971	18·4	0	1·2649	0	1·6000	0
1972	21·2	1	1·3264	1	1·7593	1·3264
1973	27·4	2	1·4377	4	2·0670	2·8754
		0	6·4506	10	8·3584	0·5734

The correlation coefficient

$$r = \frac{0\cdot5734}{\sqrt{\left\{10\left(8\cdot3584 - \frac{(6\cdot4506)^2}{5}\right)\right\}}}$$

$$= 0\cdot5734/0\cdot6033$$

$$= 0\cdot95$$

which shows that there is some justification for assuming that the actual correlation is exponential.

The regression coefficient

$$b = \Sigma xy/\Sigma x^2$$
$$= 0\cdot5734/10$$
$$= 0\cdot05734.$$
$$a = \bar{y} - 0\cdot05734\bar{x}$$
$$= 6\cdot4506/5$$
$$= 1\cdot2901.$$

Hence
$$y = 0\cdot05734x + 1\cdot2901$$
or
$$\log_{10} Y = 0\cdot05734x + 1\cdot2901.$$

Taking the antilogarithms of both sides of this equation,

$$Y = (\text{antilog}_{10} 1\cdot2901) \times 10^{0\cdot05734x}$$
$$= 19\cdot5 \, e^{0\cdot132x} \quad (\text{since } 10^{0\cdot05734} = e^{(2\cdot3026 \times 0\cdot05734)})$$
$$= 19\cdot5 \, e^{0\cdot132(X - 1971)} \quad (\text{since } x = X - 1971).$$

In order to obtain a reasonably accurate result in such calculations, it is usually necessary to retain as many decimal places as possible when obtaining the logarithm of Y. This is because quite a considerable change in the value of Y may be associated with a relatively small change in the value of its logarithm, so that an error in even the third or fourth decimal place of the logarithm may mean a high relative error.

EXERCISES 8

1. Why is *weighting* used in the construction of index numbers? Explain what is meant by *price relative*.

   Calculate, correct to one decimal place, a cost of living index from the following table:

	Price Relative	Weighting
Food	103·4	25
Transport	112·5	12
Housing	111·2	11
Durable House-hold goods	115·3	6
Services	100·6	8
Clothing	107·2	8
Tobacco	100·8	3

2. (a) From the information stated below construct a quantity index for the products made by Multiproducts Ltd. for the period 1966–69, weighted as to 1966 prices, and (b) explain the purpose of preparing a quantity index.

   State what the indices calculated in (a) above indicate about the production of Multiproducts Ltd. for the years 1966–69, and discuss the influence of individual products on the index.

   MULTIPRODUCTS LTD.

Product	1966 Average Price £	1966 Production (000's)	1967 Production (000's)	1968 Production (000's)	1969 Production (000's)
Pliers	2·00	62	65	66	90
Wrenches	3·00	138	120	110	80
Bolts	0·50	500	540	580	800
Drills	4·50	10	10	10	10

3. Calculate the index of service costs for 1971, taking 1970 as base, and using the following data:

Items	Weighting	% Increase on 1970 Costs
Travelling	20	5
Meals	15	8
Labour charges	45	14
Tools and equipment	10	7
Protective clothing	10	5

4. The index number of vehicles in the United Kingdom taking 1958 as base year (i.e. 1958 = 100) is shown below.

Year	Annual Average Index
1964	152
1965	160
1966	168
1967	176
1968	184

(a) If the number of vehicles in 1968 was 14·5 millions, calculate the number for the year 1965.

(b) If the trend over the years 1964–1968 continued, in which year was the number of vehicles double the 1958 figure?

5. The Index of Retail Prices for 1970 was 140 (Jan. 1962 = 100) whilst the Index for 1962 (Jan. 1956 = 100) was 118. Recalculate the index for 1970 using Jan. 1956 as base.

6. Recordings of a variable are taken once every day for two weeks and 7-day moving averages are calculated. How many values of the moving average are there?

7. The index numbers, calculated on the chain base method, for a particular commodity, are shown below. Calculate the 1970 index, to the nearest whole number, using 1968 as base.

1968	1969	1970
100	107	108

8. The population of a certain area on January 1st in each specified
   year was recorded as follows:

1911	10,000
1921	13,000
1931	17,000
1951	28,600

By plotting the above data on semi-logarithmic graph paper,
estimate the population in 1941 when a census was not taken.

Why is a semi-logarithmic graph particularly useful for this
kind of data? Estimate the average rate per decade at which
population increased from 1911 to 1951.

9.   PERSONAL SAVINGS AS A PERCENTAGE OF PERSONAL
                      DISPOSABLE INCOME

	1968	1969	1970
1st Quarter	9·6	12·1	11·4
2nd Quarter	8·1	7·1	8·2
3rd Quarter	7·5	7·1	7·8
4th Quarter	5·3	5·7	6·7

Correct the series for seasonal variation. Forecast the percentage of personal disposable income saved in the first quarter of
1971.

10.   MANUFACTURERS' SALES OF WOMEN'S FOOTWEAR (m. pairs)

	1966	1967	1968
1st Quarter	20·9	17·5	17·0
2nd Quarter	17·3	14·7	13·5
3rd Quarter	15·6	13·5	13·5
4th Quarter	13·9	13·1	13·7

Is there any evidence that manufacturers' sales of women's
footwear are subject to seasonal variation? Predict manufacturers' sales during the first quarter of 1969.

11. The following table indicates the quarterly sales returns for a
    small engineering company:

	1st Quarter	2nd Quarter	3rd Quarter	4th Quarter
1964	27	40	31	42
1965	52	77	69	89
1966	92	123	108	132

Plot a graph of these figures showing the sales per quarter throughout the period.

Calculate the four-quarterly moving averages and plot these using the same axes. Discuss briefly the significant features of the two graphs.

12.   PERSONAL INCOME AND SAVING IN THE U.K. (£th. m.)

	Personal Saving	Personal Income	Price Indices for Consumer Goods and Services (1963 = 100)
1959	0·8	19·6	90·8
1960	1·2	21·2	91·8
1961	1·7	22·9	94·5
1962	1·6	24·1	98·1
1963	1·6	25·6	100·0
1964	1·8	27·7	103·3
1965	2·0	30·1	108·0
1966	2·2	32·1	112·1
1967	2·1	33·7	114·9
1968	2·0	36·2	120·1

Prepare a graph illustrating the relationship between real personal saving and real income. What proportion of personal income would you expect to be saved in 1978?

13. Circulation of National Morning Newspapers

Year	1960	1961	1962	1963	1964
Average Daily Circulation (mil.)	15·1	15·9	15·7	15·6	15·9
Year	1965	1966	1967	1968	1969
Average Daily Circulation (mil.)	15·6	15·6	15·6	15·3	14·8

(a) Prepare a graph of the data on circulations of national morning newspapers.

(b) Discuss possible reasons for the trend of circulation shown.

(c) Forecast circulation in 1972.

14. Use the data given to forecast production of aircraft in 1975. How confident are you of the accuracy of the forecast?

Year	1960	1961	1962	1963	1964	1965
Production of new aircraft	518	395	487	450	319	415

Year	1966	1967	1968	1969	1970
Production of new aircraft	431	312	278	500	450

15. (a) Represent the following information by a semi-logarithmic graph:

Year	Currency Circulation (£ million)	Index Number of Wholesale Prices (1958 = 100)
1957	1,842	99·4
1958	1,905	100·0
1959	1,969	100·3
1960	2,062	101·8
1961	2,151	104·4
1962	2,161	106·8
1963	2,210	107·9
1964	2,332	111·5
1965	2,483	116·7
1966	2,637	119·9

(b) What conclusions do you draw from the graph?

16. What are the advantages of a semi-logarithmic graph over one constructed on a natural scale?

17. Calculate and draw a Z-chart of the sales (in thousands of pounds) of the Premier Furniture Stores Ltd. for the year 1971, from the details given below:

VALUE OF MONTHLY SALES OF THE
PREMIER FURNITURE STORES LTD.,
1970 and 1971
(£000's)

	1970	1971		1970	1971
January	109	121	July	118	125
February	96	103	August	107	110
March	96	104	September	110	113
April	103	108	October	123	128
May	107	116	November	130	134
June	107	114	December	136	141

18. Exponentially smooth the following observed series of values:

$$40, \quad 35, \quad 39, \quad \mathbf{44}, \quad 45, \quad 43, \quad 46.$$

The old forecast for the first observed value should be taken as 40 with $\alpha = 0.2$.

19. Exponentially smooth the series in No. 14. What is the new forecast for the production of aircraft in 1971? (Take $\alpha = 0.25$).

20. For the data in No. 8, let Y ('000) be the level of population in Year X. Fit an exponential curve to this data of the form

$$Y = A \ e^{b(X - 1921)}.$$

(a) Use your equation to estimate the population in 1941.
(b) Is there any reason to suppose that your equation is a good fit to the data?

CHAPTER 9
Official Statistics

1. Introduction

Government official statistics on the state of the economy serve a dual purpose: they are essential for an effective formulation of government policies and they are invaluable in providing guides to policy in both the public and private sectors of industry. Their value in both capacities is clearly illustrated by the need, at the present time, to control inflation by controlling wages and prices. No informed negotiations between Trade Unions and management would be possible without an extensive knowledge, on both sides of industry, of price trends and the state of the labour market. Official statistics on wage rates in different occupations, hours of work, levels of unemployment and price trends are clearly of the highest importance for this purpose.

In formulating economic policy, governments clearly need to be well-informed as to trends in unemployment, the regional distribution of population and industry, the state of trading relations of this with other countries, housing and education. The collection of data on these topics is, of course, very expensive; but the burden of cost is unavoidable in a scientifically planned economy which aims at the best utilisation of national resources whilst, at the same time, ensuring an equitable distribution of the national wealth among the individual members of the population.

Responsibility for the collection of official statistics devolves mainly upon the relevant government departments: Department of Trade and Industry, Department of Employment, Department of Education and Science, Ministry of Agriculture, Fisheries and Food, Department of the Environment and so on. The work of coordinating the findings of these agencies is undertaken by the Central Statistical Office which is responsible for the preparation of digests of the principal statistical data. This data is derived either from *sample enquiries* or from *censuses*. A sample enquiry has the advantage of being less expensive than a complete survey and of producing results in a fairly short time. By adjusting the sample size and employing a proper sampling method, the error involved in an incomplete enquiry of this kind can be minimised and measured. On the other hand, there are certain topics about which complete information is essential; and here the census method is the appropriate one to use. For example, certain information is required about every member of the population; not only its size but also its distribution, housing conditions, occupational distribution and so forth, all of which is obtained by the Census of Population which extends to every member of the population. Complete censuses are, of course, often supplemented by sample enquiries between census dates, but there is much information of a detailed nature which can be obtained only by a full census.

2. Main Sources of Official Statistics

The following table summarises some of the principal topics about which statistical data is supplied, together with the government departments responsible for collecting it and the chief publications in which it appears.

Topic	Department Collecting Data	Publications
I Population and vital statistics	Office of Population Censuses and Surveys	Registrar General's Statistical Review. Census 1971 Great Britain, Summary Tables
II Social Services, Expenditure on Social Services: Housing, Education, etc. National Insurance	Central Statistical Office Dept. of Health and Social Security Dept. of Environment	Annual Abstract of Statistics Annual Report of DHSS Housing Statistics, Great Britain (quarterly)
	Dept. of Education and Science	Statistics of Education
III Manpower and Earnings: numbers employed and unemployed, industrial disputes, basic wage rates, output per head and labour costs	Dept. of Employment Central Statistical Office	Dept. of Employment Gazette Economic Trends Monthly Digest of Statistics New Earnings Survey
IV Science and Technology: Expenditure on research and development	Dept. of Education and Science	Statistics of Science and Technology
V Agriculture, forestry and fishing: land utilisation, agricultural prices	Ministry of Agriculture, Fisheries and Food Forestry Commission	Agricultural Statistics Annual Report of Forestry Commissioners

Topic	Department Collecting Data	Publications
VI Production: volume indices, wholesale prices, census of production, individual industries	Central Statistical Office Business Statistics Office Dept. of Trade and Industry	Monthly Digest of Statistics Reports on the Census of Production Trade and Industry; Business Monitor
VII Energy: Production and consumption of coal, oil, gas and electricity	Dept. of Trade and Industry	Digest of Energy Statistics
VIII Distribution and Service trades	Dept. of Trade and Industry	Census of Distribution and other Services
IX Transport and communications	Dept. of Environment Registrar of Shipping and Seamen	Passenger Transport; Highway Statistics Registry of Ships
X External trade	Dept. of Trade and Industry Central Statistical Office	Trade and Industry; Overseas Trade Statistics (monthly) United Kingdom Balance of Payments; Economic Trends; Financial Statistics
XI National Income and Expenditure	Central Statistical Office	National Income and Expenditure
XII Financial institutions; credit and money supply, banks, insurance, building societies, securities	Central Statistical Office Bank of England Dept. of Trade and Industry	Financial Statistics Annual Report Insurance Business Statistics
XIII Public finance	Dept. of National Savings Board of Inland Revenue	Annual Report of the National Savings Committee Inland Revenue Statistics
XIV Personal income, expenditure and wealth	Dept. of Employment Central Statistical Office Board of Inland Revenue	Family Expenditure Survey; Dept. of Employment Gazette National Income and Expenditure Inland Revenue Statistics

The data presented in the publications listed above is nearly all available in summary form in the *Monthly Digest of Statistics* or the *Annual Abstract of Statistics*. In addition to the official statistical publications, the *Financial Times*, Building Societies Association, the Institute of Actuaries and other private organisations provide important material on financial matters. Information on the World

Economy and the EEC is available in United Nations publications (*Demographic Year Book* and *Statistical Yearbook*); the *Yearbook of Labour Statistics*, published by the International Labour Organisation; and the *Statistical Yearbook* of UNESCO. The ministries concerned provide the Statistical Office of the European Community (SOEC) with a large and varied amount of United Kingdom statistical data for inclusion in their Eurostat series of publications. For the most part, statistics are given on a comparable basis for each of the nine member countries. The statistics appear in summary form in *Basic Statistics of the Community*, and in more detailed form in specialised publications such as the *Yearbook of Agricultural Statistics*. Copies of these publications are available from: Office des Publications Officielles des Communautés Européennes, Boîte postale 1003, Luxembourg, or, in some cases, from HMSO.

3. Index of Retail Prices

Each month the Department of Employment publishes the latest level of its Index of Retail Prices. This is popularly known as the cost of living index, though this description became obsolete in 1947. The original cost of living index was established in July 1914 to measure the percentage monthly increase in the cost of maintaining the standard of living among working-class households, which was then regarded as a minimum standard. Since the War of 1939–45, this is no longer a valid assumption, and the present index covers a wider range of commodities and income groups than its predecessor, and is now interpreted largely as an economic indicator. The Cost of Living Advisory Committee (now renamed the Retail Prices Index Advisory Committee), which is responsible for the general superintendence of the Index, do not accept the view that the index should measure only changes in the cost of necessities since, apart from the difficulty of deciding what to include as a necessity, this would severely limit the usefulness of the index.

The current index is the result of a report in March 1962 by the Advisory Committee, and has Jan. 1974 = 100 as base. In accordance with a previous report of the Committee, a continuous enquiry —the Family Expenditure Survey—has obtained, since January 1957, details of the spending habits of private households. The enquiry covers the whole of the United Kingdom, including both rural and urban areas, as well as all income groups and family sizes. A two-stage random sample is used. First a random sample of 56 areas is selected; each month a systematic sample of 16 households from each area is chosen from the Electoral Register. Altogether, about

11,000 addresses are chosen and visited in rotation during the year. Each individual spender over 16 years of age in the household is asked to keep records of all payments made for 14 consecutive days; and information about regular, longer period, items such as mortgage payments, gas and electricity bills, insurance and so forth is also obtained, together with the number of income receivers and their incomes. The head of each respondent household receives a payment of £1 provided that the records are properly kept. From 1971 the payment was increased to £2. Although the most immediate bearing of the enquiry is on the Retail Price Index, the scope of the information obtained entitles it to be considered a multi-purpose survey. It provides source material for researches of a general economic nature; and also data is made available for market research purposes.

The Family Expenditure Survey is conducted partly by personal interview and partly from records of expenditure completed directly by household members. As with all voluntary enquiries a proportion of the sample fails to co-operate; in the Family Expenditure Survey this accounts for about 30% of the pre-selected sample. Virtually all non-response arises from refusal to co-operate, since interviewers make repeated attempts to contact each individual in the pre-selected sample. In 1971, for example, it was estimated that only about 1% of the pre-selected sample could not be contacted. Hence the final achieved sample may differ substantially from the sample originally selected which could introduce considerable bias into the results of the Survey. The reasons for non-response are complex, but it has been established that age is an important factor. The response rate seems to show a consistent decline the higher the age of the head of the household.

The findings of the Family Expenditure Surveys result in a weighting pattern which is changed every year. The following table illustrates the changes which have taken place in the weights from 1962 to 1978.

The index is the weighted average of the price relatives of each group and is a chain base index which is re-weighted every January on the information obtained from the sample households for the three consecutive years ended the previous June. The prices required for the calculation are obtained from a large number of price quotations covering a wide range of commodities and services in all parts of the country. Strictly speaking it is only movements in these prices which are measured by the index. Even so, the importance of this particular set of prices and the fact that they are used in wage negotiations and for the determination of prices and incomes policies has led to the index being regarded as a general purpose

GROUP	WEIGHT (for 1962)	WEIGHT (for 1978)
1. Food	326	233
2. Alcoholic Drink	61	85
3. Tobacco	77	48
4. Housing[1]	102	113
5. Fuel and Light	62	60
6. Durable Household Goods	65	64
7. Clothing and Footwear	99	80
8. Transport and Vehicles	88	140
9. Miscellaneous Goods	62	70
10. Services	58	56
11. Meals-Out[2]	—	51
	Total 1000	Total 1000

[1] Includes owner-occupiers' mortgage interest from February 1975.
[2] Introduced in 1968 as a separate group. Until then, half the expenditure on meals out was allocated to the food group, the other half being proportionately spread over all groups including the food group.

index. For example, it was proposed to use it for the current purchasing power (CPP) method of inflation accounting. The object of inflation accounting is to eliminate the effects of price movements on the calculation of profit. This means, for example, that estimates made of the allowance for annual depreciation of capital equipment must be based on replacement cost rather than historic cost. The assumption of the CPP method was that movements in the index of retail prices can be validly used as a guide to replacement cost. This view was challenged in the Report of the Sandilands Committee on *Inflation Accounting* which maintained that, since such items as capital equipment are not represented in the index it cannot, even indirectly, reflect changes in the prices of such items accurately. The alternative method now adopted by accountants, the current cost accounting (CCA) method, depends on the evaluation of the assets of each company by individual valuers. The great advantage of the CPP method was that it is relatively simple to apply, relying on the movement of a single index. However, it is a commonplace of Statistics that it is unwise to make general inferences from data which can be validly applied only within a restricted field, and this is the basis of the rejection of the CPP method. In response to recommendations by the Sandilands Committee, the CSO has prepared since 1978 index number series for revaluing specific assets. These are published in *Price Index Numbers for Current Cost Accounting*.

4. Index of Industrial Production

Index numbers of production are designed to measure changes in the volume of industrial production in particular industries, groups of industries, and industry as a whole. They are therefore quantity indices which are based, wherever possible, on physical units of output. In some cases, however, this provides only a misleading measure of output; for example, the numbers or weights of machines are not good indications of the real volume of machinery output. When this is so, alternative measures are adopted such as the value of output, quantity of materials used or the number of persons employed.

In order to obtain weights for calculating the Index of Industrial Production, an estimate must be made of the importance of each industry in relation to industry as a whole. Now the gross output of an industry, which is the market value of its products, will clearly not be adequate for this purpose, since it includes the cost of all materials, labour, interest, etc. and so does not reflect the value added by that industry alone. The net output of the industry, which is really its value added, will however, be quite appropriate for this purpose. Accurate net output figures for each industry are obtained in the periodic Censuses of Production.

For weighting purposes, industries are grouped according to the Standard Industrial Classification 1968. This classifies industry into 20 groups which comprise Orders II–XXI of the SIC, Order I being Agriculture, forestry and fishing. This classification, together with the weights used in computing the present index, are shown opposite.

The present Index of Industrial Production has 1975 = 100 as reference base. Before 1968, industries were analysed by the 1958 SIC in which Orders IV and V of the 1968 classification were combined into a single order as were also Orders VII to IX. This fact must be remembered when making comparisons between index numbers since 1968 and those before that year.

Further revisions of the SIC are being considered to achieve a closer correspondence to the *Nomenclature générale des activitiés économique dans les Communautés Européennes* (NACE). This has not yet passed the consultative stage, but its importance for the British economy as part of the European Community should be obvious.

5. Manpower Statistics

Manpower statistics cover all aspects of the use of the labour force of the country in economic activity; such as distribution of total

STANDARD INDUSTRIAL CLASSIFICATION 1968

Order No.	Industrial Group	Weight
II	Mining and quarrying	37
III	Food, drink and tobacco	84
IV	Coal and petroleum products	7
V	Chemicals and allied industries	58
VI	Metal manufacture	57
VII	Mechanical engineering	100
VIII	Instrument engineering	15
IX	Electrical engineering	67
X	Shipbuilding and marine engineering	16
XI	Vehicles (including aircraft)	72
XII	Metal goods not elsewhere specified	48
XIII	Textiles	49
XIV	Leather, leather goods and fur	3
XV	Clothing and footwear	24
XVI	Bricks, pottery, glass, cement, etc.	27
XVII	Timber, furniture, etc.	22
XVIII	Paper, printing and publishing	64
XIX	Other manufacturing industries	31
XX	Construction	147
XXI	Gas, electricity and water	72
	Total	**1000**

working population, employment, unemployment, industrial stoppages, wage rates and weekly hours, and output per head and labour costs. The most important general sources of statistics on these topics are the Census of Population, the Census of Production, the Census of Distribution and the publications of the Department of Employment.

Statistics of unemployment relate to the number of persons registered at the local offices of the Department of Employment as unemployed on a specified Monday in each month. The number registered as unemployed is expressed as a percentage of the estimated total number of employees. Since there is a good deal of seasonal variation in unemployment, monthly fluctuations must be corrected to obtain the trend of unemployment. The situation is also complicated by the number of school leavers coming on to the labour market at the end of each term who accordingly are placed in a separate category. A distinction is also made between those registered as wholly unemployed and those only temporarily un-employed.

Information on the structure and distribution of earnings in industry is obtained in the *New Earnings Survey*, a sample survey which has been conducted annually since 1972. In 1974, for example, the sample consisted of 81,718 men and 33,511 women and was distributed throughout Great Britain on a regional basis. The complete results of the survey are published annually in a six-part publication. The main general results and streamlined analyses of key results for particular collective agreements, industries, occupa-tions, age groups and regions are published in the Department of Employment Gazette. These give a wide range of results in a very compact and convenient way, especially for those who may not require the more detailed analyses.

Earnings, which include overtime pay, tend in most periods to rise faster than basic wage rates. In periods of increasing produc-tivity, labour costs, that is earnings per unit output, tend to rise more slowly. Comparative data on these series and the retail price index are given monthly in *Economic Trends*.

6. Population Census

The question of determining the number of people in a country is one of the greatest importance, for the figure is used in a variety of comparisons to give ratios expressed "per head of the popula-tion", "per family", etc. Such comparisons must, of course, be made between groups which are similar in relevant respects; for example, legitimate births should be compared with the total of married women of child-bearing age and not with total population or total number of women. The data required for a study of demography in the United Kingdom is collected mainly by the Registrars-General of England and Wales, Scotland and Northern Ireland. Each Registrar-General works according to a similar plan, so that the results for each part of the Kingdom are uniform and com-parable.

With the exception of 1941 a full decennial census has been held in England and Wales since 1801. The questions asked have varied a good deal at different periods; partly in order to obtain more reliable and useful information, but also in order to collect special information on topics of current interest. For example, in 1911 special information was collected on fertility; whilst in 1931 questions were introduced which enabled the numbers of unemployed in different industries and their age distribution to be ascertained.

In this country the distribution of population has always been recorded *de facto*, that is, according to the actual residence of the individual at the time of the census. This may differ somewhat from the *de jure* population, that is, the population distributed according to its normal place of residence; but the date of the census is always fixed so that these two coincide as closely as possible. Before every census, there is a good deal of preparatory work which is undertaken with the object of training enumerators and testing the effectiveness of questionnaires. Preliminary investigations of this kind are known as *pilot surveys*, and add greatly to the efficiency of the census itself. Questions may also be included in the census with the object of improving the results of future censuses. In the 1931 census, for example, the "usual residence" enquiry was introduced in order to provide evidence for determining how far a *de facto* enumeration will suffice.

7. Census of Population 1971

In the 1971 census, all questions had to be answered by every household. The basic demographic questions on age, sex, marital condition, relationship to head of household and usual residence were included in much the same form as in previous censuses. A question on country of birth was again included, and a new question was added on the countries of birth of each person's father and mother, but no information was sought on nationality or citizenship. The questions on address one year ago and address five years ago first introduced in 1961 and 1966 respectively, were repeated.

The date of first or only marriage and date of termination of that marriage were included as in 1961, but addressed only to women aged under 60. Information was also collected on dates of birth of all children born alive to such women in marriage, an innovation which will provide valuable data for the examination of trends in family size and spacing.

The main questions on occupation, industry and place of work were unchanged, but a description of work done was asked for under the occupation question. It is hoped that this will improve the coding of occupation of some groups where job titles are insufficiently specific. A new question asked for occupation on a date a year before the census to provide information on occupational mobility. The distinction between part-time and full-time work was dropped, but normal hours of work were asked for all employed persons.

A question on educational qualifications was first asked in 1961, limited to qualifications in science and technology. This was extended in the 1966 Sample Census to cover qualifications (other than those normally obtained at school) in all subjects, and was repeated in much the same form in 1971. A new question was asked on the possession of certain specified qualifications, broadly equivalent to G.C.E. "A" level. This extended the scope of the questions on educational qualifications, and also in some measure replaced the former question on the age at which full-time education ceased.

In all censuses since 1801 information has been collected on housing and households. Because of difficulties in defining and identifying structurally separate dwellings in a way that can be easily applied by enumerators in the field, no such definition was used in 1971. Instead a question on the form asked if any room, hall, passage, landing or staircase was shared with another household. If "Yes", the enumerator then enquired as to whether the shared space was used by the respondent household only for the purpose of access to its accommodation or was used for other purposes such as internal movement, and as to the number of shared rooms. This information will be used to classify household spaces according to the degree of sharing there is with other households. Questions on the shared or exclusive use of cookers, sinks, fixed baths, hot water supplies and inside or outside toilets were repeated much as before. Information on housing tenure, number of rooms and number of cars was collected as in 1966. Questions on usual residents who were absent on Census night, introduced in 1961, were repeated.

8. 1966 Sample Census of Population

Except for a few special study areas in Scotland, the 1966 Census was not a complete enumeration of the population but a 10 per cent. sample enumeration.

The sample selected for each local authority area in the country was:

(a) one in ten of the structurally separate private dwellings and "small" non-private establishments.

(b) one person in ten present at every "large" non-private establishment.

The main sampling frame was the 1961 Census record. A computer program was written to examine this and to print out for each 1961 census enumeration district a list of one in ten of each of the categories (a) and (b) above. These lists were then brought up to date to allow for new building since the 1961 Census and to include residential caravans.

Tests were carried out as part of the validation programme of the census to estimate the number of private dwellings that had no chance of selection for the census because they did not appear in any of the sampling frames. The sample selected for the census was stratified by local authority area.

The early reports on the census contain an interesting account of a method of making a preliminary estimate of sampling errors. For example, if in an area there are 625 widowed females in the sample, then the standard error of this figure is approximately $\sqrt{625}$ or 25. The estimate of widowed females in the population is 6250 and there are odds of 20 to 1 that the correct population total lies within the range $(625 \pm 2 \times 25) \times 10$ or 5750 to 6750. It is important to remember that all such calculations must be made using the actual sample number, i.e., 625 and not the population estimate i.e., 6250.

An example of the kind of results obtained, together with the 1961 figures for comparison, are shown in the following table:

Area	Total Population		
	Persons	Males	Females
	1961		
Great Britain	51,283,892	24,786,567	26,497,325
	1966		
Great Britain	52,303,720	25,319,330	26,984,390

It was originally intended that intercensal sample censuses should become a permanent feature of the collection of demographic statistics. In January 1975 it was proposed that a full census should be held in 1976 and, thereafter, every five years. This was suggested because of the increasing concern of the government with social policy and the consequent need for greater and more accurate data on the condition of the population. However, the idea had to be abandoned for economy reasons, nor has there been a sample census during the 1970s.

9. Balance of Payments

Balance of payments transactions are those between a country's residents and the rest of the world. They include payments for goods, which are classified as *visible* imports and exports; and as services and investment income, which are known as *invisible* imports and exports. Balance of trade transactions consist solely of visible items. In general, imports are measured c.i.f. (that is, their value includes carriage, insurance and freight), whilst exports are measured f.o.b. (free on board). There is therefore some discrepancy between the values of world imports and exports which reflects the world's consumption of international transport, insurance and so on. In the balance of payments accounts, both these items are valued f.o.b., since transport and insurance are included among the invisible items.

Before 1970, the official form in which the Balance of Payments was presented distinguished between Current Account transactions and those on Long-term Capital Account. Since then, a new form of

U.K. Balance of Payments 1974

	£ million
Current Account	
Exports (f.o.b.)	15,886
Imports (f.o.b.)	21,120
Visible balance	−5,234
Invisible balance	+1,566
Current Balance	−3,668
Investment and Other Capital Flows	
Official long-term capital	− 275
Overseas investment in United Kingdom public sector	+ 764
Overseas investment in United Kingdom private sector	+2,110
United Kingdom private investment overseas	−1,128
Trade credit	− 372
Other identified capital transactions	+1,542
Balancing item	+ 462
Total currency flow	− 565
Allocation of special Drawing Rights	—
Gold subscription to IMF	—
Total of above	− 565
Official Financing	
Foreign currency borrowing by H.M. Government	+ 644
Drawings on (+)/additions to (−) official reserves	− 79
Total official financing	+ 565

presentation of the balance of payments has been adopted, the main object of which is to show the means by which overseas trade is officially financed. The grouping of items into a Long-term Capital Account has been replaced by a group comprising Investment and Other Capital Flows in which no distinction is made between short- and long-term capital movements. The table shown on page 218 is prepared from the *United Kingdom Balance of Payments, Pink Book.* The three main groups in the table are:

(a) *Current account*, covering exports and imports of goods and services, investment income and transfers.

(b) *Investment and other capital flows*, covering official long-term capital transactions, investment flows, changes in the balances of other countries held in London, trade credit and other capital flows. In this group, (−) represents an increase in assets or a decrease in liabilities and (+) represents a decrease in assets or an increase in liabilities. Other capital flows include changes in the gross balances of sterling area and non-sterling area countries held by the U.K., foreign currency transactions of U.K. banks and other short-term flows.

(c) *Official financing*, covering changes in the official reserves and foreign currency borrowing by H.M. Government. This consists of drawings on a Euro-dollar facility to a limit of £4,000 million. Until 1972 official financing also included net borrowing from the IMF but since 1972 this has been included as changes in official reserves.

The *current balance* shows whether the U.K. had added to or consumed its net external assets in any period. The current balance and the net balance of investment and other capital flows, together with the net total of the unidentified transactions reflected in the balancing item, are brought together to show the *total currency flow* resulting from all external transactions. The balance of changes in the reserves and other official financing transactions thus reflects the total currency flow, together with gold subscriptions to the IMF, and (from 1970) the allocation by the IMF of the reserve asset, Special Drawing Rights.

10. National Income

The Balance of Payments and National Income Accounts together provide an essential means of assessing the state of the country's economy and the level of economic activity. The official definition of National Income is *the money value of goods and services becoming available to the nation from economic activity.* The National Income can be regarded from three different points of view: (a) output: how the value added was produced; (b) incomes: how earnings were distributed; (c) expenditure: how incomes were spent. These are essentially different ways of classifying the same thing, and each provides a method of estimating National Income. The table below illustrates two of these methods, namely (b) and (c). Total income earned yields Gross National Income in the sense that no allowance is made in this total for depreciation. Both Gross National Income and Expenditure are valued at *factor cost*, i.e. Income or Expenditure valued at market prices less indirect taxes plus subsidies. Hence

National Income at Factor Cost

= National Income at Market Prices
  — Indirect Taxes + Subsidies

The two methods of measuring National Income produce a small discrepancy which is allowed for by introducing the Residual Error

U.K. National Income and Expenditure, 1974 (£ millions)

Shares in National Income		Spending (at market prices)	
Income from employment	52,001	Consumers' expenditure	51,670
Income from rent and self-employment	13,601	Public authorities' current expenditure	16,641
Gross trading profits of companies	9,706	Gross fixed capital formation at home	16,247
Gross trading surpluses of public corporations	2,426	Value of physical increase in stocks and works in progress	1,082
Gross surpluses of other public enterprises	119	Total domestic expenditure at market prices	85,640
Total domestic income	77,853	Exports and income from abroad	22,205
less stock appreciation	− 5,964		
Residual error	736		
Gross domestic income at factor cost	72,625	*less* imports and income paid abroad	− 26,813
Net property income from abroad	1,352	*less* taxes on expenditure	− 11,351
		Subsidies	2,944
Gross national income at factor cost	73,977	Gross national expenditure at factor cost	72,625
Less capital consumption	− 8,590		
National Income	65,387		

item in the left-hand column of the table. Net National Income is obtained by deducting from Gross National Income an amount equivalent to what is necessary to replace capital consumed during the year. This is roughly equivalent to the accounting concept of depreciation, and some estimate of its amount can be obtained from the returns in which it is included to obtain net income for tax purposes. It is doubtful, however, whether this accounting estimate really provides a sufficiently accurate valuation of capital consumption, and so the figure for Net National Income must be cautiously interpreted.

In the table above, the income and spending methods are shown. Preliminary estimates of national income are given in the *National Income and Balance of Payments White Paper*, published in March just before the budget. The following table shows National Income measured from the output side, the data being derived from the *National Income Blue Book*.

U.K. National Product, 1974 (£ millions)

Agriculture, forestry and fishing	2,265
Mining and quarrying	1,093
Manufacturing	22,097
Construction	6,042
Services and distribution	46,356
Total domestic income	77,853
less Stock appreciation	− 5,964
Residual error	736
Gross domestic product at factor cost	72,625
Net property income from abroad	1,352
Gross national product at factor cost	73,977

Apart from providing an alternative means of measuring National Income, the output method is intrinsically valuable since it shows the industrial composition of output. The table shows, for example, that Manufacturing accounts for only 28 % of total domestic income; whilst Service and Distribution, which includes distributive trades, insurance, banking and many public sector enterprises accounts for 60 %. In fact, the contribution of this sector has increased by 10 % since 1970 and this growth is causing some concern since it suggests that the economy is becoming unbalanced, particularly in the public sector.

A definitive account of the sources of data and methods used to estimate National Income are given in *National Accounts Statistics: Sources and Methods* (H.M.S.O.) September 1968.

11. Standardised Death Rates

The Census of Population provides complete information about the age-structure of the whole country. This information is important from many points of view; among others, it provides a means of comparing death rates in different regions of the country. It is more or less self-evident that death rate, expressed per thousand of the population, will depend to a significant extent, on the age-distribution of the population. An area in which there is a large proportion of elderly persons can expect, other things being equal, to have a higher mortality rate than one in which this proportion is lower. It follows that in order to determine whether there are other factors, apart from age-structure, which affect mortality in different regions, it is necessary to eliminate the effects of this specific factor. This can be done by calculating the weighted average of the death rates of each age-group in the region concerned, using the numbers in the standard population as weights.

For any region, there are, in fact, two death rates: (a) the *crude death rate*, which is simply the aggregate number of persons per 1000 of the population who die in a given year; and (b) the *standardised death rate*, which is the number per 1000 dying, on the assumption that the age composition of the region is the same as that of the standard population. The crude death rate clearly does not allow for different age-structures in the regions being compared, whilst the standardised death rate does allow for this and so enables one to consider whether differences in mortality are due to factors other than differing age composition.

Calculations of the crude and standardised death rates for the following data illustrate the problem.

	Town *A*		Town *B*		
Age Group	% of Ppn.	Death Rate (per thousand)	% of Ppn.	Death Rate (per thousand)	Standard Population % of Ppn.
0–15	30	2	20	1·8	24
16–30	31	1	10	0·9	21
31–50	27	4	40	3·8	26
51–	12	6	30	4·7	29

For Town A, total number of deaths per 100,000 of the population

$$= 2 \times 30 + 1 \times 31 + 4 \times 27 + 6 \times 12 = 271$$

Crude death rate $= \dfrac{271}{100,000} \times 1000 = 2 \cdot 71$ per thousand.

Standardised death rate

$$= \frac{2 \times 24 + 1 \times 21 + 4 \times 26 + 6 \times 29}{100,000} \times 1000$$

$$= 3 \cdot 47 \text{ per thousand.}$$

For Town B, total number of deaths per 100,000 of the population

$$= 1 \cdot 8 \times 20 + 0 \cdot 9 \times 10 + 3 \cdot 8 \times 40 + 4 \cdot 7 \times 30 = 338$$

Crude death rate

$$= \frac{338}{100,000} \times 1000 = 3 \cdot 38 \text{ per thousand.}$$

Standardised death rate

$$= \frac{1 \cdot 8 \times 24 + 0 \cdot 9 \times 21 + 3 \cdot 8 \times 26 + 4 \cdot 7 \times 29}{100,000} \times 1000$$

$$= 2 \cdot 97 \text{ per thousand.}$$

The crude death rate for the region will be lower than the standardised rate if there is a larger proportion of people in the lower age-groups than in the standard population. This is the case in Town A. In Town B, the situation is reversed, though the age-structure here is closer to that of the standard population than that of Town A. An inference which might be drawn from comparing the standardised rates is that Town B is somewhat healthier than Town A. For the United Kingdom, the death rate in 1970 for the whole population was about 17·5 per thousand, so that the above figures are rather notional. In practice, it is usual to calculate male and female death rates separately, since there is a considerable divergence between them.

EXERCISES 9

1. How are official statistics useful (a) to Government, (b) to the private sector of industry?

2. What sources of statistics are available for (a) expenditure on social services, (b) earnings, (c) industrial production and (d) the world economy?

3. Give an example of (a) an official price index, (b) an official quantity index, and explain how each is constructed.

4. Distinguish between gross output and net output. For what purpose is this distinction important in the preparation of official index numbers?

5. Name three fields of enquiry for which the Standard Industrial Classification is necessary.

6. What are the main kinds of information provided by the Census of Population?

7. How was information obtained on occupational mobility in the 1971 Census of Population?

8. What is the purpose of (a) a pilot survey, and (b) a sample census?

9. Distinguish between visible and invisible exports, giving examples of each kind.

10. How was the method of presenting the U.K. Balance of Payments Accounts modified in 1970. What reasons were there for this change?

11. Comment on the use of National Income Accounts (a) as a guide to economic policy, (b) as a means of determining the industrial composition of output.

12. Why is the accounting concept of depreciation not a reliable method of measuring capital consumption?

13. It is a common complaint that Government departments require too many statistics. Give examples of statistical information which you think it is absolutely necessary that businesses should supply to the Government on request, and give your reasons for the selection you have made.

14. If you were a director of a company in a highly competitive manufacturing industry in the United Kingdom, which official statistics might you find useful? Name the sources of such statistics and state likely reasons for your interest.

15. (a) Why is it important for governments to collect and maintain manpower statistics?
(b) Suggest four subjects to which you would give priority in the collection of manpower statistics and give reasons for your choice.

16. (a) Describe the construction of the Official Retail Prices Index used in the United Kingdom, and

(b) explain how it could be used by:

    (i) Businessmen,
    (ii) Consumers, and
    (iii) Trade unions.

17. (a) What does the information in the table below indicate about the earnings of full-time men and women workers in the retail drapery, outfitting and footwear trades at October 1966 and April 1970?
(b) What does the data indicate about the relative earning positions of the lowest paid men and women workers in these trades?

WEEKLY EARNINGS IN RETAIL DRAPERY, OUTFITTING AND FOOTWEAR TRADES

	Full-time Men Workers			Full-time Women Workers		
	Lowest Decile £	Lower Quartile £	Median £	Lowest Decile £	Lower Quartile £	Median £
October 1966	12·36	14·33	16·89	7·78	8·43	10·00
April 1970	15·20	17·60	21·10	9·20	10·30	12·00

18. The age distribution and number of deaths in the population of a town in a certain year is given below. Calculate the crude and standardised death rates for males and females separately. Can it be inferred from this evidence that women live longer than men?

Age Group	Population (thousands)	Deaths	Standard Population % of Ppn.
Males: 0–10	5	100	11
10–25	6	20	14
25–55	8	80	18
Over 55	3	150	5
Females: 0–10	5	90	11
10–25	6	15	15
25–55	9	81	20
Over 55	4	200	6

19. The crude birth rate of a town containing many new housing estates will be very different from that of a town in which many retired elderly people live.

(a) Explain why this is so.

(b) Explain how the use of the standardised rate could reduce this difference.

20. The table below shows the number of deaths occurring in a particular year in each of two towns, X and Y, together with the population of each town and of the country; all are classified by age group.

Age group (years)	Number of Deaths		Population		
	Town X	Town Y	Town X	Town Y	Country (millions)
0—	21	48	3000	8000	15
20—	7	15	3500	7500	14
40—	32	77	2500	3500	13
60 and over	88	80	1000	1000	8

Calculate the crude and standardised death rates for each town.

21. "The concept of 'general price changes' in the abstract, unrelated to the purchasing pattern of any class of individual or entities, is unquantifiable."

"For measuring the average price changes experienced by individuals or entities, the goods and services whose price changes are to be measured and the relative weights to be attached to them must be determined before an appropriate price index can be constructed."

A colleague studying the Sandilands Report on *Inflation Accounting* has come across these two statements and asked for an explanation of their meaning. Draft such an explanation.

CHAPTER 10

Social Surveys

1. Introduction

In the present chapter, consideration is given to some of the practical problems which arise in the collection of statistical data with particular reference to social surveys. But although this discussion has special reference to social surveys, the problems and methods of solution connected with them are of general interest and validity in almost every field of statistical enquiry. An Office, Factory or Hospital are social units which, in many respects, are similar to society as a whole.

Particular points likely to be of interest in any enquiry are the way in which decisions about what data to collect are related to the *clearly defined* purpose of the enquiry; and also the way in which the expense of collection is likely to modify the methods of collection used. The statistician should be always alert to the possibility of reducing the cost of an enquiry, taking account of the loss which will result from the inaccuracy or inadequacy of the data which occurs when such economies are practised. This involves considerations of *utility*, measured in terms of money, and in particular estimates of the loss which is incurred by being wrong. Choice of significance levels and sample size are obvious factors in relation to which considerations of utility in decision-making can occur. This is a matter which can be meaningfully discussed within the context of traditional statistics of the kind with which this book is concerned. A great deal of work has been done in recent times, however, to modify the traditional approach to statistics with the object of introducing the cost aspect into statistical calculations. The results of much of this work are still controversial, and it is not appropriate to include an account of it at the present elementary level of study.

2. Planning of Social Surveys

In beginning any survey, it is important to know as much as possible about existing sources of data in the same or related fields, since much reduplication in the collection of data will thereby be avoided. Much statistical data published by Government departments is multi-purpose and is useful for Market Research work in Industry as well as for the specific object for which the data was obtained. The Family Expenditure Survey is an example.

In order to see the kind of problems which arise in planning a survey, consider a specific example, say a B.B.C. enquiry into the listening habits of the population of a large town. Such an enquiry is likely to have more than one purpose, but in any event it is important to define clearly what information is required and what inferences are expected to be made from it. The *unit of the enquiry* will clearly be the individual and it will be important to classify individuals into "listeners" and "non-listeners". In order to do this, it is necessary to define the meanings of these terms precisely. For example is a "non-listener" one who has access to a radio but does not use it or does the category include those who have no radio? Secondly, it will presumably be necessary to know something of the number of hours of listening devoted to each service; and thirdly the types of programme chiefly listened to (Light Music, Serious Music, Talks, etc.). Each of these questions involves a clear definition of terms which serves the dual purpose of enabling the data to be clearly related to the overall purpose of the survey and also to facilitate the unambiguous formulation of the questions which are to be put. The next step is to decide how the information is to be obtained with sufficient accuracy at the least cost. There may be many alternatives, e.g. street enquiries, mail questionnaires, door-to-door enquiries, and so on. In choosing between these, it will be necessary to determine their efficiency in terms of *non-response rate*, *accuracy of answers*, degree of skill and amount of *training* required by the research personnel and so on. Many of these factors might be evaluated on the basis of previous experience, but some may be special to this particular enquiry, in which case it will be necessary to pre-test the methods by small-scale enquiries. When the best method has been decided upon, there will be matters of detail to be finalised, such as the exact wording of questions to avoid ambiguity, and the alternatives will be compared by carrying out small-scale pilot surveys.

3. Experiments and Investigations

A descriptive social survey may incidentally produce data which illuminates relationships between variables. If more detailed knowledge of these relationships is required, then the survey must be specially designed to meet the logical and methodological requirements incident to any scientific research into causal relations. It is the special purpose of statistical experiments and investigations to examine these relationships. The object of any experiment is to examine the effects of changes in some variable on another variable whilst other conditions are held constant. In the laboratory, where the relevant physical factors can be clearly defined and enumerated, there is tolerable certainty that these extraneous factors have been held constant. On the other hand, in a social experiment involving human subjects, these extraneous factors are more difficult to define and isolate. For example, to study the relative efficiency of programmed learning and traditional teaching methods among school children, there are several obvious differences between children such as age, sex, I.Q., which may affect the result and the effects of which must be isolated in order to obtain a clear picture of the single effect of programmed learning. But considerable knowledge of the subject matter is clearly necessary in order to be reasonably certain that no relevant factors have been overlooked. Is interest in sport, ability in the various arts, occupation of parents, etc., also important? Clearly, the list of possibilities might be extended indefinitely.

Investigations differ from experiments in that the proposed causal variable cannot, in the nature of things, be controlled in the former. Thus whilst it is possible to examine the effects of a drug by actually administering it to the subject, it is not possible to observe the relationship between height and weight on the one hand and degree of introversion and extroversion on the other experimentally. We cannot increase a person's height in order to discover whether or not he becomes more extroverted: height is not a variable which can be controlled. We can however examine individuals of different heights in relation to extroversion, but this introduces the problem of eliminating the effects of individual differences apart from height. Thus one method is eliminated which is always available to the experimenter, namely that of noticing the effect of a change in the variable on the *same* subject. With this exception, the problems of designing valid experiments and investigations are much the same.

One point which must be cleared up, or at least mentioned, straight away is that to demonstrate statistical association is not sufficient to prove the existence of a causal relationship. Apart from statistical analysis, a collateral knowledge of the subject matter is necessary as well, i.e., it will be necessary to have a knowledge of psychological, biological or other scientific laws appropriate to the field of investigation. This difficulty is commonly pointed out, for example, when interpreting a correlation coefficient. It is clear, however, that the better an experiment is designed, the more likely are we to discover a true causal connection between variables. In a perfectly designed experiment, full account is taken of all the variables apart from those in which we are interested so that their effects can be properly allowed for. In this case, if A is followed by B, it can be said that A is a sufficient cause of B. It would probably be asking too much even of a perfectly designed experiment to prove that A was both a sufficient and necessary cause in view of the elaboration such an experiment would require and quite apart from the uncertainty of whether such causes exist in nature at all. In practice we cannot even be certain of the sufficiency condition, because there is always the possibility that some relevant factor has been overlooked.

Reverting to our example of the efficiency of programmed learning, this might be determined by a "before and after" experiment in which the same subjects were used with and without programmed learning. The object here would be to see whether or not this kind of instruction were effective rather than whether it was better than other methods. A pre-test could be given to the group and an average mark obtained. The group would then be given the course of instruction and then be submitted to another test, different from but comparable with the pre-test. The two average marks could then be compared. This method of exactly paired comparisons eliminates the possible effects of significant individual differences such as sex, I.Q., etc. But the experiment may still be defective if there is any significant change in the attitude of the group which is independent of the programmed learning. For example, experience with the pre-test may produce greater efficiency in working the post-test, even when the questions differ. To eliminate this source of invalidity, a control group could be used so that only *one* test was administered to each group, one of which received instruction and the other not. In this case, of course, it is necessary to match the two groups so that individuals correspond at least with respect to major significant attributes. As already indicated, there will still be a residue of rather vaguely defined or unknown attributes which might be influencing the result of the experiment but which cannot, for obvious reasons, be eliminated by matching. To reduce to a minimum the effects of these residual attributes is the purpose of *randomisation*. This experiment can, by an obvious extension, be used to compare the effects of programmed and traditional instructional techniques. This can be achieved by using three groups, with matching and randomisation, one of which is the control group receiving no instruction. (One of the purposes of such a group is to eliminate the influence of *existing* knowledge.) The resemblance between a "blocking" experiment of this kind and the blocking used in an agricultural experiment (see Chapter 6, section 8) should be noted, the blocks in the present experiment consisting of the matched individuals, each set of which should form a homogeneous group.

One reason for introducing several groups is to test the effect of a change in more than one variable. For example, we might wish to discover whether programmed instruction with or without traditional methods were more effective. An experiment to test various combinations of these two is termed a *factorial experiment*. There are four possible combinations of two variables, giving rise to a 2×2 factorial experiment so four groups will be needed to which the following types of instruction are given:

(1) PT',
(2) $P'T$,
(3) PT,
(4) $P'T'$; where P and T indicate respectively, programmed and traditional instruction and P', T' indicate the absence of these two. To examine the effects of n variables requires a 2^n factorial design. The great value of such designs is that they enable one to measure *the interaction effects* of the different variables as well as the main effects.

The above points in sample design are relevant to the *internal* validity of the experiment, i.e., they should lead to valid conclusions about causal relationships *within* the population investigated—in the limit, within the experimental group. An experiment with only internal validity will clearly have limited value, and attention must also be paid to those features of experimental design which enable one to generalise the findings to large populations. To secure the external validity of the experiment clearly involves the problem of a correct choice of sampling frame and an appropriate sample design (stratified, multi-stage, etc.).

4. Sources of Data

The value of a survey will be greatly reduced if the methods adopted for the collection of data lead to inaccuracies. Bias on the part of the investigator can to some extent be removed by proper training and, in the case of those imbued with a scientific attitude acquired in training as social or natural scientists, the degree of objectivity attained may be sufficient to overcome such bias. In studying human populations, however, the investigator is interested in attitudes and attributes subjectively as well as objectively, since he is also a member of the society which he is studying. It is therefore desirable to have several methods of data collection, if only as a means of checking the accuracy of the data. In addition, some methods of data collection are more appropriate than others to a particular field of study and also at certain stages in a particular study. On the side of the respondent, training is usually possible only to a limited extent. For example, even though a respondent is carefully instructed about the manner of completing a questionnaire and warned about the pitfalls leading to incorrect answers, it may still be difficult to overcome his innate tendency to approach the questions in a subjective way coloured by personal prejudices. For this reason, it is often preferable, where possible, to choose a method of enquiry in which the respondent is unaware of his participation in an investigation.

Personal documents, such as diaries and other notes, which have not been prepared with the specific object of assisting in an enquiry may often be freer from bias than answers in the same area obtained by an interviewer.

Observations of behaviour when the subject is unaware that he is being observed may also be a useful source of data—in motion study, for example.

Both sources of data, however, have limitations, the most important being that it is often difficult or impossible to obtain the specific information required by the enquiry which is the end product of the more precise and goal-orientated method of the questionnaire. This difficulty is brought home, even more forcibly when one considers that both these methods are difficult to combine with precisely defined sampling techniques. The observer, for example, is forced to notice only what comes immediately within his observation, and there may be some (unknown) reason why he remains unacquainted with the whole of a possible field of enquiry. This source of bias could, of course, disappear if the observation were continued over a prolonged period as is frequently the case with *participant observation* in which an observer becomes part of the community which he is set to observe.

5. Mail Questionnaires

The use of mail questionnaires is well adapted to obtaining data from certain types of population such as firms and members of a professional body. In such cases, it is usually possible to count on the cooperation of respondents because they are usually in a position to understand the purpose of such surveys. Even in the case of a survey covering the general population, mail questionnaires have a good deal to recommend them. In the first place, they are usually cheaper than the interview method, particularly where a population is widely scattered. It is true, that in this case some form of cluster sampling can be used with interviewing in order to reduce cost, but this can be adopted only at a sacrifice of the precision of results. Another advantage of mail questionnaires is that they almost infallibly reach the respondent, whereas a personal interviewer may frequently find no one at home. Furthermore, there are certain types of question which, although having a simple answer, cannot be answered without a certain amount of investigation on the part of the respondent. For example, if the unit of enquiry is the family and information is needed on travelling expenses to and from work, such information can be obtained only by seeing each working member of the family who may not be available all at once.

On the other hand, mail questionnaires have certain disadvantages, among which are the following:

(1) The questions must be sufficiently simple to be understood with the help of only a few printed instructions. This could limit the scope of the enquiry.

(2) There is usually no possibility of checking the answers, for instance by observation.

(3) They permit discussion between members of a group or family about answers to the questions and so are inappropriate where the unassisted answer of a single person is required.

(4) Questions are not answered independently of each other, since the respondent can see them all at once.

(5) The right person may not complete the questionnaires.

(6) There is no possibility of obtaining background material by observation as there is in a personal interview.

In addition to the foregoing and, perhaps, most important of all, is the high non-response rate to which this type of enquiry is supposed to be liable. Investigations on methods of obtaining data have shown that this disadvantage has been exaggerated. In particular, various methods of increasing the response rate have been tried, some of which have proved very successful. There are certain obvious precautions which should be taken, such as enclosing a pre-paid envelope for a reply and a clear statement of the objectives of the survey with each questionnaire. But in addition to these, many other devices have been found to increase response rate significantly. Among these are:

(a) Follow-up enquiries sent after a suitable time-interval to those who have not responded;

(b) Despatch of questionnaires by an authoritative body, e.g. a Government Department;

(c) Offers of an incentive such as free samples for completed questionnaires, though this, of course, increases the cost of the enquiry;

(d) Inclusion of a small sum of money with each questionnaire;

(e) Attention to small details such as the use of a stamped envelope instead of a business-reply envelope.

A low response rate may render a postal survey as expensive as one by personal interview. But the main drawback with non-response is that it may produce a biased sample, thus vitiating its inferential value. Checks on bias can be built into questionnaires, e.g. by asking subsidiary questions on educational background, but even though these show a random distribution the check does not prove absence of bias for other reasons. The reasons why people do not respond, e.g. because they feel they are unable to answer questions "adequately", may form an important part of the information which the survey is seeking and without which the enquiry will be incomplete.

6. Interviews

By far the most important means of collecting data in a statistical survey is the personal interview. Even here, there is a "non-response" problem which is quite independent of whether an interviewer is able to contact respondents and which arises simply from a refusal on the part of the respondent to cooperate. Tests have shown that certain classes of interviewer, e.g. university students, are particularly liable to meet with non-response whilst carefully chosen interviewers working for professional research organisations do much better. It has not, however, been clearly established that training of interviewers makes any significant difference in their ability to secure cooperation, though they do, in fact, usually undergo some period of training in interviewing techniques, *per se*. This training is distinct, of course, from the briefing as to how questions in the questionnaire are to be asked and the answers recorded, which is to some extent a routine matter.

There are obvious reasons why a formal interview is preferable, other things being equal and depending on the subject matter, to an informal one. In the formal interview, the form and wording of questions, including the order in which they are asked, is all worked out beforehand, and such an interview clearly demands less skill to conduct than an informal one in which the nature of the questions and direction taken by the interview is in the control and at the discrimination of the interviewer. In addition, the information obtained by a formal interview is much easier to process for statistical purposes than that obtained by an informal one. Interviewer bias is also diminished by the formal method, since the interviewer is bound to adhere to the exact form of the questionnaire.

In the formal interview there are two types of question asked:

(a) the closed question,
(b) the open question.

In the closed type question, the alternative answers are clearly and exhaustively specified and the respondent simply chooses the one appropriate to him. To each answer corresponds a code symbol, and the response can be immediately coded by the interviewer at the time it is given. Example:

	Answer:	
"For what purpose do you mainly use your car?"	Travelling to and from work	1
	Taking children to and from school	2
	Shopping	3
	Holidays and other pleasure trips	4
	Social Work	5

In the open type question, the respondent answers in his own words, the number of alternatives in this case being unrestricted. Example: "What are your principal hobbies?" Pre-coding of the answers to open questions is more difficult than for the closed type, though it is sometimes done, in which case the interviewer can sometimes code the answers himself. But generally the coding has to be done in the survey office. Clearly, the closed question presents less difficulty in respect of the accuracy of the answers obtained, since it involves less constructive thought on the part of the respondent and his answers are less likely to be influenced by the attitude of the interviewer because less prompting is needed, so that the risk of interviewer bias is less.

In addition to asking the questions in the questionnaire, an interviewer can enhance the value of the data thus obtained by making his own observations of the respondent (educational or social standing, economic group, and other factors not specifically mentioned in the questionnaire), which he can record on the questionnaire itself at the time of or following the interview. Such additional information usually enables answers to be more effectively evaluated and also provides a check on bias in the answers of the respondents. It may also help to show whether there is any sampling bias resulting in a misleading sample.

Since not everyone is a good interviewer, this being often quite independent of intelligence and educational level, and since the work is often tedious if too many interviews are carried out in a limited time, it is necessary to have some check on the efficiency of interviewers. This is independent of any check which may happen to be made on the accuracy of responses, which will mainly depend on the efficiency of the questionnaire design; and which will, to some extent have been dealt with in the pilot survey. The efficiency of the interviewer will be measured by the number of adequately completed questionnaires he obtains and some check, such as a follow-up postal enquiry to a sample of respondents, is often made on the interviewer's integrity in the reported number of returns he makes.

The numerous qualities that an interviewer should possess will not be enumerated here. They may be summarised by one word— discipline. It is essential that the interviewer follows the survey instructions, and asks the questions exactly as they are given on the questionnaire. In this respect the interviewer's basic training will have prepared her for this, and communal briefings of fieldworkers by the survey executive are held for the more complicated surveys. Those interviewers who are inexperienced are accompanied by their supervisor and random fieldchecks on interviewer's work are carried out regularly by the area supervisors. Some of the checking is done by personally contacting the respondent to ascertain whether the interview has been carried out correctly with the right respondent. The duration of the interview may range from a short questionnaire taking only a few minutes to one lasting up to two hours. The most popular duration time is about thirty minutes.

The questionnaire is likely to be structured, with the questions in a set order, to be asked exactly as they are written. Not all questions are required to be answered by all respondents and interviewers will have to follow the filtering instructions. At certain points during the interview the respondent will be handed "showcards". These might consist of lists of brands in a product field, where prompted recall of brands is required. There is no compulsion for respondents to give an interview, but the proportion of refusals is often very low. What helps in this respect is that interviewers always stress to the respondent that his responses will be kept confidential and only used in the compilation of grouped statistics.

7. Design of Questionnaires

Questionnaire design is much influenced by whether the questionnaire is to be completed by the respondent himself (as in postal enquiries) or by the interviewer. There are, however, a few general rules to be observed in framing questions.

The questions should be:

(1) Relatively few in number.
(2) Such that they require (as far as possible) a numerical answer, or yes or no.
(3) Simple enough to be readily understood.

(4) Such as will be answered without bias.
(5) Not unnecessarily inquisitorial or personal.
(6) As far as possible corroboratory.
(7) Such as directly and unmistakably cover the point about which information is required.

Where the interviewer records the answers, the questionnaire is, in fact, a *recording schedule* as well. In this case, it will be designed with respect both to the convenience of the interviewer and also to the convenience of the office staff processing the data. Whilst observing the above rules for framing questions, the value of a questionnaire used by an interviewer can be enhanced by including questions which need not be answered by all respondents or which are asked or not according to what responses have been given to other questions. These are complications which need not concern the respondent and so the response rate will be unaffected by their inclusion. All that is necessary is that there should be clear filtering instructions to guide the interviewer as to the way in which the questions are to be asked.

8. Response Errors

It may be assumed that every question put to a respondent has a true answer. The actual answer may differ from this either through the activity of the interviewer (inaccurate recording of answers, or interviewer bias) or through that of the respondent or through an interaction between the two. In order to be able to assess the precision of the results, it is necessary to measure both the bias of the answers (called the *response bias*, i.e. the mean difference between true and actual answers) and the *response variance* (i.e. the mean of the individual response variance over several interviews using the same questions for all the individuals in the group surveyed). It may well happen that individual response bias may cancel out for the group as a whole so that the overall response bias is zero. But the precision of results is still affected by response variance, which will not be zero unless all answers are perfectly accurate.

Among the factors influencing response errors are:

(1) The personal characteristics of the interviewer: age, sex, education, etc.
(2) Opinions of interviewers. Tests have shown that these produce bias to a much smaller extent than might be expected.
(3) Interviewer expectations. These operate chiefly by the way in which interviewers code doubtful or marginal answers. For example, if an answer is difficult to code considered by itself,

it may be coded in a way which appears consistent with answers previously given.

(4) Respondent errors, due to lack of knowledge, faulty memory, unwillingness to give the right answer, etc.

Methods for detecting response errors in a survey may have a dual purpose:

(a) to check the accuracy of responses in that particular survey so as to form some estimate of the precision of results; and

(b) to locate the possible sources of response error for guidance in future surveys.

The methods of detecting individual response errors (termed also *gross errors*) are:

(1) Record checks: comparison of completed questions with personal documents, birth certificates, etc.;

(2) Consistency checks: asking the same question of more than one person each of whom should give the same answer to it, or asking the same person the same question more than once but in different forms. In either case, if the answers are consistent, there is some ground for believing they are correct, though there still remains a doubt. If they are inconsistent there remains the problem of discovering which, if any, are correct.

(3) Re-interviewing: the interviews should be independent if they are to serve as a check, e.g. there must be no opportunity for a respondent to give the same (incorrect) answer on two occasions merely for the sake of consistency. Re-interviewing by interviewers of similar quality indicates response variance, whilst if an interviewer of better quality is used, an indication of bias will be obtained. Such checks are known as quality checks or Post-Enumerative checks and are employed, for example, as a check in the U.K. Census of Population—on a sampling basis, of course.

Errors revealed by these means are particularly valuable as a general indication as to why errors occur and so as an indication of how they can be avoided. Checks on overall bias (sometimes called *net errors*) are often simpler to make but give very little information about the sources of error and are only valid for the whole of some particular samples.

9. Analysis of Data

In the previous sections, survey planning has been considered with reference to two objectives:

(a) to obtain accurate data, or at least data the accuracy of which can be measured, and

(b) to obtain this data in a form suitable for processing, analysis and interpretation.

In opinion and market research surveys the simplest analysis that may be done is simply to sort the questionnaires into piles according to their responses to one or more questions, and count the number in each pile. This may be thought of as not being a very sophisticated analysis technique in this computer age, but it is very valuable when key results of a survey are required very quickly. It may be the only analysis technique used for smaller-scale surveys, with only a few questions and a limited number of respondents. Most survey questionnaires, however, will be converted into a faster access medium. The first conversion of the data is almost always into punched cards. This enables the data to be analysed on Hollerith-type machines such as counter-sorters and provides input for computer analysis. For some computers the punched cards are converted into magnetic tape records, though the punched card stage may be by-passed by using magnetic tape encoders to convert the data straight from questionnaires to tape. Another development that is being increasingly used is to employ "mark-sensing". With this technique, the interviewer makes marks in boxes on the questionnaire and a special machine "reads" the questionnaire and takes notice of which boxes are marked. The boxes represent pre-coded answers to questions and one drawback is that open-ended questions are more difficult to handle. Both punched cards and tapes may be produced by the sensing machine much faster than by conventional punching or encoding. The survey questionnaire has to be specially designed and printed accurately to fit the sensing machine. With every survey having its own special questionnaire, it is not surprising that the mark-sensing technique has, in the past, only proved profitable for continuous surveys which use the same questionnaire each time. However, the technical problems are now being overcome and in future the technique could become a standard one in survey analysis.

The statistical techniques used for the analysis of data have been discussed elsewhere. Particularly in the investigation of causal relationships, the considerations outlined in section 3 will have to be borne in mind when choosing the appropriate techniques. If there are a number of factors likely to be important causally, then some kind of factorial analysis is indicated. In any event, the aim will be to use the data as economically as possible with a view to obtaining as many valid conclusions as possible bearing on the purpose of the survey, not only for the data as a whole, but also possibly for subsets of data. In this respect, it is necessary that an estimate not only of aggregate response error and deviation should have been made, but also of gross error, in order to evaluate the precision of the results in the subsets. Aggregate error, for example, might be a vanishing quantity, whilst error in the subsets, though compensating in the aggregate, is not vanishing. It is probably the analysis of subsets which has the greatest value in the survey, for whilst there is necessarily a good deal of confounding of causes in the aggregate result, so that the exact nature of the causal relationship is impossible to determine from the aggregate alone, the deeper analysis by subsets which reduces the number of causal factors operating in each case will throw much explanatory light on the total causal relationship under study.

EXERCISES 10

1. Statistical data may be obtained by census or sample enquiry. Describe both methods and explain why sample enquiry is more frequently used than census enquiry.

2. In what way is a questionnaire design influenced by the method of conducting a survey? Consider both postal and interviewer techniques.

3. Compare and contrast the types of error which may affect the results obtained in sample surveys by: (a) interviewing, and (b) postal questionnaires.

4. Describe the various methods available for the collection of statistical information, mentioning any advantages or disadvantages of such methods.

5. Explain what is meant by (a) response error, and (b) interviewer bias. Describe some of the methods by which each can be counteracted.

6. One of the first considerations in any sample survey is the decision on the size of the sample. Explain the general factors governing this decision.

7. What rules should be observed in compiling questionnaires to ensure successful investigation. Compile a questionnaire for determining the travel habits of a firm's employees.

8. What are the primary functions of a statistical department in a large industrial organisation?

9. The owners of a local newspaper, *The Evening Star,* wish to obtain information on any improvements that could be made to increase the paper's circulation. They decide to publish a questionnaire in an edition of the paper, asking the following questions:

> What is your name?
> Do you like *The Evening Star*?
> What features of *The Evening Star* do you read first?
> Do you read a daily newspaper?
> Do you like sport?
> What is your income group?

Criticise the method of collecting the information and, where necessary, replace questions by more suitable ones.

10. What are the general objectives of a statistical experiment? What features of experimental design contribute to the attainment of these objectives? Describe some statistical experiment with which you are familiar, showing how it illustrates your answers to the first two parts of this question.

CHAPTER 11

Business Applications of Calculus

1. Coordinate Systems

In discussing the graphical presentation of statistical data, scatter diagrams and regression equations, some knowledge has been assumed of the method of representing a number by a point referred to two axes intersecting at right angles. Since it is necessary, in the work which follows, to have clear ideas about this method of representing numbers, an independent account of it is given here. The graphical representation now to be considered is a two-dimensional one for which only two axes are required. Two dimensions only are needed because the discussion is limited to cases in which the relationship between two variables is investigated. Even in this case, there is a choice between types of coordinate systems; the type used in this book is that in which two axes intersect at right angles. But data can also be recorded in a graph the axes of which intersect at some other angle. In certain parts of Mathematics, there are advantages in this procedure, but for present purposes the rectangular system is the only one which need be considered.

A pair of rectangular coordinate axes, such as those shown in Fig. 43, partition the plane into four quadrants. Though many variables in practice take only positive values, a complete account of the graphical representation of the relationship between two variables requires a consideration of all four quadrants. The point of intersection of the two axes (O in the diagram) is the *origin* of the graph from which the values of the two variables x and y are measured along the respective axes representing them. Values of x to the right of O along the horizontal axis are positive, whilst those to the left of O are negative. Similarly, along the vertical axis, values of y above O are positive, whilst those below O are negative. Any point on the graph is uniquely specified by two numbers called the *coordinates* of the point which, by convention, are always written so that the x coordinate is first and the y coordinate second. Numbers of this kind are known as *ordered pairs*. Thus the point P in the diagram is uniquely specified by the ordered pair of numbers (2, 3); its position being located by measuring 2 units along the Ox axis and 3 units parallel to the Oy axis above O. In a similar way, the point R whose coordinates are $(-3, -3)$ is found by measuring 3 units to the left of O along Ox and 3 units parallel to Oy below O.

2nd Quadrant   **1st Quadrant**

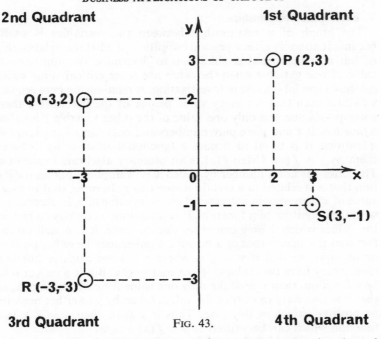

3rd Quadrant   Fig. 43.   **4th Quadrant**

In using graphs of this kind, the further convention is adopted that an *increase* in the value of either of the variables is counted as positive, whilst a *decrease* in the values of either is counted as negative. For example, an increase in the value of x from $x = 2$ to $x = 3$ is a change of $+1$ unit; whilst a decrease in this value from $x = 3$ to $x = 2$ is a change of -1 unit. Similarly, an increase in the value of y from $y = -1$ to $y = 3$ is a change in the value of y by $+4$ units; whilst a decrease from $y = 3$ to $y = -1$ is a change of -4 units. This convention might be summarised by saying that an increase is a positive change, whilst a decrease is a negative increase and so is a negative change.

It will be observed that the graphs here considered are natural scale graphs, for a change in the value of either x or y by ± 1 unit (say) is represented anywhere on the appropriate axis by the same distance. This does not mean, of course, that the scales along the two axes are necessarily the same. For example 1 unit might be represented along Ox by a distance of 1 cm and along Oy by a distance of 3 cm, the important point being that these distances represent 1 unit anywhere along the respective axes provided that the graph is a natural scale graph.

2. Functional Relationships

The graph of a relationship between two variables is useful because it not only gives a general indication of what this relationship is, but also because it enables one to determine the approximate value of one variable when the other has some critical value which one has a special interest in investigating. A relationship between two variables such that for every value of one of the variables x there corresponds one and only one value of the other variable y is called a *function*. If x and y are pure numbers and not units of any tangible quantities, it is usual to denote a functional relationship between them by $y = f(x)$. Often $f(x)$ is an ordinary algebraic expression. The letter f is not a number by which x is multiplied, but an indication that x is related in a certain manner to y. In order that to every value of x there should correspond only one value of y, in accordance with the definition of a function, it is sometimes necessary to restrict the values which x or y can take. For example, it is a well-known fact that the square root of a positive number may be either positive or negative, so that if $y = \sqrt{x}$, where x is some positive number, then y may have two values: $+\sqrt{x}$ and $-\sqrt{x}$. But if $y = \sqrt{x}$ is to be a function, then y can take only one value for each value of x, so that it is necessary to restrict the values taken by y to either negative or positive values in this case. Thus if $y \geqslant 0$, then $y = \sqrt{x}$ is a function which can be written as $y = f(x) = \sqrt{x}$.

Functions in which the variables are pure numbers have a rather marginal importance in real life, where one is interested in the relationship between tangible quantities such as output, cost and sales. Fortunately, the functions of pure mathematics provide a model for relationships of this practical kind. Two important examples of practical relationships are the cost function, denoted by $y = C(x)$ and the sales function, denoted by $y = S(x)$. The cost function shows the total cost of producing output x, where x is measured in units of output and $C(x)$ is measured in money units. In like manner, the sales function shows the total receipts obtained from the sale of x units of output, these total receipts being denoted by $S(x)$ and also measured in money units. It is useful for illustrative purposes to regard these two functions as *mappings* of output onto costs or receipts. Thus there are two ways in which these relationships can be stated:

$$\text{Either} \quad C : x \longrightarrow y \quad \text{Or} \quad y = C(x)$$
$$S : x \longrightarrow y \quad \quad y = S(x)$$

Both ways are equivalent, for they show that output x is mapped by the cost function C onto cost y or by the sales function S onto receipts y. The fact that y is used here for both costs and receipts should cause no confusion provided it is remembered that y in both cases is a variable quantity which may have divergent values under the mappings C or S for the same value of x, but which might also be equal for one or more values of x.

The simplest kind of cost or sales functions are those whose values increase in proportion to output produced or sold. These are linear functions which can be represented by algebraic expressions similar to that used for a linear regression equation (see Chapter 7). Considering first the cost function, suppose that the amount of fixed cost (buildings, plant, machinery, etc.) is £a and that each unit of output incurs an additional variable cost £b. Then the cost of producing x

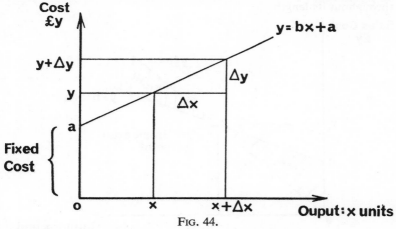

FIG. 44.

units of output is $C(x) = bx + a$. The graph of this function (Fig. 44) is a straight line which intersects the verticle axis at the point $(0, a)$ which is a units from O and whose direction in relation to the axes depends on the value of b. The graph enables one to determine the cost £y of producing x units of output. An increase in output from x to $x + \Delta x$ increases total cost from £y to £$(y + \Delta y)$. The symbol Δ (Greek capital delta) is here used to denote an increment in the output x or the cost y. Now the cost of producing output $x + \Delta x$ is

$$y + \Delta y = C(x + \Delta x) = b(x + \Delta x) + a$$
$$= bx + a + b\,\Delta x$$

Hence
$$\Delta y = bx + a + b\,\Delta x - y$$
$$= bx + a + b\,\Delta x - (bx + a)$$
$$= b\,\Delta x$$

It follows that
$$b = \Delta y / \Delta x.$$

The graph shows that the ratio $\Delta y/\Delta x$ measures the *gradient* of the line whose equation is $y = bx + a$, and so the gradient is also equal to the coefficient b in this equation. Since Δx and Δy represent an increase in x and y respectively, these increments are both positive (see section 1) so that the ratio $\Delta y/\Delta x$ is also positive. The same result is attained by considering that a decrease in x is accompanied by a decrease in y also so that, in this case, Δx and Δy are both negative whilst the ratio $-\Delta y/-\Delta x$ is positive as before. Both ratios are, in fact, equal to b which measures the rate at which y changes as x changes. A distinguishing feature of a linear function is that this rate of change is the same whatever the value of x, corresponding to the fact that the gradient of a straight line is constant throughout its length.

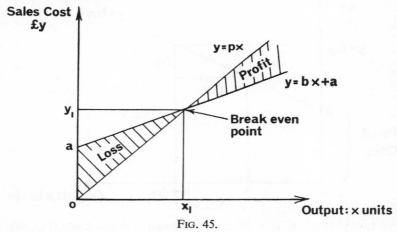

FIG. 45.

The properties of a linear sales function are similar to those of the cost function just described. If there is only one price £p per unit at which every unit of output can be sold, then the receipts from the sale of x units are $S(x) = px$. The graph of this function passes through the origin since, as is obvious, the receipts from selling none of the output are zero.

Fig. 45 shows the graphs of both cost and sales functions. The gradient of the sales line is p and, since this is greater than b (the gradient of the cost line), the two lines intersect at the point (x_1, y_1). When output is less than x_1, costs exceed revenue $(C(x) > S(x))$ so that at these levels of output, the producer incurs a loss, even though he sells the whole of his output. On the other hand, for outputs greater than x_1, sales exceed costs $(S(x) > C(x))$, so that the producer realises a profit provided that he sells the whole of his output. At the point of intersection of the two graphs, $C(x) = S(x)$, so that, in this case, there is neither profit nor loss and the producer breaks even.

It is convenient to introduce a third function, the profit function $y = R(x)$, which shows net profit from the sale of x units of output. $R(x)$ can clearly be defined in terms of cost and sales functions, for

$$R(x) = S(x) - C(x)$$
$$= px - (bx + a)$$
$$= (p - b)x - a.$$

If the producer can break even, then there is some positive output x for which $R(x) = 0$, i.e., $(p - b)x - a = 0$. The break even value of x is thus

$$x = a/(p - b).$$

Now a, the fixed cost, is positive; so that if x is positive it follows that p is greater than b ($p > b$) or, in other words, that the price per unit of the product is greater than the variable cost per unit. A numerical example should clarify this point.

Let Fixed cost $a =$ £5000
    variable cost $b =$ £50 per unit
    selling price $p =$ £70 per unit.
Then $C(x) = 50x + 5000$
              $S(x) = 70x$
              $R(x) = S(x) - C(x) = 20x - 5000.$

The graph of the function $R(x) = 20x - 5000$ is shown in Fig. 46. The graph intersects the Ox axis at $x = 250$. for which output, profit is zero. Hence this is the break even point. When output is 400 units then, provided this output is sold, a positive profit of £3000 is realised; whilst if only 100 units are produced, there is a loss of £3000. Fig. 47 illustrates the situation when the selling price is only £30, which is less than the variable cost b. In this case, the profit function $R(x) = -20x - 5000$ so that there is no positive output for which $R(x) = 0$. The break even point here occurs when there is a negative output of -250 units which is, of course, an entirely fictitious possibility, so that the producer can only incur a loss whatever his output. The graph of $y = -20x - 5000$ slopes downwards from left to right, so that as x increases, y decreases indicating that the rate of change of y on x is negative. This is also indicated by the negative sign of the coefficient of x in this function (-20) which shows that the line has a negative gradient.

The value of a function $f(x)$ at some value x_1 of the variable x is

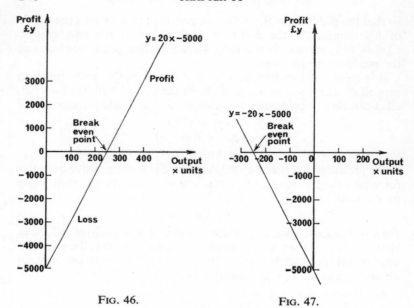

FIG. 46.   FIG. 47.

often denoted by $f(x_1)$. Thus, in the above illustration, when $x = 250$ the values of the three functions C, S and R are

$$C(250) = 50 \times 250 + 5000 = 17500$$
$$S(250) = 70 \times 250 = 17500$$
$$R(250) = 20 \times 250 - 5000 = 0.$$

3. Quadratic Functions

The linear cost and sales functions of the preceding section are mathematical models of actual functions. It is unlikely that the cost function will be exactly represented by a straight line, for expanding output may require not just a change in the normal variable factors of production such as labour and raw materials, but also capital expenditure on new equipment. Hence there will probably be some variation in costs away from a strictly linear relationship with output. It may still be true, however, that a linear trend line can be approximately fitted by the methods of Chapter 7 which will give a sufficiently accurate solution of the problem of determining the best output for practical purposes. A more serious objection to using a linear model for both cost and sales is that it leads to unrealistic results. The situation portrayed in Fig. 46 of section 2, for example, shows that there is no output which will yield a maximum profit, but that this

can be increased indefinitely by increasing output beyond the break
even point provided, of course, that the market will buy all that the
producer is prepared to produce at a fixed price. For the small
producer, this assumption may not be too unrealistic; but the large-
scale firm will be unable to sell unlimited quantities of its product
without lowering the selling price per unit. In this situation, the sales
function will not be linear. Instead, sales revenue will tend to increase
when sales increase at a low sales level and decrease as sales increase
when the sales level is high, this tendency continuing until so much is
offered for sale that it can all be disposed of only by lowering the
selling price to zero, when sales revenue will also be zero. A possible
mathematical model for a sales function of this type is

$$S(x) = bx - cx^2,$$

known as a quadratic function since the highest power to which x
occurs is the second. It should be noted that neither of the coefficients
a and b represent the price at which different levels of output can be
sold, for it is now being assumed that this price is variable, whereas
c and b are constant numbers. However, although price does not
explicitly occur in the quadratic sales function as it does in the linear
function, it is reflected by it. For practical purposes, the function can
be thought of as approximately representing data on sales which has
been obtained during a producer's previous experience.

A graphical representation of a quadratic function can be obtained
by calculating its value for different values of x. Thus suppose the
function to be graphed is $S(x) = 40x - 8x^2$, and consider the values
which $S(x)$ has when x takes whole number values from $x = 0$ to
$x = 5$. These are shown in the following table.

x	0	1	2	3	4	5
$40x$	0	40	80	120	160	200
$8x^2$	0	8	32	72	128	200
$S(x)$	0	32	48	48	32	0

The graph of the function is symmetrical about a vertical line
through $x = 2\cdot5$ and at this value of x, y has a maximum value and
is neither increasing nor decreasing as x increases or decreases (Fig.
48). The price at which any quantity x is sold is simply the revenue
obtained from selling that quantity divided by the quantity sold, i.e.,

$$\bar{S}(x) = (40x - 8x^2)/x = 40 - 8x.$$

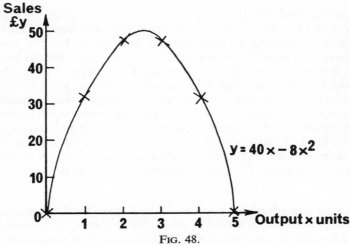

FIG. 48.

For example, when $x = 2$, selling price per unit is $40 - 8 \times 2 = £24$. It will be seen that $S(x)$ is just the average revenue per unit obtained from selling x units and is not constant but varies with the number of units sold.

Suppose now that the cost function is linear, as before, and has the value $C(x) = 3x + 20$. It follows that the profit realised from the sale of x units of product is

$$R(x) = S(x) - C(x)$$
$$= 40x - 8x^2 - (3x + 20)$$
$$= 37x - 8x^2 - 20.$$

The graph of this function is obtained in a similar way to that of $S(x)$.

x	0	1	2	3	4
$37x$	0	37	74	111	148
$8x^2$	0	8	32	72	128
20	20	20	20	20	20
$R(x)$	-20	9	22	19	0

In this case, there are two break even points corresponding to the two values of x at which the graph intersects the Ox axis, for at both these points $y = R(x) = 0$. Inspection of the graph (Fig. 49) shows

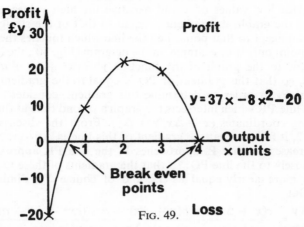

FIG. 49.

that these critical values are $x = 4$ and $x = 0.6$ (the exact value is
0.625); and the sale of output between these values yields a profit
which is maximum at $x = 2$ (approximately). Hence in existing
market and production conditions, this will be the producer's
optimum output. An important use of the differential calculus is
that it enables one to determine this value precisely.

4. Differential Calculus

It will be seen that the gradients of the two graphs in section 3 are
not constant as x changes, as is the case with a linear graph, but are

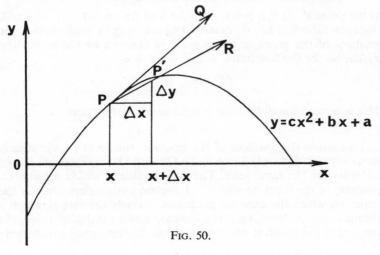

FIG. 50.

positive for low values of x and negative for high values. At any point on the graph, its gradient is equal to that of the straight line which is tangent to that point, i.e., the line which touches the graph at that point only. For example, in the diagram (Fig. 50), the line PQ is tangent to the graph of the function $y = cx^2 + bx + a$ at the point P, so that the gradient of PQ is equal to the gradient of the graph at P. In order to determine this gradient, consider another straight line PR which intersects the graph a second time at the point P' having coordinates $(x + \Delta x, y + \Delta y)$. From the discussion in section 2, it follows that the gradient of this line is $\Delta y / \Delta x$. Now as Δx decreases so that P' approaches P, the line PR approximates more closely to the line PQ; so that the gradients of these two lines become more nearly equal as Δx, and of course Δy, diminish in value. But

$$\frac{\Delta y}{\Delta x} = \frac{c(x + \Delta x)^2 + b(x + \Delta x) + a - (cx^2 + bx + a)}{\Delta x}$$

$$= \frac{2cx\,\Delta x + c(\Delta x)^2 + b\,\Delta x}{\Delta x}$$

$$= 2cx + c\,\Delta x + b.$$

As Δx decreases in value, the term $c\,\Delta x$ approaches zero so that the gradient of PR approaches the value $2cx + b$. This is clearly the limiting value of $\Delta y / \Delta x$ as Δx approaches zero and since PR coincides with PQ when this happens, it follows that $2cx + b$ is the gradient of PQ and hence the gradient of the graph of

$$y = cx^2 + bx + a$$

at the point P. At this point, both Δy and Δx are actually zero and, since the ratio $0/0$ has no determinate meaning in mathematics, the gradient of the graph at the point P is denoted by the expression dy/dx. So for the function $y = cx^2 + bx + a$,

$$\frac{dy}{dx} = 2cx + b.$$

This is termed the *differential coefficient* of the function

$$y = cx^2 + bx + a$$

and measures the gradient of the graph at the point (x, y). Strictly speaking this will only be so if the Ox and Oy axes are graduated according to the same scale. The actual value of dy/dx measures a property of the function which is, however, quite independent of the scales on which the axes are graduated, namely the rate at which y changes with x. Now when the function has a maximum value, the tangent to the graph is horizontal and so has zero gradient showing that at this point the rate at which y changes with x is zero, so that $dy/dx = 0$ at the value of x for which y is maximum. For example, when $y = 37x - 8x^2 - 20$,

$$\frac{dy}{dx} = 37 - 16x.$$

The maximum value of y thus occurs when $dy/dx = 0$ or $37 - 16x = 0$. The corresponding value of x is easily found, by solving this equation, to be $x = 37/16$ so that the maximum value of y is

$$y_{\max} = 37(37/16) - 8(37/16)^2 - 20$$
$$= 22 \text{ (approximately).}$$

This result can be verified by inspecting the graph of this function at the end of the preceding section.

Since it is also useful to be able to find the differential coefficients of functions other than quadratic, a few others will now be given. Firstly, it is clear that the linear function $y = bx + a$ has the differential coefficient $dy/dx = b$, since b measures the rate at which y changes with x in this case. It can be proved that any function of the form $y = kx^n$, where k is a constant, has differential coefficient nkx^{n-1}. This is true even when n is negative. For example, if $y = k/x = kx^{-1}$, then $dy/dx = -1 \times kx^{(-1-1)} = -kx^{-2} = -k/x^2$.

The graph of the function $y = k$ is a straight line parallel to the Ox axis, so that a change in x produces no change in the value of y and $dy/dx = 0$ in this case. This can also be deduced from the general formula for a differential coefficient by writing the function as $y = kx^0$ so that $dy/dx = 0 \times kx^{0-1} = 0$. A table of useful differential coefficients is given below.

Function y	Differential Coefficient dy/dx
kx^4	$4kx^3$
kx^3	$3kx^2$
kx^2	$2kx$
kx	k
k	0
kx^{-1}	$-kx^{-2}$
kx^{-2}	$-2kx^{-3}$

It is usual to denote the differential coefficient of any function $f(x)$ by $f'(x)$. Thus the differential coefficients of the cost and sales functions are denoted respectively by $C'(x)$ and $S'(x)$. A useful rule when applying the above table is that the differential coefficient of the sum or difference of two functions is the sum or difference of their separate differential coefficients. For example,

if $$R(x) = S(x) - C(x)$$
then $$R'(x) = S'(x) - C'(x).$$

This can be verified for the cost and sales functions of section 3. Here

$$R(x) = (40x - 8x^2) - (3x + 20)$$
so $$R'(x) = (40 - 16x) - (3)$$
$$= 37 - 16x.$$

Obtaining the differential coefficient of $R(x)$ directly,

$$R(x) = 37x - 8x^2 - 20$$
so $$R'(x) = 37 - 16x \text{ (as before)}.$$

The general form of a quadratic function is $y = cx^2 + bx + a$, the numerical coefficients c, b and a being either negative or positive. When the coefficient of x^2, namely c, is negative, this function always has a maximum value. This is the situation illustrated in the diagram at the beginning of this section. When c is positive, on the other hand, the function always has a minimum value. The value of x for which this is so is found by differentiating the function and setting the resulting differential coefficient equal to zero, the procedure being exactly the same as when finding a maximum value in the case when c is negative. Some functions have both minimum and maximum values, in which case it is necessary to differentiate the differential coefficient in order to distinguish the maximum from the minimum values. Moreover, certain functions such as $y = x^3$ have values for which $dy/dx = 0$ which are not minimum or maximum values but at which the gradient of the curve decreases to zero and then increases again without changing sign. It is often intuitively obvious from the context of a problem whether a function has a maximum or minimum value and which of these two possibilities obtains. In certain cases, however, it is useful to have a method of distinguishing the various possibilities, and this is considered in more detail in section 8.

There are some functions which either have no differential coefficients at all or none at certain values of x. For example, the function $f(x) = 1$ when x is an even integer, $f(x) = -1$ when x is an odd integer, x taking only integral values, consists of a series of isolated points so that it is discontinuous. In this case, $f(x)$ jumps from one value to another so that it is meaningless to speak of the rate at which this change takes place. Moreover, it is not sufficient that a function is continuous for it to have a differential coefficient at all points. Thus $y = |x|$, where $|x|$ is the absolute or positive value of x, has a graph which is represented by the equations $y = x$ when x is positive and $y = -x$ when x is negative. When $x = 0$, $y = 0$, so that the graph of the function is continuous for all values of x but changes direction suddenly at $x = 0$, so that there is no definite rate of change at this point and therefore no differential coefficient. The functions $y = k/x$ and $y = k/x^2$ shown in the foregoing table are discontinuous at $x = 0$ and so the differential coefficient does not exist at this point, though it does exist at all others.

5. Unit Cost and Sales Functions

The functions $C(x)$ and $S(x)$ show the total cost or sales revenue from output x. It has been already seen that the price at which any output x can be sold is given by $\bar{S}(x) = S(x)/x$. This is termed a unit sales function and is the familiar demand function of economists. In a similar way, the average cost per unit of x units of output is given by $\bar{C}(x) = C(x)/x$. This is the unit cost function, termed also by economists the average cost function. To illustrate the relationship between these two functions, consider the cost and sales functions of section 3:

$$C(x) = 3x + 20$$
$$S(x) = 40x - 8x^2.$$

The corresponding unit cost and sales functions are:

$$\bar{C}(x) = (3x + 20)/x = 3 + \frac{20}{x}$$

$$\bar{S}(x) = (40x - 8x^2)/x = 40 - 8x.$$

The graphs of these two functions are shown in Fig. 51.

The break even points are at the intersections of the unit cost and sales graphs, namely $x = 4$ and $x = 0.6$ (approx.), for at these points $\bar{S}(x) = \bar{C}(x)$ so that net profit for these outputs is zero. The graphs of the differential coefficients of the cost and sales functions are also shown in this diagram. Now the profit function

$$R(x) = S(x) - C(x)$$

is maximum when

$$R'(x) = S'(x) - C'(x) = 0,$$

i.e. when $S'(x) = C'(x)$,

so that output is optimum at the value of x for which the graphs of these two functions intersect, namely at $x_{opt} = 2.3$ (approx.). The total variable cost of producing this output is equal to the area $x_{opt} \times C'(x_{opt})$, i.e., to the shaded portion of the graph. The function

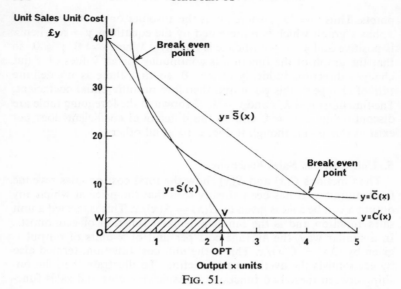

FIG. 51.

$y = C'(x)$ is sometimes known as the marginal cost function and shows the additional cost incurred by producing one additional unit of output at each level of output. Since the cost function in this case is linear, marginal cost is the same at all levels of output. The function $y = S'(x)$ is the marginal revenue function, showing at each level of sales the addition made to total sales revenue when the quantity offered for sale is increased by one unit. Since it is necessary to lower price in order to sell a larger quantity, marginal revenue is not constant but decreases as the amount offered for sale increases.

The additional revenue obtained by increasing the quantity offered for sale from x to $x + \Delta x$ is

$$S(x + \Delta x) - S(x) = \frac{S(x + \Delta x) - S(x)}{\Delta x} \times \Delta x$$

$$= \frac{dy}{dx} \times dx \text{ (when } \Delta x \text{ approaches zero)}$$

$$= S'(x)\, dx.$$

The total revenue obtained from the sale of n units is the sum of the additions to revenue due to each small increment in x which is usually denoted by

$$\int_0^n S'(x)\, dx.$$

This is known as the definite integral of the function $S'(x)$ between the limits $x = 0$ and $x = n$ and since the total revenue from the sale of n units is $S(n)$, it follows that

$$\int_0^n S'(x)\,dx = S(n).$$

Now $S'(x)\,dx$ is the area of a very narrow rectangle under the graph of $y = S'(x)$; so the sum of all such areas between $x = 0$ and $x = n$ is the total area between the graph and the Ox axis over this range of values of x. Hence the difference between total revenue and total variable cost when x is optimum is equal to the area of the triangle UVW in the diagram. An increase or decrease of x above or below x_{opt} clearly reduces this difference and so results in a lower net profit. To obtain the actual net profit, the amount of fixed cost must, of course, be deducted from the difference between total revenue and variable cost represented by the area UVW; but since, by definition, fixed cost is constant, this modification will not affect the value of x_{opt}.

The process of finding the definite integral $\int_0^n f'(x)\,dx$ of a function $f'(x)$ is known as *integration*, which is the inverse process of differentiation discussed in section 4. It follows that

$$\int_0^n f'(x)\,dx = f(n) - f(0)$$

$$= f(n) \text{ (in the special case when } f(0) = 0).$$

The limits of integration $x = 0$ to $x = n$ have been chosen here because $x = 0$ suits the particular problem which has been discussed. But any limits might have been chosen, for instance $x = \alpha$ to $x = \beta$, in which case, the value of the definite integral is

$$\int_\alpha^\beta f'(x)\,dx = f(\beta) - f(\alpha).$$

Examples

$$\int_2^3 x\,dx = \left[\frac{x^2}{2}\right]_2^3 = \frac{9}{2} - \frac{4}{2} = 2 \cdot 5.$$

$$\int_1^6 (x^2 + x)\,dx = \left[\frac{x^3}{3} + \frac{x^2}{2}\right]_1^6 = \frac{216}{3} + \frac{36}{2} - \left(\frac{1}{3} + \frac{1}{2}\right)$$

$$= 89\tfrac{1}{6}.$$

$$\int_{-1}^4 2\,dx = \left[2x\right]_{-1}^4 = 8 - (-2) = 10.$$

It will be seen that the integral of a function $y = x^n$ has the form

$$\frac{x^{n+1}}{n+1}$$

because the differential coefficient of this integral function is

$$(n+1)\frac{x^{n+1-1}}{n+1} = x^n = y.$$

This illustrates what is meant by saying that integration and differentiation are inverse processes.

6. Applications to Statistics

Differential calculus can be usefully applied to one or two problems in Statistics which have been raised in previous chapters. For example it was stated in Chapter 4, section 6 that the sum of the squared deviations of a set of numbers from their mean is less than the sum of the squared deviations of these numbers from any number apart from the mean. Let

$$y = \Sigma (x - A)^2$$

be the sum of the squared deviations of a set of numbers x from some arbitrarily chosen number A. It is easily verified, by actually expanding the expression $(x - A)^2$ and differentiating with respect to A that

$$\frac{dy}{dA} = -2(x - A).$$

Hence if $y = \Sigma (x - A)^2$, then

$$\frac{dy}{dA} = \Sigma -2(x - A) = -2 \Sigma (x - A).$$

Since the coefficient of A^2 is positive in the expansion of $(x - A)^2$, it follows that y (as a function of A) has a minimum value for some value of A. From the foregoing discussion, this value of A is that for which

$$\frac{dy}{dA} = 0 \text{ or } -2 \Sigma (x - A) = 0.$$

This equation is satisfied when $\Sigma x - \Sigma A = 0$, or $\Sigma x = nA$. Hence y is minimum when $A = \Sigma x/n = \bar{x}$, i.e. when A is equal to the mean of the set of numbers x.

The coefficients b and a in the linear regression equation $\hat{Y} = bX + a$ (see Chapter 7, section 3) are such that the sum of the squared deviations of the observed values of y about the regression line, namely $\Sigma\,(y - \overline{bx + a})^2$ is minimum. The values of b and a for which this is so are found by differentiating the function

$$S = \Sigma\,(y - \overline{bx + a})^2$$

first with respect to b and then with respect to a and setting the resulting differential coefficients equal to zero. Thus

$$\frac{dS}{db} = -2\,\Sigma\,(y - \overline{bx + a})x$$

$$\frac{dS}{da} = -2\,\Sigma\,(y - \overline{bx + a}).$$

When $\quad\quad \dfrac{dS}{db} = 0, \quad \Sigma\,xy - b\,\Sigma\,x^2 - a\,\Sigma\,x = 0$

$$\frac{dS}{da} = 0, \quad \Sigma\,y - b\,\Sigma\,x - na = 0.$$

These equations should be compared with those on page 155 for estimating b and a in the regression equations.

7. The Exponential Function

The functions so far considered in this chapter are known as algebraic functions in which y is a function of x, x^2, and so on. There is a class of functions which are important in both Statistics and Business in which the independent variable x occurs as the index or exponent of a number, an example being the function $y = 2^x$. Now any number can be expressed as the power of some other number by choosing an appropriate index. For example $8 = 2^3$, $27 = 9^{1.5}$. For mathematical purposes, it is convenient to express all exponential functions in terms of a number e whose value is given by the series

$$e = 1 + \frac{1}{1!} + \frac{1}{2!} + \frac{1}{3!} + \ldots + \frac{1}{n!} + \ldots$$

$$= 1 + 1 + 0.5 + 0.1667 + 0.0417 + 0.0083 + 0.0014 + \ldots$$

$$= 2.718 \text{ (correct to 4 significant figures).}$$

The reason why this number is chosen is that the differential coefficient of the function $y = e^x$ is equal to e^x. For e^x can be expressed in terms of the series

$$y = e^x = 1 + \frac{x}{1!} + \frac{x^2}{2!} + \frac{x^3}{3!} + \ldots + \frac{x^n}{n!} + \ldots$$

It follows that $\dfrac{dy}{dx} = 0 + 1 + \dfrac{2x}{2!} + \dfrac{3x^2}{3!} + \ldots + \dfrac{nx^{n-1}}{n!} + \ldots$

$$= 1 + \frac{x}{1!} + \frac{x^2}{2!} + \ldots + \frac{x^{n-1}}{(n-1)!} + \ldots$$

$$= e^x.$$

Since all exponential functions can be expressed in terms of e^x, this is a very convenient property when it is required to apply calculus to problems in which such functions occur.

It will be remembered that, when dealing with logarithmic graphs, proportional rate of change was defined as the ratio between the rate at which a quantity y was changing for a given value of x and that value of y. In calculus notation, proportional rate of change is given by $(dy/dx)/y$. Now if $y = e^x$, then $dy/dx = e^x$ so that

$$\frac{dy}{dx} \bigg/ y = e^x/e^x = 1.$$

This means that for the exponential function $y = e^x$, the proportional rate of change is constant for all values of x (and y). Hence if the logarithm of y is plotted against x, a straight line graph will result, since this indicates constant proportional rate of change. The logarithm tables in general use give logarithms to the base 10, but there is no reason (apart from practical convenience) why any other positive number should not be chosen as a base for logarithms. If the number e is chosen, then the logarithm of e^x to the base e, usually denoted by $\ln e^x$ is equal to x. Hence if $y = e^x$, then $\ln y = x$, and the graph of this function will clearly be a straight line.

The logarithm of any number y to the base B is denoted by $\log_B y$, so that if $x = \log_B y$ then $y = B^x$. The logarithm of y to the base B is easily converted to the base e by multiplying $\log_B y$ by $\log_e B$. For example, if $B = 10$ then, since $\log_e 10 = 2\cdot3026$,

$$\log_e y = 2\cdot3026 \times \log_{10} y.$$

Hence

$$10^x = y = (e^{2\cdot3026})^x.$$

Using the result of Exercises 11, No. 12, it follows that

$$\frac{dy}{dx} = 2\cdot3026\, e^{2\cdot3026x} = 2\cdot3026y.$$

So if $y = 10^x$ it is still true that the proportional rate of change of y is constant and the graph of y against x on semi-logarithmic graph paper will still be a straight line.

8. Maximum and Minimum Values

It has been seen that, in the case of a quadratic function there is a simple method of determining whether the function has a maximum or minimum value. For functions in which higher powers of x than the second occur a more complicated rule is needed to distinguish these two values, supposing that the functions in question possess them. Consider, for example, the cubic function

$$y = \frac{x^3}{3} - 3x^2 + 8x.$$

The graph of this function between $x = 0$ and $x = 6$, which might be a firm's variable cost curve in suitable units, is shown in Fig. 52.

x	0	1	2	3	4	5	6
y	0	5·33	6·67	6	5·33	6·67	12

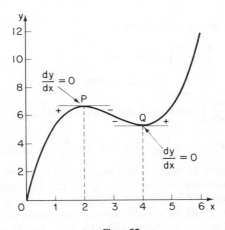

FIG. 52.

In this case y has both a maximum and a minimum value. The differential coefficient of the function is

$$\frac{dy}{dx} = x^2 - 6x + 8.$$

The maximum and minimum values occur when $dy/dx = 0$, that is, when

$$x^2 - 6x + 8 = 0.$$

The values of x at which the maximum and minimum values of y occur are given by the solution of this quadratic equation, namely

$$(x - 2)(x - 4) = 0$$

or

$$x = 2 \text{ or } 4.$$

By inspecting the graph of the function it is easy to see which value of x corresponds to the maximum value of y and which to the minimum. Fortunately, it is also possible to do this without drawing the graph of the function. At the point P on the curve, corresponding to y_{max}, the slope of the curve changes from positive to negative as x *increases* in value. Hence at the value of x at which y is maximum, the graph of dy/dx crosses the x-axis and is *downward* sloping. At this value of x, therefore, the differential coefficient of dy/dx is negative. Since

$$\frac{dy}{dx} = x^2 - 6x + 8$$

the differential coefficient of dy/dx is

$$\frac{d}{dx}\left(\frac{dy}{dx}\right) = 2x - 6$$
$$= -2 \quad \text{(when } x = 2\text{)}.$$

The symbol $\dfrac{d}{dx}\left(\dfrac{dy}{dx}\right)$ represents the *second* differential coefficient of y and is usually written as $\dfrac{d^2y}{dx^2}$. The fact that $\dfrac{d^2y}{dx^2}$ is negative at $x = 2$ shows that y attains its maximum value at this value of x.

By similar reasoning, at the point Q where y is minimum, the slope of the graph of y changes from negative to positive as x *increases*. So the graph of dy/dx crosses the x-axis and is *upward* sloping at the value of x corresponding to y_{min}. In other words, the second differential coefficient $\dfrac{d^2y}{dx^2}$ is positive at this value of x. In fact,

$$\frac{d^2y}{dx^2} = 2x - 6$$
$$= +2 \quad \text{(when } x = 4\text{)}$$

which shows that at $x = 4$, y attains its minimum value.

If the whole range of values of x for which the graph is drawn is considered ($0 \leqslant x \leqslant 6$), it will be seen that although P and Q are maximum and minimum points, respectively, the value of y is sometimes above P and sometimes below Q. In this range of values of x, therefore, y_{max} and y_{min} are not absolute maximum and minimum values of the function: they are called *local* maximum and minimum values. However, if the range of values of x is restricted to $0 \leqslant x \leqslant 4 \cdot 5$, then P is an absolute maximum, though Q is still only a local minimum value. Very often in a practical problem one is interested only in a restricted range of values of x so that, in the context of the problem the maximum or minimum values may be absolute, although if one considered a wider range of values of x, the maximum and minimum values of y would be only local. The need to consider the second differential coefficient when determining the maximum and minimum values of a function becomes even more pressing when account is taken of the fact that the condition $dy/dx = 0$ is only one condition for the existence of maximum or minimum values. There are functions for which, at some value of x, $dy/dx = 0$ but which do not have either a maximum or minimum value at that vaue of x. The graph of the function

$$y = \frac{x^3}{3} - 2x^2 + 4x,$$

which is shown in Fig. 53, is horizontal at the point R so that $dy/dx = 0$ at the value of x corresponding to this point. However,

x	0	1	2	3	4
y	0	2·33	2·67	3	5·33

the graph is *upward* sloping on both sides of this point which means that dy/dx is positive except at the value of x corresponding to the point R, at which value it is zero. Hence dy/dx is minimum at this value of x so that d^2y/dx^2 is zero. This can be verified by determining the precise value of x at which $dy/dx = 0$. Thus

$$\frac{dy}{dx} = x^2 - 4x + 4$$
$$= 0 \quad \text{(when } x = 2\text{)}.$$

Differentiating again with respect to x to obtain the second differential coefficient,

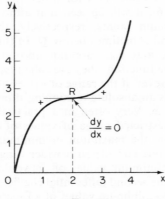

$$\frac{d^2y}{dx^2} = 2x - 4$$
$$= 0 \quad \text{(when } x = 2\text{)}.$$

Hence the point R on the curve corresponds to neither a maximum nor minimum value of y although the curve is horizontal at that point. R is sometimes called a *point of inflexion*.

The results just obtained can be summarised by saying that if y is a function of x, then a *necessary* condition for y to have a maximum or minimum value is that at some value of x, $dy/dx = 0$. But, in addition, it is also necessary that, at the same value of x, $d^2y/dx^2 \neq 0$. Taken together, these conditions are necessary *and* sufficient for y to have a maximum or minimum value. If $d^2y/dx^2 < 0$ then y is maximum, and if $d^2y/dx^2 > 0$ then y is minimum.

9. A Note on Quadratic Equations

The determination of the maximum and minimum values of a function often involves the solution of a quadratic equation. For example, the differential coefficient of the cubic function

$$y = \frac{ax^3}{3} + \frac{bx^2}{2} + cx + d,$$

where a, b, c and d are constants, is

$$\frac{dy}{dx} = ax^2 + bx + c.$$

To find the values of x at which y is maximum or minimum, it is necessary to solve the quadratic equation

$$ax^2 + bx + c = 0.$$

A solution of such an equation is a value of x which satisfies it. There is a sense in which all quadratic equations have exactly two solutions. However, if solutions which are real numbers only are permissible, then some quadratic equations have no solution. For example, the equation $8x^2 - 6x + 1 = 0$ has two solutions which are real numbers, namely, $x = \frac{1}{2}$ and $x = \frac{1}{4}$; but the equation $8x^2 - 5x + 1 = 0$ has no solutions which are real numbers.

Ideally, all quadratic equations which are soluble in the above sense can be solved by factorising the quadratic expression $ax^2 + bx + c$ into two linear algebraic expressions containing only x and real numbers. However, this is only feasible when the factors are obvious. Thus the factors of $x^2 + 2x - 8$ are obviously $(x - 2)(x + 4)$, but the expression $x^2 + 2x - 7$ has no obvious algebraic factors. If the quadratic expression has obvious factors, then the easiest way to obtain the solutions of the corresponding equation is to find these factors. Thus $x^2 + 2x - 8 = 0$ can be expressed in the form $(x - 2)(x + 4) = 0$. This shows that the equation is satisfied if either $x - 2 = 0$ or $x + 4 = 0$, that is, if $x = 2$ or $x = -4$. Obtaining the factors in such cases is largely a matter of practice. However, it is worth noting that if the coefficient of x^2 is 1, then the two algebraic factors of $x^2 + bx + c$ must contain numbers which are arithmetic factors of the coefficient c. Hence if one is looking for solutions which are whole numbers, then the choice of algebraic factors is restricted by the number of ways in which c can be factorised into whole numbers. For example, $7 = 1 \times 7$ can be factorised in only one way; but 8 can be factorised in two ways (1×8 and 2×4). Moreover, the sum or difference of the numerical factors of $|c|$ chosen must be equal to $|b|$. Thus if $|b| = 2$ and $|c| = 8$ only the factors 2 and 4 of $|c|$ meet this requirement.

When $ax^2 + bx + c$ has no obvious algebraic factors, the solutions of the equation $ax^2 + bx + c = 0$ can be found by substituting the values of a, b and c in the formula:

$$x = \frac{-b \pm \sqrt{(b^2 - 4ac)}}{2a}.$$

For example, in the equation $x^2 + 2x - 7 = 0$, $a = 1$, $b = 2$ and $c = -7$. So the (two) solutions of this equation are obtained from

$$x = \frac{-2 \pm \sqrt{\{2^2 - (4 \times 1 \times -7)\}}}{2 \times 1}$$
$$= -1 \pm 2\sqrt{2}$$
$$= 1 \cdot 8284 \text{ or } -3 \cdot 8284.$$

A quadratic expression may have two equal algebraic factors, in which case the corresponding quadratic equation has, numerically, only one solution. However, it is a *repeated* solution and in this sense the equation still has two solutions. For example, $x^2 - 4x + 4 = 0$ can be expressed as $(x - 2)(x - 2) = 0$ so that it has the repeated solution $x = 2$. Interpreted geometrically, this means that the graph of the function $y = x^2 - 4x + 4$ just touches the x-axis at $x = 2$ and attains its minimum value at that point. All quadratic equations can, of course, be solved graphically, though the solutions obtained will be only approximate. Since the object of using calculus methods to obtain the maximum and minimum values of a function is to determine these values precisely, it is obviously important to use a non-graphical method for solving any quadratic equation which may arise in this process.

EXERCISES 11

1. Plot on a graph the points P(2, 3), Q(−1, 4) and R(0, 5). Calculate the gradients of the lines PQ, QR and RP.

2. Draw the graphs of $y = 2x + 3$ and $y = 5x + 2$. Find the coordinates of the point of intersection of these two graphs.

3. Draw the graphs of the functions

$$f(x) = x + 3 \text{ and } g(x) = 4 - 3x$$

and determine the value of x for which $f(x) = g(x)$.

4. Draw the graph of $y = x^2 - 4x + 3$ between $x = 0$ and $x = 5$ and from it find the values of x for which y is zero.

5. (a) Draw the graphs of the equations:
$$2x + y = 8$$
$$y = x^2 - 2x + 4$$
for the values of x from and including -2 to $+4$.
(b) From the graph state the points at which the graphs intersect and prove the accuracy of your graph by solving the simultaneous equations.

6. The life of a certain machine depends upon the effort it is called upon to make. In an experiment to determine how the effort E lb. varies with the load W lb. the following results were recorded:

W lb.	30	40	50	60	70	80
E lb.	10·1	12·8	15·7	18·4	21·3	24·0

(a) Plot these results on a graph and from it deduce a relation connecting E and W.

(b) Use the graph to find the percentage increase in the effort E required if the load W is doubled from 32 lb. to 64 lb.

7. Find the differential coefficient of $y = x^2 - 2x + 4$. Hence calculate the value of x for which the value of this function is minimum and find this value.

8. A certain production process requires a fixed cost of £1000 and each unit of product incurs a cost of £5. If the sales function for the product is given by $S(x) = 755x - 125x^2$ where x is the number of units sold, find graphically the break even values of output. Write down the function $R(x)$ which gives net profit and determine the value of x for which net profit is maximum by differentiating $R(x)$. Calculate also the selling price and the average cost per unit when x has this value.

9. If $R(x) = 29x - 6x^2 - 15$, find the values of $R(0)$, $R(3)$ and $R(5)$. Find the value of x, correct to the nearest whole number, for which $R(x)$ is maximum.

10. Using the same axes, draw the graphs of the functions
$$y = 4x^2 - 17x + 43$$
$$y = 46x - 5x^2 - 47.$$

Determine from the graph the coordinates of the two points of intersection of these graphs. Find also the maximum or minimum value of each function, distinguishing clearly between them.

11. What is the coefficient of x^5 in the expansion of (a) e^x, and (b) e^{2x}?

12. By expanding $e^{\lambda x}$ in the form of a series, show that the differential coefficient of the function $y = e^{\lambda x}$ is $\lambda e^{\lambda x}$, where λ is a constant.

13. Evaluate the following definite integrals:

(a) $\int_0^4 2x \, dx$, (b) $\int_2^3 (3x^2 + 6) \, dx$,

(c) $\int_1^5 (8x + 9) \, dx$, (d) $\int_0^4 x(2x + 1) \, dx$.

14. Evaluate (a) $\int_0^1 e^x \, dx$, and (b) $\int_0^1 2e^{2x} \, dx$.

Give the answer in both cases correct to two decimal places.

15. Plot the graph of the function $y = 25x + (16/x)$ between $x = 0$ and $x = 5$, and find the positive value of x for which y is minimum.

16. Prove that $\sum_{i=1}^{m} \{S(i \, \Delta \, x) - S((i-1) \, \Delta \, x)\} = S(n) - S(0)$, where $n = m \, \Delta \, x$. Hence show that

$$\int_0^n S'(x) \, dx = S(n) - S(0).$$

17. A business sends out each month to its customers a catalogue in which is included current prices. The printer who produces the catalogues charges £316 for the first 3000 and at the rate of £60 per 1000 thereafter. The manager of the business is considering buying his own printing machine and equipment to produce the catalogues himself. He estimates that it will then cost him £395 per month and £25 per 1000 catalogues produced.

Graph the above information for quantities in steps of 1000 up to 10,000 catalogues and determine at what distribution it would pay him to buy the printing machine and equipment.

If the fixed costs of owning the machine and equipment increased to £437 per month, how would this affect the situation?

18. Between the sales range of 30 and 80 units the management has determined that the sales income follows the function:

Sales income (in £'s) = £20 × (sales units) − £0.15 × (sales units)² while total cost follows the function:

total cost (in £'s) = £450 + £2 × (sales units).

(a) Draw a graph showing the income and cost lines.
(b) Find, by differentiation, the output which will give maximum income and calculate the maximum profit.
(c) For what output is neither profit nor loss made?

19. Use tables of common logarithms (to the base 10) to find the logarithms of the following numbers and hence find the logarithm to the base e of each number.

(a) 12·45   (b) 0·436   (c) 541
(d) 5·921   (e) 291·5   (f) 951

(Use the conversion factor $\log_e 10 = 2\cdot3026$.)

20. Find the real solutions (where possible) of the following equations
    (a) $x^2 - 5x + 6 = 0$ (b) $x^2 + 5x - 126 = 0$
    (c) $2x^2 - x - 3 = 0$ (d) $x^2 - 10x + 25 = 0$
    (e) $x^2 - 3x + 1 = 0$ (f) $5x^2 - 7x + 4 = 0$

21. The following expressions define a firm's total revenue and total cost functions:

$$\text{Total revenue} = 18x - x^2 + 24$$
$$\text{Total cost} = \frac{1}{3}x^3 - 2\cdot5x^2 + 50.$$

(a) Use calculus methods to find the optimum production level.
(b) State the firm's profits at the optimum production level.
(c) Using the same axes, sketch the graphs of the total revenue and total cost curves, indicating the output at which profit is maximum.

22. The total cost of producing x units of output is given by

$$y = \frac{10000}{x} + e^x.$$

(a) Estimate, to the nearest unit, the output for which total cost is minimum.
(b) Calculate, also to the nearest unit, the minimum total cost y.
(c) Why do you think the value of y calculated in (b) is the minimum value?

CHAPTER 12

Set Theory and Probability

1. Set Theory

In Chapter 5, the addition and multiplication laws of probability were stated and also a definition of conditional probability was given. In the present chapter, proofs will be given of these laws, and it will be shown that the definition of conditional probability follows from that of the probability of a single event given in Chapter 5. For this purpose, it is necessary to consider the elementary aspects of the theory of sets and the method of counting the number of members in a set.

A *set* is defined simply as *any collection of objects which are all different*. Examples are: the points in a sample space, the even natural numbers, the kings of England. It will be seen that a set can be distinguished either by enumerating its individual members, as with a sample space containing a finite number of points; or by naming a property which all members of the set possess, for example, being an even natural number. The set consisting of all the objects which possess the properties used to define set membership is termed the *universal set* and is denoted by the symbol U. For example, the set of all points in a sample space is the universal set in relation to the way in which the sample space is defined. A selection of objects from the universal set is termed a *subset* of that set; all the subsets of a set including both the set itself and the set with no members, called the *null set*, and denoted by the symbol ø. A subset which is neither the universal set nor the null set is termed a *proper subset* of the universal set. To illustrate: when two coins are tossed, the resulting sample space has four points, $\{HH, HT, TH, TT\}$. This is the universal set U. The null set is the set $\emptyset = \{\ \}$, containing none of the points in U; whilst $A = \{HH\}$, $B = \{HT, TT\}$, $C = \{HH, HT, TH\}$, etc. are proper subsets of U. It will be seen that the number of subsets of a universal set U containing n members is the number of combinations of n things taken r at a time, where $r = 0, 1, 2, \ldots, n$ which is equal to 2^n (see Chapter 5, section 4). A sample space with four points thus has $2^4 = 16$ subsets and $2^4 - 2 = 14$ proper subsets.

Rules can be defined for combining sets to form new sets which are analogous to the rules for addition and multiplication whereby numbers are combined to form new numbers in ordinary arithmetic. The corresponding rules in set theory are *union*, denoted by the symbol ∪ and *intersection*, denoted by ∩. The union of two sets A and B is the set C consisting of all the members of both A and B, no member being counted twice. For example, let $A = \{HH, TT\}$ and $B = \{TT, HT\}$, then $A \cup B = \{HH, HT, TT\}$. Note that the order in which the members of a set are written down is immaterial so that, in particular, $A \cup B = B \cup A$. The intersection of two sets A and B is the set C consisting of the members of A and B which are common to both. Thus if A and B represent the same sets as above, then $A \cap B = \{TT\}$. Also $A \cap B = B \cap A$. The results of these two operations of union and intersection are illustrated by the diagram (Fig. 54), known as a Venn diagram, in which the rectangle represents the universal set U of which A and B are two subsets. It

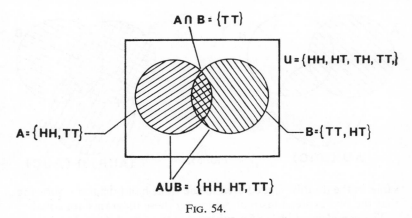

A ∩ B = {TT}

U = {HH, HT, TH, TT,}

A = {HH, TT}

B = {TT, HT}

A∪B = {HH, HT, TT}

FIG. 54.

follows from the definitions of union and intersection that the union of any set with the universal set is the universal set, for example $A \cup U = U$; and also that the union of the null set with any set is equal to that set, for instance, $\varnothing \cup A = A$. Also $A \cap U = A$ and $\varnothing \cap A = \varnothing$.

When combining more than two sets by intersection and union, it is often convenient, as in ordinary algebra, to use brackets in order to show in which order the operations must be carried out. When a single operation is used to combine all the sets this is, strictly speaking, unnecessary; for example,

$$(A \cup B) \cup C = A \cup (B \cup C)$$

and
$$(A \cap B) \cap C = A \cap (B \cap C),$$

so that the same result is reached, whatever the order of combining the sets when only a single operation is in question. This is not so, however, when both operations are involved together. There are two important rules in set theory which state that:

$$A \cap (B \cup C) = (A \cap B) \cup (A \cap C)$$
and
$$A \cup (B \cap C) = (A \cup B) \cap (A \cup C).$$

The first of these rules is similar to that of ordinary arithmetic, according to which, for example, $2 \times (5 + 8) = 2 \times 5 + 2 \times 8$. The second rule, however, has no analogue in ordinary arithmetic, for example, $2 + (5 \times 8)$ does not equal $(2 + 5) \times (2 + 8)$; this rule being peculiar to set theory. The fact that it holds for any three sets can be shown by means of Venn diagrams. It will be seen that the single-shaded area in the left-hand diagram (Fig. 55) is the

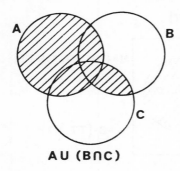

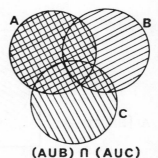

A U (B∩C)   FIG. 55.   **(AUB) ∩ (AUC)**

same as the doubly-shaded area in the right-hand diagram, showing that the two expressions represented by these diagrams are equal.

The *complement* in U of a subset A is the set A' such that

$$A \cup A' = U \quad \text{and} \quad A \cap A' = \emptyset.$$

It follows that the members of A' are all the members of U which are not members of A. The set A' is sometimes referred to as the logical negation of A. Complementation gives rise to two important rules of set theory known as the *de Morgan Rules*:

$$(A \cup B)' = A' \cap B'$$
$$(A \cap B)' = A' \cup B'.$$

Either rule can easily be shown to be true by means of Venn diagrams (see Fig. 56).

The single-shaded area of the left-hand diagram is equal to the doubly-shaded area of the right-hand one, showing that

$$(A \cup B)' = A' \cap B'.$$

Moreover, the unshaded portion of the right-hand diagram represents the set $A \cap B$, so that the whole shaded area of this diagram is the set $(A \cap B)'$ which is clearly equal to $A' \cup B'$.

Intersection and union have a useful interpretation in ordinary

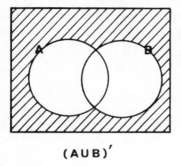
$(A \cup B)'$

FIG. 56.

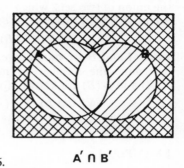
$A' \cap B'$

language. Thus an element of the set $A \cup B$ is a member of either the set A or the set B or both, so that $\cup$ is equivalent in meaning to the inclusive use of the word "or". Similarly, a member of the set $A \cap B$ is a member of the sets A and B, so that $\cap$ is equivalent in meaning to the word "and".

2. Counting Set Members

The special interest of set theory for probability is that it provides a means of counting the number of members in union or intersection sets. The number of members of the set A is denoted by $N(A)$. For example, if $A = \{HH, TT\}$, then $N(A) = 2$. It follows that $N(A) + N(A') = N(U)$ where A' is the complement of the set A in U. It is possible to add the number of members in A to those in A' in this simple way to give the number of members of U because A and A' are mutually exclusive and collectively exhaustive sets. When two sets A and B are mutually exclusive (disjoint), the number of members of A or B is equal to the number of members of the union set $A \cup B$, i.e., $N(A) + N(B) = N(A \cup B)$ when A and B are mutually exclusive. This will clearly not be the case when A and B are not mutually exclusive, as reference to Fig. 54 will show, for in this case, the sum $N(A) + N(B)$ includes the common members of A and B twice. Now the members common to A and B are also the members of the intersection set $A \cap B$. It follows that

$$N(A \cup B) = N(A) + N(B) - N(A \cap B).$$

Example

$$A = \{HH, TT\}, \quad B = \{TT, HT\}$$
$$N(A \cup B) = 2 + 2 - 1 = 3.$$

The above is a general rule for counting the number of members in the union of two sets, which applies even when A and B are mutually exclusive, for in this case, $A \cap B = \emptyset$ and $N(\emptyset) = 0$ so that

$$N(A \cup B) = N(A) + N(B)$$

when A and B are mutually exclusive. The rule also enables one to determine the number of members of $A \cap B$ when $N(A \cup B)$, $N(A)$ and $N(B)$ are known, for

$$N(A \cap B) = N(A) + N(B) - N(A \cup B).$$

EXAMPLE 1

(i) *If $N(A \cup B) = 25$, $N(A \cap B) = 5$ and $N(B) = 14$, find $N(A)$.*
(ii) *If $N(A) = 10$ and $N(B) = 6$, what are the greatest and least values of $N(A \cup B)$?*

(i) $25 = N(A) + 14 - 5$
so $N(A) = 25 - 14 + 5 = 16.$

(ii) $N(A \cup B)$ is greatest when $A \cap B = \emptyset$, in which case
$$N(A \cup B) = 10 + 6 = 16.$$

$N(A \cap B)$ is greatest when $A \cap B = B$, i.e., when $N(A \cap B) = 6$; so the least value of $N(A \cup B)$ is
$$N(A \cup B) = 10 + 6 - 6 = 10.$$

A rule for finding the number of members in the union of three sets can be obtained by repeated application of the rule for two sets:

$$
\begin{aligned}
N(A \cup B \cup C) &= N\{(A \cup B) \cup C\} \\
&= N(A \cup B) + N(C) - N\{(A \cup B) \cap C\} \\
&= N(A) + N(B) - N(A \cap B) \\
&\quad + N(C) - N\{(A \cap C) \cup (B \cap C)\} \\
&= N(A) + N(B) + N(C) - N(A \cap B) \\
&\quad - N(A \cap C) - N(B \cap C) + N(A \cap B \cap C).
\end{aligned}
$$

EXAMPLE 2

A survey of 200 investors showed the following information concerning the desirability of buying shares in one or more of three companies A, B and C.

28 *advised buying A and B*
92   „   „   *A or B but not C*
42   „   „   *B but not A or C*
122   „   „   *B or C but not A*
64   „   „   *C but not A or B*
14   „   „   *A and C but not B*

How many investors advised: (a) buying shares in all three companies,
(b) buying A and B but not C, (c) buying shares in only one company?

The data can be summarised as follows:

$$N(A \cap B) = 28, \qquad N\{(A \cup B) \cap C'\} = 92,$$
$$N(A' \cap B \cap C') = 42, \qquad N\{A' \cap (B \cup C)\} = 122,$$
$$N(A' \cap B' \cap C) = 64, \qquad N(A \cap B' \cap C) = 14.$$

The accompanying Venn diagram (Fig. 57) shows that

$$N\{(A' \cap B) \cup (A' \cap C)\}$$
$$= N(A' \cap B \cap C') + N(A' \cap B \cap C) + N(A' \cap B' \cap C)$$

i.e.,

$$122 = 42 + N(A' \cap B \cap C) + 64$$

so

$$N(A' \cap B \cap C) = 122 - 42 - 64 = 16.$$

Also,

$$N\{(A \cap C') \cup (B \cap C')\}$$
$$= N(A \cap B' \cap C') + N(A \cap B \cap C') + N(A' \cap B \cap C')$$

i.e., $92 = N(A \cap B' \cap C') + N(A \cap B \cap C') + 42$

so

$$N(A \cap B' \cap C') + N(A \cap B \cap C') = 50$$

Hence $N(A \cap B \cap C) + 50 + 42 + 14 + 16 + 64 = $ total no. of
investors $= 200$.

(a) No. of investors who advised buying shares in all three companies $= N(A \cap B \cap C)$
$$= 200 - 186$$
$$= 14$$

(b) Since $N(A \cap B) = N(A \cap B \cap C') + N(A \cap B \cap C)$
i.e., $28 = N(A \cap B \cap C') + 14,$

it follows that no. of investors who advised buying shares in
A and *B* but not $C = N(A \cap B \cap C')$
$$= 28 - 14 = 14.$$

(c) No. advising buying shares in only one company
$$= N(A \cap B' \cap C') + N(A' \cap B \cap C') + N(A' \cap B' \cap C)$$
$$= 36 + 42 + 64$$

(since $N(A \cap B' \cap C') = 50 - N(A \cap B \cap C')$)
$$= 142.$$

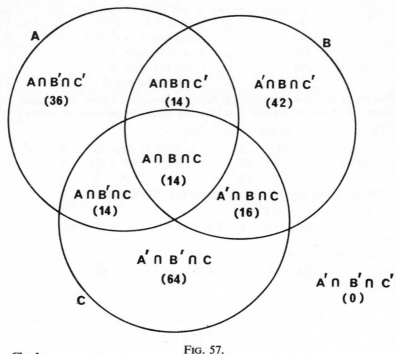

A

B

$A \cap B' \cap C'$
(36)

$A \cap B \cap C'$
(14)

$A' \cap B \cap C'$
(42)

$A \cap B \cap C$
(14)

$A \cap B' \cap C$
(14)

$A' \cap B \cap C$
(16)

$A' \cap B' \cap C$
(64)

$A' \cap B' \cap C'$
(0)

C

FIG. 57.

Check

$$N(A \cup B \cup C) = 78 + 86 + 108 - 28 - 28 - 30 + 14 = 200.$$

The foregoing example illustrates how three subsets can be used to partition the universal set into 8 mutually exclusive and collectively exhaustive subsets each of which is expressed as an intersection of all three sets or their complements. In general, n subsets of a universal set partition it into 2^n mutually exclusive and collectively exhaustive subsets, some of which may of course be empty. In the above Example, for instance, $N(A' \cap B' \cap C') = 0$, because it is assumed that no investor recommended buying none of the shares.

3. Probability Measure

If a universal set U consists of all the points in a sample space, then the number of points is $N(U)$ and the probability that a specified point is randomly selected is $1/N(U)$. It is evident, therefore, that the number of members in a set provides a measure of the probability of randomly selecting any one of the members. If A is the subset of points in the sample space which are favourable to the occurrence of the event A, then the probability that A occurs in a single trial is

$$P(A) = N(A)/N(\text{U}).$$

The reader should satisfy himself that this definition of probability in terms of sets has the three properties of a probability measure enumerated on page 95. In particular, when A is the null set ø, $P(A) = 0$; and when $A = \text{U}$, $P(A) = 1$.

If A and B are two subsets of U, then the conditional probability of B, given that A has occurred, is

$$P(B|A) = \frac{N(A \cap B)}{N(A)} = \frac{P(A \text{ and } B)}{P(A)}.$$

Since a point in A has already been chosen, only those points in B which it has in common with A could have been chosen, so the points favourable to B in this case are those in the intersection set $A \cap B$. If A and B are independent events, then the proportion of points in B which are also in A is the same as the proportion of points in B which are in U, and in this case,

$$P(B|A) = \frac{N(A \cap B)}{N(A)} = \frac{N(B)}{N(\text{U})},$$

or

$$P(B|A) = \frac{P(A \text{ and } B)}{P(A)} = \frac{P(B)}{P(\text{U})} = P(B).$$

Hence, when A and B are independent, $P(B|A) = P(B)$.

The number of points in the sample space favourable to the event A or B is $N(A \cup B)$. But

$$N(A \cup B) = N(A) + N(B) - N(A \cap B)$$

so

$$\frac{N(A \cup B)}{N(\text{U})} = \frac{N(A)}{N(\text{U})} + \frac{N(B)}{N(\text{U})} - \frac{N(A \cap B)}{N(\text{U})}$$

or

$$P(A \text{ or } B) = P(A) + P(B) - P(A \text{ and } B).$$

This is the addition law of probability (Chapter 5, section 3). When A and B are mutually exclusive events, $A \cap B = \text{ø}$ in which case $N(A \cap B) = 0$ and $P(A \text{ and } B) = 0$.

From the expression for conditional probability given above, it follows that

$$P(A \text{ and } B) = P(A) P(B|A).$$

This is the multiplication law for the probability of the joint occurrence of two events. When A and B are independent, $P(B|A) = P(B)$, in which case, the multiplication law reduces to

$$P(A \text{ and } B) = P(A) P(B).$$

EXAMPLE 3

Firm	Defective Electron Tubes per box of 100 units				
	0	1	2	3 or more	Total
Supplier A	500	200	200	100	1000
Supplier B	320	160	80	40	600
Supplier C	600	100	50	50	800
Total	1420	460	330	190	2400

From the data given in the above table, calculate the conditional probabilities for the following questions:

  (i) *If one box had been selected at random from this universe, what are the probabilities that the box would have come from Supplier A; from Supplier B; from Supplier C?*
 (ii) *If a box had been selected at random, what is the probability that it would contain two defective tubes?*
(iii) *If a box had been selected at random, what is the probability that it would have no defectives and would have come from Supplier A?*
 (iv) *Given that a box selected at random came from Supplier B, what is the probability that it contained one or two defective tubes?*
  (v) *If a box came from Supplier A, what is the probability that the box would have two or less defectives?*
 (vi) *It is known that a box selected at random has two defective tubes. What is the probability that it came from Supplier A; from Supplier B; from Supplier C?*

(i) Let $P(A)$, $P(B)$, $P(C)$ be the probabilities that a box came from Suppliers A, B, C respectively. Then

$$P(A) = 1000/2400 = 5/12,$$
$$P(B) = 600/2400 = 1/4,$$
$$P(C) = 800/2400 = 1/3.$$

(ii) Let X be the number of defectives in a box. Then
$$P(X = 2) = 330/2400 = 11/80.$$

(iii) $P(A \text{ and } X = 0) = P(A) P(X = 0|A) = \dfrac{5}{12} \times \dfrac{500}{1000} = 5/24.$

(iv) $P(X = 1 \text{ or } 2|B) = P(X = 1|B) + P(X = 2|B)$

$$= \frac{160}{600} + \frac{80}{600}$$

$$= 2/5.$$

(v) $P(X \leqslant 2|A) = P(X = 0|A) + P(X = 1|A) + P(X = 2|A)$

$$= \frac{500}{1000} + \frac{200}{1000} + \frac{200}{1000}$$

$$= 9/10.$$

Alternatively,

$$P(X \leqslant 2|A) = 1 - P(X \geqslant 3|A)$$

$$= 1 - \frac{100}{1000}$$

$$= 9/10.$$

(vi) $P(A|X = 2) = \dfrac{P(A \text{ and } X = 2)}{P(X = 2)} = \left(\dfrac{200}{2400}\right) \bigg/ \left(\dfrac{11}{80}\right) = 20/33.$

$$P(B|X = 2) = \left(\frac{80}{2400}\right) \bigg/ \frac{11}{80} = 8/33.$$

$$P(C|X = 2) = \left(\frac{50}{2400}\right) \bigg/ \frac{11}{80} = 5/33.$$

Check

$$P(A|X = 2) + P(B|X = 2) + P(C|X = 2)$$

$$= \frac{20}{33} + \frac{8}{33} + \frac{5}{33} = 1.$$

4. Inverse Probability

The conditional probability $P(B|A)$ is the probability that B has occurred or will occur when it is known that A has occurred. The inverse problem of this is to find the probability that A has occurred when it is known that B has occurred, i.e., the conditional probability $P(A|B)$. Now, by the multiplication law,

$$P(A \text{ and } B) = P(A)\, P(B|A)$$

and

$$P(B \text{ and } A) = P(B)\, P(A|B).$$

Since

$$P(A \text{ and } B) = P(B \text{ and } A)$$

it follows that

$$P(A)\, P(B|A) = P(B)\, P(A|B)$$

whence $$P(A|B) = \frac{P(A)\,P(B|A)}{P(B)}.$$

This is known as *Bayes' Theorem*, after an English mathematician the Reverend Thomas Bayes (1702–61). $P(A)$ and $P(B)$ are, as before, the unconditional probabilities of A and B arrived at by considering the whole sample space. The following example illustrates the application of the formula.

EXAMPLE 4

Of the total output of a factory, 30% is produced by workshop A and 70% by workshop B. On the average, 12 components out of 1000 produced in A are defective and 8 out of 1000 produced in B are defective. If a component drawn at random from the whole output is defective, what is the probability that it is from workshop A?

Let $P(A)$ and $P(B)$ be the probabilities of drawing an item from A and B respectively, and let $P(C)$ be the probability of drawing a defective item. The probability that if a defective item is drawn it came from A is, by Bayes' Theorem,

$$P(A|C) = \frac{P(A)\,P(C|A)}{P(C)}.$$

Now $$P(A) = 30/100 = 0.3$$

$P(C|A)$ is the probability that if an item comes from A it is defective, namely $12/1000 = 0.012$.

$P(C)$ is the probability of drawing a defective item from either A or B, i.e.,

$$\begin{aligned} P(C) &= P(A)\,P(C|A) + P(B)\,P(C|B) \\ &= 0.3 \times 0.012 + 0.7 \times 0.008 \\ &= 0.0092. \end{aligned}$$

Hence the required probability is

$$\begin{aligned} P(A|C) &= \frac{0.3 \times 0.012}{0.0092} \\ &= 9/23. \end{aligned}$$

5. Tree Diagrams

It is sometimes necessary to find the probability of occurrence of an event which happens at the end of a process involving several stages. In this case, the event may happen by several, mutually exclusive, routes; and the probability that it will happen is the sum of the probabilities of its happening by each route. Calculations in this kind of problem can be quite complicated, and it is often helpful to set them out in the form of a tree diagram, as illustrated by the following example.

EXAMPLE 5

In any trial of an experiment a rat may turn to the left or the right. If it turns left, it receives food; if it turns right it receives an electric shock. On the first trial the rat is equally likely to turn left or right. If the rat receives food on any trial, the probability that it will turn left on the next trial is $\frac{2}{3}$; if the rat receives a shock on any trial, the probability of a left turn at the next trial is $\frac{4}{5}$.

(i) *What is the probability that the rat will turn left at the third trial?*

(ii) *If the rat is observed to turn left at the third trial, what is the probability that it turned left at the first trial?*

At any trial, there are two mutually exclusive outcomes: F (food) and S (shock), and at the nth trial there are 2^n mutually exclusive

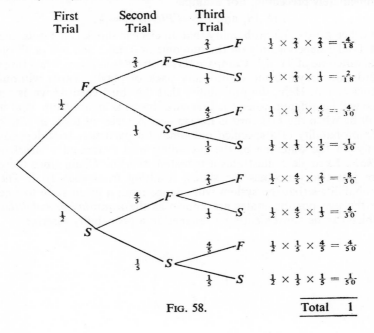

First Trial	Second Trial	Third Trial	
		$\frac{1}{2} \times \frac{2}{3} \times \frac{2}{3} = \frac{4}{18}$
		$\frac{1}{2} \times \frac{2}{3} \times \frac{1}{3} = \frac{2}{18}$
		$\frac{1}{2} \times \frac{1}{3} \times \frac{4}{5} = \frac{4}{30}$
		$\frac{1}{2} \times \frac{1}{3} \times \frac{1}{5} = \frac{1}{30}$
		$\frac{1}{2} \times \frac{4}{5} \times \frac{2}{3} = \frac{8}{30}$
		$\frac{1}{2} \times \frac{4}{5} \times \frac{1}{3} = \frac{4}{30}$
		$\frac{1}{2} \times \frac{1}{5} \times \frac{4}{5} = \frac{4}{50}$
		$\frac{1}{2} \times \frac{1}{5} \times \frac{1}{5} = \frac{1}{50}$

FIG. 58.   Total   1

routes by which these outcomes may be reached. These routes are shown in the tree diagram (Fig. 58) in which the conditional probabilities $P(F|S)$, $P(S|S)$, $P(S|F)$ and $P(F|F)$ are also indicated.

(i) Probability that rat turns left at the third trial is

$$P(F_3) = \frac{4}{18} + \frac{4}{30} + \frac{8}{30} + \frac{4}{50} = 158/225.$$

(ii) Probability that rat turned left on the first trial when it is observed to turn left on the third trial is $P(F_1|F_3)$ and, by Bayes' Theorem,

$$P(F_1|F_3) = \frac{P(F_1)\,P(F_3|F_1)}{P(F_3)},$$

where

$$P(F_1) = \tfrac{1}{2}, \quad P(F_3) = \frac{158}{225}$$

and

$$P(F_3|F_1) = \frac{2}{3} \times \frac{2}{3} + \frac{1}{3} \times \frac{4}{5} = \frac{32}{45}.$$

So

$$P(F_1|F_3) = \left(\frac{1}{2} \times \frac{32}{45}\right) \Big/ \left(\frac{158}{225}\right) = 40/79.$$

An interesting feature of this example is that the outcome of any trial is independent of the outcomes of all previous trials except that immediately preceding. For example

$$P(S_3|S_1 \text{ and } F_2) = P(S_3|F_2) = \tfrac{1}{3};$$

in other words, the probability that an electric shock is the outcome of Trial 3 depends only on the outcome of Trial 2 and not at all on the outcome of Trial 1. Compare this with what happens when three cards are drawn from an ordinary pack of playing cards without replacement. Here, the probability that the third card drawn is an ace will be different when the first card drawn is an ace from what it will be when the first card is not an ace. A series of trials in which the probability of a specified outcome at a particular trial depends only on the outcome of the preceding trial is termed a *Markov Chain*. Example 5 illustrates a two-state Markov Chain since there are just two outcomes (or states) resulting from each trial. The probabilities that the system will change from a given state to one of the two possible states are known as the *transition probabilities* which can be conveniently represented in a probability matrix:

$$
\begin{array}{c}
 \\
i
\end{array}
\diagdown
\begin{array}{c}
i+1 \\
\begin{array}{cc} F & S \end{array}
\end{array}
$$

$$
\begin{array}{c}
F \\
S
\end{array}
\begin{pmatrix}
\frac{2}{3} & \frac{1}{3} \\
\frac{4}{5} & \frac{1}{5}
\end{pmatrix}
$$

This matrix shows, for example, that if the system is in state F at the ith trial, then the probability that it is state S at the $(i + 1)$th trial is $\frac{1}{3}$. The initial probabilities for the system can be shown in the row matrix:

$$\begin{matrix} F & S \\ (\frac{1}{2} & \frac{1}{2}). \end{matrix}$$

The two matrices above can be multiplied, by the rules of matrix multiplication, to give the probabilities that the system is in states F or S after the second trial:

$$(\tfrac{1}{2} \quad \tfrac{1}{2})\begin{pmatrix} \tfrac{2}{3} & \tfrac{1}{3} \\ \tfrac{4}{5} & \tfrac{1}{5} \end{pmatrix} = (\tfrac{1}{2} \times \tfrac{2}{3} + \tfrac{1}{2} \times \tfrac{4}{5} \quad \tfrac{1}{2} \times \tfrac{1}{3} + \tfrac{1}{2} \times \tfrac{1}{5})$$

$$= \begin{matrix} F & S \\ (\tfrac{11}{15} & \tfrac{4}{15}). \end{matrix}$$

This shows that the probability that the system is in state F after the second trial is $\frac{11}{15}$, and that it is in state S is $\frac{4}{15}$; which can be easily verified from the tree diagram. The probabilities of each state after the third trial are obtained by repeating the above operation:

$$(\tfrac{11}{15} \quad \tfrac{4}{15})\begin{pmatrix} \tfrac{2}{3} & \tfrac{1}{3} \\ \tfrac{4}{5} & \tfrac{1}{5} \end{pmatrix} = (\tfrac{11}{15} \times \tfrac{2}{3} + \tfrac{4}{15} \times \tfrac{4}{5} \quad \tfrac{11}{15} \times \tfrac{1}{3} + \tfrac{4}{15} \times \tfrac{1}{5})$$

$$= \begin{matrix} F & S \\ (\tfrac{158}{225} & \tfrac{67}{225}). \end{matrix}$$

It will be observed that the sum of the elements in each row of a probability matrix is 1, because these elements are the probabilities of a set of mutually exclusive and collectively exhaustive outcomes.

6. Continuous Probability Distributions

If a variable x is continuously distributed in the interval $[a, b]$ then it can take any value in this interval. However, since the number of values which x can take is infinite, the probability that it takes any particular value at a random selection is infinitesimally small. It is denoted by the product of the probability function of x and a very small increment in x, that is the product $P(x) \, dx$. The probability distribution function of a continuous variable x is thus:

$$F(x) = \int_a^x P(x) \, dx.$$

Since x must take some value in the interval $[a, b]$ it follows that

$$F(b) = \int_a^b P(x) \, dx = 1.$$

Thus any probability function $P(x)$ must satisfy the condition that the definite integral of the function over the whole range of values taken by x is 1.

When all values of x are equally likely, then $P(x) = k$ where k is a constant whose value must satisfy the above condition for the definite integral of $P(x)$. If $P(x)$ is constant for all values of x in a specified range and zero for values of x outside that range, then x is said to have a *rectangular distribution*. For example, let x have a rectangular distribution in the interval [0, 4] so that $P(x) = k$. The value of k can be determined by solving the equation:

$$F(4) = \int_0^4 k\,dx = 1, \quad \text{i.e.,} \quad \left[kx\right]_0^4 = 1.$$

whence $4k = 1 \quad \text{or} \quad k = \tfrac{1}{4}.$

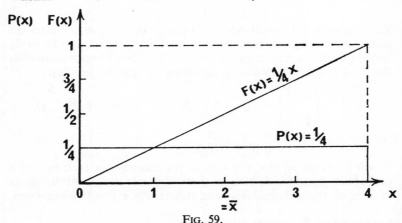

FIG. 59.

The graphs of the probability function $P(x) = \tfrac{1}{4}$ and the distribution function $F(x) = \tfrac{1}{4}x$ are shown in Fig. 59. The mean of the distribution is found in the usual way by summing the products $x\,P(x)\,dx$ over the whole range of values which x can take. Thus

$$\bar{x} = \int_0^4 (x \times \tfrac{1}{4})\,dx = \left[\frac{x^2}{8}\right]_0^4$$
$$= \tfrac{16}{8} - 0 = 2.$$

It is fairly obvious that the mean of a rectangular distribution will be the middle value of the range of values taken by x, as it is in the above case.

There are many kinds of probability function. The following example illustrates a triangular distribution.

EXAMPLE 6

Verify that the function defined by

$$P(x) = \frac{x}{6}, \qquad (0 \leqslant x \leqslant 2)$$

$$P(x) = \frac{1}{2} - \frac{x}{12}, \quad (2 \leqslant x \leqslant 6)$$

$$P(x) = 0, \qquad \text{(elsewhere)}$$

could be a probability function.

Calculate the probability that any randomly chosen value of x will lie between 0·5 and 1·5 if the probability function is that defined above. Find also the arithmetic mean of this continuous distribution.

If $P(x)$ is a probability function, then

$$\int_0^2 P(x)\,dx + \int_2^6 P(x)\,dx = 1.$$

The actual value is

$$\int_0^2 \frac{x}{6}\,dx + \int_2^6 \left(\frac{1}{2} - \frac{x}{12}\right) dx = \left[\frac{x^2}{12}\right]_0^2 + \left[\frac{x}{2} - \frac{x^2}{24}\right]_2^6$$

$$= \left(\tfrac{4}{12} - 0\right) + \left(\tfrac{6}{2} - \tfrac{36}{24}\right) - \left(\tfrac{2}{2} - \tfrac{4}{24}\right)$$

$$= \tfrac{1}{3} + \tfrac{3}{2} - \tfrac{5}{6}$$

$$= 1.$$

Hence $P(x)$ is a probability function, illustrated by the sketch (Fig. 60).

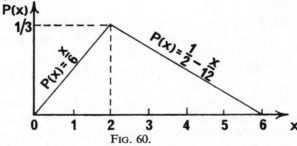

FIG. 60.

Probability that x lies in the interval [0·5, 1·5] is

$$P(0·5 \leqslant x \leqslant 1·5) = F(1·5) - F(0·5)$$

$$= \int_{0·5}^{1·5} \frac{x}{6}\,dx = \left[\frac{x^2}{12}\right]_{0·5}^{1·5}$$

$$= \tfrac{9}{48} - \tfrac{1}{48}$$

$$= 1/6.$$

The mean of the distribution is given by

$$\bar{x} = \int_0^2 \frac{x^2}{6}\, dx + \int_2^6 \left(\frac{x}{2} - \frac{x^2}{12}\right) dx$$

$$= \left[\frac{x^3}{18}\right]_0^2 + \left[\frac{x^2}{4} - \frac{x^3}{36}\right]_2^6$$

$$= \tfrac{8}{18} + \tfrac{36}{4} - \tfrac{216}{36} - \left(\tfrac{4}{4} - \tfrac{8}{36}\right)$$

$$= 2\tfrac{2}{3}.$$

EXERCISES 12

1. Write down all the subsets of the set $U = \{a, b, c\}$.

2. List all the proper subsets of the set $U = \{1, 2, 3, 4\}$ which include the digit 2.

3. List all the subsets of the set $U = \{a, b\}$, and show that two pairs of these subsets have U as their union and also have ø, the null set, as their intersection.

4. Show that the universal set U and the null set ø are the complements of each other.

5. The set $U = \{1, 2, 4, 8\}$.
Write down the four subsets of U, each of which contains three elements. If one of these subsets is chosen at random, find the probability (i) that the mean of the elements of the subset is more than 3, and (ii) that the median element of the subset is more than 3.

6. If A and B are two subsets of the universal set U, where $N(A) = 16$, $N(B) = 9$ and $N(U) = 20$, find the least and greatest possible values of $N(A \cap B)$.

7. Show that $(A')' = A$. Hence simplify $(A' \cap B')'$.

8. (i) Simplify $A \cap (B \cup B')$.
(ii) If $U = \{\text{animals}\}$, $D = \{\text{dogs}\}$ and $F = \{\text{fat animals}\}$, write a sentence equivalent to the statement $D \cap F' \neq \text{ø}$.

9. In a certain school there are 87 boys of a particular year. Of these, 43 play hockey, 42 play football and 47 play tennis; 15 play tennis and hockey, 17 tennis and football, and 21 hockey and football. If each boy plays at least one game, find the number of boys who play all three. Express these facts in a Venn diagram, showing clearly the number of boys in each separate region.

10. On the staff of a college, 48 men have a licence to drive a car, motor cycle or a public vehicle. Of these, 35 can drive a car, 8

can drive a public service vehicle and 5 can drive both a car and a motor cycle. All those who can drive a public service vehicle can also drive a car. The number who can drive a car only is twice the number who can drive a motor cycle only.

(i) Denoting by x the number of men who can drive all three types of vehicle, draw a Venn diagram to show the above facts. Write down an equation in x and hence find the value of x.

(ii) If one of the men is chosen at random, what is the probability that he can drive a motor cycle?

(iii) If one of the men who can drive a motor cycle is chosen at random, what is the probability that he can also drive a public service vehicle?

11. A firm finds that 50 of its customers are in the North of England, and 80 are in retail trade. Customers who are in at least one of these categories numbered 105. All but 20 of the firm's customers who are late in paying are in retail trade in the North. There are 61 customers who are from the North, or late with payments, or both. How many Northern customers are there who are in retail trade and/or late with payments?

What extra information would you need to work out how many customers there are altogether?

12. The probability that a construction job will be finished on time is 3/5, the probability that there will be no strikes is 2/3, and the probability that the job will be finished on time given that there are no strikes is 4/5.

(i) What is the probability that the job will be finished on time and there will be no strikes?

(ii) What is the probability that there will have been no strikes given that the job is finished on time?

13. As a result of an advertising campaign, 70% of the people using Brand X toilet soap in one month continue using it the next month. Of those people using any other brand of toilet soap in one month, 40% change to Brand X in the next month. If 50% use Brand X now, what proportion will use it in 3 months' time?

14. If a company makes a profit in a given year, the probability that it makes a profit in the following year is 0·9. On the other hand, if it makes a loss in a given year, the probability of a loss in the following year is 0·5. In Year 0 the company made a profit.

(i) Illustrate this situation by means of a tree diagram, showing the position by Year 3.

    (ii) What is the probability that the company made a loss in Year 3?

    (iii) If the company made a profit in Year 3, what is the probability that it made a loss in Year 1?

    (iv) If the company is known to have made a profit in Year 1, what is the probability that it made a profit in Year 3?

15. Form the initial probability matrix and the transition probability matrix for the data in Question 14. Hence find, by matrix multiplication, the probability that the company will make a profit in Year 4.

16. The variable x has a rectangular distribution in the interval $[0, 1]$. If the probability function for this distribution is $P(x) = k$, find k. Find also the probability that x lies between 0.3 and 0.9.

17. Verify that $P(x) = \frac{1}{2}$, $(2 \leqslant x \leqslant 4)$, may be a probability function. Find the arithmetic mean of x and, by evaluating the definite integral

$$\int_{2}^{4} (x - \bar{x})^2 \, P(x) \, dx,$$

find the variance of x.

18. If $P(x) = k(2x - x^2)$, $(0 \leqslant x \leqslant 2)$, is a probability function, where k is a constant, find k. Hence find the arithmetic mean of x, and the probability that x lies between $\frac{1}{2}$ and $1\frac{1}{2}$. By considering the value of x for which the distribution function $F(x) = \frac{1}{2}$, find the median of the distribution.

19. Three cards are drawn at random, without replacement, from an ordinary pack of playing cards.
(a) Show, by means of a tree diagram, that the unconditional (or prior) probability that the third card drawn is a heart is $\frac{1}{4}$.
(b) If the third card drawn is not a heart, what is the probability that the first card drawn was not a heart?

20. Three urns X, Y and Z each contain ten balls which are either green or red. A dice is rolled and if a 1 appears X is selected, if a 2 or 3 appears Y is selected, and if a 4, 5 or 6 appears Z is selected. X contains 2 green balls, Y contains 4 green balls and Z contains 6 green balls.
(a) What is the probability that a ball chosen at random from the urn selected is red?
(b) What is the probability that if the ball chosen is red the urn selected was X?

(c) If it is known that the urn selected was either Y or Z, what is the probability that the ball chosen is green? Draw a tree diagram illustrating this situation, showing on each branch the appropriate probability.

CHAPTER 13

Hypotheses and Significance Tests

1. Small Samples

In Chapter 6 it was stated that the means of large samples of size greater than 50 (say) are Normally distributed; and this fact was used to estimate or test hypotheses about the population mean. For this purpose, it was necessary to know the standard error of the sample means and hence the standard deviation of the population, and it was seen that a satisfactory estimate of the latter could be obtained from the sample variance

$$s^2 = \Sigma\,(x - \bar{x})^2/n$$

where n is the sample size. When n is small, a better estimate of population variance in the sense that it involves a smaller probable error, is given by

$$ns^2/(n - 1) = \Sigma\,(x - \bar{x})^2/(n - 1).$$

The standard error of the sample means is then found by taking the square root of this expression divided by n, that is $s/\sqrt{(n - 1)}$. In order to test the hypothesis that a small sample with mean $\bar{x}$ came from a population with mean μ, the statistic:

$$t = (\mu - \bar{x})/\{s/\sqrt{(n - 1)}\}$$

is computed. When n is large, t differs very little from the standard Normal variable X and so will be Normally distributed. But when n is small t has its own distribution which is shown in Table 2 at the end of the book.

For small samples, the sample size n is important so that it must be taken into account when using the t-distribution to test hypotheses. It is constructed on the assumption that the error in the estimate of population variance is much larger when n is small than when it is large. Hence when n is small a much larger value of t is necessary to be significant at a given significance level than when n is large. The amount of this probable error depends, however, not directly on n but on the number of *degrees of freedom*, given by $v = n - 1$. In drawing the random sample, n independent selections are made from the population and, at this stage, there are n degrees of freedom because the probability of making any selection is independent of any previous selections which may have been made. However, if it is assumed that the sample variance is the same as the

290

population variance in order to calculate t, the number of degrees of freedom of t must be reduced to $n - 1$.

To illustrate the use of Table 2, the probability that t is greater than 2·57 when $v = 5$ is 0·025 or 2·5%. Hence if a sample mean differs by more than this number of standard errors from the hypothetical population mean μ, then this is significant at the 2·5% level of a one-tailed test and at the 5% level of a two-tailed test, and the null hypothesis that μ is the population mean will be rejected at these levels. If, however, the sample size is increased to 11, so that $v = 10$, then the critical number of standard errors is 2·23, so that $|t| > 2·23$ is significant at the 5% level of a two-tailed test. When n is very large it will be seen, from the bottom row of Table 2, that at the 5% level, the critical value of t is 1·96 which is the same as the critical value of the standard Normal variable X at this level. Hence for large n, the Normal distribution (Table 1) can be used to test hypotheses about the population parameters.

EXAMPLE 1

The expected lifetime of electric light bulbs produced by a given process was 1500 *hours. To test a new batch a sample of* 10 *showed a mean lifetime of* 1410 *hours. The sample standard deviation is* 90 *hours.*

Test the hypothesis that the mean lifetime of the electric light bulbs has not changed, using a level of significance of: (a) 0·05 *and* (b) 0·01.

Here the standard error of sample means is $90/\sqrt{(10 - 1)}$ or 30 hours.
Hence $t = (1500 - 1410)/30 = 3$.
No. of degrees of freedom, $v = 10 - 1 = 9$.
The critical value of t at the 5% level is 2·26.
Hence the observed value of t is greater than the critical value and so the null hypothesis that the mean lifetime has not changed is rejected at the 5% level. At the 1% level, the critical value of t is 3·25, so the null hypothesis is not rejected at this level.

It should be observed that if the Normal distribution had been used in this Example, the null hypothesis would have been rejected at both the 5% and 1% level since the critical value of a standard Normal variable is 2·58 at the 1% level, and 3 is greater than this.

A limitation of the t-test is that it can be validly applied only if the sample means are normally distributed. When the sample size is small, this is possible only if the population itself is normally distributed.

2. The Sum and Difference of Random Variables

If two samples are taken under different circumstances, it may be of interest to know whether there is any significant difference between their means. For example, if an I.Q. test is given to two groups of people, each group differing in educational background, a difference between the mean scores of each group may be due either to random sampling errors or to the fact that the test is not independent of educational background.

Suppose there are two sets of measurements (which may be sample means):

$$X = \{x_1, x_2, \ldots, x_n\}$$
$$Y = \{y_1, y_2, \ldots, y_m\}.$$

Let $\bar{x}$, $\bar{y}$ and s_x^2, s_y^2 be the means and variances of the sets X and Y respectively. And let Z be the set of all differences such as $x_i - y_j$ $(i = 1, 2, \ldots, n; j = 1, 2, \ldots, m)$. Clearly the set Z contains $m \times n$ elements. If the mean of Z is $\bar{z}$, then

$$\bar{z} = \frac{\Sigma (x_i - y_j)}{mn}$$

$$= \frac{m \Sigma x}{mn} - \frac{n \Sigma y}{mn}$$

$$= \bar{x} - \bar{y}.$$

Hence the mean of differences between two sets of measurements is equal to the difference between their respective means.

Secondly, suppose that the variance of Z is s_z^2. Using the formula for variance when the assumed mean is zero:

$$s_z^2 = \frac{\Sigma (x_i - y_j)^2}{mn} - (\bar{z})^2$$

$$= \frac{m \Sigma x^2}{mn} + \frac{n \Sigma y^2}{mn} - \frac{2 \Sigma xy}{mn} - (\bar{x} - \bar{y})^2$$

$$= \frac{\Sigma x^2}{n} - (\bar{x})^2 + \frac{\Sigma y^2}{m} - (\bar{y})^2 - 2\left(\frac{\Sigma xy}{mn} - \bar{x}\bar{y}\right)$$

$$= s_x^2 + s_y^2 - 2 \operatorname{Cov.}(xy)$$

$$= s_x^2 + s_y^2 \quad \text{(when Cov}(xy) = 0\text{, i.e., when } x \text{ and } y$$
$$\text{are independent).}$$

It follows that, if two sets of measurements are independent, i.e., if there is no correlation between the x and y values, then the variance of the differences between x and y is equal to the sum of the variances of the two sets of measurements. It follows that if the two sets consist of random sample means, then the variance of the difference between the sample means is equal to the sum of the variances of each set of sample means. The square root of this sum is therefore the standard error of the difference between sample means. If only two samples are taken with means $\bar{x}$, $\bar{y}$ and variances s_x^2, s_y^2 respectively, and the respective sample sizes are n_1 and n_2, then the estimated standard error of the difference $\bar{x} - \bar{y}$ is

$$\sqrt{\left(\frac{s_x^2}{n_1} + \frac{s_y^2}{n_2}\right)},$$

where $s_x/\sqrt{n_1}$ and $s_y/\sqrt{n_2}$ are the standard errors of $\bar{x}$ and $\bar{y}$ respectively.

EXAMPLE 2

In a spelling test, the average mark for the 30 boys taking the test was 60 with a standard deviation of 7. For the 35 girls the average was 66 and the standard deviation 6. Test the hypothesis that girls are better at spelling than boys at (a) the 0·05 and (b) the 0·01 significance levels.

The sample size here is sufficiently large for a Normal distribution to be used.

Standard error of difference between means

$$= \sqrt{\left(\frac{7^2}{30} + \frac{6^2}{35}\right)} = 1 \cdot 63.$$

Difference between sample means $= 66 - 60 = 6$. Making the null hypothesis that the difference between the means is zero, the standard Normal variable

$$X = (6 - 0)/1 \cdot 63 = 3 \cdot 68$$

Since $X = 1 \cdot 96$ and $2 \cdot 58$ at the 5% and 1% significance levels respectively, the null hypothesis is rejected at the 5% and at the 1% level. Hence at both levels it can be concluded that girls are better than boys at spelling, for since the result is significant in a two-tailed test, it is also significant in a one-tailed test at the same levels of significance.

The reader should prove for himself that if x_i and y_j are independent random variables, then the mean of all sums $x_i + y_j$ is $\bar{x} + \bar{y}$ and that the variance of this sum is, as before, the sum of the variances of x_i and y_j.

3. Difference between Proportions

The standard error of a proportion in a sample of size n from a binomial population with probability of success p and of failure $q \, (= 1 - p)$ is $\sqrt{(pq/n)}$ (see Chapter 6, section 5). Suppose that two samples of sizes n_1 and n_2 are drawn from binomial populations and that the sample proportions of successes are p_1 and p_2 respectively. The estimated variances of the two proportions are then $p_1 q_1/n_1$ and $p_2 q_2/n_2$. It follows from the result in section 2 that the standard error of the difference between sample proportions $p_1 - p_2$ is

$$\sqrt{\left(\frac{p_1 q_1}{n_1} + \frac{p_2 q_2}{n_2}\right)}.$$

EXAMPLE 3

A market research agency carried out a sample survey in which of 1600 respondents 40% claimed to buy the product of a certain company. Six months previously, the same size of sample revealed that 36% were professed buyers. Test the hypothesis that the company's product is gaining ground at the expense of its competitors.

Difference between the proportions

$$= 0{\cdot}4 - 0{\cdot}36 = 0{\cdot}04$$

$$\text{Standard error of difference} = \sqrt{\left(\frac{0{\cdot}4 \times 0{\cdot}6}{1600} + \frac{0{\cdot}36 \times 0{\cdot}64}{1600}\right)}$$

$$= 0{\cdot}017.$$

Making the null hypothesis that the difference between proportions is zero, the standard Normal variable

$$X = (0{\cdot}04 - 0)/0{\cdot}017 = 2{\cdot}35.$$

This is significant at the 5% level of a two-tailed test and at the 1% level of a one-tailed test, so there is some evidence that the company's product is gaining ground.

4. Correlation and Regression

In Chapter 7, Example 3 a rather low value of the product–moment correlation coefficient r was obtained between the age of machines and the number of failures experienced with machines of a given age. It is useful, in such cases, to have a means of testing whether the observed value of r could have differed from zero due to random sampling errors or whether it provides evidence of real linear correlation. This can be done using a t test in which

$$t = \frac{r\sqrt{(n-2)}}{\sqrt{(1-r^2)}} \quad \text{(no. of degrees of freedom} = (n-2)),$$

where r is the product–moment correlation coefficient and n is the sample size. Thus when, as in Example 3, Chapter 7, $r = 0.37$ and $n = 50$

$$t = \frac{0.37\sqrt{(50-2)}}{\sqrt{(1-0.37^2)}} = 2.76.$$

From Table 2, when $\nu = 48$ degrees of freedom, the critical value of t lies between 2·70 and 2·66 at the 1% significance level, so that the observed value of t (2·76) is certainly significant of some linear correlation in the data. This is because, in spite of the rather low value of r the sample size is fairly large.

A more general test which enables one to determine whether r differs significantly from some specified value (not necessarily zero) is known as the z test, where

$$z = \tfrac{1}{2} \ln \left(\frac{1+r}{1-r} \right) = 1.1513 \log \left(\frac{1+r}{1-r} \right)$$

where ln is the logarithm to the base e and log is the logarithm to base 10, i.e., the common logarithm. z is approximately Normally distributed with mean $\bar{z} = \tfrac{1}{2} \ln \{(1+\rho)/(1-\rho)\}$ and standard error $1/\sqrt{(n-3)}$ where ρ is the population correlation coefficient. Tables of z for each value of r from 0 to 1 are tabulated in the *Cambridge Elementary Statistical Tables*, so that it is unnecessary to calculate the logarithm when these tables are used.

When making predictions using a regression equation, it is useful to have an estimate of the limits within which the prediction will lie with a given probability. For this purpose an estimate is required of the standard error of the prediction. If x_i and y_i are pairs of observations from which the least squares regression equation $\hat{Y} = bX + a$ has been calculated, then an estimate of the squared deviations of y_i about the regression line is given by

$$\begin{aligned} S^2 &= \Sigma\,(y_i - \overline{a+bx_i})^2 \\ &= \Sigma\,(y_i - \overline{a+bx_i})y_i - a\,\Sigma\,(y_i - \overline{a+bx_i}) \\ &\quad - b\,\Sigma\,(x_iy_i - \overline{ax_i + bx_i{}^2}) \\ &= \Sigma\,y_i{}^2 - a\,\Sigma\,y_i - b\,\Sigma\,x_iy_i. \end{aligned}$$

[Note that $\Sigma\,(y_i - \overline{a+bx_i}) = \Sigma\,(x_iy_i - \overline{ax_i + bx_i{}^2}) = 0$ since this is the condition for the sum of squared deviations to be minimum.]

The standard error of a prediction $\hat{Y}$ is then $S/\sqrt{(n-2)}$, and

$$\frac{Y - \hat{Y}}{S/\sqrt{(n-2)}}$$

has a t distribution with $(n-2)$ degrees of freedom (one degree of freedom being subtracted for each of the estimated parameters a and b in the regression equation). To illustrate the application of this result consider the regression equation for the data in Chapter 7, Example 1, namely

$$\hat{Y} = 0\cdot96X - 54\cdot3.$$

Here
$$S^2 = 10510 + 54\cdot3 \times 292 - 0\cdot96 \times 27378$$
$$= 80 \quad \text{(approximately)}.$$

Hence the standard error of $\hat{Y}$

$$= \sqrt{(80/(10-2))}$$
$$= 3\cdot16.$$

At the 5% level, with $(10-2) = 8$ degrees of freedom, $t = 2\cdot31$. Hence 5% confidence limits for Y (the true value of Y) are

$$\hat{Y} \pm 2\cdot31 \times 3\cdot16 = 0\cdot96X - 54\cdot3 \pm 7\cdot3.$$

The need to estimate the standard error of $\hat{Y}$ arises from the fact that the regression equation is estimated from sample observations (x_i, y_i) and these observations are subject to sampling errors. Hence for any value x_i it is unlikely that the corresponding observed y_i will lie exactly on the regression line $y = bx + a$. Instead, one can expect that the observed values will satisfy the *exact* regression equation

$$y_i = bx_i + a + e_i \quad (i = 1, 2, \ldots, n)$$

where (x_i, y_i) are a pair of observations and n is the sample size. The term e_i is a random variable and is the amount by which the observed value y_i deviates from the regression line. In these circumstances one may expect that the sum of the e_i below the regression line is equal to their sum above the regression line, so that the mean value of the error term is zero, that is, $E(e_i) = 0$. The situation is illustrated in Fig. 61.

If, as is often the case, the e_i are normally distributed about their mean zero, then the least squares estimate for the regression equation minimises Σe_i^2, the estimated variance of the error term being

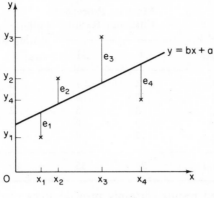

FIG. 61.

$$\hat{\sigma}^2 = \frac{\Sigma e_i^2}{n - 2}.$$

Here Σe_i^2 is just the sum of the squared deviations of y_i about the regression line which is identical with the sum S^2 calculated above using the regression equation.

5. Paired Samples

If it is required to test whether a new machining process gives better results than an existing one, two groups of operators could be randomly selected and assigned to the old and new process. This would, however, introduce a lot of variability into the results which would affect the reliability of the test. This can be avoided by using a single random sample of operators, each operator performing parallel processes by the old and new methods. The observed results of such an experiment might be as shown on page 298.

The mean of the differences in rating is $10/5 = 2$ whilst the estimate of population variance of differences is $6/(5 - 1) = 3/2$. Hence the standard error of the sample mean difference is

$$\sqrt{(\tfrac{3}{2}/5)} = 0.55.$$

Making the null hypothesis that the mean difference is zero,

$$t = (2 - 0)/0.55 = 3.64.$$

With $(5 - 1) = 4$ degrees of freedom, $t = 2.78$ at the 5% level, so

Operator	Machine Process Efficiency Rating		Difference in Rating (II–I)
	I	II	
A	4	7	3
B	6	8	2
C	3	5	2
D	5	8	3
E	7	7	0
Total	25	35	10

that the observed results certainly provide some evidence that the new process is superior to the old.

If two sets of five operators had been randomly selected and allocated to processes I and II respectively, then in order to find the standard error of the differences in performance of the two processes, it would have been necessary to estimate the population variance of the efficiency ratings from both sets of results. Thus the squared deviations about the mean of processes I and II are, respectively, 10 and 6. An estimate of population variance for small samples in this case is obtained by combining the sample squared deviations and dividing by the sum of the numbers in each sample less 2 to give

$$\text{Estimated population variance} = \frac{10 + 6}{(5 - 1) + (5 - 1)} = 2.$$

The standard error of the difference between the means of the two processes is then

$$\sqrt{(\tfrac{2}{5} + \tfrac{2}{5})} = 0\cdot 9 \text{ (approximately)}.$$

In this case, $t = 2/0\cdot9 = 2\cdot22$, whilst $t = 2\cdot31$ is significant at the 5% level with 8 degrees of freedom. Hence if the results in the above table had been obtained from unpaired samples, they would not have been significant of any real difference in efficiency, owing to the much larger standard error of the difference between the means in this case.

6. Type I and Type II Errors

As was mentioned in Chapter 6, section 4, a null hypothesis is not tested in isolation but always against some other hypothesis. If the alternative hypothesis is unspecified, then it is simply assumed that it is the contradictory of the null hypothesis. For example, if the null hypothesis is $H_0 : \bar{x} = \mu$, then the alternative hypothesis against which it is tested is $H_1 : \bar{x} \neq \mu$. On some occasions, it may be desirable to state the alternative hypothesis more precisely. For example, one might wish to test the hypothesis $H_0 : \bar{x} = \mu_1$ against the alternative hypothesis $H_1 : \bar{x} = \mu_2$ for some population from which a random sample is taken. The decision to reject or accept H_0 (and consequently to accept or reject H_1) depends on the level of significance fixed for the test. In fixing this level, however, both hypotheses must be considered, for a 5% significance level when H_0 is true may not be a 5% significance level when H_1 is true.

To illustrate this possibility, suppose that a sample of one item is randomly selected from a population which is Normally distributed, and it is decided to reject the hypothesis $H_0 : \bar{x} = \mu_1$ if the value of the item selected is greater than some specified value a $(x > a)$. The probability that H_0 will be rejected if it is true is equal to the shaded area under the Normal curve in Fig. 62. The value of x to the right of a is called the *critical region* of the test, and a may be fixed so that the probability of rejecting H_0 when it is true has some desired value, say 5%. This means that on 5% of the occasions on which

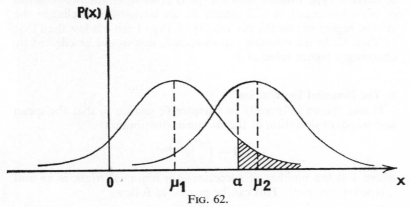

FIG. 62.

the test is carried out, H_0 will be rejected when it is true. Now suppose that H_1 is true, so that the population mean is μ_2. In this case, the probability that H_1 will be rejected is $P(x < a)$ which now corresponds to the area to the left of a under the Normal curve for which the mean is μ_2; and this is not necessarily the same as the probability of rejecting H_0 when it is true, using the same critical region for the test.

A test of this kind thus gives rise to two possible kinds of error:

that of rejecting H_0 when it is true, known as Type I error; and that of accepting H_0 when it is false, known as Type II error. The importance of the two types of error in decision-making is that one may be more costly in money terms than the other, even when the probabilities of each type of error are the same, i.e., when

$$P(x > a \mid H_0) = P(x < a \mid H_1).$$

Sample result	H_0 true	H_1 true
$x > a$	H_0 incorrectly rejected. Type I error	H_0 correctly rejected
$x < a$	H_0 correctly accepted	H_0 incorrectly accepted. Type II error

The cost of making either one of these errors can be reduced by a correct choice of critical region. If, for example, it is more expensive to make a Type I rather than a Type II error when the probabilities of both are equal, it will clearly be an advantage to change the critical region so that the probability of Type I error is less than that of Type II. In the example just discussed, this would be effected by choosing a higher value of a.

7. The Binomial Distribution

It was shown informally in Chapter 6, section 5, that the mean and standard deviation of the Binomial distribution

$$P(x) = \binom{n}{x} q^{n-x} p^x,$$

where x is the number of successes in n binomial trials, is np and $\sqrt{(npq)}$ respectively. This can be proved as follows:

The mean number of successes is

$$\bar{x} = \sum_{x=0}^{n} \frac{xn!}{(n-x)!\,x!} q^{n-x} p^x$$

$$= np \sum_{x=1}^{n} \frac{(n-1)!}{(n-x)!\,(x-1)!} q^{n-x} p^{x-1}$$

$$= np \times (q+p)^{n-1}$$

$$= np \quad (\text{since } q+p=1).$$

The variance of the number of successes

$$= \sum_{x=0}^{n} \frac{x^2 n!}{(n-x)!\,x!} q^{n-x} p^x - (\bar{x})^2$$

$$= \sum_{x=0}^{n} \frac{(x^2 - x + x)\,n!}{(n-x)!\,x!} q^{n-x} p^x - (\bar{x})^2$$

$$= \sum_{x=0}^{n} \frac{x(x-1)\,n!}{(n-x)!\,x!} q^{n-x} p^x + \sum_{x=0}^{n} \frac{xn!}{(n-x)!\,x!} q^{n-x} p^x - (\bar{x})^2$$

$$= n(n-1)p^2 \sum_{x=2}^{n} \frac{(n-2)!}{(n-x)!\,(x-2)!} q^{n-x} p^{x-2} + \bar{x} - (\bar{x})^2$$

$$= n(n-1)p^2 \times (q+p)^{n-2} + np - n^2 p^2$$

$$= np - np^2$$

$$= np\,(1-p)$$

$$= npq.$$

Hence the standard deviation of x is $\sqrt{(npq)}$.

To illustrate the use of the binomial distribution, suppose that an unbiased die is rolled and it is noted whether or not the score obtained is 1 or 2. The probability of either score at any trial is 1/3 and the probability of any other score is 2/3. Hence $p = 1/3$ and $q = 2/3$ and it follows that the expected number of times a score of 1 or 2 is obtained in 9 trials is

$$9 \times \frac{1}{3} = 3$$

and the variance of the number of times either score is obtained is

$$9 \times \frac{1}{3} \times \frac{2}{3} = 2.$$

If N experiments each comprising n trials are performed, then the expected frequency of experiments in which x successes occur is

$$N \times P(x).$$

This enables one to construct the expected frequency distribution for x when N experiments are performed. Suppose, for example, that the number of experiments performed is $3^9 = 19683$ and that two series are performed with $n = 3$ and $n = 9$. The expected frequency distribution of x, the number of times a score of 1 or 2 is obtained in a series of N experiments with the die, is given in the following table.

$$N = 19683$$

	$n = 3$			$n = 9$		
x	$C(3, x)$	$N(\tfrac{2}{3})^{3-x}(\tfrac{1}{3})^x$	Expected Frequency	$C(9, x)$	$N(\tfrac{2}{3})^{9-x}(\tfrac{1}{3})^x$	Expected Frequency
0	1	5832	5832	1	512	512
1	3	2916	8748	9	256	2304
2	3	1458	4374	36	128	4608
3	1	729	729	84	64	5376
4				126	32	4032
5				126	16	2016
6				84	8	672
7				36	4	144
8				9	2	18
9				1	1	1
Total			19683			19683

The mean and standard deviation of x for each of these distributions may be calculated in the usual way. But it should be obvious that the results obtained will be the same as the mean and standard deviation of x in a single experiment. Thus the mean value of x when N experiments are performed is

$$\frac{\Sigma x N P(x)}{N} = \frac{N \Sigma x P(x)}{N} = E(x).$$

In the two distributions above, the mean and variance of x are therefore:

When $n = 3$, $\bar{x} = 3 \times \dfrac{1}{3} = 1$ and   Var. $(x) = 3 \times \dfrac{2}{3} \times \dfrac{1}{3} = \dfrac{2}{3}$.

When $n = 9$, $\bar{x} = 3$ and   Var. $(x) = 2$.

The frequency polygons for these two expected frequency distributions are shown in Fig. 63. It will be seen that both distributions are positively skew. However, as the number of trials, n, in each experiment increases the mode of the distribution is pulled to the right and the frequencies tend to be distributed more equally about this modal point. By increasing the number of trials in each experiment, the distribution becomes more symmetrical and also tends to become continuous since, with large n, the probability of each value of x is very small—at least when neither p nor q is too small. Under these conditions, the binomial distribution is approximated well by

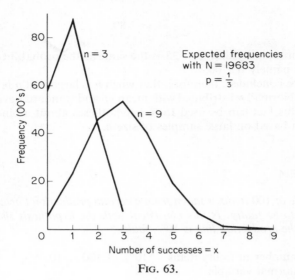

FIG. 63.

the normal distribution. This is a very convenient property since, if n is large, it is a matter of some difficulty to determine the probability that x is greater or less than a given value, using the binomial probabilities. In the die-rolling experiment, for example, the probability that x (the number of occasions on which a score of 1 or 2 is obtained) is less than 35 when the number of trials is 81 is, using the binomial probabilities,

$$\sum_{0}^{34} P(x) = \sum_{0}^{34} C(81, x)\left(\frac{2}{3}\right)^{81-x}\left(\frac{1}{3}\right)^{x}.$$

In other words it would be necessary to calculate 35 binomial probabilities and add them together in order to find the required probability. This can be avoided by noting that, since n is large, the probability distribution of x is approximately normal, so that the variable

$$X = \frac{35 - \mu}{\sigma}$$

is a standard normal variable. It is easy enough to find μ and σ for the binomial distribution. In the case considered, these are

$$\mu = 81 \times \tfrac{1}{3} = 27 \quad \text{and} \quad \sigma = \sqrt{(81 \times \tfrac{2}{3} \times \tfrac{1}{3})} = 4 \cdot 24.$$

Hence the standard normal variable

$$X = \frac{35 - 27}{4 \cdot 24} = 1 \cdot 89.$$

So the probability that $x < 35$ is the same as the probability that $X < 1\cdot89$, namely $0\cdot9706$.

It may be concluded, therefore, that when n is large and p not too small, x is Normally distributed with mean np and standard deviation $\sqrt{(npq)}$. This fact can be used to test hypotheses about a binomial population based on large samples of size n.

EXAMPLE 4

A sample of 100 *items is taken from a certain production line and* 12 *are found to be faulty. Is this consistent with the hypothesis that the output of the production line is* 10% *faulty?*

Expected number of faulty items $= 10\%$ of $100 = 10$.
Standard normal variable
$$X = (12 - 10)/\sqrt{(100 \times \tfrac{1}{10} \times \tfrac{9}{10})}$$
$$= 0\cdot66.$$

This is clearly not significant, so that as many as 12 faulty items could have resulted by chance from such a population.

EXAMPLE 5

An urn contains 60 *red marbles and* 40 *white marbles. Two sets of* 30 *marbles each are drawn with replacement from the urn and their colours noted. What is the probability that the two sets differ by* 8 *or more red marbles.*

Let x_1 and x_2 be the number of red marbles in each sample. The probability of drawing a red marble is $60/100 = 3/5$, so that the standard deviation of the number of red marbles drawn in a sample of $30 = \sqrt{(30 \times \tfrac{3}{5} \times \tfrac{2}{5})}$. It follows that the standard deviation of the difference $x_1 - x_2$ between the number of red marbles drawn is
$$\sqrt{(\tfrac{180}{25} + \tfrac{180}{25})} = 3\cdot80.$$
The mean difference $= \tfrac{3}{5} \times 30 - \tfrac{3}{5} \times 30 = 0$.
Hence the standard Normal variable corresponding to a difference of 8 is
$$X = (8 - 0)/3\cdot8 = 2\cdot11.$$

From Table 1, $P(X > 2 \cdot 11) = 0 \cdot 01743$.

Thus the probability that either $x_1 - x_2 = 8$ or more, $x_2 - x_1 = 8$ or more is $2 \times 0 \cdot 01743$ or $3 \cdot 5\%$.

8. The Poisson Distribution

When n is large and p very small, the Binomial distribution is not symmetrical but approximates to another distribution, known as the Poisson distribution, which can be used for testing hypotheses or calculating probabilities. The formula for this distribution is

$$P(x) = \frac{m^x}{x!} e^{-m},$$

where $e^{-m} = 1/e^m$ and e is the exponential constant discussed in Chapter 11, section 7 having the approximate value $2 \cdot 718$. $P(x)$ is the probability of x successes in a very large number of binomial trials when the mean number of successes in a set of such trials is m. To show that this is a probability function, the corresponding distribution function $F(x)$ may be computed, where x is infinite or very large. Thus

$$F(\infty) = \sum_{x=0}^{\infty} \frac{m^x}{x!} e^{-m}$$

$$= e^{-m} \times \sum_{x=0}^{\infty} \frac{m^x}{x!}$$

$$= e^{-m} \times \left(1 + \frac{m}{1!} + \frac{m^2}{2!} + \text{etc.} \dots \right)$$

$$= e^{-m} \times e^{m}$$

$$= 1.$$

This is so because x must take one but only one of the values 0, 1, 2 up to infinity.

The Poisson distribution has a very wide range of applications. An instructive example is its use in traffic studies. Suppose, for example, that between the hours of 1 p.m. and 2 p.m. each weekday 3 cars on the average are observed to pass a check point every minute. If the cars pass the point at random so that one is just as likely to pass in one particular second during the hour as at any other, and it takes exactly 1 second for the car to pass the point, then the number of cars passing in one minute has a binomial distribution for which $n = 60$ and $p = 3/60$ or $0 \cdot 05$. This satisfies the conditions for a Poisson distribution with mean $m = np = 0 \cdot 05 \times 60 = 3$. The probability that x cars will pass in one minute is thus

$$P(x) = \frac{3^x}{x!} e^{-3}.$$

It is easy to calculate from this expression the probability that 0, 1, 2, 3, 4, etc. cars pass the check point during any one minute. The values of the exponential function e^m are tabulated for values of m from 0 to 5 in Table 6 at the end of the book. Thus for $m = 3$, $e^3 = 20$ (approximately), so $e^{-3} = 1/20 = 0.05$. The probabilities that 0, 1, 2, 3, etc. cars pass the check point in one minute are thus given by:

$$e^{-m}\left(1, \frac{m}{1!}, \frac{m^2}{2!}, \frac{m^3}{3!}, \frac{m^4}{4!}, \text{etc.}\right)$$

$$= e^{-3}\left(1, \frac{3}{1!}, \frac{3^2}{2!}, \frac{3^3}{3!}, \frac{3^4}{4!}, \text{etc.}\right)$$

$$= 0.05 \times 1, \frac{0.05 \times 3}{1!}, \frac{0.05 \times 3^2}{2!}, \frac{0.05 \times 3^3}{3!}, \frac{0.05 \times 3^4}{4!}, \text{etc.}$$

$$= 0.05, \ 0.15, \ 0.23, \ 0.23, \ 0.17, \text{etc.}$$

The probability that no cars pass in one minute is therefore $P(0) = 0.05$. Similarly, $P(1) = 0.15$, $P(2) = 0.23$, $P(3) = 0.23$, $P(4) = 0.17$ are the probabilities that 1, 2, 3 or 4 cars pass in one minute. The probability that more than 4 cars pass in one minute is clearly

$$1 - \{P(0) + P(1) + P(2) + P(3) + P(4)\}$$
$$= 1 - (0.05 + 0.15 + 0.23 + 0.23 + 0.17)$$
$$= 0.17.$$

As for the Binomial distribution, the standard deviation of x for a Poisson distribution is $\sqrt{(npq)}$. But since p is small, it follows that $q (= 1 - p)$ is very nearly 1, so that $npq \simeq np$. Hence the standard deviation of x in the Poisson distribution is approximately $\sqrt{m}$.

When m is large, say greater than about 5, the Poisson distribution approximates to the Normal distribution. For example the number of cars passing the check point on the average every hour is $3 \times 60 = 180$. It is still true that p is very small, so that the standard deviation of x is still $\sqrt{m}$ where, in this case, $m = 180$. The probability that more than 200 cars pass the check point in one hour can thus be found by calculating the standard Normal variable:

$$X = (200 - 180)/\sqrt{180} = 1.49.$$

Hence $P(x > 200) = P(X > 1.49) = 0.0681$. (From Table 1.)

The Poisson distribution has numerous industrial applications. For example the motor accident rate per driver of commercial vehicles generally has a Poisson distribution. By calculating the Poisson probabilities from the known mean accident rate, and comparing these with the observed frequency distribution of accidents per driver, it is possible to determine whether accidents are happening at random or if some drivers are more accident-prone than others. Inventory problems, of which something will be said in a later chapter, are another field of application for the Poisson distribution. For example, the weekly sales of grand pianos may follow such a distribution. Knowing average weekly demand and hence the probability of demand for grand pianos being greater than a certain number, the dealer will know what stock to carry in order to give him a reasonable chance of not running out in the course of one week.

The goals scored by a number of football teams often have a Poisson distribution. An example is provided by the data in Exercises 4, No. 19. The mean number of goals scored by 60 teams on a particular Saturday is 1·3 whilst the standard deviation of the number of goals scored is 1·13. Hence $\sigma^2 = 1·28$ which is almost equal to the mean and is what one would expect if the distribution were Poisson. If the variance in this case had been greater than the mean it would indicate that some teams have a higher goal-scoring potential than others, so that if a team scored a large number of goals in one match, it would be more than likely to score more than the average number of goals in succeeding matches. In the case considered, this is not true, which shows that the better teams are not distinguished by a higher goal-scoring capacity.

It is instructive to compare the expected frequencies (assuming a Poisson distribution) for the data in Exercises 4, No. 19 with the observed frequencies. These are shown in the following table.

Goals Scored $= x$	$P(x)$ $= 1·3^x\, e^{-1·3}/x!$	Expected Frequencies $60 \times P(x)$	Observed Frequencies
0	0·273	16·4	14
1	0·354	21·2	26
2	0·230	13·8	12
3	0·100	6·0	6
4	0·032	1·9	0
more than 4	0·011	0·7	2

Although the observed frequencies do not agree exactly with the expected frequencies in this case, the differences could well be due to sampling errors and, in Chapter 14, it will be shown how the null hypothesis that this is the case can be tested. However, presumptive evidence in favour of this hypothesis is already provided by the fact that the mean and variance of the distribution are almost equal.

9. The F Distribution

In estimating the significance of the difference of two means using small samples (as in section 5), it is usual to estimate the population standard deviation from the combined results of both samples. Thus if s_x^2 and s_y^2 are the variances of two samples of size n_1 and n_2 respectively, the best estimate of population variance is

$$\hat{\sigma}^2 = \frac{n_1 s_x^2 + n_2 s_y^2}{(n_1 - 1) + (n_2 - 1)}.$$

In other words, the squared deviations of the sample values from their respective means are added and divided by the combined sample size $n_1 + n_2$ less 2. The square root of this quotient is the estimated population standard deviation $\hat{\sigma}$ and the standard errors of the two sample means considered separately are then $\hat{\sigma}/\sqrt{n_1}$ and $\hat{\sigma}/\sqrt{n_2}$. It follows that the standard error of the difference between the sample means is

$$\hat{\sigma}\sqrt{\left(\frac{1}{n_1} + \frac{1}{n_2}\right)}.$$

The differences between sample means then have a t-distribution with $n_1 + n_2 - 2$ degrees of freedom, the above standard error and mean zero (assuming that the samples came from the same population).

In combining the sample results to estimate the population standard deviation, it is assumed that the samples were drawn from populations with the same variance, though not necessarily with the same means. This assumption is often made without being tested, though it is possible to test it by a special significance test called the F-test. (The test was devised by the celebrated statistician Sir Ronald Fisher, which accounts for its name.) This test is based on the fact that the ratio of the sample estimates of two population variances have a known distribution called the F-distribution. Thus if $n_1 s_x^2/(n_1 - 1)$ and $n_2 s_y^2/(n_2 - 1)$ are the sample estimates of the population variance, then

$$F = \frac{n_1 s_x^2/(n_1 - 1)}{n_2 s_y^2/(n_2 - 1)}$$

where it is convenient to assume that the numerator of this ratio is greater than or equal to the denominator, so that F is greater than or equal to 1. With given sample sizes n_1 and n_2, the larger the value of F, the more likely are the two parent populations to have different variances. Significant values of F are tabulated for different degrees of freedom $v_1 = n_1 - 1$ and $v_2 = n_2 - 1$ at the 1% and 5% probability levels in many sets of statistical tables; for example, the *Cambridge Elementary Statistical Tables* and the *ICMA Mathematical Tables for Students*. An extract from these tables for the 5% significance level is given below.

		v_1 = degrees of freedom (numerator)						
		1	2	3	4	5	6	7
v_2 = degrees	1	161·4	199·5	215·7	224·6	230·2	234·0	236·8
of freedom	2	18·5	19·0	19·2	19·2	19·3	19·3	19·4
(denominator)	3	10·13	9·55	9·28	9·12	9·01	8·94	8·89
	4	7·71	6·94	6·59	6·39	6·26	6·16	6·09
	5	6·61	5·79	5·41	5·19	5·05	4·95	4·88
	6	5·99	5·14	4·76	4·53	4·39	4·28	4·21
	7	5·59	4·74	4·35	4·12	3·97	3·87	3·79

As an illustration of the use of this test, let $n_1 = 8$ and $n_2 = 6$, $s_x^2 = 9$ and $s_y^2 = 4$. Then the estimated population variances are

$$\hat{\sigma}_x^2 = (8 \times 9)/(8 - 1) = 10·29$$
$$\text{and} \quad \hat{\sigma}_y^2 = (6 \times 4)/(6 - 1) = 4·8.$$

Hence

$$F = \hat{\sigma}_x^2/\hat{\sigma}_y^2$$
$$= 10·29/4·8$$
$$= 2·14.$$

With $v_1 = 8 - 1 = 7$ and $v_2 = 6 - 1 = 5$, $F = 4·88$ is significant at the 5% level, so the observed value of F (2·14) is not significant and the null hypothesis that the samples came from populations with the same variance cannot be rejected. It would therefore be perfectly permissible to estimate the population variance in this case by pooling the sample results. Notice that the null hypothesis which is being tested is that the two population variances are the same. Nothing is said about which is to be the larger in order that the null hypothesis be rejected. So the F-test is essentially a two-tailed test.

10. Range and Standard Deviation

In quality control work (see Chapter 15) an estimate is often needed of the population standard deviation of the dimensions of a machine part. This can of course be estimated from a small sample or from a number of small samples. In such cases an alternative estimate, which is almost as good and which involves fewer computations, can be obtained from the sample range, that is, the difference between the greatest and least values in the sample of the dimension being investigated.

If the dimension is normally distributed, then the statistic σ/R_n, where σ is the population standard deviation and R_n is the range in a sample of size n, has a known probability distribution with mean a_n. The values of a_n for different sample sizes are tabulated so that it is possible to obtain either the mean range of samples of size n from the relation $\bar{R}_n = \sigma/a_n$ (assuming that the population standard deviation is known), or an estimate of the population standard deviation from the relation $\hat{\sigma} = a_n R_n$. A table of the values of a_n for small samples is shown below.

Sample Size n	2	3	4	5	6
a_n	0·8862	0·5908	0·4857	0·4299	0·3946

Thus if the diameter of a machine part in a sample of size 4 were found to vary between 3·56 cm and 3·61 cm, then the range R_4 is 0·5 mm, so that an estimate of the population standard deviation of the diameters is 0·4857 × 0·5 mm or 0·243 mm. This also enables one to estimate the standard error of the sample means $\hat{\sigma}/\sqrt{n}$ which, in the case considered, is 0·243/$\sqrt{4}$ or 0·122. Unless the process for manufacturing the part were out of control, the number of samples with means outside the limits $\pm 2 \times 0·122$ mm from the specification for the diameter of the part would be expected to be rather small.

EXERCISES 13

1. A machine is regulated to fill bags with sugar so that the net weight of sugar in each bag is 2 lb. A randomly chosen sample of 10 bags has a net mean weight of 2·1 lb with a standard deviation of 0·15 lb. Test the hypothesis that the machine needs adjusting.

2. 17 boxes of matches are selected at random from a large batch of

boxes. The mean number of matches per box in the sample is 348 with a standard deviation of 3. Test the hypothesis that the average number of matches per box in the batch is 350.

3. Estimate the population mean from the following set of sample measurements, and set 95% confidence limits for the estimate.
   Measurement x cm: 1·12 1·15 1·10 1·14 1·15 1·10 1·11
   How many more measurements would be needed to be 95% certain that the true mean was within 0·01 cm of the sample mean?

4. Samples of building material manufactured to a standard specification at two works were tested. The following results were obtained:

	Works A	Works B
Breaking point in lb:		
Mean	743	727
Standard deviation	120	140
Number in sample	200	245

   Test whether the difference between sample means is statistically significant. Would your conclusion have been different if the standard error of the difference had been 8 lb?

5. A market research company wishing to determine whether it is more usual in the North for working men to come home to a mid-day meal than in the South interviews two random samples each of 500 men. In the sample from the North 330 men come home mid-day compared with 280 in the South. Is the difference significant?

6. In 1970 the accounts section of a company issued 34,101 invoices, of which 3120 were subsequently found to contain errors. After a reorganisation of the department a series of samples of invoices were inspected.
   The following figures show the errors found:

1971	Number Inspected	Number with Errors
June	120	6
September	115	7
December	130	5

Has there been a significant improvement?

7. After a corrosion test, 42 of 536 metal components treated with primer A and 91 of 759 treated with primer B showed signs of rusting. Test the hypothesis that primer A is superior to primer B as a rust inhibitor.

8. 100 employees from company A have a mean age of 44·6 years and a standard deviation of 4·3 years. 150 employees from company B have a mean age of 41·4 years and a standard deviation of 3·9 years. Assess the evidence for the statement that the mean age of employees in company B is less than the mean age of employees in company A. What assumptions does your assessment involve?

9. In an examination the average mark for 30 men was 70 with a standard deviation of 8, and for 30 women it was 75 with a standard deviation of 7. Test the hypothesis at the 5% level of significance that women perform better at this examination.

10. A manufacturer aims to make a machine which will have a mean operating life of 10,000 hours. He draws a sample of 20 from a batch and tests it. The mean life of the sample is 9900 hours with a standard deviation of 220 hours. What conclusion can he draw from this sample?

11. The following are two sets of sample measurements:

Measurement x cm: 24·1   23·8   24·0   24·2
Measurement y cm: 24·2   24·3   24·1   23·9   24·2   24·1

  (a) Calculate the mean and standard deviation of each sample.
  (b) Use the combined sample standard deviations to estimate the population standard deviation and use this estimate to test whether there is any significant difference between the means of the two samples.

12. The number of strikes lasting one day or more in two industrial groups in the United Kingdom during a six-month period are shown below.

Duration (complete days)	Distributive Trades	Transport
1	10	32
2	9	12
3	1	6
4	2	4
5 or more	12	12

Is there any evidence of a real difference in the duration of strikes between the two groups?

13. Test whether the product–moment correlation coefficient calculated in Exercise 7, No. 19 (ii), differs significantly from zero.

14. Test whether the correlation coefficients calculated for Exercise 7, No. 5, differ significantly from zero and set 95% confidence limits for those regression equations of y on x for which there is significant correlation.

15. A random sample of 10 pairs of observations showed a product–moment correlation coefficient of 0·6. Could this sample have come from a population for which the correlation coefficient was 0·5? [$\ln 3 = 1·10$ and $\ln 4 = 1·39$.]

16. The following table appeared in *The Observer* on 24th January 1971, concerning trade within the Commonwealth:

Country	Proportion of Exports sold to Britain		Proportion of Imports bought from Britain	
	% 1965	% 1969	% 1965	% 1969
Australia	18	12	26	22
Canada	14	7	7	6
Ceylon	26	20	18	17
Ghana	13	26	25	27
Hong Kong	14	12	11	8
India	18	12	11	7
Malawi	50	36	25	26
Malaysia	7	5	20	13
New Zealand	48	39	37	31
Nigeria	38	28	31	34
Pakistan	13	11	15	12
Singapore	5	4	10	7
Zambia	38	27	20	22
Others	26	23	22	21

Use a paired sample test to determine how far this data confirms the view that Britain's trade with the Commonwealth has declined in importance within the period given.

17. In order to test the hypothesis $H_0 : \bar{x} = 2$ against the alternative hypothesis $H_1 : \bar{x} = 5$ a sample of one item is taken from a Normal population whose standard deviation is known to be 1. It is decided to reject H_0 if the sample measurement is greater than 3·64. Calculate the size of the Type I and Type II errors.

18. A single item is selected from a Normal population with standard deviation 2. Find the critical region for testing $H_0 : \bar{x} = 3.5$

against $H_1 : \bar{x} = 1$ if the size of the Type I error is to be 0·01 and the Type II error is to be kept as small as possible. Find the size of the Type II error in this case.

19. (a) The probability of rejecting H_0 when it is true is sometimes known as the "size" of a statistical test, whilst the probability of rejecting H_0 when H_1 is true is known as the "power" of the test. A widely used principle of significance testing is that the size of a test should be as small as possible whilst the power of the test should be as large as possible. How does this principle affect the choice of critical region for the test?

(b) Describe two situations in the practice of personnel management in which the concept of testing an alternative hypothesis against a null hypothesis is appropriate.

20. Two fair coins are tossed 5 times and the number of times on which two heads appear is noted. If the experiment is repeated 1024 times, calculate the expected frequencies of the number of experiments in which heads appear together 0, 1, 2 up to 5 times. Verify that the mean number of occasions on which heads appear together in an experiment is 1·25 and that the standard deviation is 0·97.

What is the probability of obtaining more than 2 pairs of heads in any experiment?

21. (i) The binomial probability distribution involves n independent trials in each of which the probability of some event occurring is a constant p.

Sketch the distribution for (a) $n = 10, p = 0·1$, and (b) $n = 1000$, $p = 0·3$, labelling the horizontal axis clearly in each case, and finding the standard deviation for the second distribution. (Other calculations are unnecessary.)

(ii) A research worker examined 1000 individuals to discover the incidence of a characteristic. On the assumption that this characteristic is possessed by 30% of the population, use the Normal distribution to calculate the probability that the number found with the characteristic was between 300 and 320 inclusive.

22. A bag contains 4 green balls and 1 red ball, which are identical apart from colour. A trial consists of making a random selection of a ball from the bag, noting its colour and returning it to the bag. A success consists of drawing a red ball.

(a) Calculate the probability of at least two successes in 5 trials.

(b) If the trial is repeated 100 times, calculate the approximate value of the probability of drawing the red ball at least 30 times, using the Normal distribution.

(c) If two sets of 100 trials are carried out, what is the probability that the number of red balls obtained in each set differ by 5 or less?

23. In a traffic study, observations were made on the number of buses passing a particular point each minute over a period of five hours. It was found that, on the average, one bus passed the point every minute. Calculate the Poisson probabilities that in any minute, the number of buses passing is 0, 1, 2, 3, 4. Find the probability that at least one bus passes the point in any one minute.

Estimate the mean number of buses passing the check point every hour and set 95% confidence limits on the mean.

24. In a transport organisation, the motor accident rate was considered unduly high. As a result, an intensive programme of education and training was undertaken. The accident rates before and after the programme were then measured.

(a) What general form of distribution of numbers of drivers with 0, 1, 2, . . . accidents would you expect in each of these periods?

(b) Give a mathematical expression for the probability of an integer number, k, of accidents and state the mean and variance of the distribution.

(c) If the average number of accidents is relatively large, to what form of continuous distribution does the discrete distribution of drivers with given number of accidents approximate?

(d) If the average number of accidents per driver during a long period before the training programme is known to have been 16 per year and the average rate recorded in the year after the programme was 9, is there any evidence of a significant improvement?

25. A manufacturer uses high-speed weighing and packing machines with an accuracy adequate to ensure that only one bag in twenty is likely to be underweight when the machines are set to weigh a given weight. A customer receives a consignment of 60 bags. What are the chances that four or more will be underweight?

26. Estimate the population standard deviation from the following sample readings:

$$8 \quad 9 \quad 17 \quad 11 \quad 18 \quad 16 \quad 14 \quad 13 \quad 12 \quad 9$$

Given that $a_{10} = 0.3249$ compute an alternative estimate of population standard deviation using the range. What assumption about the distribution of the population must be justified if this estimate is to be valid?

27. There are two methods of assembling a piece of equipment. The times taken (in minutes) by ten men using one method and by ten men using another method are given below.

Method A	Method B
2·2	2·0
1·7	1·6
2·4	2·3
1·8	2·6
2·3	1·8
3·2	2·7
2·5	2·4
2·2	2·2
2·4	2·5
3·1	1·9

Is there any evidence that Method B is quicker than Method A? State any assumptions you have made.

28. On average, 1% of the staff on a particular shift are absent on any one day. If the shift is made up of 150 men, what is the probability that two or more men will be absent tomorrow? What assumptions have you made?

CHAPTER 14

The Chi Squared Test and Non-Parametric Tests

1. The χ^2 Distribution

In a binomial trial there are just two mutually exclusive and collectively exhaustive outcomes, usually designated "success" and "failure". If the probability of success is p, then the expected number of successes in n trials is np. To test whether the observed number of successes x differs significantly from the expected number, the Normal distribution is used provided that n is large and p not too small, the standard Normal variable being $(np - x)/\sqrt{(npq)}$. When there are more than two possible outcomes, the population is no longer a binomial one; but the expected frequency of each outcome can be computed if their respective probabilities are known. In this case, it is still possible to test whether the observed frequencies of each outcome differ significantly from the expected frequencies by using the χ^2 test (χ is the Greek letter chi). If O and E are the observed and expected frequencies respectively, then the value of χ^2 for a set of n trials is given by

$$\chi^2 = \sum \frac{(O - E)^2}{E},$$

where the number of terms in the sum is equal to the number of possible outcomes of a trial.

Whether or not a particular value of χ^2 is significant depends not only on its magnitude, but also on the number of degrees of freedom of the test, which is determined by the number of independent outcomes. If, for example, there are r outcomes then there are r corresponding probabilities to be estimated, the sum of which is 1. Hence the number of independent outcomes cannot exceed $r - 1$ since when $r - 1$ probabilities have been estimated, the rth probability is 1 less the sum of the other $r - 1$ probabilities. If these $r - 1$ probabilities are independent, then the number of degrees of freedom for the test is $r - 1$. The probability that a given value of χ^2 will be exceeded when the number of degrees of freedom is ν is tabulated in Table 4, and the graphs of the probability function $P(\chi^2)$ for $\nu = 3, 4, 5, 6$ are shown in Fig. 64.

The value of the distribution function $F(\chi^2)$ is equal to the area under a graph between 0 and χ^2 corresponding to a specified number of degrees of freedom, so the probability that χ^2 is exceeded with that number of degrees of freedom is $1 - F(\chi^2)$ which is equal to the

317

area under the graph to the right of χ^2. For example, the probability that the value $\chi^2 = 6\cdot25$ is exceeded when the number of degrees of freedom is 3 is $0\cdot1$. It will be seen from the graph that the areas to the right of $6\cdot25$ are greater as the number of degrees of freedom increases, so that the probability that this value of χ^2 is exceeded increases with the number of degrees of freedom, the value thus becoming less significant.

When the number of outcomes is just two, the number of degrees of freedom is $2 - 1 = 1$ and the χ^2 test is equivalent to a test using

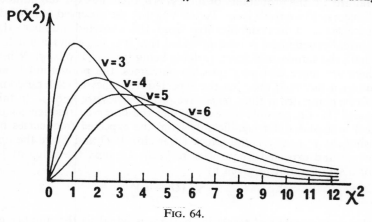

FIG. 64.

the Normal distribution. Thus suppose that the expected proportion of successes is p, then p is the only independent probability since $p + q = 1$, and

$$\chi^2 = \sum \frac{(O - E)^2}{E}$$
$$= \frac{(np - x)^2}{np} + \frac{(nq - \overline{n - x})^2}{nq}$$
$$= \frac{(np - x)^2}{np} + \frac{(np - x)^2}{nq}$$
$$= (np - x)^2/(npq).$$

This is the square of the corresponding Normal variable, so that if a value of χ^2 is significant at the 5% level (say) with 1 degree of freedom, the corresponding Normal variable will be significant at this level. For example, a value $1\cdot96$ is significant at the 5% level for the standard Normal distribution whilst the value $1\cdot96^2 = 3\cdot84$ is significant at the same level in the χ^2 distribution. If the number of degrees of freedom exceeds 1, then, of course, the two distributions are no longer comparable.

2. Contingency Tables

In order to determine whether two sets of measurements are associated, it is often appropriate to compute a correlation coefficient between sample pairs of the measurements. This method is clearly not available for testing the association between two attributes because these are non-measurable characteristics. In this case, a χ^2 test can be used in which the observed frequencies with which items in a sample do or do not possess both attributes are compared with the expected frequencies estimated on the assumption that the two attributes are independent. Now a sample item can be classified with respect to an attribute into at least two mutually exclusive and collectively exhaustive classes. Where the number of classes is just two, then items possessing the attribute fall into one class and those not possessing it fall into the other. If the sample items are classified with respect to a second attribute, also into two classes, then each item falls into one of four possible classes according to whether or not it possesses both the first and second attributes.

Attribute A

		A	A'	Total
Attribute B	B	a	b	$a + b$
	B'	c	d	$c + d$
	Total	$a + c$	$b + d$	n

A sample of size n is thus classified into four mutually exclusive classes $A \cap B$, $A \cap B'$, $A' \cap B$ and $A' \cap B'$, the observed frequencies for each class, namely a, b, c and d being shown in the above table. If the attributes A and B are independent, then the probability that an item possesses attribute A is independent of the probability that it possesses attribute B, so that the conditional probability $P(A|B) = P(A)$ and also $P(B|A) = P(B)$. In this case, the probability $P(A \cap B)$ that an item possesses both attributes is equal to the product $P(A) P(B)$. These two probabilities must be estimated from the sample. Thus

$$P(A) = (a + c)/n \quad \text{and} \quad P(B) = (a + b)/n.$$

It follows that the probability that an item falls in the set $A \cap B$ when A and B are independent is

$$(a + c)(a + b)/n^2.$$

The expected frequency of items in the top left-hand cell of the table is thus

$$n(a + c)(a + b)/n^2 = (a + c)(a + b)/n.$$

The other expected frequencies are calculated in a similar way; for example, the expected number in the set $A' \cap B'$ (the bottom right-hand cell of the table) is

$$(b + d)(c + d)/n.$$

Let e_1, e_2, e_3, e_4 denote the expected frequencies in each cell of the table, then

$$\chi^2 = \frac{(a - e_1)^2}{e_1} + \frac{(b - e_2)^2}{e_2} + \frac{(c - e_3)^2}{e_3} + \frac{(d - e_4)^2}{e_4}$$

when $e_1 = (a + c)(a + b)/n$, $e_2 = (b + d)(a + b)/n$,

$e_3 = (a + c)(c + d)/n$ and $e_4 = (b + d)(c + d)/n$.

When $P(A)$ and $P(B)$ have been estimated $P(A') = 1 - P(A)$ and $P(B') = 1 - P(B)$, so that $P(A)$ and $P(B)$ have one degree of freedom each, whilst the product $P(A)P(B)$ has $1 \times 1 = 1$ degree of freedom. Once this probability has been determined, the probabilities for the remaining three cells can be deduced so that χ^2 has 1 degree of freedom for this table. The table is known as a *contingency table*, and as the classification is into two classes with respect to each attribute it is a 2×2 contingency table.

EXAMPLE 1

Use the following data to test whether the number of defective items produced by two machines is independent of the machine on which they were made.

| | Machine Output | | |
	Defective Articles	Effective Articles	Total
Machine A	25	375	400
Machine B	42	558	600
	67	933	1000

Machine	Output			
	Defective		Effective	
A	25	26·8	375	373·2
		−1·8		+1·8
B	42	40·2	558	559·8
		+1·8		−1·8

The expected frequencies on the assumption of no association are shown in the top right-hand corner of each cell. For example, the expected frequency of the top left-hand cell is $(67 \times 400)/1000 = 26·8$. In the lower half of each cell the value $O - E$ is shown. Thus

$$\chi^2 = \frac{(1·8)^2}{26·8} + \frac{(1·8)^2}{373·2} + \frac{(1·8)^2}{40·2} + \frac{(1·8)^2}{559·8}$$

$$= 0·22. \quad \text{(Degrees of freedom} = 1.)$$

This value of χ^2 is far too low to be significant, so that there is no evidence that one machine is more likely to produce defective items than the other.

A set of individuals can be classified with respect to an attribute into more than two classes. For example, M.P.s can be classified, according to political party, into Conservative, Labour, Liberal, etc. Suppose that such a set is classified into s classes according to attribute A and into r classes according to attribute B. The probability that a randomly selected item falls into the ith class of A is $P(A_i)$, whilst the probability that it falls into the jth class of B is $P(B_j)$. It follows that the probability of the item selected falling into class $A_i \cap B_j$ is $P(A_i) P(B_j)$ when A and B are independent. Because the classes of A and B are mutually exclusive and collectively exhaustive,

$$\sum_{i=1}^{s} P(A_i) = 1 \quad \text{and} \quad \sum_{j=1}^{r} P(B_j) = 1.$$

So there are $(s - 1)$ independent probabilities $P(A_i)$ and $(r - 1)$ independent probabilities $P(B_j)$. Hence in an $r \times s$ contingency table, where $r =$ number of rows and $s =$ number of columns, there are $(r - 1)(s - 1)$ cells to which independent probabilities can be assigned. The number of degrees of freedom for an $r \times s$ table is accordingly $(r-1)(s-1)$. For example, for a 3×3 table, the number of degrees of freedom is $(3-1)(3-1) = 4$.

EXAMPLE 2

Given the following data, use the χ^2 test to determine whether the number of accidents in a group of factories is independent of the age of the worker.

Number of Accidents	Age		
	Under 21	21–44	45–65
0	120	360	220
1	40	28	2
2	13	5	2
3 or more	7	2	1

No. of Accidents	Age			Total
	Under 21	21–44	45–65	
0	120 157·5 −37·5	360 345·6 +14·4	220 196·9 +23·1	700
1	40 15·7 +24·3	28 34·6 −6·6	2 19·7 −17·7	70
2 or more	20 6·8 +13·2	7 14·8 −7·8	3 8·4 −5·4	30
Total	180	395	225	800

The expected frequencies are calculated in the same way as for a 2×2 contingency table. For example, the expected frequency for the bottom right-hand cell is $(225 \times 30)/800 = 8·4$. The expected frequencies are rounded, where necessary, to make their column and row totals agree with those of the observed frequencies.

$$\chi^2 = \frac{(37\cdot5)^2}{157\cdot5} + \frac{(14\cdot4)^2}{345\cdot6} + \frac{(23\cdot1)^2}{196\cdot9} + \frac{(24\cdot3)^2}{15\cdot7} + \frac{(6\cdot6)^2}{34\cdot6}$$

$$+ \frac{(17\cdot7)^2}{19\cdot7} + \frac{(13\cdot2)^2}{6\cdot8} + \frac{(7\cdot8)^2}{14\cdot8} + \frac{(5\cdot4)^2}{8\cdot4}$$

$$= 100\cdot22.$$

No. of degrees of freedom $= (3 - 1)(3 - 1) = 4$. With 4 d.f., $\chi^2 = 13\cdot28$ is significant at the 1% level, so the above value is highly significant of an association between number of accidents and age. The observed frequencies are greater than the expected frequencies for the lower age group as the accident rate increases, so that this group is more accident-prone.

It will be seen from the graph on page 318 that the χ^2 distribution, like the Normal distribution, is continuous. Hence it can be validly applied only when the sample size n is large. Moreover, the continuity requirement demands also that no expected cell frequency should be less than 5. For this reason, it is often desirable to combine cell frequencies when the observed frequencies in any row (or column) are small. For example, the data tell us that only 1 individual in the 45–65 age group had 3 or more accidents, the expected frequency being $(10 \times 225)/800 = 2\cdot4$. This is too low to meet the continuity requirement, and so the third and fourth rows of the data are combined for the purpose of calculating χ^2. A continuity correction, called *Yates' correction*, is sometimes applied to the data by deducting $\frac{1}{2}$ from the difference $O - E$ for each cell. When the differences are large, however, this makes no appreciable difference to the result.

3. Goodness of Fit

As well as testing association between attributes, the χ^2 test can also be used to test whether an observed frequency distribution differs significantly from a theoretical distribution.

EXAMPLE 3

An urn contains red, green and white balls which are identical in every respect but colour. 60 balls are drawn from the urn, each ball being replaced immediately it is drawn and the colour noted. The numbers of different colours obtained are Red: 15, Green: 26, White: 19. Test the hypothesis that the number of balls of each colour in the urn is the same.

	Colour			Total
	Red	Green	White	
Observed frequency	15	26	19	60
Expected frequency	20	20	20	60
$O - E$	-5	6	-1	0

If the numbers of balls of each colour in the urn are equal, then the probability of drawing a ball of any particular colour is $\frac{1}{3}$. Since there are three probabilities to be estimated, corresponding to the three outcomes, the number of degrees of freedom is $3 - 1 = 2$.

$$\chi^2 = \sum \frac{(O - E)^2}{E}$$
$$= \tfrac{25}{20} + \tfrac{36}{20} + \tfrac{1}{20}$$
$$= 3 \cdot 1.$$

With 2 d.f., $\chi^2 = 5 \cdot 99$ is significant at the 5% level, so that the null hypothesis that the numbers of balls of each colour are equal is not rejected.

In this Example, the hypothesis tested is whether an observed set of sample frequencies could have been obtained from a population with a rectangular distribution. In a similar way it can be tested whether a population has a Binomial, Poisson, Normal or some other distribution for some measurable characteristic.

EXAMPLE 4

Four coins were tossed 100 times and the observed number of occasions on which 0, 1, 2, 3, 4 heads were obtained was, respectively, 8, 17, 51, 18, 6. Test the hypothesis that the four coins were unbiased.

If the four coins are unbiased, then the probability of a head from each is $\frac{1}{2}$. Accordingly the frequency of the number of heads obtained should have a binomial distribution, the probabilities of each number being given by the terms of the expansion of $(\frac{1}{2} + \frac{1}{2})^4$.

For example, the probability of 0 heads is $(\frac{1}{2})^4$, so that the expected frequency of 0 heads in 100 trials is $100 \times (\frac{1}{2})^4 = 6\cdot25$. The observed and expected frequencies are shown below.

			No. of Heads			
	0	1	2	3	4	Total
Observed frequency	8	17	51	18	6	100
Expected frequency	6·25	25	37·5	25	6·25	100
$O - E$	1·75	−8	13·5	−7	−0·25	0

$$\chi^2 = \frac{(1\cdot75)^2}{6\cdot25} + \frac{(8)^2}{25} + \frac{(13.5)^2}{37\cdot5} + \frac{(7)^2}{25} + \frac{(0\cdot25)^2}{6\cdot25} = 9\cdot88.$$

The number of independent expected frequencies is $(5 - 1) = 4$. With 4 d.f. $\chi^2 = 9\cdot49$ is significant at the 5% level. Hence at this level, the null hypothesis that the coins are fair is rejected.

In order to test whether an observed frequency distribution is approximately normal, it is first necessary to fit the Normal frequencies to the distribution using the observed mean and standard deviation as estimates of the population parameters. The expected frequencies are found by calculating the area under the Normal curve for each class interval and then multiplying this relative frequency by the total observed frequency. The following example shows what is involved.

EXAMPLE 5

A random sample of businessmen were asked to rate the success of an industrial advertising campaign. The rating scale was from 0 to 100. The results were:

Scale	Rating frequency
0 and < 10	0
10 and < 20	0
20 and < 30	0
30 and < 40	8
40 and < 50	16

50 and < 60	13
60 and < 70	23
70 and < 80	15
80 and < 90	16
90 and < 100	9
	100

Test the hypothesis that the ratings given by the sample are normally distributed, using the 5% level of significance.
(*The mean $\bar{x} = 65\cdot5$, and the standard deviation $s = 17\cdot6$*).

Interval	X	A	p	O	E = 100p
0—	−3·72	0·0000	0·0008	0	0·08
10—	−3·15	0·0008	0·0040	0	0·40
20—	−2·59	0·0048	0·0169	0	1·69
30—	−2·02	0·0217	0·0518	8	5·18
40—	−1·45	0·0735	0·1159	16	11·59
50—	−0·88	0·1894	0·1889	13	18·89
60—	−0·31	0·3783	0·2243	23	22·43
70—	0·26	0·6026	0·1913	15	19·13
80—	0·82	0·7939	0·1238	16	12·38
90—	1·39	0·9177	0·0823	9	8·23
100—	1·96	1·0000			
				100	100·00

The first column shows only the lower limit, i, of each interval which is transformed in column 2 to the standard normal variable

$$X = \frac{i - 65\cdot5}{17\cdot6}.$$

The area under the normal curve giving the probability that an item is less than X is then tabulated in the third column headed 'A', using the values in Table 1. Hence this column shows the cumulative relative frequencies of items less than 0, 10, 20, etc. The last relative frequency in this column is necessarily 1 since all items must be accounted for. The values in column 4 are the differences between successive values of A so that, for example, the probability, p, that an item lies in the interval 30–40 is $0\cdot0735 - 0\cdot0217 = 0\cdot0518$. On the null hypothesis that the distribution is normal, the expected frequency in each interval is $100p$.

Hence

$$\chi^2 = \sum \frac{(O - E)^2}{E}$$
$$= 9 \cdot 26$$

There are 10 cells and three constraints on the number of degrees of freedom, namely the total observed frequency 100, and the estimates of the population parameters based on the observed mean and standard deviation. The number of degrees of freedom for the test is therefore $10 - 3 = 7$. With 7 d.f., $\chi^2 = 14 \cdot 067$ is significant at the 5% level so there is no reason to reject the null hypothesis that the distribution is normal.

In this example, the observed distribution, like the Normal distribution itself, is continuous, so that the intervals used to group the frequencies are exactly coterminous. To test whether a discrete variable has an approximately normal distribution it is accordingly necessary to construct adjacent intervals based on the discrete values of the variable. For example, if the variable takes the values 0, 1, 2, etc. it is natural to group the frequencies in the intervals $0 \pm \frac{1}{2}$, $1 \pm \frac{1}{2}$, $2 \pm \frac{1}{2}$ and so on. The cumulative relative frequencies in column 'A' are then calculated for values of the variable $< -\frac{1}{2}$, $< \frac{1}{2}$, $< 1\frac{1}{2}$, etc. An example is given in Exercises 14, No. 17.

In Chapter 13, section 8 the Poisson frequencies for the data in Exercises 4, No. 19 were calculated and found to be fairly close to the observed frequencies. The null hypothesis that the observations come from a Poisson distribution can now be tested using chi squared.

Goals Scored	Observed Frequencies	Poisson Frequencies	$O - E$	$(O-E)^2/E$
0	14	16·4	−2·4	0·3512
1	26	21·2	4·8	1·0868
2	12	13·8	−1·8	0·2348
3	6⎫	6·0⎫		
4	0⎬ 8	1·9⎬ 8·6	−0·6	0·0419
more than 4	2⎭	0·7⎭		
				1·7147

The frequencies in the last two cells are too low to be considered separately, so these are combined with the number of teams scoring three goals. The observed value of χ^2 is 1·71 with $4 - 1 = 3$ degrees of freedom which is well below the 5% significance level (7·815), so the null hypothesis that this is a Poisson distribution is not rejected. In effect, this means that the distribution of the number of goals scored is random, so that one team is just as likely to score a goal as another.

4. Non-Parametric Tests

The tests of significance which have been discussed in previous chapters have been based on assumptions about the distribution of the variable being sampled. For example, in order to use the t-test for small samples, it must be assumed that the basic variable is normally distributed. Moreover, all of the tests have employed either the known population means and standard deviations or sample estimates of them. It sometimes happens, however, that it is uncertain how the basic variable is distributed. To meet such situations, special tests have been devised which are known as *distribution-free* or *non-parametric* tests since they make no assumptions about the distribution of the basic variable nor utilise the distribution parameters. These tests are sometimes also called "quick-and-easy" tests since they can often be used where a parametric test would be valid and involve fewer calculations than such a test. However, if a parametric test can be validly applied it is usually more reliable than a non-parametric test, and the main justification for using the latter is when a parametric test cannot be applied.

The chi squared test already considered shares several features in common with non-parametric tests. For example, it is based on observed frequencies and not on sample estimates of population parameters. Also it can be applied whatever the distribution of the basic variable; for example it can be used to test goodness of fit of observed frequencies with those expected on the assumption of a normal distribution or a Poisson distribution and so on, without making any pre-empting assumption about the type of frequency distribution to which the basic variable actually does belong.

In the sections which follow, several tests which are specifically non-parametric will be considered.

5. The Sign Test

In a paired sample test based on a small sample the differences between pairs of readings can be computed and a t-test used to determine whether the mean of the differences is significantly different from zero, provided that it is known that the differences are normally distributed. If this is unknown, then one possibility is to consider the number of occasions on which the readings in one sample are greater than those in the other. If it is true that the two samples come from the same population, then one would expect that the first member of a pair of sample values was greater than the second on about half the occasions on which samples are taken. Owing to sampling errors, the proportion of these occasions will probably not be exactly one-half, but any difference from this value can be tested for significance using the binomial probabilities or, if the sample size is large enough, the normal approximation to the binomial probabilities.

An example will clarify the procedure. Suppose that the performance of each member of the staff of a company is assessed annually by his or her immediate superior in terms of a five-point scale, the positions being labelled 1, 2, 3, 4, 5 in order of increasing success. The company concerned runs short staff training courses and the effectiveness of these courses is evaluated in terms of the annual assessments. The scores obtained before and after attending the course by a group of 26 subjects were as follows:

Subject	A	B	C	D	E	F	G	H	I	J	K	L	M
Before (b)	3	2	4	2	4	5	1	3	5	3	3	1	3
After (a)	5	4	3	2	5	1	3	4	4	4	5	3	1

Subject	N	O	P	Q	R	S	T	U	V	W	X	Y	Z
Before (b)	2	4	4	5	3	1	3	4	1	4	1	3	2
After (a)	3	5	2	2	4	5	1	5	3	1	5	2	3

On the assumption that there is no significant difference in performance before and after the course, it is to be expected that the number of subjects for whom $a < b$ is about the same as the number of subjects for whom $a > b$. If the differences $a - b$ are considered, a series of numbers is obtained some of which are positive and some negative. For the above data, the sign distribution is:

Sign of $a - b$: + + − 0 + − + + − + + + −
                  + + − − + + − + + − + − +

Ignoring the tied value for subject D, there are 25 positive and negative signs of which 16 are positive. On the null hypothesis that a sign is equally likely to be positive or negative, the mean number of positive signs is $\frac{1}{2} \times 25$ or 12·5. In order to test whether the difference between the observed number of positive signs and the expected number is due to chance, one could compute the binomial probabilities for $p = \frac{1}{2}$ and $n = 25$ to determine the probability that the number of positive signs is at least as great as 16. If this probability is less than 5% one could then say that the difference is significant at the 5% level. With such a large value of n this is, of course, somewhat laborious. However, with a sample size greater than 20 and, particularly as the binomial distribution with $p = \frac{1}{2}$ is already symmetrical, it is reasonable to use a normal approximation. Thus the mean number of positive signs in a sample of size n is $\frac{1}{2}n$, the variance of this number being $\frac{1}{2} \times \frac{1}{2}n$ or $\frac{1}{4}n$. Hence if the number of positive signs obtained is x, one tests the significance of the standard normal variable

$$X = \frac{\frac{1}{2}n - x}{\frac{1}{2}\sqrt{n}}.$$

In the case considered,

$$X = \frac{16 - 12\cdot5}{\frac{1}{2}\sqrt{25}} = 1\cdot4$$

which is not significant at the 5% level of a one-tailed test. So the null hypothesis that the course did not make any difference could not be rejected.

6. The Median Test

In comparing the results of two samples, the sign test is inapplicable if the samples are not paired or if the sample sizes are not the same. A suitable test to use in such cases, known as the median test, consists in combining the sample results and determining the median for the combined data. On the null hypothesis that the results of the two samples do not differ, one would expect the median of the combined results to be also the median of the results considered separately. In other .words one would expect to find 50% of the readings above and 50% below the combined median for both sets of data.

To illustrate, suppose that the same test in Statistics is given to two sets of pupils from two different schools, the marks for the two sets being as follows:

School A: 25, 25, 24, 24, 23, 23, 22, 22,
21, 20, 19, 19, 18, 18, 17, 15,
15, 14.
School B: 23, 22, 21, 19, 19, 18, 17, 17,
16, 16, 16, 15, 15, 15, 14, 14.

Altogether there are 34 marks and it is easily verified that the median mark for the combined data is 18·5. The distribution of the marks above and below this value for each school is:

	School A	School B
Above median	12	5
Below median	6	11

To test whether or not this is a chance distribution, a chi squared test of association can be used; the contingency table is as follows:

	School A	School B	Total
Above median	12 9 +3	5 8 −3	17
Below median	6 9 −3	11 8 +3	17
Total	18	16	34

Here, $\chi^2 = 4·25$ with 1 degree of freedom, and this is significant at the 5% level. Hence there is evidence to show that the performance of the pupils in School A is better than in School B.

7. The Rank Sum Test

Another way of testing whether the level of performance of the pupils in the two schools in section 6 differs is to use a rank sum test. This consists of arranging the combined results in order of magnitude and assigning a rank to each mark. If the two schools are the same it might be expected that the mark ranks will be more or less evenly distributed between them. This is indicated by comparing the means of the rank sums for each school.

The combined ranks for each test are as follows:

School A	25	25	24	24	23	23		22	22		21		20	19	19		
School B						23		22		21				19	19		
Rank	1·5	1·5	3·5	3·5	6	6	6	9	9	9	11·5	11·5	13	15·5	15·5	15·5	15·5

School A	18	18		17						15	15				14		
School B			18		17	17	16	16	16			15	15	15		14	14
Rank	19	19	19	22	22	22	25	25	25	29	29	29	29	29	33	33	33

In assigning the ranks, account must be taken of tied items. For example, the mark 19 occurs four times and occupies the 14th, 15th, 16th and 17th ranks. Hence the rank 15·5 is assigned to each of its occurrences. The rank sums for each school are:

Rank sum for School A = 1·5 + 1·5 + 3·5 + 3·5 + 6 + 6 + 9
$\qquad$ + 9 + 11·5 + 13 + 15·5 + 15·5 + 19
$\qquad$ + 19 + 22 + 29 + 29 + 33 = 246·5.

Rank sum for School B = 6 + 9 + 11·5 + 15·5 + 15·5 + 19 + 22
$\qquad$ + 22 + 25 + 25 + 25 + 29 + 29
$\qquad$ + 29 + 33 + 33 = 348·5.

A check on these totals is provided by the fact that the sum of the natural numbers from 1 to 34 is

$$\frac{34(34 + 1)}{2} = 595$$

which agrees with the total

$$246·5 + 348·5 = 595.$$

The formula used to test the significance of the rank sums is

$$U = n_1 n_2 + \frac{n_1(n_1 + 1)}{2} - R_1.$$

In the case considered, $n_1 = 18$ and $n_2 = 16$. R_1 is the sum of the ranks of the sample of size n_1, that is, 246·5. The mean of R_1 is easily found; for the expected value of any random selection of one item from the first $n_1 + n_2$ positive integers is $\frac{1}{2}(n_1 + n_2 + 1)$. So

$$E(R_1) = \tfrac{1}{2} n_1(n_1 + n_2 + 1).$$

The formula for the variance of R_1 is rather more difficult to derive and is merely quoted here, namely

$$\text{Var. }(R_1) = \frac{n_1 n_2(n_1 + n_2 + 1)}{12}.$$

It follows that

$$E(U) = n_1 n_2 + \tfrac{1}{2} n_1 (n_1 + 1) - E(R_1)$$
$$= \tfrac{1}{2} n_1 n_2$$

and

$$\text{Var. } (U) = \text{Var. } (R_1)$$
$$= n_1 n_2 (n_1 + n_2 + 1)/12.$$

It can be shown that when n_1 and n_2 are both greater than 8, U is approximately normally distributed, so that

$$X = \frac{U - E(U)}{\sqrt{\text{Var. } (U)}}$$

is a standard normal variable. Hence the normal distribution can be used to determine whether the difference between the observed and expected values of a rank sum is significant. In the present instance,

$$E(U) = \tfrac{1}{2} \times 18 \times 16 = 144$$

and

$$\text{Var. } (U) = (18 \times 16 \times 35)/12 = 840$$
$$R_1 = 246 \cdot 5$$
$$U = 288 + \tfrac{1}{2}(18 \times 19) - 246 \cdot 5 = 212 \cdot 5.$$

So

$$X = \frac{212 \cdot 5 - 144}{\sqrt{840}} = 2 \cdot 36$$

This value is almost significant at the 1% level and confirms the result of the median test which showed that the null hypothesis that no difference in performance between the two schools existed must be rejected.

In carrying out this test, it is immaterial which rank sum is chosen as R_1 provided, of course, the corresponding value of n_1 is used. When the sample sizes are small, the normal distribution cannot be used and reference must be made to specially constructed tables for the distribution of U. The rank sum test is known as the *Mann-Whitney test* (or the U test).

EXERCISES 14

1. State the probability levels at which the following values of χ^2 are significant: (a) 12·23 with 5 d.f., (b) 10·02 with 2 d.f., (c) 14·12 with 10 d.f., (d) 6·51 with 1 d.f.

2. A coin is tossed 100 times and the number of heads obtained is 32. Test the hypothesis that the coin is fair, using both a Normal and a χ^2 distribution.

3. Outline and explain by means of a numerical example, the steps involved in a χ^2 test of association, the type of data on which such a test is used and the way in which the value of χ^2 is interpreted.

4. In an experiment to study the effect of smoking on lung cancer, a sample of 500 people were randomly selected, of which 300 were smokers and 200 were non-smokers. After 10 years, 40 smokers and 10 non-smokers had died. Arrange this data in a contingency table, and test the hypothesis that the death-rate of smokers and non-smokers was the same.

5. A sample survey of users of Public Libraries was conducted to investigate the reading habits of men and women. The results of the investigation were as follows.

| | Type of Literature Preferred | | |
	Fiction	Non-Fiction	Total
Men	132	102	234
Women	168	98	266
	300	200	500

Is there any evidence that women show a greater preference for fiction than men?

6. The data in the following table show television ownership by social class in a random sample of 120 households in a certain town. Test whether there is an association between ownership of a television set and social class

Social Class of Head of Household	Owner	Non-Owner
Upper	15	5
Middle	38	7
Lower	37	18
Total	90	30

7. In a survey of 120 firms the replies were classified by size (employment) and rate of absenteeism to produce the following frequency table:

Size (employees)	Absenteeism Rate			
	less than 1%	1% to 3%	more than 3%	Total
1–100	19	17	4	40
101–1000	19	29	12	60
1001 or more	4	8	8	20
Total	42	54	24	120

Is there any evidence that the level of absenteeism and size are related?

8. In a random sample of 100 examination candidates, it was found 45 did best in English, 35 did best in French and 20 did best in Mathematics. Test the hypothesis that the proportion of candidates doing best in the respective subjects is $4:3:3$.

9. Six coins are tossed 100 times and the observed and expected number of heads obtained were as follows:

	No. of Heads							
	0	1	2	3	4	5	6	Total
Observed frequency	0	5	14	20	40	17	4	100
Expected frequency	1·6	9·4	23·4	31·3	23·4	9·3	1·6	100

Does the observed differ significantly from the expected distribution?

10. The figures given below relate to the frequency of major strikes reported in the former Ministry of Labour Gazette during a twelve-year period. The number of weeks in which 0, 1, 2, 3 and 4 or more strikes occurred is shown together with the corresponding number of weeks expected on the basis of a Poisson distribution.

	No. of Strikes per Week					
	0	1	2	3	4 or more	Total
Actual number of weeks	242	244	109	23	8	626
Expected number of weeks	254	229	103	31	9	626

Consider whether the observed frequencies differ significantly from the Poisson series.

11. Calculate the mean and standard deviation of the following empirical distribution:

Failures/week	No. of weeks
0	4
1	16
2	21
3	23
4	17
5	11
6	6
7	2
8 or more	0

What distribution could be used to describe this data?
Calculate the expected frequencies and test the goodness of fit.

12. In a survey of sheep's teeth obtained from a number of post-mortem examinations of mountain sheep, it was found that of the four lower incisor teeth the number missing was distributed as follows:

Number of missing teeth:	0	1	2	3	4
Number of cases:	227	42	26	15	22

What distribution would you expect if each tooth has the same chance of being lost? Fit this distribution to the data and test for goodness of fit. What conclusion can you draw?

13. The following sample of ten items is known to have come from a population which has a symmetrical, but not necessarily a normal distribution:

$$2 \quad 5 \quad 9 \quad 8 \quad 6 \quad 3 \quad 11 \quad 5 \quad 3 \quad 7$$

Use the sign test to test the hypothesis that the population mean is as high as 10.

14. A new wage agreement involving a major re-grading exercise and the introduction of bonus payments is being negotiated. A random sample of employment and production records was selected and two sets of calculations were made of weekly remunerations: (a) under the existing system, plus 20% to cover the rise in the cost of living, and (b) under the proposed new system.

The results obtained, in £ per week, were as follows:

Subject	1	2	3	4	5	6	7	8	9	10	11	12	13
Old (plus 20%)	56	43	59	62	38	49	53	37	71	53	47	39	37
New	67	58	58	75	47	51	52	49	75	59	56	41	42

Subject	14	15	16	17	18	19	20	21	22	23	24	25
Old (plus 20%)	68	27	68	75	42	53	61	56	58	35	46	37
New	65	31	72	84	45	54	65	61	57	39	49	39

Use a sign test to determine whether, on average, the new agreement will lead to an increase of wages of more than 20%.

15. Use the median test to determine whether the following two samples come from the same population:

Sample A: 6, 11, 6, 1, 11, 5, 7, 2,
5, 9, 9, 3, 8, 3, 9, 3.
Sample B: 14, 9, 3, 5, 9, 12, 9, 3,
6, 10, 3, 8, 12, 7, 10, 1,
7, 10, 10, 7.

16. Test the hypothesis that the two samples in No. 15 come from the same population using the rank sum test.

17. Fit a Normal distribution to the binomial frequency distribution $100(0·7 + 0·3)^8$ and test for goodness of fit. (Take $\sigma = 1·3$).

CHAPTER 15

Quality Control

1. Objectives of Quality Control

The quality of products at various stages of a production run necessarily suffers a certain amount of variability. The dimensions of a standard part of a machine, for example, will not be precisely the same from one unit to another, nor will otherwise identical products precisely resemble each other in surface finish. Bags of fertiliser, sugar and so forth having the same advertised net weight may not have precisely the same weights. Inspection methods of some kind are therefore necessary in order to ensure that products meet minimum quality requirements before delivery to the consumer. Traditionally, inspection has usually been of the finished product or component, the product being passed or rejected, often on the basis of a sample inspection. This method has the disadvantage of *determining* the quality of the product only when the manufacturing process is complete, and is responsible for a great deal of avoidable waste. Modern practice is to aim at *controlling* quality, i.e., not to look for defective products or components after they have been made, but to anticipate tendencies in the process that might cause them to become defective. This is achieved by maintaining a continuous inspection, at regular stages during the manufacturing process, by examining samples of a product or its components and charting the results in a particular way. The chart gives visual indication enabling corrective action to be taken as soon as the productive process begins to go wrong.

Quality control has several advantages over traditional methods. It cuts costs because the number of defectives is reduced and also because less inspection is needed, most of the work of final inspection being eliminated. It helps to create confidence and goodwill among consumers not only because adherence to specification will generally be closer, but also because details of control charts can be supplied to consumers, enabling them to dispense with much of their own routine inspection. Production planning is facilitated by the information provided by control charts because they show whether a production process is capable of working to the tolerances given in a specification. Finally, it helps to improve the morale of the workers, since they can often be trained to maintain the control charts themselves, thereby giving them a greater sense of participation and responsibility.

338

2. Control Charts

Experience shows that, even under mass production, machines cannot turn out parts which are exactly interchangeable, so that some degree of *tolerance* has to be allowed. Modern Quality Control is based on two main principles. One is the variability inherent in any process. The other is that small samples if drawn in a particular way and examined, can yield a useful picture of a bulk lot (e.g., the output of an automatic lathe). Inspection of random samples can show whether a machine is stable, that is whether the variability of the product is solely due to the inherent variability of the machine or whether it could be reduced by better tool-setting, more skilled operation or material of a higher grade. It also enables one to determine the level of precision of this stable state, i.e., its extreme limits of tolerance and what percentage of defectives is likely to be turned out, should parts be required to be produced to closer limits. If the machine is unstable, then inspection indicates whether this instability produces too high a proportion of defectives.

The mean of sample measurements has a known distribution which, in the present context, can be assumed Normal. If a machine is used to bore a hole 3 mm in diameter in a component and the stable state of the machine gives a tolerance of 0·24 mm either way, then one may expect the diameter of a hole to lie within $(3 \pm 0·24)$ mm provided the machine is stable. Every component could be examined to see whether this criterion were actually being fulfilled, but this would obviously be unfeasible if the number of components was large, in which case sampling must be used. The measurements obtained from the samples must lie within limits which are less than the tolerance, since sampling does not permit one to say, with certainty, that the limits are being maintained. If several sample measurements are made, of n measurements each, then an estimate can be made of the standard deviation of the sample means, i.e., $\sigma/\sqrt{n}$, where σ is the population standard deviation of the measurements. The process average is the mean of the sample means. Having obtained a value of the standard error of the sample means by initially taking a sufficient number of measurements, the theory of the Normal curve is used to find limits between which any new sample mean can be expected to lie with a given degree of probability. Thus there is only a 1/1000 chance that any sample mean lies 3·09 (approximately 3) standard errors above the process average and a 1/40 chance that it will lie 1·96 (approximately 2) standard errors above the process average. The former of these limits gives an *outer control limit* (OCL); so that if $\bar{x}$ is the process average, the OCL lies at $\bar{x} \pm 3$ s.e. The 1/40 limit gives the *inner control limit* (ICL), located at $\bar{x} \pm 2$ s.e. The OCL must, of course, lie within the tolerance if it is to be accepted *ab initio*.

The foregoing information is indicated on a control chart such as that shown in Fig. 65. Sample means are plotted on the chart at regular intervals as they become available. Very often, additional limits lying between ICL and OCL are calculated, and if any sample mean lies outside these limits, the process should be checked to see that it is properly functioning. Even if all the means lie within the

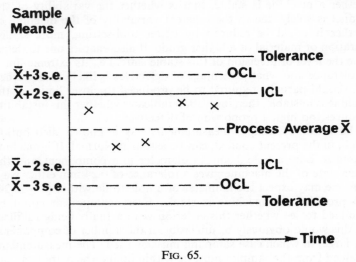

FIG. 65.

ICL it may still be necessary to take action, e.g., if they lie mainly on one side of the process average and particularly if this is so with consecutive samples.

As well as controlling the mean, it is necessary to check that there are no extreme items. Individual measurements may exceed the tolerance but still give a series of averages which lie within the control limits for the mean. The use of the mean, by itself, is therefore unsatisfactory for controlling a measurable magnitude. It must therefore be coupled with a test based on the *range* of items in each sample, i.e., by the difference between extreme items, say w. The average range $\bar{w}$ is estimated from a number of samples and indicated on a control chart for the range, shown in Fig. 66. Alternatively, if the population standard deviation is known, it can be used to estimate the mean range by the method explained in Chapter 13, section 10, assuming that population measurements are normally distributed. The control limits for w are closely related to the population standard deviation; but are usually obtained from a specially prepared table of constants. From such a table, a value of a coefficient D is obtained corresponding to a sample of size n, such that $D\bar{w}$ is the control limit for the range. This limit and the average range are indicated on a control chart for the range (Fig. 66). If tolerances are not being met, three possibilities are open: to improve the accuracy of the machine, to widen the tolerances laid down in the specification, or to accept a certain percentage of defectives.

Some features of products requiring control are not measurable; for example, the surface finish of metal components. The general characteristic of such products is that they can be classified as "pass" or "reject"; there is no intermediate decision. The same principles of variability and sampling are used for the Quality Control of these products, but calculations are made from the percentage of defectives

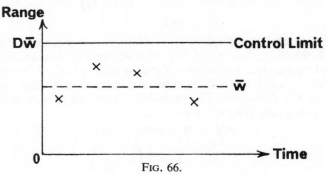

Fig. 66.

found. The probability of a defective is usually quite small so that, in a large sample, the number of defectives follows a Poisson distribution with mean m, the average number of defectives per sample. If the sample size is sufficiently large, m will be large enough for the sample proportions of defectives to be Normally distributed with mean m and standard deviation $\sqrt{m}$. The tolerance in this case will be a maximum number of defectives per sample, whilst the ICL and OCL will, as before, be located at $m + 2\sqrt{m}$ and $m + 3\sqrt{m}$. In this case, of course, there are no lower control limits and no control chart for the range.

3. Acceptance Sampling

Quality checks on a finished product usually involve the inspection of a random sample from a batch. The number of defectives in a fairly large sample can be expected to have a Poisson distribution, and this fact can be used to find the probability that a sample with a given number of defectives came from a batch with, at most, a given percentage of defectives. For example, if a batch contains 2% defectives, then the mean number of defectives in a sample of 100 is 2. But a sample of 100 containing 2 defectives might easily have come from a batch in which the proportion of defectives is greater or less than 2%. If a lot is rejected when the sample contains 2 or more defectives, it could well happen that the lot itself contains less than 2% defectives. Thus when the lot contains only 1% defectives, the mean number of defectives in a sample of 100 is $m = 1$, and the probability that a sample from this population contains 2 or more defectives is, using the Poisson distribution,

$$P(x \geqslant 2) = 1 - \{P(0) + P(1)\}$$
$$= 1 - e^{-1}\left(1 + \frac{1}{1!}\right)$$
$$= 0.26.$$

When a lot is rejected if a sample of 100 contains 2 or more defectives, there is thus a probability of 26% of rejecting a lot containing only 1% defectives. This probability is thus a measure of the *producer's risk* that a good lot will be rejected. Suppose now that the lot contains 3% defectives. The probability that the sample contains fewer than 2 defectives when $m = 3$ is

$$P(x < 2) = P(0) + P(1)$$
$$= e^{-3}\left(1 + \frac{3}{1!}\right)$$
$$= 0.2.$$

This probability is a measure of the *consumer's risk* that he will accept a bad lot containing 3% defectives under this sampling plan. The probabilities of rejecting a lot sampled when the sample size is n and the permissible number of defectives in a sample is less than m, are tabulated for various values of n and m and different values of percentage of defectives in the lots sampled. For each pair of values of n and m, it is possible to construct an *Operating Characteristic Curve* from which can be estimated the producer's and consumer's risk of rejection or acceptance of a lot with a given percentage of defectives. The O.C.C. for $n = 100$, $m = 2$ is shown in Fig. 67.

The graph shows that the producer's risk of 10% is that a good lot with only 0.6% defectives will be rejected by this plan; whilst the consumer's risk of 10% is that he will accept a poor lot with 3.8% defectives. Assuming that 2% is the maximum proportion of defectives which the consumer will accept, increasing the sample size will lower the consumer's 10% risk to accepting a poor lot with something less than 3·8% defectives, though at the same time, this will increase the producer's risk that a very good lot is rejected. The

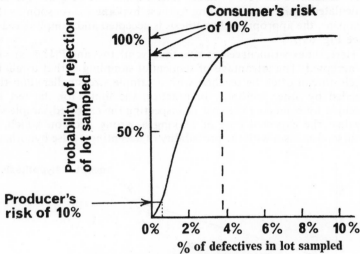

O.C.C. when sample size = 100
permissible no. of defectives = 1 or less

FIG. 67.

converse situation obtains if the sample size is reduced, so that a small sample favours the producer, whilst a large sample favours the consumer, though, of course, a large sample will prove more expensive.

Acceptance sampling is used in auditing to check the accuracy of ledgers. Here the *acceptable quality level* (AQL) is, say, less than 2 errors per 100 entries. The "Producer's" risk now is that a complete check would be ordered, even though the ledger were quite up to standard; whilst the "Consumer's" risk is that of accepting a poor ledger.

4. Sequential Sampling

In sequential sampling, the sample size is not fixed in advance. It consists of selecting single items in sequence from the same batch or lot and an accept/reject decision is made when enough evidence has been obtained, i.e., enough samples of 1 have been taken. This accept/reject decision is dependent on the number of samples taken and the cumulative results of these samples. For example, suppose a coin is tossed and it is required to test the hypotheses: (i) $P(\text{Heads}) = 0.5$, or (ii) $P(\text{Heads}) = 0.7$. Tossing is continued until the cumulative number of heads falls outside one or other specially calculated limits corresponding to these hypotheses. As soon as this happens, the appropriate hypothesis is accepted and sampling ceases (see Fig. 68).

Here, the experiment ceases after the seventh toss and $P(\text{Heads})=0.7$ is accepted. The advantage of sequential sampling is that a reliable decision can often be reached with a sample size smaller than that needed by other methods. In practice, the limits for the test are decided by balancing the cost of inspecting the expected sample size against the expected cost of making a wrong decision which, of course, decreases with the probability of accepting a false hypothesis.

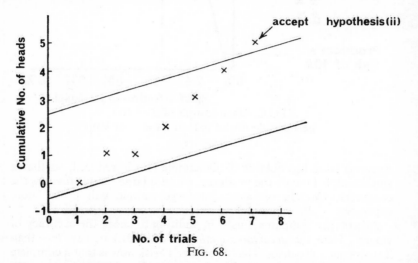

FIG. 68.

This probability decreases as the limits are made wider, entailing a larger sample size and increased cost of inspection. Sequential sampling is thus an extremely useful tool in statistical decision-making. The best sampling plan is chosen by constructing a loss function which balances the cost of sampling against the cost of wrong decisions for different sampling plans, on the assumption that there is some prior knowledge of the possible range of values of the population parameter being investigated. This knowledge is provided by the prior distribution of the parameter in question, obtained by applying Bayes' theorem.

EXERCISES 15

1. A chemical plant shows the following hourly production over a period of ten hours:

   Hour: 1   2   3   4   5   6   7   8   9   10
   Production: 140 131 142 121 134 145 131 148 132 136

   Assuming that the mean production rate is as expected, calculate from this data the upper and lower control limits for use on a control chart, so that these limits cover a 1/20 risk, in order to warn the plant operator of possible changes in the process. Illustrate the chart and show on it the control limits with some specimen hourly recordings.

2. What advantages has statistical quality control over other methods of inspection?

3. What are the principal factors to be considered when adopting an acceptance sampling plan to check the quality of finished products?

4. Draw the Operating Characteristic Curve for the following data:

% defective in lot	0·5	1	2	3	5	9
m in sample	1	2	4	6	10	18

Probability that lot is rejected	0·6%	5%	40%	70%	97·5%	100%

   If the sample size is 200 and a lot is rejected if 5 or more defectives are found, find the consumer's and producer's risk of 10%.
   Explain the meaning of these results.

5. Explain what is meant by sequential sampling and comment on its advantages or disadvantages, if any.

6. A manufacturer produces packets of paper which he states contain a minimum of 100 sheets each. When he checks his output he finds that 4% of packets contain less than 99 sheets of paper and 22·5% of packets contain more than 104 sheets. What is the mean and standard deviation of the number of sheets in a packet? Do you think that the product meets the manufacturer's specification?

7. A sample of size ten is taken from each batch of production in a factory and the batch is rejected if one or more defective items are found in this sample. Construct the operating characteristic curve of this scheme. What is the probability of accepting a

batch containing 20% defectives under this scheme? What is the technical name for this probability?

8. Ten samples, each consisting of four items, gave the following results:

Sample	Mean	Range
1	49·8	9·9
2	46·4	8·6
3	51·2	10·8
4	48·1	10·8
5	50·3	10·7
6	58·1	12·0
7	47·2	9·5
8	48·6	10·6
9	49·7	10·3
10	46·0	9·4

(a) Given that $a_{10} = 0\cdot3249$, use the mean range to obtain an estimate of population standard deviation.

(b) Calculate the control limits for the mean.

(c) Are these results consistent with the manufacturer's specification that each item must fall within the range 48 ±10 units? (You may assume a Normal distribution for the individual items.)

CHAPTER 16

Mathematical Expectation

1. Mathematical Models

The application of mathematical techniques to production planning constitutes what is called Operational Research. Carrying out operational research in a particular industry may call for a good deal of technological knowledge as well as mathematics, but it is to the latter aspect that attention will be directed in the remainder of this book. It very seldom happens that a process of industrial change can be described in exact mathematical terms. On the other hand, it is very often possible to deduce what will happen as a consequence of a change in output or technique from an approximate mathematical formulation of the underlying laws involved. An approximate formulation of this kind is known as a *mathematical model* of the situation in question. Examples of mathematical models have been already given in Chapter 11 in the discussion of cost and sales functions. Thus a cost function of the form $C(x) = bx + a$ is a linear model of the relationship between output and cost which is supposed to represent the actual relationship sufficiently closely to be used in the calculation of optimum or some other output. Whether this is so or not depends on how far the assumptions of the model which are used to obtain the coefficients of the function summarise the facts about the production process. The model assumes, for example, that an increase in output by a given amount involves always the same additional employment of labour and other resources, which can be obtained at constant cost. In practice, such an assumption might be quite unjustified, in which case the model will be invalid and unusable for the purpose for which it is designed, namely to predict costs.

Mathematical models are of two kinds: *probabilistic* (sometimes also called *stochastic*), and *deterministic*. In many situations, a model which takes no account of uncertainty will clearly be unrealistic. For example, the cost function $C(x)$ is intended to be applicable over some pre-determined time period, during which production conditions and factor prices may change in a way which can be predicted only at a given level of probability. The cost of a given output will almost certainly have a probability distribution, so that instead of being able to say that an output x has a definite cost, it can only be said that the cost may be somewhat less or somewhat greater than a certain cost with given probabilities; the probabilities

347

in question being determined on the basis of past experience. In this case the cost function will be designed to indicate, not the actual cost of output x, but the *expected* cost. In a similar manner, the sales function can be designed to take account of the possibility that the total revenue obtainable from the sale of x units of output is uncertain, whilst the probabilities of selling an output which is more or less than x at a fixed price are known. The sales function then indicates the *expected* revenue to be derived from offering x units of output for sale which will almost certainly be less than that derived from a sales function which takes no account of uncertainty.

A deterministic model takes no account of uncertainty. In certain situations, it may be perfectly valid to assume that no uncertainty is present in a process. For example, in a given technological situation, physical units of input may be related in a fixed way to physical units of output, so that if one is changed, the other will also change in an entirely predictable manner. But a deterministic model will clearly be an over-simplification when factors, such as prices, are introduced to which uncertainty attaches. Even so, deterministic models are often extremely useful as a guide to planning, particularly when no reliable information is available to provide a measure of the uncertainties involved. This chapter will be concerned with several aspects of probabilistic models, whilst the remaining chapters deal with both kinds of model.

2. Expected Values

If a variable can take the n values x_i each with probability p_i, then $\Sigma p_i = 1$ and the expected value of the variable is

$$E(x) = \sum_{i=1}^{n} x_i p_i = x_1 p_1 + x_2 p_2 + \ldots + x_n p_n.$$

As thus defined, the expected value of x is simply its mean value. In the present context, the variable x may be either a sum of money or units of a commodity. The gambling situation provides an illustration of the former of these possibilities. Suppose that a trial consists of tossing two fair coins, and that A pays B £2 if no heads occur, £1 if 1 head occurs and nothing if 2 heads occur. Then B's expected gain from one trial is

$$£2 \times P(T, T) + £1 \times P(H, T \text{ or } T, H) + £0 \times P(H, H)$$
$$= £2 \times \tfrac{1}{4} + £1 \times \tfrac{1}{2} + £0 \times \tfrac{1}{4} = £1.$$

If B stakes £1 on the outcome of the trial, then his expected loss is

$$£(1 - 2) \times \tfrac{1}{4} + £(1 - 1) \times \tfrac{1}{2} + £(1 - 0) \times \tfrac{1}{4} = £0.$$

It follows that it is worth at most £1 to B in order to participate in the game, for if he stakes less than £1, his expected gain is positive, whilst by staking more than £1, he will lose, on the average, in a long series of trials. The parallel situation in business is the case in which a man is faced with the decision of investing $£X$ in a business when he expects returns of $£Y_i$ with probability p_i and, at the current rate of interest, demands an expected profit of $£R$. The expected value of R is

$$E(R) = \sum_{i=1}^{n} £Y_i p_i - £X,$$

and he will not make the investment unless $E(R) - £R$ is positive, for otherwise there is some more profitable alternative investment.

The essence of any decision-making process lies in the *comparison* of the profitabilities of alternative policies. The first step in this comparison is the formulation of the alternatives followed by the evaluation of their expected profitability.

EXAMPLE 1

An oil company is contemplating working an area of the North Sea. The profits from different quantities of oil found and the probabilities of finding them are:

Quantity (units)	Profit (units of currency)	Probability
5	30	0·1
4	15	0·3
3	5	0·2
2	0	0·2
1	−10	0·1
0	−15	0·1

(*a*) *How much should the company pay for a survey which would say for sure whether oil was there or not?*

(*b*) *How much should the company pay for a survey which would say for sure how much oil is there?*

(a) The two policies to be compared here are working the area with and without a survey. If the area is worked without a survey, then

$$\text{Expected profit} = 30 \times 0·1 + 15 \times 0·3 + 5 \times 0·2 + 0 \\ \times 0·2 - 10 \times 0·1 - 15 \times 0·1$$

$$= 6 \text{ units.}$$

If the area is worked if and only if a survey shows that oil is present, then the loss of -15 which arises when no oil is found will be replaced by zero profit. So in this case,

$$\text{Expected profit} = 30 \times 0\!\cdot\!1 + 15 \times 0\!\cdot\!3 + 5 \times 0\!\cdot\!2 + 0$$
$$\times 0\!\cdot\!2 - 10 \times 0\!\cdot\!1 + 0 \times 0\!\cdot\!1$$
$$= 7\!\cdot\!5 \text{ units.}$$

Hence it would be an advantage to have this survey made and to pay an amount for it not exceeding $7\!\cdot\!5 - 6 = 1\!\cdot\!5$ units.

(b) In this case the policies to be compared are working the area without a survey and working it only if a survey shows that there are more than two units of oil present. In the latter case, there will be zero profit if there are 0, 1 or 2 units present, and

$$\text{Expected profit} = 30 \times 0\!\cdot\!1 + 15 \times 0\!\cdot\!3 + 5 \times 0\!\cdot\!2 + 0 \times 0\!\cdot\!4$$
$$= 8\!\cdot\!5 \text{ units.}$$

This shows that it would be worth the company's while to pay not more than $8\!\cdot\!5 - 6$ or $2\!\cdot\!5$ units for a survey which would say *how much* oil is present.

An alternative situation in which expected profit can be estimated with a view to its maximisation is that in which the probability distribution of the number of units of a commodity which can be sold at a given price is known. A shopkeeper may wish, for example, to stock up in October with calendars and is able to order calendars in batches of 100 at a cost of £35 per batch. From past experience, the probability distribution of the number of calendars sold is that shown in the following table.

Number sold	Probability
0	0·0
100	0·2
200	0·4
300	0·3
400	0·1
500 or more	0·0
	—
	1·0
	—

If he purchases 300 calendars, the expected number sold

$$= 100 \times 0\!\cdot\!2 + 200 \times 0\!\cdot\!4 + 300 (0\!\cdot\!3 + 0\!\cdot\!1)$$
$$= 220.$$

Hence if each one can be sold for 50p, the shopkeeper's expected profit when he purchases 300 is

$$2 \cdot 2 \times £50 - 3 \times £35 = £5.$$

In order to determine the best purchasing policy, the expected profit from each policy must be evaluated in a similar way. This can be done conveniently by exhibiting the profit or loss from each policy in a Pay-off matrix. For each 100 sold, the profit will be

$$£(50 - 35) = £15,$$

whilst the loss will be $-£35$ per 100 not sold. Hence the Pay-off matrix in £'s will be:

Sold \ No. Purchased	100	200	300	400
0	−35	−70	−105	−140
100	15	−20	−55	−90
200	15	30	−5	−40
300	15	30	45	10
400	15	30	45	60

To find the expected profit of each alternative purchasing policy, each entry in the above table must be multiplied by the appropriate probability. This gives the expected profit of each policy in £'s shown in the following table.

Probability	Sold \ No. Purchased	100	200	300	400
0·0	0	0	0	0	0
0·2	100	3	−4	−11	−18
0·4	200	6	12	−2	−16
0·3	300	4·5	9	13·5	3
0·1	400	1·5	3	4·5	6
Expected profit		15·0	20·0	5·0	−25

Expected profit is highest when 200 calendars are purchased, so that this is the shopkeeper's best policy. The Pay-off matrix shown in the first table is a concept of general applicability and shows the loss or gain arising from intersecting strategies.

In the absence of any knowledge of the probable number sold, apart from the fact that selling zero or 500 or more calendars is totally impossible, the best assumption the shopkeeper can make is that the four remaining outcomes are equally likely, i.e., each has a probability of 0·25. In this case, if he purchases 400, for example, his expected profit will be

$$(-£90) \times 0.25 + (-£40) \times 0.25 + £10 \times$$
$$0.25 + £60 \times 0.25 = -£15.$$

3. Decision Trees

A decision tree is essentially a probability tree applied to the evaluation of expected values. Consider the following situation: A firm makes a profit each year which can take the values £5000, £6000, £7000 or £8000. The managing director notices that whatever profit he makes this year, the next year there is a probability of 0·2 that his profit will be £1000 higher (when an upward move is possible), and there is a probability of 0·3 that his profit will be lower by £1000 (when a downward move is possible). Otherwise his profit next year is unchanged. His profit this year is £8000 and he wishes to determine the expected value of profit in two years' time. The situation can be represented by means of a decision tree (Fig. 69).

It will be observed that the transition probabilities at any stage depend only on the outcome of the preceding stage; so that the

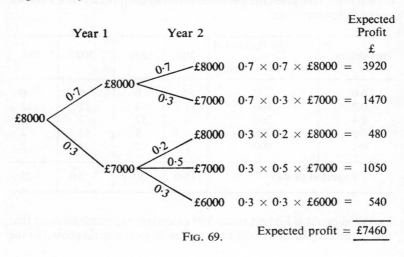

FIG. 69.

stages here form a Markov chain for which the initial and transition probabilities matrices are:

$$
\begin{array}{cccc}
5 & 6 & 7 & 8 \\
(0 & 0 & 0 & 1)
\end{array}
\quad \text{and} \quad
\begin{array}{c|cccc}
 {}_{i}\backslash^{i+1} & 5 & 6 & 7 & 8 \\
\hline
5 & 0.8 & 0.2 & 0 & 0 \\
6 & 0.3 & 0.5 & 0.2 & 0 \\
7 & 0 & 0.3 & 0.5 & 0.2 \\
8 & 0 & 0 & 0.3 & 0.7
\end{array}
$$

An alternative method of finding the distribution of probabilities at the end of Year 2 is to multiply these matrices as explained in Chapter 12, section 5. Thus the probabilities at the end of Year 1 are:

$$
(0 \quad 0 \quad 0 \quad 1)
\begin{pmatrix}
0.8 & 0.2 & 0 & 0 \\
0.3 & 0.5 & 0.2 & 0 \\
0 & 0.3 & 0.5 & 0.2 \\
0 & 0 & 0.3 & 0.7
\end{pmatrix}
=
\begin{array}{cccc}
5 & 6 & 7 & 8 \\
(0 & 0 & 0.3 & 0.7)
\end{array}.
$$

At the end of Year 2, they are thus:

$$
(0 \quad 0 \quad 0.3 \quad 0.7)
\begin{pmatrix}
0.8 & 0.2 & 0 & 0 \\
0.3 & 0.5 & 0.2 & 0 \\
0 & 0.3 & 0.5 & 0.2 \\
0 & 0 & 0.3 & 0.7
\end{pmatrix}
$$

$$
= (0 \quad 0.09 \quad 0.15 + 0.21 \quad 0.06 + 0.49)
$$

$$
\begin{array}{cccc}
 5 & 6 & 7 & 8 \\
= (0 & 0.09 & 0.36 & 0.55).
\end{array}
$$

Expected profit

$$
= £5000 \times 0 + £6000 \times 0.09 + £7000 \times 0.36
$$
$$
+ £8000 \times 0.55 = £7460.
$$

Although the transition probabilities at any stage are independent of all except the outcomes of the stage immediately preceding, the probabilities of each outcome at the end of Year n are not independent of the initial state. For example, if the profit now were £5000, then the expected profit in Year 2 would be different from that calculated above. Many Markov chains tend, however, to a steady state, after a long period of time, which is independent of the initial state; which means that the row matrix $(p_1 \, p_2 \, p_3 \, p_4)$ will be the same in Year $n + 1$ as in Year n. For the above illustration, the condition for a steady state to exist at some stage is that

$$(p_1 \quad p_2 \quad p_3 \quad p_4) = (p_1 \quad p_2 \quad p_3 \quad p_4) \begin{pmatrix} 0{\cdot}8 & 0{\cdot}2 & 0 & 0 \\ 0{\cdot}3 & 0{\cdot}5 & 0{\cdot}2 & 0 \\ 0 & 0{\cdot}3 & 0{\cdot}5 & 0{\cdot}2 \\ 0 & 0 & 0{\cdot}3 & 0{\cdot}7 \end{pmatrix}$$

$$= (0{\cdot}8p_1 + 0{\cdot}3p_2 \qquad 0{\cdot}2p_1 + 0{\cdot}5p_2 + 0{\cdot}3p_3$$
$$0{\cdot}2p_2 + 0{\cdot}5p_3 + 0{\cdot}3p_4 \quad 0{\cdot}2p_3 + 0{\cdot}7p_4).$$

If the row matrix on the left of this equation is equal to that on the right, then

$$0{\cdot}8p_1 + 0{\cdot}3p_2 = p_1$$
$$0{\cdot}2p_1 + 0{\cdot}5p_2 + 0{\cdot}3p_3 = p_2$$
$$0{\cdot}2p_2 + 0{\cdot}5p_3 + 0{\cdot}3p_4 = p_3$$
$$0{\cdot}2p_3 + 0{\cdot}7p_4 = p_4.$$

Solving these equations, we find that $p_1 = \frac{3}{2}p_2$, $p_2 = \frac{3}{2}p_3$, $p_3 = \frac{3}{2}p_4$. But $p_1 + p_2 + p_3 + p_4 = 1$. So $\frac{27}{8}p_4 + \frac{9}{4}p_4 + \frac{3}{2}p_4 + p_4 = 1$, and $p_4 = 8/65$, $p_3 = 12/65$, $p_2 = 18/65$, $p_1 = 27/65$. In the long-run, therefore, the expected profit will be

$$£5000 \times \tfrac{27}{65} + £6000 \times \tfrac{18}{65} + £7000 \times \tfrac{12}{65}$$
$$+ £8000 \times \tfrac{8}{65} = £6015 \text{ (approx.)}$$

A fuller account of the matrix solution of this kind of problem is given in Chapter 20, Section 12.

4. Queuing Theory

Queues develop whenever the rate at which individuals arrive for servicing exceeds the rate at which they are serviced. It is obviously important that an agency providing a service should ensure that its capacity to meet demand for the service is adequate; otherwise queues will develop which involve loss of time and consequently expense to the consumer and possibly loss of custom. Queuing theory provides a method of adjusting capacity to meet demand so that this kind of situation can, as far as possible, be avoided. Now arrivals at a servicing unit are likely to be irregular and possibly random, and the best regulated agency may find that at certain times demand exceeds supply. In these circumstances, the best policy is to ensure that the probability that such a situation arises is as small as possible rather than to try to eliminate it altogether. The latter policy will almost certainly involve an uneconomic cost; whereas the former enables one to maximise the difference between expected revenue and expected cost.

The solution of the queuing problem depends on the construction of the appropriate probability model. One must therefore begin by making assumptions about the structure of the queuing system being studied. A typical queuing situation is the *simple* queue illustrated in Fig. 70. A simple queue consists of a single channel service facility

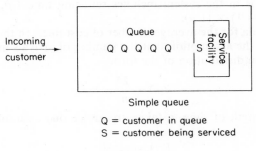

Simple queue

Q = customer in queue
S = customer being serviced

FIG. 70.

at which customers arrive at random intervals for servicing at the average rate of λ per unit time. The length of time taken to service each customer is also random but, on the average μ customers are serviced per unit time. It is clear that if the average number of customers arriving per unit time is greater than the number serviced per unit time ($\lambda > \mu$), then not only will there be a queue but the length of the queue will increase indefinitely as time goes on. One condition for the system to be viable, therefore, is that it be designed so that $\mu > \lambda$. However, even though this is the case it does not follow that there will be no queue. Since arrival and service times are both randomly distributed, the probability that an incoming customer will have to wait because someone is being serviced is never zero so the expected or average number of customers in the queue at any time is also never zero.

The probability that a customer has to wait is given by the ratio

$$\frac{\text{mean rate of arrival}}{\text{mean rate of service}} = \lambda/\mu = \rho$$

where the condition for the queue to settle down is that ρ is less than 1. This ratio measures the *traffic intensity*. It is not difficult to see that the average interval between arrivals is $1/\lambda$ ($\lambda \times 1/\lambda = 1$ time unit) and that $1/\mu$ is the average time taken to service one customer. At any time there may be n customers in the system, comprising $n - 1$ in the queue and 1 customer just about to be serviced. But though n is variable, there is an average number $\bar{n}$ in the system, which is a permanent condition of the system, and which a new customer joining the queue at any time will expect to find. Hence the average length of time a new arrival will have to wait before reaching the servicing point is $\bar{n} \times (1/\mu)$, and this is the average length of time the new arrival is in the queue. The average length of time the new arrival is in the system includes servicing time $1/\mu$, so this is given by $(\bar{n} + 1) \times (1/\mu)$.

The formula for the average number of customers in the system is obtained on the assumption that the number of arrivals in unit time has a Poisson distribution of the form

$$P(n) = \frac{\lambda^n}{n!} e^{-\lambda}$$

whilst the length of time, t, taken to service one customer has the distribution

$$P(t) = \mu e^{-\mu t}.$$

(The latter distribution is known as a *negative exponential distribution*.) On these assumptions it can be shown that the average number of customers in the system is

$$\bar{n} = \frac{\rho}{1 - \rho}$$

where $\rho =$ traffic intensity.

It follows that, for a single channel system,

Average time an arrival
is in queue (waiting time) $= \bar{n} \times (1/\mu)$

$$= \frac{\rho}{1 - \rho} \times \frac{1}{\mu}.$$

Average time an arrival
is in system $\qquad = (\bar{n} + 1) \times (1/\mu)$

$$= \frac{1}{1 - \rho} \times \frac{1}{\mu}.$$

Three further assumptions of a single queue concern queue discipline:

(a) There is no limit to the permissible length of the queue.
(b) Customers will neither be repelled by the length of the queue when they arrive nor, when they join it, leave before being serviced.
(c) Customers are served on a "first in first out" (FIFO) basis.

As a numerical illustration of the foregoing results, suppose that the average service rate μ is 12 per hour, then the average time an arrival is in the queue when customers arrive at rates of 3, 4, 6, 8 and 10 per hour is as follows:

Arrival Rate Per Hour $= \lambda$	$\rho = \lambda/\mu$	$\rho/(1 - \rho)$	Average Time in Queue (minutes) $= (\rho/(1 - \rho))\,(1/\mu)$
3	$\frac{1}{4}$	$\frac{1}{3}$	$\frac{1}{3} \times \frac{60}{12} = 1\cdot67$
4	$\frac{1}{3}$	$\frac{1}{2}$	$\frac{1}{2} \times 5 = 2\cdot5$
6	$\frac{1}{2}$	1	$1 \times 5 = 5$
8	$\frac{2}{3}$	2	$2 \times 5 = 10$
10	$\frac{5}{6}$	5	$5 \times 5 = 25$

The graph below shows the relationship between the varying arrival rate and waiting time with constant mean service time.

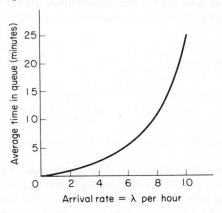

FIG. 71.

The graph (Fig. 71) shows that as the mean arrival rate approximates more closely to the mean service rate, the rate at which waiting time increases becomes very great. When $\lambda = \mu$ (i.e. $\rho = 1$) the queue length may oscillate between zero and infinity so that the average queue length becomes infinitely great as well as the average waiting time.

When the system consists of several channels in parallel it is known as a *complex system* (see Fig. 72). Suppose that the number of channels is c and the servicing rate is μ for each channel. Then for the whole system the servicing rate is clearly $c\mu$. Hence for a complex system

$$\rho = \lambda/c\mu.$$

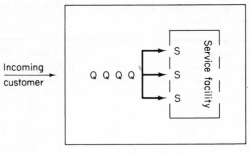

Complex queue

FIG. 72.

The formulae derived for average times in a simple queuing system do not, in general, give the corresponding times for a complex queue. Instead, the average time a customer is in a complex queue is given by the formula

$$t = \frac{(\rho c)^c}{c!\,(1-\rho)^2\,c\mu}\,P_0 \dots\dots\dots(1)$$

where $P_0 = \dfrac{c!\,(1-\rho)}{(\rho c)^c + c!\,(1-\rho)\left\{\sum\limits_{n=0}^{c-1}\dfrac{1}{n!}\,(\rho c)^n\right\}}$

is the probability that, at any time, there are no customers in the system.

It is easy to verify that when $c = 1$ (a simple queue) formula (1) is equivalent to the formula for the average length of time a customer has to wait in a single channel queue. Also from formula (1) the length of time a customer is in a multi-channel system is clearly

$$t + \frac{1}{\mu}.$$

EXAMPLE 2

An enquiry desk was set up in the hallway of a company's offices. Callers, all of whom were on the company's business, arrived at the rate of 20 per hour, and were dealt with on an average at the rate of 30 per hour. If the cost of one clerk to staff the desk for an 8-hour day is 75p per hour and the average cost of the visitor's time is £3 per hour, consider the case for employing a second clerk at the desk at 75p per hour.

When one clerk is employed, traffic intensity $\rho = 20/30 = 2/3$.
Average number of visitors in system $= \rho/(1 - \rho) = (\frac{2}{3})/(\frac{1}{3}) = 2$.

Average time a visitor is in the system $= 2 \times \frac{1}{30} + \frac{1}{30} = 0\cdot1$ hr.
Average cost per visitor $= £3 \times 0\cdot1 = £0\cdot30$.
There are 160 visitors each day, so that total cost per day to company
$= 160 \times £0\cdot30 + 8 \times £0\cdot75 = £54$.

The use of two clerks results in a complex system with $c = 2$. In this
case, $\rho = 20/(2 \times 30) = 1/3$.

Using the formula for a complex queue,

$$P_0 = \frac{2\,!(1 - \frac{1}{3})}{(\frac{2}{3})^2 + 2\,!(1 - \frac{1}{3})(1 + \frac{2}{3})}$$

$$= \frac{4/3}{(4/9) + (20/9)}$$

$$= \tfrac{1}{2}.$$

So

$$t = \frac{(\frac{2}{3})^2}{2\,!(\frac{2}{3})^2 \times 2 \times 30} \times \tfrac{1}{2}$$

$$= \frac{1}{240}\ \text{hour.}$$

Hence the length of time each caller is in the system is

$$\frac{1}{240} + \frac{1}{30} = \frac{3}{80}\ \text{hour.}$$

Total cost per day to company $= 160 \times £\dfrac{3 \times 3}{80} + 8 \times £1\cdot5$

$$= £30.$$

There is thus a definite saving in employing two clerks.

5. Simulation

An alternative method of determining the characteristics of a
queue is to obtain an observed frequency distribution of arrival
times, random numbers being assigned to the arrival times in
proportion to their frequencies. By means of a random number
table, or by using some random number generating device, a model
of arrival times can be constructed for a typical interval, from which,
for example, average waiting time per item can be calculated. To
illustrate, suppose that a machine can process an article in 5 minutes
and that the arrival times of articles to be processed have the following frequency distribution:

Interval between
  arrivals (min.):   2   3   4   5   6   7   8   Total
% frequency: 2   5   11   20   22   31   9   100

If the articles arrive at random it can be said, for example, that the probability that 4 minutes will elapse until the arrival of the next article when one has just arrived is $11/100$. In order to determine a

Interval between Arrivals (min.)	Frequency	Random Number
2	2	00–01
3	5	02–06
4	11	07–17
5	20	18–37
6	22	38–59
7	31	60–90
8	9	91–99

probable total waiting time in a given interval of, say, 1 hour, a model is constructed of the way in which articles are likely to arrive during that hour. This is done by assigning random numbers to each interval, so that the number of numbers assigned is proportional to each frequency.

Using the first column of two-figured numbers in Table 5, the first number 23 corresponds to an interval of 5 minutes, the second 05 to an interval of 3 minutes, and so on. Continuing in this way, the sequence of arrival times (shown opposite) is obtained. A positive entry in the last column of the table indicates that an item is waiting that length of time for processing, whilst a negative entry indicates machine-idle time. The average waiting time per item is $9/11$ minutes, whilst the average machine idle time is 5 minutes per hour. It should be observed that the results obtained here do not agree with those obtained by the methods of the preceding section, since they were derived on the assumption that arrivals per unit time had a Poisson distribution, whereas the distribution in the present example is not. The above method is known as the *Monte Carlo Method,* and is particularly useful when it is difficult to obtain a theoretical distribution to fit the observed frequency distribution, or when the queuing situation is complex, involving more than one service channel.

Item	Arrival Time (min.)	Cumulative Total of Arrival Times (1)	Cumulative Total Processing Time (2)	Waiting Time (2)–(1)
1	5	5	5	0
2	3	8	10	2
3	4	12	15	3
4	6	18	20	2
5	8	26	25	−1
6	4	30	31	1
7	6	36	36	0
8	8	44	41	−3
9	6	50	49	−1
10	5	55	55	0
11	4	59	60	1

Total waiting time = 9 min.

In the foregoing model, it is assumed that service time for each item is constant. In certain situations this may not be unrealistic, for example items arriving for processing in a purely mechanical system may have a uniform processing time. However, the general rule is that, although items arrive for the same kind of service, there will be detailed differences in the service required which will result in a probability distribution of service times. This possibility has already been mentioned in section 4, and it is also possible to take account of it in the simulation model. Suppose, for example, that the inter-arrival times of customers at a counter, and the servicing time per customer have the following observed probability distributions:

Inter-arrival time (min.)	3	5	7	9	11
Probability:	0·08	0·20	0·50	0·12	0·10

Service time (min.)	3	5	7	9	> 9
Probability	0·15	0·40	0·30	0·15	0

A simulation model for both distributions is prepared in exactly the same way as that for one. Random numbers are assigned to each distribution as follows:

Inter-arrival Time (min.)	R. Ns.	Service Time (min.)	R. Ns.
3	00–07	3	00–14
5	08–27	5	15–54
7	28–77	7	55–84
9	78–89	9	85–99
11	90–99		

Two series of random numbers are now needed to simulate the time sequence for each distribution. Thus to obtain the inter-arrival times of the first five items, select the first five two-digit random numbers in the final column of Table 5 and use these to simulate the inter-arrival times of the first five items. Similarly, use the next five two-digit random numbers in this column to simulate the first five service times. The results are shown in the following table.

Item	A/T (min.)	Cu. Total A/T (1)	S/T (min.)	Cu. Total S/T (2)	Waiting Time (2) − (1)
1	7	7	5	5	−2
2	7	14	5	12	−2
3	7	21	7	21	0
4	11	32	5	26	−6
5	5	37	7	39	2

Again it is assumed that, at the start, there is an item already in the system which takes 5 minutes to service. The first customer arrives 7 minutes later, also taking 5 minutes to service and so on. The cumulative total arrival times are simply the cumulative totals of the arrival times in the preceding column. However the total service time must be cumulated with reference both to the individual service times and to the cumulative total arrival times. The counter appears to be idle about 25 % of the time during the first 40 minutes, although the fifth customer is kept waiting for 2 minutes.

6. Replacement Policies

The age at failure of pieces of equipment is not usually even approximately the same for all pieces, but has a probability distribution. This means that there is no obvious time at which all pieces should be replaced. Generally speaking, when a piece of equipment fails, it has to be replaced at once; but, on the other hand, it is possible that individual replacement for all pieces of equipment is more expensive than group replacement at fixed intervals, since individual replacement cost per unit is usually higher than group replacement cost per unit. Hence there is usually a choice between replacement policies and a consequent need to determine their relative costs in order that a decision between them can be made.

EXAMPLE 3

A unit of electrical equipment is subject to failure. The probability distribution of its age at failure is:

Age at failure (weeks)	2	3	4	5
Probability	0·2	0·4	0·3	0·1

Initially 1000 new units are installed, and any unit which fails is replaced by a new unit at the end of the week in which it fails.

(a) *Calculate expected numbers of units to be replaced in each of weeks 1 to 7.*
   What rate of failures can be expected in the long run?

(b) *Among the 1000 installed units at the start of week 8, how many can be expected to be aged 0 weeks, 1 week, 2 weeks, 3 weeks, or 4 weeks. Compare this with the expected frequency distribution in the long run.*

(c) *Replacement of individual units on failure costs 5 pence each. An alternative policy is to replace all units after a fixed number of weeks (at a cost of £30) and to replace any units failing before the replacement week at the individual cost of 5 pence each. Should this preventative policy be adopted?—if so, after how many weeks should all units be replaced?*

(a) End of week — Number replaced

End of week		Number replaced
1		0
2	$0·2 \times 1000$	$= 200$
3	$0·4 \times 1000$	$= 400$
4	$0·2 \times 200 + 0·3 \times 1000$	$= 340$
5	$0·4 \times 200 + 0·2 \times 400 + 0·1 \times 1000$	$= 260$
6	$0·3 \times 200 + 0·4 \times 400 + 0·2 \times 340$	$= 288$
7	$0·1 \times 200 + 0·3 \times 400 + 0·4 \times 340 + 0·2 \times 260$	$= 328$

Average age at failure
$$= 2 \times 0.2 + 3 \times 0.4 + 4 \times 0.3 + 5 \times 0.1 = 3.3 \text{ weeks.}$$
Hence average rate of failure in the long run $= 1000/3.3 = 303$ per week.

(b) Expected frequency distribution of ages at beginning of week 8

Age (weeks)		Number
0		328
1		288
2	$0.8 \times 260 =$	208
3	$\{1 - (0.2 + 0.4)\} \times 340 =$	136
4	$\{1 - (0.2 + 0.4 + 0.3)\} \times 400 =$	40
		1000

Since 303 units are replaced on the average each week, the expected number of units at any time having ages 0 and 1 week is 303 each. The long run expected age distribution is therefore:

Age (weeks)		Number
0		303
1		303
2	$(1 - 0.2) \times 303 =$	242
3	$\{1 - (0.2 + 0.4)\} \times 303 =$	121
4	$\{1 - (0.2 + 0.4 + 0.3)\} \times 303 =$	31
		1000

(c) With individual replacement, the average replacement cost is $303 \times £0.05 = £15.15$ per week.
If there is group replacement once every two weeks, there will be no individual replacements, and the weekly average replacement cost $= £30/2 = £15$. So it will certainly be worth while adopting a group replacement policy.
With group replacement,

(i) Every 3 weeks: Individual replacement cost $=$
$$200 \times £0.05 = £10$$
Average cost $= £(10 + 30)/3 = £13.33$ per week.
(ii) Every 4 weeks: Individual replacement cost $=$
$$(200 + 400) \times £0.05 = £30$$
Average cost $= £(30 + 30)/4 = £15$ per week.

The minimum cost replacement policy is group replacement every 3 weeks at a cost of £13·33 per week.

For an alternative solution of this problem by matrix methods, see Exercises 20, No. 17.

EXAMPLE 4

The manager of a fleet of hire cars wishes to establish a purchasing policy for tyres. The cost of a new tyre is £5, but the cost of a tyre failure in use is estimated as an average £15. Observation of past tyre performance shows the following failure rates:

Mileage	% Fail	Mileage	% Fail
Under 10,000 miles	0	16,000–	12
10,000–	2	18,000–	22
12,000–	4	20,000–	35
14,000–	5	Over 22,000	20

On these data establish the most economic replacement policy.

The choice is between replacing tyres after 10,000 miles, 12,000 miles, 14,000 miles, etc. If tyres are replaced every 14,000 miles (say), then expected replacement cost = £5 + (0·02 + 0·04) × £15 = £5·90 and the average cost of replacement per 10,000 miles is £5·9/1·4. The average replacement costs of the alternative policies may be found in a similar way.

Replace after	Total Expected Cost	Expected Cost per 10,000 miles
10,000 miles	£5 + 0 × £15 = £5	£5
12,000 miles	£5 + 0·02 × £15 = £5·30	£4·42
14,000 miles	£5 + 0·06 × £15 = £5·90	£4·21
16,000 miles	£5 + 0·11 × £15 = £6·65	£4·16
18,000 miles	£5 + 0·23 × £15 = £8·45	£4·69

The average mileage of a tyre before failure is 19,600 miles, so that the average cost per 10,000 miles of replacing a tyre only when it fails is £15/1·96 or £7·63. This compares unfavourably with all of the above policies. The cheapest policy is therefore to replace each tyre after 16,000 miles if it has not failed earlier.

EXAMPLE 5

Makalu Ltd. uses a large number of machines which incoporate a special component, liable to failure. Its present policy is to replace each component individually following failure. Records have been kept of the working lives, before failure, of 500 components and have revealed the following results:

Number of Components	Length of Life (months)
75	1
225	2
150	3
50	4
500	

Assuming that component lives are always an exact number of months, compare a policy of bulk replacement at intervals of one, two and three months with the existing policy of individual replacement. The cost of individual replacement is £42 per unit and the cost of bulk replacement is £24 per unit, in both cases including the cost of the component.

The average life of a component is 2·35 months.
Hence average cost of individual replacement is
$$\frac{£42}{2·35} = £17·87 \text{ per month per unit.}$$

If all components are replaced after 1 month, then the average cost per unit per month is £24.

Average cost of bulk replacement after 2 months
$$= \frac{1}{2}\left(\frac{75}{500} \times £42 + £24\right) = £15·15.$$

Average cost of bulk replacement after 3 months

$$= \tfrac{1}{3} \{(0 \cdot 15 + 0 \cdot 45 + 0 \cdot 15^2) \times £42 + £24\} = £16 \cdot 72.$$

Hence the cheapest policy is bulk replacement every 2 months at an average cost of £15·15 per month per unit.

7. Simulation and Replacement Policies

In Example 5 it is assumed that the lives of components have a discrete probability distribution. The distribution will certainly be continuous so that more detailed information about the cost of the various policies might be obtained by simulation. Since the simulated model can be constructed by the aid of a computer it is possible to consider the performance of a large sample of components using a model which is based on the observed probability distribution. This procedure has the advantage that it can be carried out quickly and without any further recourse to the physical situation being modelled.

The procedure may be illustrated using the data in Example 5. First convert the frequencies to percentage frequencies and assign random numbers to each life span:

Life (months)	% Fail	R. Ns.	Cu. Frequency (%)
0–1	15	00–14	15
1–2	45	15–59	60
2–3	30	60–89	90
3–4	10	90–99	100

Next draw the cumulative frequency graph showing the percentage of components which fail at less than a specified age. (see Fig. 73).

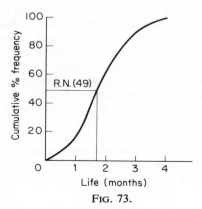

FIG. 73.

Select a number (say 5) of components for study and also the same number of random numbers: 11, 32, 25, 49, 31 (see bottom row of Table 5). Each of these random numbers corresponds to a randomly chosen life. For example, the random number 49 corresponds to a life of 1·7 months which is obtained by interpolation from the cumulative frequency graph. The lives of the remaining components are ascertained in the same way and recorded in the table below.

| | Component No. | | | | | | Cumulative |
	1	2	3	4	5	Clock	Failure No.
R.N.	11	32	25	49	31	0	
Life (months)	0·7	1·4	1·2	1·7	1·4	0·7	
R.N.	42	—	—	—	—		1
Life (months)	1·6	0·7	0·5	1·0	0·7	1·2	
R.N. Life, etc.						0	

The "Clock" is initially set to zero and then advanced to indicate the life of the component with the shortest life (0·7 months). If the policy being considered is bulk replacement after 1 month, then this item will have failed before this time has elapsed. So "1" is recorded in the cumulative failure column. A new random number is then chosen to represent the replacement of component no. 1 and the life of the new component ascertained from the cumulative frequency graph. The clock reading (0·7) is deducted from the remaining lives and the shortest among the five new readings is added to the clock. In the case considered the shortest life is 0·5 and so the clock is reset to 1·2 months. Since this exceeds the replacement period being considered there are no more failures in the current period, so the clock is returned to zero and five new random numbers selected and the whole process repeated. A large number of replacement periods are simulated in this way and the average number of failures per replacement period is calculated, from which it is a simple matter to find the average cost of the replacement policy. This can be compared with alternative policies by constructing a fresh model for replacement periods of two months, three months or even an intermediate number of months. It is thus possible to obtain a refined picture of the replacement process which will lead to a more informed decision than was possible by the method of Example 5.

Notice that simulation consists of making random selections from a probability distribution, so that it is essentially similar to any other process of statistical sampling. As was pointed out in section 5, simulation is certainly useful when a theoretical approximation to an observed distribution with well-defined mathematical properties cannot be established. It may, however, also be an advantage to use a simulation model when such a theoretical distribution is applicable. This may be so if the situation being modelled is at all complex and involves several interacting probability distributions. In such cases, the theoretical distributions can be used as the basis of the model, enabling one to assign random numbers with high accuracy.

8. A Note on Queuing Theory

It was stated in section 4 that the probability that an arrival has to wait for servicing in a simple queuing system is $\rho = \lambda/\mu$. This is, of course, the probability that the arrival will not find the system free. Also the probability that the arrival will not have to wait is $1 - \rho$ which is also the probability that no one is being serviced. In order to derive the formula for the average number of units in the system at any time it is first necessary to obtain the probability function $P(n)$ giving the probability that there are, at any time, n units in the system. This function can be obtained rigorously from the basic mathematical distributions of arrivals and service times by methods which lie beyond the scope of this book. Instead, one may use an informal argument. When a new arrival comes to the system he will find 0, 1, 2, etc., units in the system which must be serviced before he reaches the service point himself. The probability that there are n units in the system is the probability that he must wait for just these n units to be serviced and then be serviced himself. The situation is, in fact, equivalent to a series of independent trials in which there are n "failures" (probability $= \rho$) followed by one "success" (probability $= 1 - \rho$). This probability is clearly $\rho^n(1 - \rho)$, so that the probability function giving the probability that there are n units in the system is

$$P(n) = (1 - \rho)\rho^n \qquad (n = 0, 1, 2, \ldots).$$

Hence the expected or mean value of n (the average number in the system) can be found in the ordinary way:

$$E(n) = \sum_{n=0}^{\infty} n(1 - \rho)\rho^n$$
$$= (1 - \rho)(0.\rho^0 + 1.\rho + 2.\rho^2 + 3.\rho^3 + \ldots) \qquad (1)$$

The sum of the series on the right can be obtained by applying the theory of convergent geometric progressions which, for the benefit of readers who are not conversant with it, is explained in Chapter 19. Thus $E(n)$ is multiplied by ρ to give

$$\rho E(n) = (1 - \rho)(1.\rho^2 + 2.\rho^3 + \ldots) \qquad (2)$$

Subtracting (2) from (1) then gives

$$(1 - \rho)E(n) = (1 - \rho)(\rho + \rho^2 + \rho^3 + \ldots)$$

So

$$\begin{aligned} E(n) &= \rho + \rho^2 + \rho^3 + \ldots \\ &= \rho(1 + \rho + \rho^2 + \ldots) \\ &= \rho\left(\frac{1}{1 - \rho}\right) \qquad \text{(since } 0 \leqslant \rho < 1) \\ &= \rho/(1 - \rho). \end{aligned}$$

This is the result stated in section 4 for the average number of customers in the system.

The probability function $P(n)$ can also be used to obtain the average queue length, that is, the average number in the system who are not actually being serviced. Now there are times when there is no queue, so one may first determine the average queue length when this possibility is allowed for. If $n = 0$ or 1, then there is no queue, so that if the number of people in the queue is m, then $m = 0$ when $n = 0$ or 1. Hence the expected value of m is

$$E(m) = \sum_{n=0}^{\infty} m(1 - \rho)\rho^n \quad (m = 0 \text{ when } n = 0,$$
$$m = n - 1 \text{ when } n > 0)$$
$$= (1 - \rho)(0.\rho^0 + 0.\rho + 1.\rho^2 + 2.\rho^3 + \ldots) \qquad (3)$$

Also

$$\rho E(m) = (1 - \rho)(1.\rho^3 + 2.\rho^4 + \ldots) \qquad (4)$$

Subtracting (4) from (3) then gives

$$(1 - \rho)E(m) = (1 - \rho)(\rho^2 + \rho^3 + \rho^4 + \ldots)$$

So

$$\begin{aligned} E(m) &= \rho^2(1 + \rho + \rho^2 + \ldots) \\ &= \rho^2/(1 - \rho). \end{aligned}$$

Hence the average number of people in the queue, counting occasions on which the queue length may be zero, is given by the formula

$\rho^2/(1 - \rho)$. For example if $\rho = 2/3$, as for the single channel system in Example 2, then the average queue length is

$$\frac{(2/3)^2}{\left(1 - \dfrac{2}{3}\right)} = 1 \cdot 33.$$

In a practical queuing situation, one may not be so much interested in the average queue length, including those occasions on which there is no queue, as in the average queue length when queues develop. In this case $m = 1, 2, 3, \ldots$ and $n > 1$, so that the probability function of m is given by the conditional probability

$$P(m \mid n > 1) = \frac{P(m)P(n > 1 \mid m)}{P(n > 1)} \quad (m = 1, 2, 3, \ldots)$$
$$= \frac{P(n)P(n > 1 \mid n)}{P(n > 1)} \quad (n = 2, 3, 4, \ldots).$$

Here $P(n > 1) = 1 - (1 - \rho) - (1 - \rho)\rho = \rho^2$, and under the stated condition for the value of n, $P(n > 1 \mid n) = 1$. So

$$P(m \mid n > 1) = \frac{(1 - \rho)\rho^n}{\rho^2}$$
$$= (1 - \rho)\rho^{n-2} \quad (n = 2, 3, 4, \ldots).$$

Hence the expected value of m when m is greater than zero is

$$E(m \mid m > 0) = \sum_{n=2}^{\infty} m(1 - \rho)\rho^{n-2} \quad (m = n - 1)$$
$$= (1 - \rho)(1 . \rho^0 + 2 . \rho + 3 . \rho^2 + \ldots) \quad (5)$$

Also
$$\rho E(m \mid m > 0) = (1 - \rho)(\rho + 2 . \rho^2 + 3 . \rho^3 + \ldots) \quad (6)$$

Subtracting (6) from (5) then gives
$$E(m \mid m > 0) = 1 + \rho + \rho^2 + \ldots$$
$$= 1/(1 - \rho).$$

Hence if only occasions on which queues develop are considered, the average queue length is given by the formula $1/(1 - \rho)$. For example, if $\rho = 2/3$ (as in Example 2), then the average queue length when there is a queue is

$$\frac{1}{\left(1 - \dfrac{1}{3}\right)} = 1 \cdot 5.$$

The results obtained in this section are valid only for a *simple* queue. The equivalent results for a complex queuing system are, of course, a good deal more complicated. However, it is worth noting that if T hours is the average time a customer spends in the system, *whether simple or complex*, then the number of arrivals during that time is λT, where λ is the number of arrivals per hour. Since a customer takes T hours to pass through the system before any new arrival can leave it, the expected number in the system must be λT. Hence if T is known it is easy to find $E(n)$, the expected number in the system.

EXERCISES 16

1. In three tosses of a fair coin, a player wins £3 if 3 tails occur, £2 if 2 tails occur and he loses £3 if no tail occurs. If one tail occurs, no one wins. Find the expected value of a game to a player and determine whether the game is fair. If the game is not fair, state how much a player should win or lose when one tail occurs in order to make it fair.

2. A fair coin is tossed 5 times and A pays B £1 for each head which appears. If B pays A £4 at the outset, calculate the expected value of the game to A.

3. Two dice are rolled and a player receives £10 if the difference between the scores on the two dice is two or less. Find how much a player should pay when the difference is greater than two in order to make the game fair.

4. A fair coin is tossed 100 times and a player receives £2 if 60 or more heads appear. Find the expected value of the game to him if he pays 30 pence to the banker at the outset.

5. Two dice are rolled 72 times and A pays B £1 for every double six which occurs. What is B's expected gain?

6. A Travel Agency plans to open another branch in one of two locations. As a result of a survey, it is estimated that one location will yield an annual profit of £5000 if it is successful and a loss of £1000 otherwise. For the other location the estimated profit if successful is £7000 and the loss £2000 otherwise. The probability of success at each location is $\frac{1}{2}$. Which location should the management choose in order to maximise profit?

7. A baker makes a special loaf each day which cost 10p each and sells at 15p each. Any loaves not sold at the end of the day must be thrown away. Experience shows that he sells 48, 49, 50, 51 or 52 loaves per day and that probability of specific sales are 0·1, 0·3, 0·4, 0·1, 0·1.

    (a) How many loaves should the baker produce?
    (b) What would be his profit if he knew exactly how many loaves would be sold each day?
    (c) Discuss the advantages and disadvantages of a decision theory approach to this problem.

8. At the market in the morning, before any customers are about, a retailer buys bunches of flowers which cost him £0·10 each to sell at £0·25 each. The retailer buys only in the morning, does not reduce his price and gives any stock not sold by the evening to the local hospital. The various quantities he can buy each morning are 100, 200, 300 or 400 bunches.

    He estimates the demand characteristics each day to be:

Bunches	Probability
0	0·05
100	0·20
200	0·40
300	0·25
400	0·10
500 or more	0·00
	1·00

    Calculate:
    (a) the expected value for each alternative purchasing policy;
    (b) the most probable result of a day's trading if the retailer bought 400 bunches;
    (c) the maximum the retailer should agree to pay for advance knowledge of the exact demand for the following day.
        (Consider how many bunches he would sell in the long run if he bought *exactly* the right number each day.)

9. A manufacturer has three inspection plans A, B and C. The chance that a faulty unit will pass undetected is 2% in plan A, 5% in plan B and 10% in plan C. The respective inspection costs per unit are £0·35, £0·10 and £0·01. All defective units not detected by the manufacturer will be found by the customer and will incur rectification costs of £3·00 for each unit.

(a) Determine the most economic inspection plan.
(b) State in what circumstances a policy of no inspection should be recommended.

10. Using the information below,
    (a) Draw a decision tree diagram to illustrate the relationships between the two sets of outcomes.
    (b) Calculate the net expected monetary value of undertaking both investments.

The following table gives the probabilities associated with three possible outcomes of two investments. The outcomes relate to a set of mutually exclusive, mutually exhaustive and independent events.

Investment Y Net Outcomes (£)	Investment X Net Outcomes (£)			
	0	2000	4000	
0	·04	·12	·04	·20
2000	·12	·36	·12	·60
4000	·04	·12	·04	·20
	·20	·60	·20	

11. A company is considering whether to work one of its North Sea natural gas concessions. It has two options: either to conduct an initial study which would cost £100,000, or not to conduct it. Experience in similar areas has been that initial studies indicate a 5% probability that a workable gas field was likely to exist in the area, and a 95% probability that there would not be one. If the company decides to start drilling, the cost will be £2,000,000. If gas were found, the present worth of gas obtained would be £20,000,000 but if gas were not found the return would be nil.
    The probabilities of finding gas are as follows:
    (1) if an initial study is conducted, and the likelihood of the existence of a field is indicated, the probability is 90%;
    (2) if an initial study is conducted, and the likelihood of the existence of a field is found to be remote, the probability is 2%;
    (3) if no initial study is conducted, the company believes that in its particular area the probability is 6·4%.
    What advice, with supporting arguments and figures, would you give the company?

12. A manufacturer decides to invest £10,000 in modernising the plant and equipment of his factory. There is a 0·7 probability each year that maintenance costs will be £2000 and a 0·3 probability that they will be £1500. The expected addition to annual income is £8000. Draw a decision tree covering the first three years of the project and find the manufacturer's expected profit for Year 3. Find also his expected annual profit in the long run.

13. (a) State the properties relevant to a simple queue.
    (b) Define traffic intensity and calculate the expected length of time a customer will be in a queue if the service rate is 10 per hour and the traffic intensity is 0·8.

14. Explain the characteristics of problems that arise in commerce and industry which would be amenable to solution by use of queuing theory. In what way does simulation help?

15. Show graphically how the average time that one has to wait for a sole telephone operator to answer varies with the number of calls made per hour if the operator can deal with 60 calls per hour. Discuss how the principles behind your graph can be applied to a wide variety of situations.

16. The probability that a customer has to wait longer than time t in a queue is given by $\dfrac{\lambda}{\mu}e^{(\lambda-\mu)t}$. A coin-operated telephone is installed in a canteen for use by the staff. On average 8 people per hour use the telephone, and each call lasts 3 minutes. What is the probability that a member of the staff will have to wait more than 3 minutes before using the telephone?

17. A factory manager has to decide which of two shop maintenance engineers, A or B, to employ. Machines break down on an average at one per hour. The cost of a machine being idle is estimated at £2 per hour. A asks for £1 per hour while B asks for 75p per hour. It is known that A can repair 2 machines per hour while B can repair only $1\frac{1}{2}$ machines per hour. Which is the more economical engineer to employ?

18. A company is about to install a new manufacturing process. Essential to the success of the process is a control unit for which the probability distribution of failures during the lifetime of the installation is estimated to be:

Number of failures	0	1	2	3	4
Probability	0·30	0·25	0·20	0·15	0·10

Spares of the unit can be purchased only at the time of the initial order when their cost will be £2000 each. If there is a failure and no spare is available it has been estimated that the loss of production while the control unit is being repaired together with the direct cost of the repair will cost the company £10,000.

(a) Calculate the expected number of failures.
(b) State the number of spares, if any, the company should purchase at the time of the initial order.
(c) State how many spares the company would have purchased if the probabilities of failure were not known but that it was considered extremely unlikely there would be more than four failures during the life of the machine.

19. A component required in a main assembly is supplied to a company by one of its subsidiaries. Inspection of the component is carried out by the parent company and it is considered by them that the rejection rate is too high; this is thought to be due to poor machining of certain critical dimensions of the component. If a component has to be scrapped, the cost is £5. Production is in batches of 1000 components.

The parent company proposes to send a trained operator to the subsidiary each time a batch of these components goes into production, to carry out the machining of the critical dimensions. It will cost £150 each time to send one of its operators to the subsidiary, but it is expected that the scrap rate will be held at 2%.

The prior probabilities of the percentage defectives under the present circumstances are given in the following table:

Defective components %	Prior probability
2	0·07
4	0·23
6	0·29
8	0·35
10	0·06

(a) Explain the likely derivation of the "prior" probability distribution in this case.
(b) From the given data, determine whether or not the proposed action should be taken.

20. The manager of a fleet of 10 lorries costing £2200 each knows that every lorry will on average require a major overhaul every

2 years. There is, however, a 30% probability that the lorry will have a major breakdown at the end of the first year but not before. The vehicle supplier with whom the manager deals is prepared to replace the whole fleet at a cost of £15,000 at the end of one year's life; £17,500 at the end of two years' life; or £20,000 at the end of three years' life. What is the most economic policy for the manager to follow:

(a) replace the whole fleet after one year;
(b) replace the whole fleet after two years;
(c) replace the whole fleet after three years;
(d) replace each lorry individually?

You may assume that the cost of a major breakdown and overhaul is the same, i.e., £2200 and that after the first year, surviving lorries are subject to the same annual risk of breakdown.

21. As accountant of a manufacturing company you are asked to advise whether or not a new product should be launched on the market. Estimates of annual demand are given as:

Demand	8,000 units	9,000 units	10,000 units
Probability	25%	50%	25%

Estimates of cost per unit are given as:

Cost	£4	£5
Probability	25%	75%

No units can be held in stock for any appreciable time.

(a) What is the minimum price per unit at which the product could be sold at a profit?
(b) If the product was to sell at £6·50 per unit, how many units per year would you recommend should be produced and what will be the resulting profit?

22. A factory has two machines, each of which is liable to break down once every twenty-eight hours. These are maintained by a single repairman who takes two hours, on average, to service one machine.
Assuming the conditions of a simple queue, calculate

(a) the expected number of machines which are not running at any time, i.e. the expected number of machines that are either being serviced or awaiting servicing;
(b) the expected length of time a machine which has just broken down must wait for servicing;

    (c) the expected length of time a machine which has just broken
        down is idle;

    (d) the expected number of machines in the queue when there
        is a queue.

In the light of your answer to (d) are any of the assumptions
that the conditions of a simple queue are satisfied in this case
invalid?

23. A production line can be used for making three different
products, but no more than one type of product can be made in
one day. The probability p_{ij} of manufacturing product j on
day $(t + 1)$, given that product i was manufactured on day t,
is independent of t and given by

$$(p_{ij}) = \begin{array}{c} \\ 1 \\ 2 \\ 3 \end{array} \begin{array}{ccc} & j & \\ 1 & 2 & 3 \\ \begin{pmatrix} \cdot 7 & \cdot 3 & \cdot 0 \\ \cdot 5 & \cdot 3 & \cdot 2 \\ \cdot 0 & \cdot 4 & \cdot 6 \end{pmatrix} \end{array}$$

    (a) On day 1, product 1 is produced. What is the probability
        that it is not produced on day 3?

    (b) In the long run, on what proportion of days will each pro-
        duct be manufactured?

    (c) There is a set-up cost c_{ij} of producing product j the day
        after product i, given by

$$(c_{ij}) = \begin{array}{c} \\ 1 \\ 2 \\ 3 \end{array} \begin{array}{ccc} & j & \\ 1 & 2 & 3 \\ \begin{pmatrix} 0 & 3 & - \\ 1 & 0 & 5 \\ - & 2 & 0 \end{pmatrix} \end{array}$$

In the long-run what average cost per day can be expected?

24. Machines break down on an average of one every two hours. A
single maintenance engineer takes one hour to repair a machine
and is paid £2 per hour. The cost of a machine being idle is £3
per hour. Calculate

    (a) the expected number of machines which are idle at any time;

    (b) the expected total cost of a breakdown.

The firm is considering employing a second engineer at the same
wage as the first and of the same efficiency. Assuming that both
engineers are employed, calculate

    (c) the expected length of time a machine which breaks down
        is idle;

(d) the expected total cost of breakdowns.
Would you advice the firm to employ both engineers?

25. Cars arriving at a garage at the rate of 15 per hour are served at a single pump. Find the service rate which must be achieved if the average time a car waits for petrol is not to exceed two minutes. What is the expected length of time a car is delayed at the garage in this case?

26. The following percentage failure rates refer to lift motors in a busy office block:

	% Fail in Period
Under 10 weeks	5
10–	10
20–	20
30–	30
40–50	35

If the motors are replaced over the weekend the total cost is £200 each. If they fail during the week the replacement cost is £1000 each. Is it best to replace the motors before failure and if so, when? (Work in 10 week periods.)
How could this problem be solved by simulation?

CHAPTER 17

Network Analysis and Economic Order Quantity

1. Networks

A network is a set of points (called nodes or vertices) with one or more lines (called arcs or edges) connecting a pair of points. The tree diagrams discussed earlier in the book are networks in this sense which can be used to analyse a complex situation. Other examples of networks are highway systems, business communication systems and social organisations. By representing each of these situations in the form of a network, their properties can be analysed with the object of securing better organisation of the systems and obtaining some idea of their flexibility so that the systems can be adapted in the most economical way when circumstances change. Very often, it is possible to summarise the properties of networks algebraically, by means of matrices; and this is a powerful technique for discovering properties of networks which may not be at all obvious from a visual inspection. Even so, the visual appearance of a network can often reveal a surprising amount of information about the situation it represents, and it is this aspect of the subject which is considered in this chapter.

In the context of Operational Research, the most important application of networks is to production planning. An example of a network of this kind, which is used in planning the construction of a house, is shown in Fig. 74. The whole process from start to finish is technically known as a *project*, which is subdivided into jobs or *activities*. In the example in Fig. 74, the names of the activities appear at the nodes of the network, though these, in fact, indicate the termination of the activities to which these names refer. Each arc represents the activity named at the head of each arrow. A solid arrow represents an activity with a definite duration, the activity time being indicated in days, or in whatever units the total project time happens to be measured. A broken arrow represents a *dummy activity*, having zero duration, and shows only that the activities thus connected must both be completed before the next activity can begin. The direction of a broken arrow depends on the sequencing of activities and, in particular is determined by the priorities which must be satisfied before a new activity can begin. For example, a large number of preliminaries must be concluded before work can begin on the jobs following the erection of the shell, and so all the preliminary activities must terminate at the node immediately prior to these later activities. A network of this kind is known as a *directed network*,

380

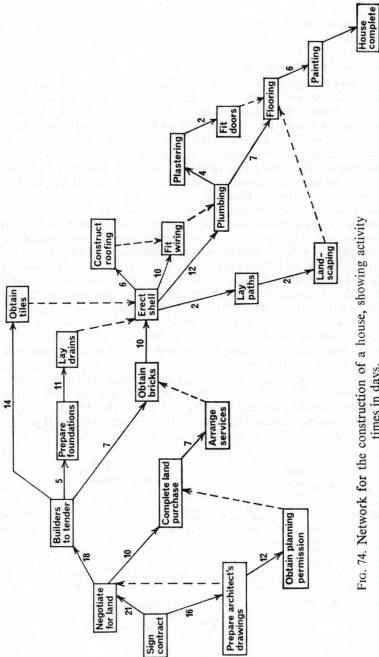

FIG. 74. Network for the construction of a house, showing activity times in days.

since no activity can be begun until all preceding activities have been completed.

2. Critical Path Analysis

It will be seen from the network illustrated in Fig. 74 that more than one series of activities may begin and end at single activities. For example, the sequences: Erect shell → Lay Paths → Landscaping → Flooring and Erect shell → Plumbing → Flooring both begin and end at the same nodes. This means that both series start simultaneously and both must be completed before the next activities are begun. The first series, however, occupies less time than the second, so that there is some time to spare in the activities of the first series. Hence a longer time can be taken over these activities than the scheduled time without increasing the total duration of the project. The total amount of this margin is known as the *total float time* for the activities in question. The first series above occupies a total time of 4 days whilst the second series occupies 19 days, so for laying paths and landscaping there is a total float time of $19 - 4 = 15$ days. This is an *interfering float*, because the total float time is shared between both activities; so that, for example, if laying paths takes 5 days longer than the scheduled time, then there is only 10 days float time remaining by which the duration of landscaping can be increased. There is a *free float* when each of two series beginning and ending with the same activities consists of a single activity in the series with shorter duration. For example, the series: Builders to tender → Obtain tiles → Erect shell and Builders to tender → Obtain bricks → Erect shell, gives a free float to the activity "Obtain tiles" of $17 - 14 = 3$ days. The duration of this activity may be increased by 3 days without affecting the total project time or the float time of any other activity.

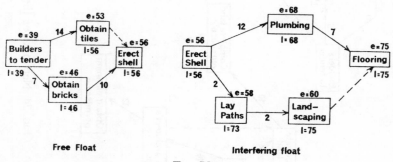

Free Float   Interfering float

FIG. 75.

In order to facilitate the calculation of float times, the earliest and latest times at which an activity can be completed without altering total project time are sometimes shown against the relevant node of the network. Denoting by e and l earliest and latest completion time of an activity, the networks with both these times indicated for the series of activities mentioned above are shown in Fig. 75.

The difference between the earliest and latest completion times for any activity is the total float time for the activity, which may be either a free or an interfering float depending on the nature of the network in that region. A general equation for finding the total float time of any activity $i - j$ is

Total float of activity $i - j =$ latest time of event j
— earliest time of event i
— duration of activity $i - j$.

Thus for activity: erect shell $\rightarrow$ lay paths,

Total float $= 73 - 56 - 2 = 15$ days.

For some activities, for example, "negotiate for land" and "erect shell", earliest and latest completion times are the same; so that there is a float time of zero in these cases. This means that increasing the duration of these activities is only possible at the expense of a longer project time. Now it is fairly obvious that for any network there must be at least one unbroken sequence of nodes, extending from the initial to the terminal nodes, for which total float times are zero. The total duration of such a sequence of activities is the shortest time in which the project can be completed and is known as the *critical path*. Critical path activities are all those activities on the critical path. For the network of Fig. 74, the critical path activities and times are as follows:

Activity	Time (days)
Negotiate land	21
Builders to tender	18
Obtain bricks	7
Erect shell	10
Plumbing	12
Flooring	7
Painting	6
Total project time	81

Whilst a network may have more than one critical path, the total duration times for each must, by definition of the critical path, be the same for each.

The fact that a network allows float times and critical path times for a project to be calculated shows clearly its information value; for such calculations enable one to assess the flexibility of the project and to discover how scheduled times may be revised with the object of reducing costs and avoiding bottlenecks. Shortening the total project time may result in considerable saving, although this must be balanced by the increased cost of completing some of the activities in a shorter time. The obvious activities to consider for this purpose are those on the critical path, but it must, at the same time, be remembered that when such activities are shortened, some activities not formerly on a critical path, may now become critical path activities. Shortening the critical path therefore requires a very careful selection of activities to ensure that those activities are selected which produce the maximum reduction of project time at the least additional cost. The following example illustrates how a network may be used to modify the production plan in the most economical manner.

EXAMPLE 1

A project consists of six activities A to F inclusive, with the following sequential relationships:

A must follow C and E.
B must follow A and F.
D must follow B.
F must follow C.

Activities C and E may take place at the same time; and similarly activities A and F.

The normal duration of each activity is, in weeks:

Activity	A	B	C	D	E	F
Duration	4	5	4	1	2	3

Associated with each activity are the following crash durations and the corresponding extra cost which is linearly related for each activity.

Activity	A	B	C	D	E	F
Crash duration, in weeks	1	3	2	1	2	1
Associated extra cost, in £'s	240	200	120	—	—	80

The customer requires the project to be completed in 13 weeks and there is a penalty of £200 per week for excess time with a bonus of £90 per week for earlier completion.

You are required to:

(a) *draw a logical network based on normal durations for the project and show on the network the duration, earliest start time and the latest start time for each activity;*

(b) *indicate the critical activities and the normal duration of the project;*

(c) *derive the data which would enable you to plot the cost/time curve for the project;*

(d) *state with reasons, whether or not the normal duration for the project should be changed.*

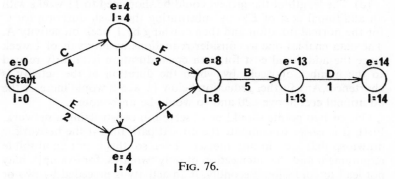

FIG. 76.

(a) The network is shown in Fig. 76 together with the earliest (*e*) and latest (*l*) start times for each activity. The small circles indicate the nodes of the network and the activities are represented by the arcs.

(b) The critical activities are C, A, B and D. Hence the normal project time $= 4 + 4 + 5 + 1 = 14$ weeks.

(c) In deriving the data for the cost/time curve, it can be arranged that there is some constant cost, which is basic cost for the project, to which must be added (or subtracted) any cost changes due to changes in the duration of the project. The cost/time curve, therefore need reflect only these changes if all one is interested in is to find the optimum duration of the project. In finding these changes in cost, only those changes in the project-times which involve the smallest additional cost for a particular duration need be considered. For normal duration, there is an additional cost of £200. This duration can be reduced to 13 weeks, with least addition to cost, by substituting the crash duration for C (for 1 week), the net additional cost being £120/2 = £60. The duration can be further reduced from 12 to 11 weeks by substituting the crash duration for A (for 1 week) at an extra additional cost of £240/3 = £80. Continuing in this way, the following data is obtained relating the duration of the project to least additional cost:

Duration (weeks)	14	13	12	11	10	9	8
Additional Cost (£'s)	+200	+60	+120	+200	+300	+400	+520
Bonus (£'s)	0	0	−90	−180	−270	−360	−450
Net Cost (£'s)	200	60	30	20	30	40	70

Note that to reduce duration from 9 to 8 weeks, both A and F must be reduced by 1 week (cost £80 + £40) since both these activities are now on the critical path.

(d) The length of the project could be shortened to 11 weeks with an additional cost of £20 by substituting the crash duration for C for the normal duration and then crashing by 1 week on activity A. The data enables one to consider reductions by intervals of 1 week since the additional cost for each crash duration is linearly related to the number of weeks by which the duration of the activity is shortened. Any further reduction below 11 weeks would increase the additional cost above £20 and so would be uneconomic.

One or two points should be observed in constructing a network. First, it is easier to compute the critical path time if the network is drawn so that arcs do not intersect. Even so, this is not an absolute requirement and the intersection of only two arcs, for example, may not lead to confusion. Secondly, if an activity is preceded by two or more activities, then these preceding activities must come together in a single node from which the succeeding activity starts. Thus in Example 1, B follows A and F so that A and F must join at the node from which B starts. On the other hand, it sometimes happens that an activity follows two or more activities, and that another activity follows some but not all of these preceding activities. The network must then be drawn so that the activity following the smaller number of activities does not appear to follow them all, whilst at the same time, the activity following the larger number of activities does in fact do so. This is achieved by bringing the smaller number of precedent activities together in a single node and joining this node to the remaining precedent activities by a broken arrow. In Example 1, A follows both C and E, whilst F follows only C. Hence C and E are connected to two distinct nodes which are joined by a broken arrow from C to E. The direction of this broken arrow is determined by the fact that A follows both C and E, whilst F follows only C. If the direction of the arrow were reversed it would mean that A followed only E whilst F followed both C and E. The same principle applies whatever the number of activities preceding a given activity.

Various symbols may be employed in drawing a network with the object of making the position clearer and recording a greater amount of information. In a complicated network, for example, it is useful to mark the critical path by means of a double arrow. One may also wish to indicate in the diagram information concerning crash duration and the costs associated with it. An alternative way of drawing the network for Example 1 and the symbols which may be used are illustrated in Fig. 77.

One limitation of critical path planning is that whilst it may be possible to separate the different activities and establish their chronological sequence with more or less certainty, an estimate of the duration of each activity may be attended with a good deal of uncertainty. There are many external factors such as strikes, late delivery of materials and so forth which could produce this result and which will upset the production plan and call for a modification of the network. Assuming that estimates of duration times are based on past experience, the best that can be done is to compute the average time for each activity. If the dispersion about this average time is small, then critical path analysis can be effectively used; but a high dispersion of duration times may entail too much uncertainty for the critical path to be computed reliably. In this case, any estimate of saving resulting from the use of alternative procedures may be liable to considerable error. The uncertainty of activity times is allowed for in a technique known as PERT (Program Evaluation and Revue Technique). This can be used to assess the probabilities that production deadlines will be met.

3. Economic Order Quantity

Analytical techniques are important for Management because a choice nearly always exists between several policies for achieving the same end. Scientific management has evolved mathematical techniques for determining the most profitable among a number of competing policies. The present topic affords a good illustration of this point. When a manufacturer obtains some essential factor of production from an external source, it is important that he ensures that he always has sufficient of the factor in stock for his needs and it will be assumed that he never runs out of stock and consequently always re-orders in time to avoid this happening. The interval between orders will, of course, depend on the rate of usage and the

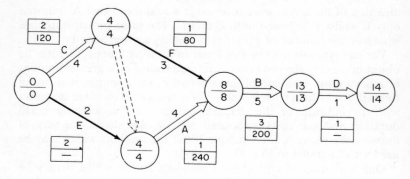

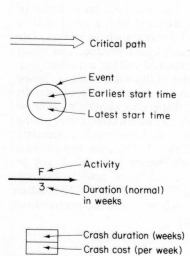

Critical path

Event
Earliest start time
Latest start time

F — Activity
3 — Duration (normal) in weeks

Crash duration (weeks)
Crash cost (per week)

FIG. 77.

quantity ordered. Now he could adopt a simple procedure of always re-ordering at fixed intervals of, say, 1 year—knowing his annual usage he will know exactly how many units to order. But it can be shown mathematically that this simple method will usually not be the least expensive. Two important factors which affect the decision are the cost of holding stock, which will be greater the more units ordered, and the cost of delivery, which is usually constant whatever the quantity ordered and which will therefore be less per annum, the fewer the deliveries, i.e. the greater the quantity ordered each time.

The various factors required in the analysis are as follows:

Q = quantity to be ordered
Y = annual usage
Cs = delivery cost per order
C = price per unit
I = stockholding cost p.a. as a percentage of cost of average quantity in stock p.a.

To find the average stock held per annum, the simplifying assumption is made that the demand rate is constant throughout the year so that stock decreases as a linear function of time (see Fig. 78).

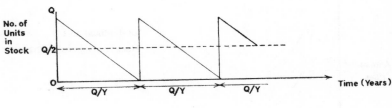

FIG. 78.

On this assumption, it is clear that:

Annual average stock = $Q/2$ units

Also   Interval between orders = Q/Y (measured in years)
Stockholding cost p.a. = $IC/100$

Hence   Total annual stockholding cost = $ICQ/200$
Annual delivery cost = YCs/Q

Hence   Total cost p.a. = $\dfrac{ICQ}{200} + \dfrac{YCs}{Q}$

and this will clearly vary with the size of each order (Q), which is the point made in the first paragraph. If values are assigned to the constants I, C, Y, Cs and a graph of cost plotted as a function of Q, it will be found to be a U-shaped curve, falling for small values of Q and rising for high values. So somewhere between these extremes, the curve will attain its lowest point and, for the value of Q at which it does so, total annual cost is a minimum. This, then, is the economic order quantity (E.O.Q.). To obtain a formula for this value of Q, it is necessary to use elementary differential calculus. Thus cost is minimum for that value of Q for which

$$\frac{d \text{ (total annual cost)}}{dQ} = \frac{IC}{200} - \frac{YCs}{Q^2} = 0.$$

Whence it follows that E.O.Q. $= \sqrt{\left(\frac{200\ YCs}{IC}\right)}$.

The minimum total annual cost is then

$$\frac{IC}{200}\sqrt{\left(\frac{200\ YCs}{IC}\right)} + YCs\sqrt{\left(\frac{IC}{200\ YCs}\right)}$$
$$= 2\sqrt{\left(\frac{IC\,YCs}{200}\right)} = \sqrt{\left(\frac{IC\,YCs}{50}\right)}.$$

Fig. 79 shows the curves for total cost, stockholding cost and delivery cost.

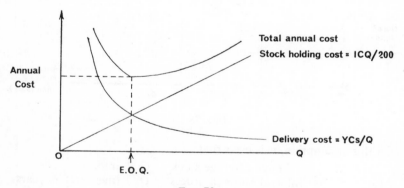

FIG. 79.

An interesting feature of this graph is that the E.O.Q., which gives minimum total cost, is also that value of Q for which

$$\text{stockholding cost} = \text{delivery cost.}$$

This is no accident, but arises from the conditions of the problem. In fact, it is not difficult to verify that when

$$Q = \sqrt{(200\,YCs/IC)}, \quad ICQ/200 = YCs/Q.$$

EXAMPLE 2

The annual carrying cost of stocks of raw material is £0·10 per unit. Production is steady throughout the year, there are no delivery problems with suppliers, so safety stocks need not be held. It is therefore decided to time purchases to be received just as the stocks of raw material reach zero. Each raw material order incurs a procurement cost of £20 which includes invoicing, transportation, etc. The annual demand for raw material is 1,000,000 units. Determine the economic order quantity, and least annual cost at which the raw material can be obtained.

Here, $Y = 1,000,000$;

$$\text{Stockholding cost p.a.} = £0·10 \times Q/2$$
$$\text{annual delivery cost} = £20 \times 1,000,000/Q$$
$$\therefore \text{Total annual cost} = 0·05Q + \frac{20,000,000}{Q}.$$

To find the E.O.Q., differentiate total annual cost with respect to Q and set the result equal to zero. Thus

$$\frac{d\,(\text{total annual cost})}{dQ} = 0·05 - \frac{20,000,000}{Q^2} = 0,$$

whence

$$\text{E.O.Q.} = \sqrt{\left(\frac{20,000,000}{0·05}\right)}$$
$$= 20,000 \text{ units.}$$

$$\text{The least annual cost} = £\left(0·05 \times 20,000 + \frac{20,000,000}{20,000}\right)$$
$$= £2000.$$

In this Example the solution is independent of the price of raw materials because stockholding costs are dependent, not on price, but only on quantity ordered. In this kind of problem, therefore, the formula for E.O.Q. should not be applied unthinkingly; but first principles should be used to obtain a solution if necessary. The student should draw a graph illustrating the specific solution obtained above.

Another simplifying assumption of the formula for E.O.Q. is that C, the price per unit, is constant whatever the quantity ordered. But if, for example, discounts are allowed on large orders then this assumption is not valid. In deriving the formula for E.O.Q. the total annual cost considered includes only stockholding costs and delivery costs. Total annual costs, including the cost of Y units, is obtained by adding YC to the other two cost elements; but if C is constant then the term YC disappears on differentiation so that it does not affect E.O.Q. If C is variable on the other hand, the optimum order size is that which minimises total annual cost, including the cost of the goods, that is:

$$\text{Total cost p.a.} = YC + \frac{ICQ}{200} + \frac{YCs}{Q}.$$

To illustrate the method of solving this kind of problem, suppose that annual demand for material is 10,000 units and that the prices per unit for different order sizes are:

Quantity ordered (units):   less than 1000   1000–2500   2500–5000
Price per unit (C):   £2   £1·75   £1·50

Stockholding costs are 25% of material costs per annum and delivery cost is £50 per order.

The square root formula can be used to calculate the E.O.Q. at each price. Thus

$$\text{When } C = \pounds2, \quad \text{E.O.Q.} = \sqrt{\left(\frac{200\ YCs}{IC}\right)}$$

$$= \sqrt{\left(\frac{200 \times 10,000 \times 50}{25 \times 2}\right)}$$

$$= 1414 \text{ units.}$$

$$\text{When } C = \pounds1\cdot75, \text{ E.O.Q.} = 1414 \times \sqrt{\left(\frac{2}{1\cdot75}\right)}$$

$$= 1512 \text{ units.}$$

$$\text{When } C = \pounds1\cdot50, \text{ E.O.Q.} = 1512 \times \sqrt{\left(\frac{1\cdot75}{1\cdot50}\right)}$$

$$= 1633 \text{ units.}$$

In each case, the E.O.Q. lies in the range 1000–2500 units for which the price is £1·75, so the only valid order quantity given by the formula is 1512 units. On the other hand, it is clear that, delivery and stockholding costs will be minimum at a price of £2 when the quantity ordered is as large as possible (i.e. 1000 units), and will also be minimum at a price of £1·50 when the quantity ordered is as small as possible (i.e. 2500 units). To find which of the three quantities is optimum it is only necessary to evaluate the total cost (including YC) in each case:

When $C = \pounds2$ and $Q = 1000$,
total cost p.a. (£'s)

$$= 10,000 \times 2 + \frac{25 \times 2 \times 1000}{200} + \frac{10,000 \times 50}{1000}$$

$$= \pounds20,750.$$

When $C = £1·75$ and $Q = 1512$,
total cost p.a. (£'s)

$$= 10,000 \times 1·75 + \sqrt{\left(\frac{ICYCs}{50}\right)}$$

$$= 17,500 + \sqrt{\left(\frac{25 \times 1·75 \times 10,000 \times 50}{50}\right)}$$

$$= £18,161.$$

When $C = £1·50$ and $Q = 2500$,
total cost p.a. (£'s)

$$= 15,000 + 669$$
$$= £15,669.$$

Hence the optimum order quantity in this case is 2500 units resulting in a minimum annual total cost of £15,669.

4. Lead Time

The analysis in the foregoing section is based on simplifying assumptions. The model is a deterministic one and, moreover, it is assumed that no time elapses between the placing of the order and delivery. If demand is predictable with certainty, then the existence of a time lag between order and delivery, called *lead time* presents no problem, and the calculation of E.O.Q. is performed as in section 3. When demand is not exactly predictable, the existence of lead time necessitates the holding of buffer or "safety" stocks, for there is some probability of a *stock-out* (i.e., running out of stock) before delivery can be effected; and this will almost certainly involve additional costs due, for example, to the need to make special deliveries to waiting customers. The two commonest methods for dealing with this situation are the *two-bin system* and the *periodic review system*. The two-bin system consists of re-ordering whenever stock falls below a certain level and has the advantage that it responds fairly promptly to fluctuations in the rate of usage and is not over-dependent on accurate forecasting of demand. Under the periodic review system, re-order dates are fixed and orders are placed at constant intervals of time, producing substantial savings in administrative costs and price concessions from suppliers. With this system, however, buffer stocks tend to be higher than under the two-bin system, leading to higher average stock and stockholding costs.

For both re-ordering systems, E.O.Q. can be found as in section 3, but it is necessary to allow for lead time by calculating the *re-order point*, i.e., the level below which stock should not be allowed to fall. Secondly, if a buffer stock is held, this increases the average stock held by the amount of the buffer stock and so increases the annual stockholding cost from $ICQ/200$ to $IC(Q + 2B)/200$, where B is the size of the buffer stock in units. Suppose that a company currently orders lots of 50,000 units at a time at a price of £0·25 per unit with a lead time of 15 days, the buffer stock being 20,000 units and daily usage 2000 units. The re-order point is given by:

$$\text{re-order point} = \text{lead time} \times \text{daily usage} + \text{buffer stock}$$
$$= 15 \times 2000 + 20,000$$
$$= 50,000 \text{ units.}$$

This means that stock is re-ordered when the level falls to 50,000 units. If E.O.Q. is 50,000 units and stockholding costs are 20% per annum, then
Minimum stock held (i.e. immediately before delivery) = 20,000 units.
Maximum stock held (i.e. immediately after delivery) = 70,000 units.
Hence average stock held $= \dfrac{20,000 + 70,000}{2} = 45,000$ units.

Annual stockholding cost = 20% of 45,000 × £0·25 = £2250 p.a.

Once the size of the buffer stock has been fixed, the resulting cost of holding it is a fixed cost and so will not vary with Q (the quantity ordered). This means that total annual cost is still a function of Q only, and so the formula for E.O.Q. is the same whether or not there is lead time or a buffer stock. The size of the buffer stock is determined at an optimum level by considering the probability distribution of demand. Suppose, for example, that re-ordering is 10 times per year and that, within the lead time, average demand is 16 units. The number of units actually demanded might have a Poisson distribution with mean 16 and standard deviation $\sqrt{16} = 4$. Since the mean is large, the Poisson distribution approximates to a Normal distribution from which the probability that demand will be greater than 0, 1, 2, 3, etc. units above the mean can be calculated. If the cost of a stock-out of any size is £5 and the cost of holding stock is £2 per unit per annum, then the annual cost of a buffer stock of size x, together with the expected cost of stock-outs is

$$£2x + £5 \times 10 \times P\{X > (x + 16 - 16)/4\},$$

where X is the standard Normal variable. The size of the buffer stock is fixed so that this cost is minimum. The following table illustrates. The probabilities in column (a) are obtained in the usual way from Table 1. For example, when $x = 3$, $X = 3/4 = 0·75$ and $P(X > 0·75) = 1 - 0·7734 = 0·2266$ or 0·23 (approximately). The optimum size of buffer stock is either 5 or 6 units at an annual total cost of £15·50.

Buffer Stock x	(a) Probability of demand $> x + 16$	Stockholding Cost £2x	Expected Cost of Stock-out £50 × (a)	Annual Total Cost (£'s)
0	0·50	0	25·00	25·00
1	0·40	2	20·00	22·00
2	0·31	4	15·50	19·50
3	0·23	6	11·50	17·50
4	0·16	8	8·00	16·00
5	0·11	10	5·50	15·50
6	0·07	12	3·50	15·50
7	0·04	14	2·00	16·00

In practice, of course, the cost of a stock-out will vary with its size, in which case it is necessary to calculate the average cost of stock-out per lead time when demand exceeds supply by 1, 2, 3, etc. units. For example, if no buffer stock is held, the average amount by which demand exceeds supply per lead time is simply the sum of the probabilities in column (a), including the probabilities for higher values of x than 7. It is left to the student to show that this will, in fact, be the average excess of demand above the mean 16, in this case.

Instead of making assumptions about the theoretical distribution of demand, the estimate of buffer stock may be based on an observed probability distribution of demand during lead time. The following example illustrates.

EXAMPLE 3

A company has an annual demand for material X of 1000 tons. Order lead time is 5 days and usage during lead time as shown by past records is:

Usage (tons)	Probability
less than 18	0
18	0·10
19	0·20
20	0·25
21	0·15
22	0·15
23	0·10
24	0·05

The cost price is £20 per ton and stockholding cost is 25% per annum of the stock value. Delivery cost per batch is £100 and the cost of a stock-out (per ton) is £6.

(a) *Calculate the economic order quantity.*

(b) *Assuming that there are 250 working days in the year, calculate the re-order level.*

(a) Here, annual demand, Y = 1000 tons

delivery cost, Cs = £100 per order

purchase price, C = £20 per ton

stockholding cost = 25% of £20 per ton per annum.

Hence

$$\text{E.O.Q.} = \sqrt{\left(\frac{200 \times 1000 \times 100}{25 \times 20}\right)}$$
$$= 200 \text{ tons.}$$

(b) Average number of orders per annum will be $1000/200 = 5$.

Cost of a stock-out per ton = $5 \times £6 = £30$ per annum.

Cost of buffer stock = 25% of £20 = £5 per ton.

Since there are 250 working days in the year,

average daily usage = $1000/250 = 4$ tons.

Hence average usage during lead time = $5 \times 4 = 20$ tons.

To find the re-order level it is necessary to determine the optimum size of buffer stock which is done by considering the average number of stock-outs of each size. The calculations are shown in the following table.

Buffer Stock x	Probability of Demand $> x + 20$	(a) Av. Number of Stock-outs	Stockholding Cost £5x	Expected Cost of Stock-out £30 × (a)	Annual Total Cost £
0	0·45	0·95	0	28·50	28·50
1	0·30	0·50	5	15·00	20·00
2	0·15	0·20	10	6·00	16·00
3	0·05	0·05	15	1·50	16·50
4	0·00	0·00	20	0·00	20·00

The table shows that the optimum buffer stock is 2 tons at a minimum annual total cost of £16. Hence

Re-order level = Buffer stock + Lead time × daily usage
$$= 2 + 20$$
$$= 22 \text{ tons.}$$

When zero buffer stock is held, the probability that there is a stock-out of exactly 1 ton is $0.45 - 0.30$, the probability that there is a stock-out of exactly 2 tons is $0.30 - 0.15$ and so on. Hence the average number of stock-outs in column (a) when $x = 0$ is

$$1 \times (0.45 - 0.30) + 2 \times (0.30 - 0.15) + 3$$
$$\times (0.15 - 0.05) + 4 \times (0.05 - 0)$$
$$= 0.45 + 0.30 + 0.15 + 0.05$$
$$= 0.95$$

Similarly, when $x = 1$, the average number of stock-outs is

$$0.30 + 0.15 + 0.05 = 0.50.$$

The remaining averages in column (a) are calculated in a similar manner.

5. Producing for Stock

Instead of ordering goods from an external supplier a firm may decide to produce them itself. So far as the cost of different stock levels is concerned, the essential difference between these two cases is that an external supplier can supply the whole order at one delivery, whereas a certain length of time is needed, depending on the annual production rate, for a producer to produce the whole quantity required for stock. During this time, some of the stock will be sold, so that stock levels are not so great as when a quantity is delivered all at once by an external supplier. In fact, if the rate of production exactly equalled the rate of demand and both rates were uniform throughout the year, there would be no stock at all. This is, of course, an unrealistic possibility; the rate of production is generally greater than the rate of demand, so that production is not continuous throughout the year.

The costs associated with the production of items held in stock by the producer are:

(a) Direct cost per unit, consisting of variable costs, the cost of labour and materials, and so on, which is denoted by C.

(b) Set-up cost per production run, which is the cost involved in preparing for the production of a batch of goods, denoted by Cs.

(c) Stockholding cost, which is denoted by H per unit per year, or by I if this cost is given as a percentage per annum of the direct cost of producing the average quantity held in stock.

The problem in this case is to obtain a formula giving the optimum quantity, or economic batch quantity (E.B.Q.), to produce in each production run, that is, the quantity which will minimise annual set-up and stockholding costs.

Let Q = batch size
C = direct costs per unit
P = production rate per year
Y = annual demand
t = time occupied by a production run (in years)
t_1 = interval between production runs (in years).

During time t, stock increases at the rate of $P - Y$ per year and reaches a peak at time t after the commencement of production. Stock then declines during the remainder of time t_1 until the beginning of the next production run. Average stock held throughout the year is half the peak stock at time t, assuming that production and demand rates are uniform. The diagram (Fig. 80) illustrates the position.

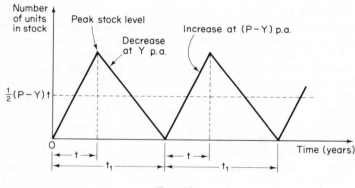

FIG. 80.

The diagram shows that the peak stock held is $(P - Y)t$, so that average stock held is $\frac{1}{2}(P - Y)t$. Hence total stockholding and set-up costs are given by

$$\text{Total cost p.a.} = \frac{\frac{1}{2}IC(P - Y)t}{100} + \frac{YCs}{Q}$$

$$= \frac{IC(P - Y)Q}{200P} + \frac{YCs}{Q} \quad \text{(since } Q = Pt\text{)}.$$

Differentiating with respect to Q,

$$\frac{d(\text{total annual cost})}{dQ} = \frac{IC(P - Y)}{200P} - \frac{YCs}{Q^2}$$

and total cost is minimum when

$$\frac{IC(P - Y)}{200P} - \frac{YCs}{Q^2} = 0.$$

It follows that

$$\text{E.B.Q.} = \sqrt{\left(\frac{200P\,YCs}{IC(P - Y)}\right)}.$$

In this formula $IC/100$ is the cost per unit of holding stock when this cost is given as a percentage I of direct costs. If the stockholding cost is given as H per unit, then the formula becomes

$$\text{E.B.Q.} = \sqrt{\left(\frac{2P\,YCs}{H(P - Y)}\right)}.$$

The graph showing the relationship between the elements of total annual cost for the batch size is similar to that for E.O.Q. given on page 390 (see Fig. 81).

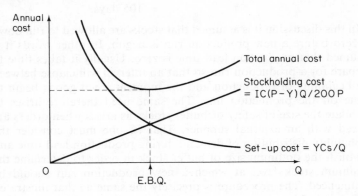

FIG. 81.

EXAMPLE 4

Annual demand for bicycles is 3000 *per year and they can be produced at the rate of* 4000 *per year. The direct cost of producing each machine is* £30. *Set-up cost is* £500 *per batch whilst holding cost is* 25% *per annum. Calculate*

(a) *the quantity to be manufactured in each batch,*
(b) *the manufacturing cost (i.e. excluding storage cost) of each bicycle,*
(c) *the interval between each production run, assuming that there are* 250 *working days in a year.*

(a) Using the notation in the formula for E.B.Q.,

$$P = 4000 \qquad Y = 3000 \qquad I = 25\%$$
$$C = £30 \text{ and } Cs = £500.$$

So

$$\text{E.B.Q.} = \sqrt{\left(\frac{200 \times 4000 \times 3000 \times 500}{25 \times 30 \times (4000 - 3000)}\right)}$$
$$= 1265.$$

(b) Set-up cost $\quad = \dfrac{£500}{1265}$ per machine

$$= £0{\cdot}40$$

Manufacturing cost $= £30 + £0{\cdot}40$
$$= £30{\cdot}40 \text{ per machine.}$$

(c) Interval between production runs $= (1265 \times 250)/3000$ days
$$= 105 \text{ days.}$$

In this discussion it is assumed that stocks are allowed to run down to zero before a new production run is begun. In other words it is assumed that production lead time is zero. Usually it takes time to prepare for a production run so that an interval will elapse between the beginning of production and the moment when goods begin to come off the production line. The same need therefore arises to calculate the size of safety or buffer stocks as arises when orders are placed with an external supplier. That is, one must consider the probability distribution of demand during production lead time and establish the optimum size of buffer stock in order to determine the minimum stock level at which a new production run should be commenced. The procedure is precisely the same as that illustrated in Example 3.

6. Replacement of Capital Equipment

In deciding the best replacement policy for items of capital equipment which fail (see Chapter 16, section 6), it is appropriate to use a probabilistic model. The replacement of capital equipment with a long term of useful life requires a different approach because, in this case, the equipment does not usually fail completely, but incurs maintenance charges and also has some resale value. The average annual cost of the equipment up to a specified year is the total maintenance (or operating) costs to that year, plus the difference between the purchase and resale price in that year, divided by the number of years the equipment has been in use. The following example illustrates the method of calculation.

EXAMPLE 5

A transport company buys road tankers costing £5000 each. From the data below advise management when a tanker should be replaced:

Year	1	2	3	4	5	6
Operating costs (£'s)	750	800	850	900	1000	1225
Resale price (£'s)	4500	4050	3750	3600	3450	3325

Year	Operating Cost (£'s)	Total Operating Cost to Date (£'s)	£5000 −Resale Price	Total Cost to Date (£'s)	Average Annual Cost (£'s)
1	750	750	500	1250	1250
2	800	1550	950	2500	1250
3	850	2400	1250	3650	1217
4	900	3300	1400	4700	1175
5	1000	4300	1550	5850	1170
6	1225	5525	1675	7200	1200

Average annual cost is minimum in Year 5, which suggests that a tanker should be replaced in its fifth year of life.

EXERCISES 17

1. For the network in Fig. 82 (a) write down the critical path activities, (b) find the critical path time and (c) indicate what float time is available.

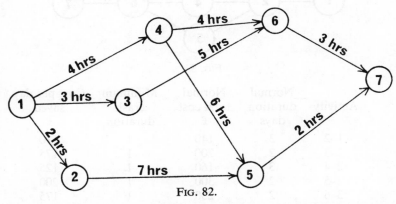

FIG. 82.

2. What are the principal types of application of network analysis?

3. From the following activities construct a network indicating the critical path and the sub-critical activities.

Initial Activity Node	Terminal Activity Node	Activity Time (days)
0	1	2
0	2	4
1	3	3
2	4	5
3	4	12
3	5	11
3	6	10
4	7	14
5	8	4
6	8	6
7	8	7
8	9	3

4. Calculate the float times for each of the activities in Fig. 74, clearly distinguishing the cases in which there is a free float. What effect might possible variations in the durations of the activities: Construct roofing, Lay drains and Fit wiring, have?

5. The network in Fig. 83 was prepared before the start of a project:

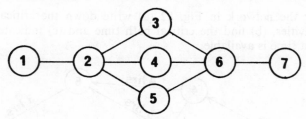

FIG. 83.

Activity	Normal duration days	Normal total cost £	Minimum crash duration	Cost per day saved £
1–2	3	140	1	110
2–3	2	200	1	175
2–4	3	160	1	125
2–5	2	300	1	200
3–6	2	250	1	175
4–6	6	400	1	70
5–6	5	230	1	70
6–7	5	220	1	90

There is a bonus of £100 per day for every day saved below the contract period of 15 days and a penalty of £200 for each day after the 15 days.

  (a) Calculate the normal duration and the normal cost.
  (b) Calculate the cost of completing the project in 15 days.
  (c) State the optimum plan for the company to attempt.
  (d) Revert to the normal programme and normal costs and state what action you would recommend to ensure completion by the original date if, after the tenth day the actual situation was as follows:

      activities completed at normal cost;
      1–2;   2–3;   3–6;   2–4;   2–5

      activities not yet started:
      4–6;   5–6;   6–7.

Calculate also the revised cost of the project under these circumstances.

6. You have been provided with the following durations and costs of the activities necessary to complete project K:

Activity	Normal duration, days	Normal cost £	Crash duration, days	Crash cost £
0–1	4	80	4	80
0–2	3	60	3	60
1–3	6	150	5	180
1–4	3	80	2	150
2–4	5	100	4	120
3–5	8	160	8	160
4–5	15	300	10	400
5–6	10	200	8	290

  (a) Construct the network.
  (b) Calculate the shortest time within which the project can be completed at normal cost.
  (c) Calculate the total float for each activity.
  (d) Calculate the normal cost of completing the project.
  (e) Calculate the revised cost and duration of the optimal programme if the project will produce profits at the rate of £40 per day saved and there are no physical limits on the resources needed.

7. Use the square root formula to determine the economic order quantity and total supply costs of tyres costing £5 each for a transport undertaking that uses 500 tyres per year. The holding

cost is 15% of the average stock value and the average cost per order is £0·60.

Discuss critically the square root formula for stock control purposes.

8. A wholesaler distributes 20,000 units of a product costing 50p per unit during the course of one year. It costs him £100 for each delivery to his warehouse and the capital tied up in stock can be invested elsewhere at a rate of 15%. What is the optimal quantity that the wholesaler should keep and what is the total cost? How realistic is this solution? What other information would you need to improve your solution?

9. Best Value Supermarkets Limited buys an economy size instant coffee to market under its own brand name. The monthly sales in all its stores, assuming 25 days in a month, are 40,000 units. The sales occur evenly throughout the month. The company currently orders in lots of 40,000 at a time at a price of £0·30 per unit with a lead time of 10 days. A base inventory of 10,000 is kept as a buffer stock.

(a) Calculate the re-order point.
(b) The supplier has offered to reduce the price to £0·28 per unit if the order size is increased to 150,000 units for delivery within 20 days. If these terms were accepted the company would still keep a base inventory of 10,000 units but would have to rent additional storage at a cost of £5,000 per annum. Carrying costs to the company, excluding additional storage space, are 20% per annum. Terms of settlement are the same under both current and proposed delivery patterns. Determine whether or not the new terms should be accepted.

10. A firm is able to obtain quantity discounts on its orders of material as follows:

Price per ton £	Tons
6·0	less than 250
5·9	250 and less than 800
5·8	800 and less than 2000
5·7	2000 and less than 4000
5·6	4000 and over.

The annual demand for material is 4000 tons.
Stockholding costs are 20% of material cost per annum.

The delivery cost per order is £6·00.
Calculate the best quantity to order.

11. The average demand for a product per lead time is 25 units. If demand has a Poisson distribution, find the size of buffer stock needed to reduce the risk of a stock-out to 5%.

12. Cost of holding stock is £1 per unit and stock is replenished 10 times a year. Average demand per lead time is 9 units, and the cost of special delivery to waiting customers is £2 per unit. During lead time, demand has a Poisson distribution. Calculate the optimum size of buffer stock which should be held.

13. From the data in Question 9, calculate the risk of a stock-out under both the current and proposed arrangements, and assuming that demand has a Poisson distribution.

14. The annual costs of running a motor vehicle whose purchase price is £3000 are given below.

Year	1	2	3	4	5	6	7	8
Running costs	500	600	700	900	1150	1400	1700	2000
Resale price	1500	750	357	100	100	100	100	100

Find the age at which the vehicle should be replaced.

15. An Operational Research project consists of the following activities:

	Activities	Duration (days)
A	Preliminary meeting	1
B	Problem formulation	8
C	Plant visits	5
D	Data collection	14
E	Data analysis	10
F	Supplementary data	14
G	Preliminary notes	15
H	Model construction	11
J	Solution	5
K	Discussions	3
L	Devise operating rules	6
M	Draft report	18
N	Final report	12

Construct a project graph incorporating the following sequence restrictions:

B to follow A	H to follow C and E
C to follow B	J to follow H
D to follow B	K to follow F and J
E to follow D	L to follow K
F to follow E	M to follow C, E and G
G to follow B	N to follow L and M

What is the critical path through the network? Give the least time to project completion.

If model construction should prove shorter than expected, what effect would this have?

How many paths are there through the network, and which would you assess as sub-critical (that is, liable to be critical paths should small deviations from expected activity durations occur)?

16. A company uses the products given below at a steady rate:

Product	Annual Demand	Cost per Unit (£)
1	800	1
2	1600	0·25
3	400	4
4	225	16

The cost of placing an order is £2 and is independent of the number of products and quantities ordered. The cost of holding a unit in stock for one year is estimated to be £1. There are a number of suppliers for the above products, who use varying selling policies:

Supplier 1. Can supply all products—no discounts.
Supplier 2. Only products 1 and 2—discount of 5% if the order is for more than £100.
Supplier 3. Only products 2 and 4—discount of 2% if the order is for more than £500.
Supplier 4. Only products 1 and 3—discount of 5% if the order is for more than £200.

Which suppliers do you recommend, and what order quantities of each product does this involve?

17. The average demand for a product which is priced at £0·25 a unit is 250 items per week. The lead time is four weeks and distribution of demand during lead time is as follows:

Demand (units)	Probability
800	0·05
900	0·12
1000	0·24
1100	0·25
1200	0·20
1300	0·11
1400	0·03

The cost of placing an order is £0·50 and the total annual stock-holding costs are estimated to be 13 % of the average stock value.

(a) Assuming that there are 50 working weeks in the year, calculate the economic order quantity.

(b) If there is a penalty of £20 for each 100 items by which demand exceeds supply during lead time, what size buffer stock should be held?

18. Your company sells Rollum at the rate of 500 per day throughout a working year of 250 days. The product is normally purchased by your company ready for sale at £7 per unit. Investigations have shown that it could be made at the rate of 800 per day in a part of the factory at present unoccupied. The direct costs per unit involved would be material £1·25, labour £0·50 and variable overheads including hire of machinery £2·25. The set-up cost per batch would be £600 and stockholding costs have been estimated at 25 % per annum.

(a) Derive the economic batch formula to be used in these circumstances.

(b) Calculate the quantity to be ordered in each batch.

(c) Calculate the total cost of manufacture for the year and per unit.

(d) What is the average stock held?

19. The firm which at present purchases the product in Question 17 plans to produce it for itself instead. The production rate is 300 units per week and production lead time is 4 weeks. Other data is unchanged. Calculate the stock level at which the firm should begin to prepare for a new production run.

20. Use the formulae for E.B.Q. in section 5 to derive formulae for the minimum total set-up and stockholding cost.

CHAPTER 18

Linear Programming Techniques

1. Allocation

In any business undertaking, a desired objective may be attainable by a number of different routes. Management is then faced with the problem of choosing that route by which the end can be attained at least cost. The solution of this problem is usually a matter of deciding on the best allocation of resources. For example, a given output may be produced either by 20 men and 1 machine or by 10 men and 2 machines, the choice between these two alternatives naturally depending on the relative costs of men and machines. The first step in its solution is to formulate the problem in mathematical terms by introducing variables to represent alternative allocations. The simplifying assumption is usually made that costs or output vary as a linear function of the variable quantities of input. This may not always be true, but is often a good approximation for a wide range of values of the variables. The solution of a production planning problem on the assumption of linear relationships between variables is known as *linear programming* and can be applied to a wide variety of situations in which the essence of the problem is one of allocation. Examples of such problems are: the determination of the best proportions between inputs, finding the best output or product mix when the proportions between inputs are fixed by technological considerations, deciding on the most economic combination of routes for transporting materials when a number of different routes are available and planning the best way of combining sales strategies in a monopolistic or quasi-monopolistic situation. Linear programming techniques exist for the solution of all these problems and, since they are very flexible, can be used for solving other kinds of problem as well, such as optimum stockholding problems.

The best production plan does not necessarily entail the full utilisation of resources if the object is to obtain maximum profit, so that the data of a linear programming problem are usually limits within which the problem must be solved rather than precise magnitudes. Thus although the final solution of a linear programming problem is in terms of equations between variables, its formulation requires one to consider inequalities as well. For example, the availability of an input may be limited so that more than a certain quantity of it cannot be employed; the problem then being to decide whether, taking into account other aspects of the data, to employ the

408

whole available amount of the input or less than this amount. A useful preliminary to the discussion of linear programming is therefore a consideration of the relationships between linear inequalities.

2. Linear Inequalities

It was seen in Chapter 11, section 2, that a linear equality between two quantities x and y can be represented graphically by means of a straight line, the general form of the equation for which is $y = bx + a$. The line consists of a set of points, the coordinates (x, y) of any one of which satisfy the equation of the line. This can be expressed by saying that the solution set of the equation is the set of all points on the line $y = bx + a$. All linear equations between two variables have solution sets of this kind. In a similar manner, a linear inequality between two variables also has a solution set; for example, the inequality $y \leqslant bx + a$ has, as part of its solution set, all the points on the line $y = bx + a$, for these certainly satisfy the relationship $\leqslant$, which is a non-strict inequality. But the inequality has many other solutions as well, for it is obviously true of any point *below* the line $y = bx + a$. Similarly, the inequality $y > bx + a$ is satisfied by any point above the line, though not by a point on the line, since the inequality is strict in this case.

If two linear equations in two unknowns are consistent and distinct, then there is a unique pair of numbers (x, y) which simultaneously satisfies them. More than two equations in two unknowns are inconsistent unless the coefficients of the additional equations are all multiples of the coefficients of one or other of the original pair of equations. If the equations are inconsistent, then there is no pair of values (x, y) which simultaneously satisfies them all. Inequalities in two unknowns, provided they are consistent, are also simultaneously satisfiable; but in this case, the number of number pairs which satisfy them may be infinite and, moreover, it is possible for more than two inequalities in two unknowns to be consistent, even though they are all essentially different. To illustrate, consider the inequalities $y - x < 0$, $y + x < 2$, $y > 0$ and $x > 1$. The graphs of the equations $y = x$ and $y = 2 - x$ are shown in Fig. 84. The Ox axis represents the equation $y = 0$ whilst the vertical line at $x = 1$ represents the equation $x = 1$. The inequality $y > 0$ is satisfied by the set of all points lying above the Ox axis, whilst the inequality $y < x$ is satisfied by all points lying below the line $y = x$. The inequality $y + x < 2$ (or $y < 2 - x$) is satisfied by all points lying below the line $y = 2 - x$. All these inequalities are satisfied by points lying in the whole triangular shaded area, i.e., the intersection of the three sets of points satisfying each inequality separately.

The set of points satisfying $x > 1$ lies in the region to the right of the line $x = 1$, and so all four inequalities are satisfied by points lying in the triangular cross-shaded portion of the diagram. The intersection of all four sets of points satisfying the inequalities separately is not the null set, and so these four inequalities are consistent, the solution set being the cross-shaded triangular area, excluding, of course, points on the boundary lines.

Consider now the inequalities $y - x < 0$, $y > 0$, $x < 1$ and $y + x > 2$. The first three of these inequalities are consistent, the solution set being the single-shaded triangular region of the diagram. But the points satisfying the inequality $y + x > 2$ lie above

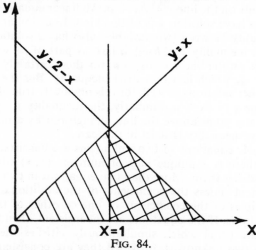

FIG. 84.

the line $y = 2 - x$, and the intersection of this region with the single-shaded triangular area is the null set. Hence all four inequalities in this case are not simultaneously satisfiable and so are inconsistent. Inequalities may be consistent though some of them are redundant for determining a specific solution. For example, the inequalities $x > 0$, $y > 0$, $y - x < 0$ and $y + x < 2$ are satisfied by points in the shaded region of the diagram, whilst the three latter inequalities are also satisfied by these points, so that the first inequality, $x > 0$, really contributes nothing to the solution and is redundant, though not inconsistent with the remaining inequalities.

3. Graphical Solutions

In a production planning problem the conditions of the problem are usually given in the form of *constraints* which can be expressed as linear inequalities. The constraints indicate that certain quantities or combinations of quantities cannot be less or greater than a specified magnitude. The problem consists of determining the conditions under which a quantity Z, called the *objective function*, can be maximised or minimised under the given constraints. This involves finding the optimum values of the variables of which Z is a function. When the number of these variables is just two, a solution to the problem can be found graphically, as the following example shows.

EXAMPLE 1

Two soap powders Rub and Rinse are manufactured in 1lb. packets and each hour one man produces x lb. of Rub and y lb. of Rinse. Each powder is produced by using any one of 3 machines A, B and C and the number of minutes required by each machine in the production of 1 lb. of Rub or 1 lb. of Rinse is as follows:

	A	B	C
Rub	1·5	3	2·5
Rinse	2·5	1	1·5

Write down three inequations which can be deduced from this table. If the profit on a packet of Rub is 6p and on a packet of Rinse is 4p, find the maximum profit which one man can make in one hour from the production of these two powders.

Let x and y be the number of lb. of Rub and Rinse produced on machines A, B or C. In one hour's production, the time spent on any machine cannot exceed 60 minutes. Hence the constraints are:

$$\text{for machine A } 1·5x + 2·5y \leqslant 60$$
$$\text{for machine B } 3x + y \leqslant 60$$
$$\text{for machine C } 2·5x + 1·5y \leqslant 60$$

The objective function for Z, which gives the profit arising from one man's production for one hour is

$$Z = 6x + 4y,$$

where Z is in pence. The graph of the inequalities is shown in Fig. 85. All the points in the shaded region of the graph represent *feasible solutions* of the problem, and among them is one solution which maximises Z. To find this solution, the graph of the function Z when Z is zero is drawn, and a line parallel to this is drawn as far to the

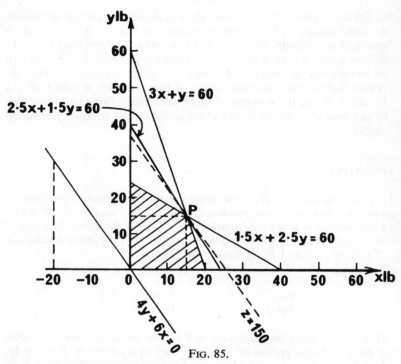

FIG. 85.

right on the graph as possible so that at least one point on it is a
feasible solution (i.e. is consistent with the constraints). This point
(P in the diagram) gives the optimum feasible solution, namely
$x = 15$ lb. and $y = 15$ lb. The fact that the three constraint lines
intersect at P shows that there is no advantage in using one machine
rather than another. Moreover, the quantities of both Rub and
Rinse produced are the same when Z is maximum. Maximum profit
is given by

$$Z_{max} = 6 \times 15 + 4 \times 15$$
$$= £1 \cdot 50.$$

The shaded region of the above graph is known as a convex
polygon, having the property that a straight line joining any two
points in or on the boundaries of it lies wholly within or on a boundary of the polygon. This shows why the method adopted above
gives an optimum solution, for the line Z_{max} passes through only one
point of the polygon, namely the vertex P. If it passed through any
point other than P, it would also pass through other points within

the polygon, some of which would represent feasible solutions not on a boundary. All these points would give the same value of Z, but it is clear that a point not on a boundary yields a solution which could be improved by increasing one of the variables at the same time keeping the other constant. All linear programming problems with a solution give rise to a convex polygon of the above type, one of the vertices of which is a solution. This is true also when the objective function has to be minimised, in which case, the line representing the function should lie as far to the left on the graph as possible consistent with the constraints. This situation is illustrated by the following example.

EXAMPLE 2

Minimise the objective function $Z = 6x + 5y$ subject to the constraints $2x + 5y \geqslant 10$, $2x + y \geqslant 4$, $3x + 4y \leqslant 12$.
In this case, the optimum solution is at the vertex Q of the shaded

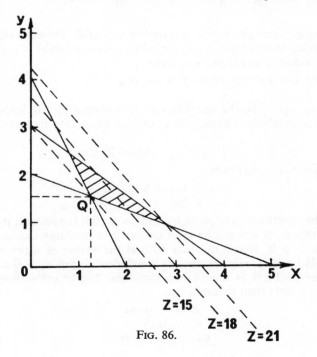

FIG. 86.

area representing all feasible solutions. Z is minimum when $x = 1 \cdot 25$, $y = 1 \cdot 5$ (Fig. 86).

In the example which follows, it is helpful to illustrate the problem by means of a graph, though some calculation is also needed in order to obtain a solution.

EXAMPLE 3

A firm combines raw materials A and B to manufacture a product X. There are three ways A and B can be combined, all of which give a profit of £1 per unit of X produced. The quantities of A and B required for the manufacture of 1 unit of X by each method is:

	Method			
	I	*II*	*III*	
A	1	3	8	*tons.*
B	6	2	0	

The firm has available a *tons of A and 48 tons of B. Assuming that the firm wishes to maximise profit, for which range of values of* a *should it use methods I and II (but not III)?*

Which methods should the firm use if a $= 7$?

Let x_1, x_2, x_3 be the quantities of X produced by Methods I, II and III respectively. The objective function which is to be maximised is:

$$Z = x_1 + x_2 + x_3 \quad \text{(where } Z \text{ is in £'s)}.$$

There are two constraints:

$$x_1 + 3x_2 + 8x_3 \leqslant a$$
$$6x_1 + 2x_2 \qquad \leqslant 48.$$

Since the contribution to profit by each method is the same, it is clear that Method III will not be used unless there are large stocks of A compared to B. Hence in order to find the values of a for which Methods I and II only are used, it is sufficient to put $x_3 = 0$ and to solve the problem as one in two variables. The objective function and constraints then become:

$$Z = x_1 + x_2$$
$$x_1 + 3x_2 \leqslant a$$
$$6x_1 + 2x_2 \leqslant 48.$$

The position is illustrated graphically in Fig. 87.

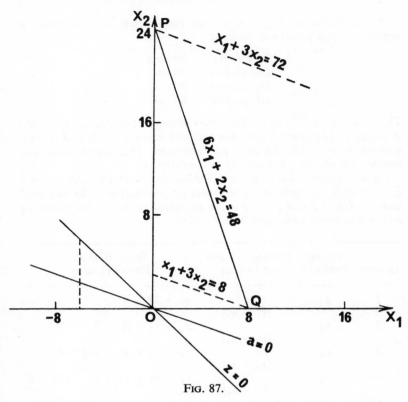

Fig. 87.

Since the line $Z = x_1 + x_2$ has a steeper negative gradient than the line $x_1 + 3x_2 = a$, it follows that the vertices of the area of feasible solutions which give the maximum values of Z for different values of a all lie on the line PQ. If $a = 8$, the graph shows that only Method I will be used, whilst if $a = 72$, only Method II will be used. Hence if $8 < a < 72$, both methods will be used. When $a \leqslant 8$, only Method I will be used, and this is the case when $a = 7$.

The following example, which must be solved algebraically, illustrates the adaptability of linear programming methods.

EXAMPLE 4

A manufacturer of specialist cars knows that demand forms a regular cyclical pattern as follows:

1st quarter	20 *cars*
2nd quarter	30 *cars*
3rd quarter	50 *cars*
4th quarter	60 *cars*

The initial stock, i.e., at the beginning of the first quarter, is zero, and a charge of £80 is made for each car held in stock at the end of each quarter. It costs £50 for each unit difference of output between one quarter and the next to vary the level of output.

An economist advises against holding stock at the end of each quarter while an engineer recommends the production of 40 cars each quarter. Use a linear programming technique to advise the managing director as to his most economical policy.

Quarter	Number Produced	Change in Level of Output	Stock Held at End of Quarter
1	x_1		$x_1 - 20 \geqslant 0$
		$\lvert x_2 - x_1 \rvert$	
2	x_2		$x_1 + x_2 - 50 \geqslant 0$
		$\lvert x_3 - x_2 \rvert$	
3	x_3		$x_1 + x_2 + x_3 - 100 \geqslant 0$
		$\lvert x_4 - x_3 \rvert$	
4	x_4		$x_1 + x_2 + x_3 + x_4 - 160 = 0$
		$\lvert x_1 - x_4 \rvert$	
1	x_1		

Total stock held per quarter $= 3x_1 + 2x_2 + x_3 - 170$.
If $x_1 = x_2 = x_3 = 40$, then

cost of holding stock $= £80 \times (240 - 170) = £5600$ p.a.,

whilst the cost of changing the level of output is zero. If no stocks are held, then
cost of changing level of output

$$= £50 \times \{(30 - 20) + (50 - 30) + (60 - 50) + (60 - 20)\}$$
$$= £4000 \text{ p.a.}$$

The economist's advice not to hold stocks is therefore preferable to the engineer's.

4. The Simplex Method

When the objective function in a linear programming problem contains more than two variables, the graphical method of the preceding section cannot usually be applied and it is necessary to use an algebraic procedure by which a solution is obtained in a number of steps, or iterations, beginning with a trial solution which is improved at each step, the process continuing until an optimum position is reached. There are several algebraic techniques for dealing with particular types of linear programming problems, but the method in most general use, due to G. B. Dantzig, is that known as the Simplex method.

The first step in the Simplex method is to convert each of the constraint inequalities into equalities by introducing a single *slack variable* into each—one slack variable for each constraint. The reason for this is that in the optimum solution, supplies used may be less than the total availabilities, and the existence of a slack variable in the corresponding equality enables this result to be obtained whilst, at the same time, satisfying the constraints. The steps in the procedure are best set out in tableau form and the method of doing this is illustrated in the following example. This is actually an example in which only two variables have to be determined, so that a graphical method could be used; however, it still provides an illustration of the Simplex method which can be applied to problems involving a greater number of variables.

EXAMPLE 5

A company manufactures two products x_1 and x_2. The contribution margin per unit of x_1 = £8 and of x_2 = £10. There are three machine centres through which the products pass. Product x_1 requires one hour's machining time in machine centre 1, and two and one hours respectively in machine centres 2 and 3. The machining requirements for product x_2 are one, one and two hours respectively in machine centres 1, 2 and 3. The maximum machine time available is 80 hours in machine centre 1, 100 hours in machine centre 2, 120 hours in machine centre 3. The company wishes to maximise the total contribution from these two products.

Determine the optimal values of x_1 and x_2 by the Simplex method.

The data of the problem is shown in tabular form below.

Product	Machine Centre		
	1	2	3
x_1	1	2	1
x_2	1	1	2
Available	80	100	120

The objective function is $Z = 8x_1 + 10x_2$.
The constraints are:

$$x_1 + x_2 \leqslant 80$$
$$2x_1 + x_2 \leqslant 100$$
$$x_1 + 2x_2 \leqslant 120$$
$$x_1, x_2 \geqslant 0.$$

The three constraint inequalities are converted into equalities by introducing slack variables $x_3, x_4, x_5 \geqslant 0$ as follows:

$$\left. \begin{array}{l} x_1 + x_2 + x_3 = 80 \\ 2x_1 + x_2 + x_4 = 100 \\ x_1 + 2x_2 + x_5 = 120. \end{array} \right\} \text{(A)}$$

The first tableau for the solution is:

C_i	x_i	x_1	x_2	x_3	x_4	x_5	b_i
0	x_3	1	1	1	0	0	80
0	x_4	2	1	0	1	0	100
0	x_5	1	2	0	0	1	120
	C_j	8	10	0	0	0	
	Solution	0	0	80	100	120	$(Z = 0)$
	Δ_j	8	10	0	0	0	
	b_i/a_{i2}	—	—	80	100	60	

The numbers in the body of the table are the coefficients of the terms on the left-hand side of the equations (A). The column b_i contains the coefficients on the right-hand side of these equations, so that $b_1 = 80$, $b_2 = 100$, $b_3 = 120$.

The row C_j contains the coefficients of x_j in the objective function Z.

The variables included in a solution are called the *basis variables* which cannot exceed in number the number of constraints. The first feasible solution includes as many as possible of the slack variables. In this example all the slack variables can be included in the first feasible basis, and the three equations are satisfied by $x_3 = 80$, $x_4 = 100$, $x_5 = 120$, whilst the non-basis variables x_1 and x_2 are zero.

It is now necessary to find how the basis can be changed so as to increase the value of Z. Here we proceed one step at a time, discarding a slack variable and introducing another variable which was previously zero. To find the new variable to enter, the row Δ_j is computed by multiplying the numbers in the column C_i by the corresponding coefficients in columns x_1, x_2, x_3, etc., summing the products and subtracting this sum from the appropriate C_j. The column C_i consists of the coefficients in the equation Z corresponding to the variables in the basis. In the first tableau, these are the coefficients of x_3, x_4, x_5 which in the maximising equation are all zero. Now $C_1 = 8$, so to find Δ_j for the first column we have

$$\Delta_1 = 8 - 0 \times 1 - 0 \times 2 - 0 \times 1 = 8$$

also
$$\Delta_2 = 10 - 0 \times 1 - 0 \times 1 - 0 \times 2 = 10$$

and so on.

The new variable to be entered corresponds to the value of Δ_j which is largest and non-negative. In this case it is $\Delta_2 = 10$ so the new variable to come into the next basis is x_2.

The departing variable is found by computing the row b_i/a_{ir} where a_{ir} is the coefficient in the ith row of the variable x_r, the entering variable, in the body of the table: in this case $r = 2$ and the corresponding coefficients are $a_{12} = 1$, $a_{22} = 1$, $a_{32} = 2$. Now b_i are the values occurring in the basis, because the coefficients of the basis variables are all equal to 1.

Hence,

$$b_1/a_{12} = 80/1 = 80, b_2/a_{22} = 100/1 = 100, b_3/a_{32} = 120/2 = 60,$$

and these values are entered in the positions shown in the row b_i/a_{12} corresponding to the basis variables in the solution. The basis variable to depart is that for which b_i/a_{ir} takes its smallest non-negative value, x_r being the entering variable. Thus b_i/a_{12} is smallest for x_5 viz. 60 so x_5 goes out and x_2 comes in.

Since x_5 is in the third equation x_2 must come into the third equation in place of it with coefficient 1. Hence the coefficient of x_2

in this equation must be reduced to unity by dividing all the co-efficients in the equation by 2. The intermediate coefficients are:

$$
\begin{array}{ccccc|c}
1 & 1 & 1 & 0 & 0 & 80 \\
2 & 1 & 0 & 1 & 0 & 100 \\
\tfrac{1}{2} & 1 & 0 & 0 & \tfrac{1}{2} & 60
\end{array}
$$

Since each equation should contain only one basis variable, all the coefficients of x_2, except the last, must be reduced to zero, which is done by taking appropriate multiples of the coefficients in the last equation from corresponding coefficients in the other two. In this case the multiple is unity, and the coefficients for the second tableau are:

$$
\begin{array}{ccccc|c}
\tfrac{1}{2} & 0 & 1 & 0 & -\tfrac{1}{2} & 20 \\
\tfrac{3}{2} & 0 & 0 & 1 & -\tfrac{1}{2} & 40 \\
\tfrac{1}{2} & 1 & 0 & 0 & \tfrac{1}{2} & 60
\end{array}
$$

Second Tableau

C_i	x_i	x_1	x_2	x_3	x_4	x_5	b_i
0	x_3	$\tfrac{1}{2}$	0	1	0	$-\tfrac{1}{2}$	20
0	x_4	$\tfrac{3}{2}$	0	0	1	$-\tfrac{1}{2}$	40
10	x_2	$\tfrac{1}{2}$	1	0	0	$\tfrac{1}{2}$	60
	C_j	8	10	0	0	0	
	Solution	0	60	20	40	0	$(Z = 600)$
	Δ_j	3	0	0	0	-5	
b_i/a_{i1}		—	120	40	$\tfrac{80}{3}$	—	
		$\uparrow$			$\downarrow$		
		E			D		

In this case

$$\Delta_1 = 8 - 0 \times \tfrac{1}{2} - 0 \times \tfrac{3}{2} - \tfrac{1}{2} \times 10 = 3$$

$$\Delta_2 = 10 - 0 \times 0 - 0 \times 0 - 10 \times 1 = 0$$

etc. Δ_j is largest for x_1 (entering variable) and b_i/a_{i1} is smallest for x_4 (departing variable). The final tableau is now obtained by reducing the coefficient of x_1 in the *second* equation to unity by multiplying it throughout by $\tfrac{2}{3}$. The coefficients for the third tableau are then obtained, as above for the second tableau.

Third Tableau

C_i	x_i	x_1	x_2	x_3	x_4	x_5	b_i
0	x_3	0	0	1	$-\frac{1}{3}$	$-\frac{1}{3}$	$\frac{20}{3}$
8	x_1	1	0	0	$\frac{2}{3}$	$-\frac{1}{3}$	$\frac{80}{3}$
10	x_2	0	1	0	$-\frac{1}{3}$	$\frac{2}{3}$	$\frac{140}{3}$
	C_j	8	10	0	0	0	
	Solution	$\frac{80}{3}$	$\frac{140}{3}$	$\frac{20}{3}$	0	0	$(Z = 680)$
	Δ_j	0	0	0	-2	-4	

No improvement is now possible because all the items Δ_j are either zero or negative. Hence the optimum solution is

$$x_1 = 80/3 = 26\cdot67 \qquad x_2 = 140/3 = 46\cdot67$$
$$x_3 = 20/3 = 6\cdot67 \qquad x_4 = x_5 = 0$$

The values of the slack variables in this solution have a significance which is apparent from equations (A). Thus the first of these equations is satisfied only if $x_3 = 6\cdot67$ so that machine centre 1 shows $6\cdot67$ hours idle time. The fact that $x_4 = x_5 = 0$ shows that machine centres 2 and 3 are fully occupied. The negative terms in the Δ_j row show that the introduction into the basis of the variables corresponding to them would reduce Z. In each tableau the coefficients in this row show the additional contribution which results if the corresponding variable x_j is increased by 1 unit. In the third tableau, therefore, the zero coefficients show that no addition to the variables x_1, x_2, x_3 will increase profit. The negative coefficients -2 and -4 show that if either x_4 or x_5 are increased, profit will actually be reduced. However, if either of these variables can be reduced, that is, made negative, then profit will be increased. The two constraint equations for machine centres 2 and 3 can be written in the form

$$2x_1 + x_2 = 100 - x_4$$
$$x_1 + 2x_2 = 120 - x_5$$

these centres being fully utilised. Making x_4 negative by giving it the value -1 is equivalent to increasing the machine time available in machine centre 2 by 1 hour. Similarly giving x_5 the value -1 is equivalent to increasing the machine time available in centre 3 to 121 hours. The resulting increases in x_1 and x_2 which are now possible lead to an addition to profit of

$$(-1 \times -2) + (-1 \times -4) = 6.$$

This can easily be verified by finding the values of x_1 and x_2 which satisfy the simultaneous equations

$$2x_1 + x_2 = 101$$
$$x_1 + 2x_2 = 121$$

which are $x_1 = 27$ and $x_2 = 47$. The total contribution is now

$$Z = 8 \times 27 + 10 \times 47 = 686$$

which is an increase of 6 on the previous value.

The coefficients in row Δ_j at any stage are known as *shadow prices* and indicate the maximum price which can be paid for an additional unit of resources in order to obtain a net increase in profit. Thus if the capacity of machine centre 2 can be increased by 1 hour at a cost of less than £2 there will be a net addition to profit. The fact that x_3 is positive in the final solution shows that machine centre 1 has surplus capacity, so there is clearly no case for extending the availability of this resource.

In the foregoing example, the object is to maximise Z when all the constraints are expressed as "less than" inequalities. If "greater than" inequalities occur, they can be transformed to "less than" inequalities by changing the signs of both sides of the inequality. For example, the inequality $2x_1 + 3x_2 \geqslant 4$ is equivalent to the inequality $-2x_1 - 3x_2 \leqslant -4$. A non-negative slack variable can now be added, as before, to obtain the corresponding equation. In this case, when x_1 and x_2 are both zero, the slack variable must be negative, contradicting the imposed condition that it is non-negative. A modification of the procedure previously explained is thus required in order to set up the first tableau; but this matter will not be pursued further here.

If a problem requires that Z should be minimised, it can be transformed to a maximising problem by maximising $-Z$, i.e. by changing the signs of all the coefficients in the objective function. For example, minimising $Z = 2x_1 + 4x_2 + 3x_3$ is equivalent to maximising $Z = -2x_1 - 4x_2 - 3x_3$.

5. Transportation Problems

The essence of a transportation problem is to decide which, between a number of alternative routes, will enable one to achieve a specified object at minimum cost. An algebraic method is available for the solution of such problems which can be applied systematically so that *a* best solution, in the sense of one that produces *the* minimum cost, is automatically reached. There may be either several solutions or a unique solution which attain this desired end. Other things being equal, it will not matter which of these situations arises if all one is interested in is producing the minimum transportation cost. The problem may consist either of minimising distance travelled, when cost per unit distance is the same for all routes, or minimising costs when this is not so.

The algebraic method is illustrated by the following simple problem:

Office	Factory I	II	Salesmen Available
A	20	25	2
B	30	30	3
Number sent	2	3	5

Suppose that a firm has two offices at each of which are the number of salesmen shown in the above table and that it is required to send a specified number (also shown) to each of two factories. The distances in miles between the offices and factories are shown in the body of the table. Required to find which salesmen should be sent to which factories so as to minimise the mileage travelled by the salesmen.

To set up the problem algebraically, suppose that a_1, a_2 salesmen are sent from A to factories I and II respectively, and that b_1, b_2 are sent from B to factories I and II respectively. The data enables us to formulate four equations each containing two of these unknown quantities, viz.,

$$a_1 + a_2 = 2$$
$$b_1 + b_2 = 3$$
$$a_1 + b_1 = 2$$
$$a_2 + b_2 = 3$$

Although it may seem, since there are four unknowns and four equations, that this system is uniquely soluble, you will find, if you try various values, that it is indeterminate, i.e., there is no unique solution. However, there is a further condition which must be satisfied in order to produce a solution to the problem, viz., that

Total mileage $= 20a_1 + 25a_2 + 30b_1 + 30b_2$ must be minimum.

In order to find values of the unknowns which will make this minimum, we begin by rearranging the terms of this equation.

$$\begin{aligned}
\text{Total mileage} &= 20a_1 + 25a_2 + 30b_1 + 30b_2 \\
&= 20(a_1 + a_2) + 5a_2 + 30(b_1 + b_2) \\
&= 20 \times 2 + 5a_2 + 30 \times 3 \\
&= 40 + 90 + 5a_2
\end{aligned}$$

To obtain this result, the fact is used that $a_1 + a_2 = 2$ and $b_1 + b_2 = 3$. Since none of the unknowns can be negative, it is clear from this last expression that total mileage is minimum when $a_2 = 0$. Hence from the original equations, $a_1 = 2$, $b_1 = 0$, $b_2 = 3$. In other words, to minimise the mileage, both salesmen from A are sent to I and all three salesmen at B are sent to factory II. The minimum mileage will evidently be 130 miles and this is the unique solution of the problem.

A simpler method of solution, which is closely related in principle to the algebraic one, consists of reducing the cost (or distance) matrix so that as many (reduced) costs as possible are zero. This is clearly a very direct method, since it enables one to see at a glance which routes are cheapest (or shortest) and it will obviously be advantageous to utilise these routes as fully as possible in order to minimise cost (or distance). The procedure is most easily illustrated by an example.

EXAMPLE 6

The owner of a mini-cab firm controls three small garages in various parts of a town containing respectively 2, 3 and 4 cabs. At one point of time in the evening the owner receives three requests for cabs in various quantities from three parties going on in town. He calculates the distances in miles from the garages to the parties as follows:

Garage	Party		
	A needing 1 car	B needing 3 cars	C needing 5 cars
X—containing 2 cars	6	3	10
Y—containing 3 cars	4	9	5
Z—containing 4 cars	3	6	6

Calculate an optimum solution that minimises the total distances from garage to parties.

Step 1

Deduct the lowest value (mileage) from each cell of each row to give:

Garage	Party A	B	C	Available	Value deducted
X	3	0	7	2	$3 \times 2 = 6$
Y	0	5	1	3	$4 \times 3 = 12$
Z	0	3	3	4	$3 \times 4 = 12$
Required	1	3	5	9	30

Step 2

Deduct lowest value from these remaining values in each cell of each column:

Garage	Party A	B	C	Available
X	3	0	6	2
Y	0	5	0	3
Z	0	3	2	4
Required	1	3	5	9
	0	0	1	Value deducted
			$\times 5$	
			5	

Step 3

Allocate requirements to each cell in a way which yields, where possible, minimum mileage.

Thus allocate 1 to ZA, 2 to XB and 1 to ZB, 3 to YC and 2 to ZC.

These allocations, with modified mileages from Step 2, are shown in the following table:

Garage	Party			Total
	A	B	C	
X	3	0	6	2
		2		
Y	0	5	0	3
			3	
Z	0	3	2	4
	1	1	2	
Total	1	3	5	9

Additional mileage $= 1 \times 3 + 2 \times 2 = 7$.
No further improvement is possible, so this is the optimum plan.
Total mileage $= 30 + 5 + 7 = 42$.

The solution of Example 6 is straightforward, because the availabilities and requirements are equal. When demand and supply are unequal, there are two cases to consider:

(i) Supply greater than demand

To apply the transportation technique in this case, it is necessary to balance demand and supply by including in the tableau an additional demand centre called a *sink* to take up surplus supply. The transportation costs are written in the top right-hand corner of each cell in the manner illustrated in Example 6, except that the costs in cells of the sink column are all zero. The sink only uses up surplus supply, so there should be no penalty for allocating to these cells, hence the zero costs. For example, suppose there are two demand centres A and B and two supply centres X and Y, then the tableau is:

Supply	Demand		
	A	B	Sink
X	1 x_{11}	3 x_{12}	0 x_{13}
Y	2 x_{21}	4 x_{22}	0 x_{23}

Hypothetical transportation costs are also included for illustrative purposes. The quantity demanded is

$$x_{11} + x_{12} + x_{21} + x_{22}$$

whilst the amount by which supply exceeds demand is

$$x_{13} + x_{23}.$$

A reduced tableau, such as that shown in Example 6, is then easily obtained from this, noting that the lowest value to be deducted in each row is zero.

(ii) Demand greater than supply

In this case, the sink is included among the supply centres. For example:

Supply	Demand	
	A	B
X	1 x_{11}	3 x_{12}
Y	2 x_{21}	4 x_{22}
Sink	x_{31}	x_{32}

Total supply $= x_{11} + x_{12} + x_{21} + x_{22}$

Excess demand $= x_{31} + x_{32}$.

In obtaining reduced costs here, the lowest value deducted in each column is zero.

EXAMPLE 7

A company must transport vehicles that are stored in three garages to four different destinations. Let the number of vehicles stored at the three garages be 20, 20 and 24, respectively. Let the number required at each destination be 15. The cost (in pounds) of transporting a vehicle from a garage to a destination is summarised in the following table:

		Destination			
		1	2	3	4
	1	1	2	3	4
Garage	2	8	7	6	5
	3	9	10	11	12

The company wishes to minimise the cost of transport:
(a) Find two different solutions minimising the cost.

(b) *Suppose additional information is received which indicates that alternative jobs are available for vehicles in Garages 2 and 3 if they are not sent to any of the destinations. A Garage 2 vehicle can earn £30 and a Garage 3 vehicle can earn £20 in alternative jobs. The company would consider lost income as part of its total cost. Find a cost-minimising solution under these circumstances.*

(a) **Step 1**

Deduct lowest cost from each cell of each column to give:

	Destination					
Garage	1	2	3	4	"S"	Available
1	0	0	0	0	0	20
2	7	5	3	1	0	20
3	8	8	8	8	0	24
Required	15	15	15	15	4	64

Value deducted	1	2	3	4	0
	$\times 15$	$\times 15$	$\times 15$	$\times 15$	$\times 4$
	15	30	45	60	0

Step 2

Allocate requirements to each cell in a way which results, where possible, in minimum cost:

	1		2		3		4		"S"		Total
		0		0		0		0		0	
1	15		5		0		0		0		20
		7		5		3		1		0	
2	0		0		5		15		0		20
		8		8		8		8		0	
3	0		10		10		0		4		24
Total	15		15		15		15		4		64

Total cost $= 10 \times 8 + 5 \times 3 + 10 \times 8 + 15 \times 1 + 150$
$= £340.$

An alternative least-cost plan is to send 15 vehicles from Garage 3 to Destination 1, 15 from Garage 1 to Destination 2, 5 from each of the Garages to Destination 3 and 15 from Garage 2 to Destination 4.

(b) In the light of the new information, £30 must be added to each of the costs in row 2 of the matrix in Step 2 (except the "S" column), and £20 must be added to each of the costs in row 3 (also excluding the "S" column). The allocations are then as follows:

	1	2	3	4	"S"	Total
	0	0	0	0	0	
1	15	5	0	0	0	20
	37	35	33	31	0	
2	0	0	1	15	4	20
	28	28	28	28	0	
3	0	10	14	0	0	24
Total	15	15	15	15	4	64

Total cost $= 10 \times 28 + 1 \times 33 + 14 \times 28 + 15 \times 31 + 150$
$ = £1320.$

The transportation technique can also be used for maximising quantities such as profits. In this case, the *highest* cell values in each row or column of the profits matrix are subtracted from each cell value. The resulting "reduced" profits will then be either zero or negative. Allocations are first made to those cells with zero "reduced" profits and any remaining allocations to cells with the largest negative values, bearing in mind, of course, that -1 is greater than -2, for instance.

6. Theory of Games

Competitors in business are seldom restricted to only one course of action; there are usually several such courses open to each competitor, and the outcome of each course will depend upon those adopted by the other competitors. It will not be known, however, what these courses of action will be in any particular instance, although an individual may havè some knowledge of the general strategic dispositions of his rivals. Given enough information about the outcome of one's own decisions in relation to the possible decisions of one's rivals, it will be possible to formulate a policy which will lead to the maximising of gain or the minimising of loss over time. The theory of games is used to analyse the relations, in terms of outcomes, between one individual's policy decisions and those of his rivals.

A *zero-sum two-person game* is essentially a competitive activity in which there are two opponents and in which each player attempts to maximise his gain or minimise his loss and, in the final outcome of which, one person's gain exactly equals the other person's loss. Each of the two opponents is supposed to have a set of strategies such that each of one player's strategies will tell him what the outcome of the game will be when the other player plays each of his strategies. This data is represented in a *pay-off matrix* for each of the players. For example, in a 2×2 game, each player has two strategies, and their pay-off matrices might be as shown:

A's strategy	B's strategy I	II		A's strategy	B's strategy I	II
I	5	−3		I	−5	3
II	−1	2		II	1	−2

A's pay-off matrix   B's pay-off matrix

A game between two players A and B is zero-sum if, when both play their optimal strategies, A's expected gain exactly equals B's expected loss. This will clearly be the case in the above example since each player's pay-off matrix is the inverse of the other. In certain games, the pay-off matrix is such that it is to the advantage of each player to use just one strategy, i.e. to employ a *pure strategy*. This is so when the highest of the minimum gains for each strategy of A and the least of the maximum losses for B is represented by the same element of the pay-off matrix. In this case the game has a *saddle-point* which is the common element in each player's pure strategy. The following game (illustrated by A's pay-off matrix) has a saddle-point.

A's minimum gains for his strategies I and II respectively are −3 and 2, the largest of these being 2.

	B	
A	I	II
I	1	(−3)
II	②	④

B's maximum losses for his strategies I and II are, respectively, 4 and 2, the least of these being 2.

Hence the game has a saddle-point which is the intersection of A's strategy II and B's strategy I, namely the element 2; and it will pay both A and B to use these pure strategies all the time. The value of the game to A is +2 and to B is −2.

The justification of this method of selecting strategies is that, whatever strategy is adopted by one player, the other player will try to reduce the first player's gain to a minimum. Hence, when the game has a saddle-point, it will be to the advantage of the first player to use the pure strategy for which that minimum gain is greatest. On the assumption that both players act on this principle of minimising each other's gain (or maximising each other's loss), a saddle-point will be a true equilibrium for the game, since any departure from the strategy which includes the saddle-point will result in loss to the player who adopts the alternative strategy.

When a game has no saddle-point, neither player can do better than adopt a *mixed strategy*. In a 2 × 2 game, each player will play his alternative strategies at random, but in fixed proportions, the proportions being determined on the assumption that A maximises his expected gain whilst B minimises his expected loss. The calculations required to determine the proportions are illustrated by the following pay-off matrix (for A):

A's strategy	B's strategy I	II	
I	a	b	x
II	c	d	1 − x
	y	1 − y	

If A plays strategies I and II in the proportions $x : 1 - x$ respectively, $0 \leqslant x \leqslant 1$, then when B plays strategies $(y, 1 - y)$ A's expected gain is:

$$g = y\{ax + c(1 - x)\} + (1 - y)\{bx + d(1 - x)\}.$$

Since B's expected gain in a zero-sum game is $-g$, A will choose strategies which will minimise $-g$ and this will be the case when

$$\frac{dg}{dy} = \{ax + c(1-x)\} - \{bx + d(1-x)\} = 0$$

or $ax + c(1-x) = bx + d(1-x),$

whence $x = (d-c)/\{a + d - (b+c)\}.$

The optimum value of y can be obtained by a similar argument, differentiating g with respect to x and setting the differential co-efficient equal to zero to give

$$y = (d-b)/\{a + d - (b+c)\}.$$

For the game at the beginning of this section we have, from A's pay-off matrix, $a = 5$, $b = -3$, $c = -1$ and $d = 2$.

whence $x = (2+1)/(7+4) = 3/11$

$$y = (2+3)/(7+4) = 5/11.$$

Hence the expected value of the game to A is

$$g = \frac{5}{11}\left\{\frac{5 \times 3}{11} + (-1)\left(1 - \frac{3}{11}\right)\right\}$$

$$+ \left(1 - \frac{5}{11}\right)\left\{\frac{-3 \times 3}{11} + 2\left(1 - \frac{3}{11}\right)\right\}$$

$$= 7/11.$$

B's expected gain is evaluated by using B's pay-off matrix and is, of course, equal to $-7/11$.

A's expected gain can also, conveniently, be calculated using matrix algebra. Let P and Q represent A's and B's optimal strategies respectively and A represent A's pay-off matrix. Then A's expected gain is

$$G = PAQ$$

$$= \begin{pmatrix} \frac{3}{11} & \frac{8}{11} \end{pmatrix} \begin{pmatrix} 5 & -3 \\ -1 & 2 \end{pmatrix} \begin{pmatrix} \frac{5}{11} \\ \frac{6}{11} \end{pmatrix}$$

$$= \begin{pmatrix} \frac{3}{11} & \frac{8}{11} \end{pmatrix} \begin{pmatrix} \dfrac{25 - 18}{11} \\ \dfrac{-5 + 12}{11} \end{pmatrix}$$

$$= \begin{pmatrix} \dfrac{21 + 56}{121} \end{pmatrix}$$

$$= \begin{pmatrix} \dfrac{7}{11} \end{pmatrix}.$$

Before this method is applied to determining optimal strategies, the pay-off matrix should first be inspected to see whether the game has a saddle-point. If it has, the above method breaks down, for it will be found that the above formulae give values of y or x which lie outside the required interval [0, 1].

In an $m \times n$ game with no saddle-point, there are $m - 1$ values of x to be determined for A and $n - 1$ values of y for B in order to obtain the optimum mixture of strategies for both. If m and n are both greater than 2 a solution can always be obtained by linear programming methods, particularly if a computer is available. However, the situation is often simplified, in this case, if dominant strategies exist either for A or B. One strategy is *dominant* to another if each of the outcomes of one is better than or as good as the corresponding outcomes of the other from the player's point of view. In this case, the dominated strategy or strategies can be eliminated, thus reducing the dimensions of the game and facilitating its solution. The following example illustrates.

EXAMPLE 8

The pay-offs (to player A) in a zero-sum game are as shown in the matrix.

		B			
		1	2	3	4
A	1	−1	4	3	−3
	2	7	2	8	5
	3	1	5	3	6
	4	5	1	4	4

What are A's and B's optimal strategies?
How much should A pay to B to make the game fair?

Here A has two dominant strategies which he will always prefer to the remaining two. These are 2 (which is dominant to 4) and 3 (which is dominant to 1). After eliminating the dominated strategies, the pay-off matrix becomes:

		B			
		1	2	3	4
A	2	7	2	8	5
	3	1	5	3	6

From this it appears that B has two strategies which are dominant to the others, namely 1 and 2 since these result in smaller *losses* to B than strategies 3 and 4 respectively. Eliminating these others, the pay-off matrix becomes:

		B 1	B 2	
A	2	7	2	x
	3	1	5	$1 - x$
		y	$1 - y$	

The game has no saddle-point so that the formulae derived above can be used to obtain the optimum values of x and y. Thus

$$x = (5 - 1)/(7 + 5 - 2 - 1) = 4/9.$$

So A plays 2 in 4/9 of the games and 3 in 5/9 of the games. Similarly, B minimises his losses when

$$y = (5 - 2)/(7 + 5 - 2 - 1) = 1/3.$$

So B plays 1 in 1/3 of the games and 2 in 2/3 of the games. The value of the game to A is

$$g = \tfrac{1}{3}(7 \times \tfrac{4}{9} + 1 \times \tfrac{5}{9}) + \tfrac{2}{3}(2 \times \tfrac{4}{9} + 5 \times \tfrac{5}{9})$$
$$= (28 + 5 + 16 + 50)/27$$
$$= 3\tfrac{2}{3}.$$

Hence A must pay B $3\tfrac{2}{3}$ in order to make the game fair.

7. Simplex Method: Alternative Procedure

The procedure for solving a linear programming problem by the Simplex method explained in section 4 may prove rather unwieldy, particularly where several variables are involved. A more compact method which rests on precisely the same principle as that in section 4 is illustrated by the solution of the following example.

EXAMPLE 9

A company manufactures three products: tanks, trays and tubs, each of which pass through three processes I, II and III.

The table below gives the time required for each product in each process and, for a certain production period, the total process time available. The contributions to profit of each product are £2, £3, and £4 per unit respectively.

Process	Process hours per unit			Total process
	Tanks	Trays	Tubs	hours available
I	5	2	4	12,000
II	4	5	6	24,000
III	3	5	4	18,000

Determine how many units of each product should be produced in order to maximise profit and state the profit figure.

Let x_1, x_2, x_3 be the number of tanks, trays and tubs produced respectively and let x_4, x_5, x_6 be slack variables.

The objective function is

$$Z = 2x_1 + 3x_2 + 4x_3$$

and the constraint equations are

$$5x_1 + 2x_2 + 4x_3 + x_4 = 12,000$$
$$4x_1 + 5x_2 + 6x_3 + x_5 = 24,000$$
$$3x_1 + 5x_2 + 4x_3 + x_6 = 18,000.$$

The first tableau is now set up as follows:

First Tableau

	x_1	x_2	x_3	x_4	x_5	x_6	M
x_4	5	2	④	1	0	0	12,000
x_5	4	5	6	0	1	0	24,000
x_6	3	5	4	0	0	1	18,000
L	2	3	$\boxed{4}$	0	0	0	$Z = 0$

The first column shows the variables in the first feasible solution, which are all slack variables. Column M shows the availabilities, and row L shows the coefficients of each of the variables in the objective function, those of the slack variables being, of course, zero. The first step is to find a variable to come into the solution in place of one of the variables already in, the change being made so that the value of Z is increased as much as possible. This is effected by selecting the largest positive coefficient in row L (in this case 4) which fixes x_3 as the entering variable. To find the departing variable, each of the coefficients in column M is divided by the coefficient in the same row in column x_3, the row in which the smallest of these (non-negative) quotients occurs determining which of the basis variables in the first column is the departing variable. Thus the quotients are: $12,000/4 = 3000$, $24,000/6 = 4000$ and $18,000/4 = 4500$ of which 3000 in the first row is the smallest. This shows that the variable x_4 in the first row is replaced by x_3 in this row.

The coefficient (4) in row x_4 and column x_3 is called the *pivot* which is essential for the calculations necessary to set up the next tableau. In order to obtain the second tableau: (a) divide the coefficients in the first row of the first tableau by the pivot (4) in order to reduce the coefficient of x_3 in the basis to unity thus giving the coefficients in the first row of the second tableau; (b) subtract multiples of the coefficients in the first row of the second tableau from corresponding coefficients in the remaining rows of the first tableau in order to reduce the coefficients of x_3 in rows 2 and 3 to zero. That is, multiply each coefficient of the first row of the second tableau by 6 (including the coefficient in column M) and subtract the products from the corresponding coefficients in the second row of the first tableau to give the coefficients in the second row of the second tableau. Then multiply the coefficients in the first row of the second tableau by 4 and subtract the products from corresponding coefficients in the third row of the first tableau in order to obtain the coefficients in the third row of the second tableau. (c) Multiply each of the coefficients in the first row of the second tableau (excluding that in column M) by the pivotal number 4 in row L of the first tableau and subtract these products in turn from corresponding coefficients in row L of the first tableau to give the coefficients in row L of the second tableau. For example the coefficient in row L, column x_1 of the second tableau is $2 - 4 \times \dfrac{5}{4} = -3$.

Second Tableau

	x_1	x_2	x_3	x_4	x_5	x_6	M
x_3	$\dfrac{5}{4}$	$\dfrac{1}{2}$	1	$\dfrac{1}{4}$	0	0	3000
x_5	$-\dfrac{14}{4}$	2	0	$\dfrac{3}{2}$	1	0	6000
x_6	-2	$\boxed{3}$	0	-1	0	1	6000
L	-3	$\boxed{1}$	0	-1	0	0	$Z = 12{,}000$

In this case, the largest positive coefficient in row L is 1 showing that x_2 is the next entering variable. On dividing each of the coefficients in column M by the corresponding coefficients in column x_2 the smallest quotient obtained is that in row x_6 showing that this is the variable to leave and that the pivot for obtaining the next tableau is 3. The third tableau is now obtained in exactly the same way from the second tableau as the second tableau was obtained from the first.

Third Tableau

	x_1	x_2	x_3	x_4	x_5	x_6	M
x_3	$\dfrac{19}{12}$	0	1	$\dfrac{5}{12}$	0	$-\dfrac{1}{6}$	2000
x_5	$-\dfrac{26}{12}$	0	0	$-\dfrac{5}{6}$	1	$\dfrac{2}{3}$	2000
x_2	$-\dfrac{2}{3}$	1	0	$-\dfrac{1}{3}$	0	$\dfrac{1}{3}$	2000
L	$-2\dfrac{1}{3}$	0	0	$-\dfrac{2}{3}$	0	$-\dfrac{1}{3}$	$Z = 14{,}000$

All the coefficients in row L are now either zero or negative, showing that the solution cannot be further improved. The basis variables in the final solution are those in the first column and since the coefficients of each of these variables have been reduced to unity and the remaining variables are zero, it follows that the values of the basis variables are the coefficients in column M of the final tableau. Hence the solution is

$$x_2 = x_3 = x_5 = 2000$$

and the corresponding profit is

$$Z = 3 \times 2000 + 4 \times 2000 = \text{£}14,000.$$

As the slack variables x_4 and x_6 are both zero, Processes I and III are fully utilised whilst there is surplus capacity in Process II since x_5 is greater than zero. The shadow prices occur in row L. Thus an increase of 1 hour in each of Processes I and III would result in an addition to profit of $\frac{1}{3} + \frac{2}{3} = \text{£}1$ and it would not be worth making this extension unless the cost of doing so were less than £1.

The parameters of a linear programming model are usually estimates and may turn out to be wrong. Hence when an optimal solution has been reached it may need to be modified in the light of further experience. Even so, it may often be the case that quite a considerable error in the estimates will have little or no effect on the optimal solution. In Example 9, Process II is under-utilised by 2000 hours, so that if the estimate of 24,000 hours of the time available for this Process proved to be optimistic this would probably not affect the optimal solution. On the other hand, if the time available for Process I proved to be an overestimate, the final solution of the problem in the third tableau would obviously have to be modified. It is obviously important to know, in advance, how changes of this kind in the model parameters would affect the optimal solution so that a deeper investigation of the estimates can be made if the solution is likely to be materially affected. Information about this is obtained by what is known as *sensitivity analysis*. The object of sensitivity analysis is to assess the extent to which an optimum solution might have to be modified owing to a given deviation of the values of the model parameters from their estimated values. The extent of these deviations from expectations will depend on the probability distributions of the estimates, and linear programming models must be capable of adaptation to these probabilistic considerations.

The optimal solution may itself provide some indication of its sensitivity to changes in the parameters. In the third tableau of the foregoing example, the fact that the coefficient in row L, column x_1, is negative shows that quite a considerable increase in the contribution of tanks to profit would be needed before some other solution were optimum. In fact, if this contribution were increased from £2 to £4·33, the shadow price of tanks would be zero in the final tableau and the solution with $x_1 = 0$ would still be optimal. If on the other hand the contribution of tanks were increased to £5 per unit, then profit could be increased by making x_1 greater than zero so that the optimal solution before the increase would not be optimal after it had taken place. One could, in fact, find the new optimal solution by changing the negative shadow price $-2\frac{1}{3}$ to $-2\frac{1}{3} + (5 - 2) = \frac{2}{3}$ in the third tableau, and proceed from this to develop further tableaux until the new optimum solution was reached.

The existence of uncertainty is only one factor affecting the validity of a linear programming model. The basic mathematical assumptions of the model are that all the functions, i.e. the constraint and objective functions, must be linear. In the objective function, for instance, it is assumed that an increase in one of the variables will produce a proportional change in the contribution to profit. However, unit profit may change with production levels, in which case the assumption would be unjustified. Fixed overheads are another source of non-linearity. These may be established for all products collectively; but the optimum product mix may exclude one or more of the products, and this may affect fixed overheads. In other words, a change in the output of a product from 0 to 1 unit could result in a once-for-all increase in costs which would not be linearly related to output.

One requirement of the linear model is that resource usage for each product considered individually is proportional to the output of the product in question. But it is also necessary that interaction between the levels of outputs of several products has no influence on the proportionality of individual resource usage. This implies that the terms of a constraint function must be strictly additive. For instance, if the levels of output of products 1 and 2 require a_1x_1 and a_2x_2 units of resources respectively when considered individually, then if the constraint function is linear, it must also be the case that if both levels of output are achieved, the resource usage is $a_1x_1 + a_2x_2$. This would not be the case if the production of product 1 yielded a by-product which could be used in the production of product 2, but which would have to be obtained externally if product 1 were not produced. Interactions of this kind may also occur in the objective function if, for example, the market price of a product has to be adjusted when the output of some other product is changed. The small producer selling in a "perfect" market will not be faced with this problem, but it could be important to a large-scale producer or monopolist.

The optimal levels of output provided by the Simplex solution may be fractional, although the nature of the product may entail that the solution must be in integers because of the indivisibility of the final product. For example, it is perfectly possible to produce $1\frac{1}{2}$ tons of a fertiliser, but it is not possible to produce $100\frac{1}{2}$ motor vehicles. The existence of indivisibilities may not make a non-integer solution significantly invalid if the number of units of output is very large, for in this case, one can simply round the values of the Simplex solution to the nearest integer. However, if the output is small then it could happen that by rounding the values obtained to the nearest integer, the solution will become either unfeasible (i.e. not satisfy the constraints) or be significantly sub-optimal. A special technique known as integer programming has been developed to deal with situations of this kind. Non-linear programming techniques are also available where the assumptions of linearity are flagrantly unfulfilled, although these are generally applicable only to certain special cases. Very often the situation approximates sufficiently closely to linearity for the Simplex method to be used, and this is by far the most successful and universally applied programming technique.

EXERCISES 18

1. Draw the graphs of the equations $y = 6 - 2x$ and $5y = 20 - 4x$ using only the positive (i.e. the 1st) quadrant. Shade the portion of this quadrant which consists of all points satisfying the inequalities $y + 2x \leqslant 6$ and $5y + 4x \leqslant 20$. Which of the following number pairs satisfy (a) both inequalities, (b) just one inequality, (c) neither inequality?

   (i) $(1, 1)$, (ii) $(4, 2)$, (iii) $(1, 4)$, (iv) $(2, 1)$, (v) $(3, 1)$.

2. Which of the following sets of inequalities are consistent?
   (a) $x + y > 2$, $x + y > 1$; (b) $x + y < 2$, $x > 3$ where both x and y are non-negative; (c) $y + 2x \leqslant 6$, $5y + 4x \geqslant 20$.

3. If x and y are both non-negative and $2x + 3y \leqslant 6$ and $x + 3y \leqslant 3$, what is the maximum value of $x + y$?

4. An establishment for boarding animals has kennels for 20 dogs and cages for 30 cats, but a local authority regulation restricts the total number of animals kept at any one time to 36. Taking x as the number of dogs and y as the number of cats, write down the three inequalities which the above conditions impose.

Every day, 15 minutes' work has to be done for each dog kept, and 10 minutes' work for each cat, and there is only 7 hours available for this work. Show that this imposes the further condition $3x + 2y \leqslant 84$.

Draw a linear programming graph to illustrate the above data, and shade it so as to leave *unshaded* the region containing points corresponding to numbers of animals that could be kept.

If the gross profit on each dog is 20p per day and on each cat 15p per day, and the overhead cost of the establishment is £3·60 per day, shade the region containing points corresponding to numbers of animals that would cause the establishment to run at a loss.

5. (a) What is "linear programming"? Describe the type of problem to which this technique may be applied.

(b) The following table shows the time required for producing two products X and Y, each of which has to be processed on all three machines, A, B and C.

Machine	Hours per unit		Machine Hours Available
	Product X	Product Y	
A	3	1	42
B	4	2	60
C	2	4	48

What combination of the two products will give the maximum utilisation of the three machines?

6.

	Vitamin A	Vitamin C	Vitamin D
Normal needs per day per person	5000 units	75 mg	400 units
One tablet of Omnivite	1250 units	10 mg	40 units
One tablet of Helthimax	500 units	15 mg	200 units

The table shows the normal needs of a person per day of Vitamins A, C and D, together with what would be obtained by taking one tablet of each of the preparations, Omnivite and Helthimax. One particular person attempts to meet his needs solely from these preparations.

Using x and y as the number of tablets of Omnivite and Helthimax respectively, show that enough Vitamin A is taken if $5x + 2y \geqslant 20$. Find two similar conditions for enough Vitamins C and D to be taken.

Draw a linear programming graph shading the regions giving inadequate supplies of each of the vitamins.

Assuming that the tablets must be taken whole and not divided up, find from the graph the number of tablets per day of each make giving adequate supplies:

    (a) if the total number of tablets is to be a minimum.
    (b) if the cost per day is to be a minimum, given that a tablet of Helthimax costs twice as much as a tablet of Omnivite.

7. A manufacturer wishes to produce 100 tons of a product containing at least 50% of factor A and 30% of factor B. He can use two ingredients, X costing £20 per ton, which will yield 60% of A and 20% of B, and Y costing £40 per ton which will yield 40% of A and 50% of B. Determine by graphical methods the mix of X and Y to yield the minimum material cost of production.

8. Use the Simplex method to maximise $Z = 4x_1 + 8x_2 + 10x_3$ subject to

$$x_1 \geqslant 0, \; x_2 \geqslant 0, \; x_3 \geqslant 0$$
$$x_1 + x_2 + x_3 \leqslant 1000$$
$$0 \cdot 5x_1 + 0 \cdot 5x_2 + 0 \cdot 5x_3 \leqslant 1500$$
$$0 \cdot 5x_1 + x_2 + x_3 \leqslant 2000.$$

Is there any other method by which this problem can be solved?

9. Use the Simplex method to solve Question 5 (b).

10. Maximise $Z = x_1 + 2x_2 + 3x_3$ subject to

$$x_1 + x_2 \leqslant 3$$
$$x_2 + x_3 \leqslant 4$$
$$x_1, x_2, x_3 \geqslant 0.$$

11. The following table gives the costs and nutritional contents (per unit) of five different foods.

	Foods				
	1	2	3	4	5
Calories	300	400	100	100	200
Vitamins	100	100	200	100	100
Cost (£)	20	20	31	11	12

An adequate diet must provide at least 1500 units of calories and 1000 units of vitamins.

(a) Formulate as a linear programme, the problem of finding an adequate diet at the least cost.

(b) By using graphical methods, or otherwise, is it possible to say that no matter how many units of calories and vitamins are required for an adequate diet, some of the foods will never be considered in the least cost solution? Which ones?

(c) Show that the cost of the optimal solution is £115.

(d) What assumptions have you made in using linear programming to solve this problem?

12. Three operational research teams have a working capacity of 200, 300 and 500 man hours per week respectively. Four minor research problems must be resolved within one week and will require an estimated 300, 150, 400 and 150 man hours. The cost per hour in £'s of each team working on each problem is given below.

	Job			
Team	A	B	C	D
1	5	5	20	25
2	5	10	15	20
3	8	5	10	5

Using linear programming techniques find the least cost solution of resolving the four research problems in one week.

13. A steel company is concerned with the problem of distributing imported ore from three ports to four steel mills situated throughout the country.

The supplies of ore arriving at ports are:

Port	Tons per week
a	20,000
b	38,000
c	16,000

Demands at the steel mills are:

Steel mill	Tons per week
A	10,000
B	18,000
C	22,000
D	24,000

Transportation costs are £0·05 per ton mile. The distances between the ports and the steel mills are given below:

	A	B	C	D
a	50	60	100	50
b	80	40	70	50
c	90	70	30	50

Calculate the transportation plan which will minimise ore distribution costs for the steel company. State the cost of this distribution plan.

14. The transport manager of a company which has three factories and four warehouses is faced with the problem of determining the way in which factories should supply warehouses so as to minimise total transportation costs.

In a given month, the supply requirements of each warehouse, the production capacities of the factories and the cost of shipping one unit of product from each factory to each warehouse in pounds sterling are shown in the table below:

	Warehouse 1	Warehouse 2	Warehouse 3	Warehouse 4	Production available units
Factory:					
A	12	23	43	3	6
B	63	23	33	53	8
C	33	1	63	13	17
Required units	4	7	6	14	31

Determine the minimum cost transportation plan.

15. A ladies fashion shop wishes to purchase the following quantities of summer dresses:

Dress size	I	II	III	IV
Quantity	100	200	450	150

Three manufacturers are willing to supply dresses. The quantities given below are the maximum they are able to supply of any given combination of orders for dresses:

Manufacturer	A	B	C
Total quantity	150	450	250

The shop expects the profit per dress to vary with the manufacturer as given below:

			Sizes	
Manufacturer	I	II	III	IV
	£	£	£	£
A	2·50	4·00	5·00	2·00
B	3·00	3·50	5·50	1·50
C	2·00	4·50	4·50	2·50

You are required to:

(a) Use the transportation technique to solve the problem of how the orders should be placed on the manufacturers by the fashion shop in order to maximise profit.

(b) Explain how you know that there is no further improvement possible, showing your workings.

16. A manufacturer has three depots and two factories with transport costs per ton of his product as follows:

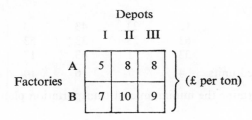

	Depots		
	I	II	III
A	5	8	8
B	7	10	9

Factories   } (£ per ton)

During week 1, his deliveries (in tons) were as follows:

	I	II	III	
A		12	18	30
B	10	28	32	70

Total available at factories

Total required at depots   10   40   50

Total transport cost = £878.

(a) Find a route (from a factory to a depot) which could be eliminated from the list of those used without affecting total deliveries from any factory or to any depot, such that the total cost of delivery is reduced.

(b) Find the minimum cost solution. Is it unique?

(c) What change in the transport cost (per ton) on the route from A to III will make the deliveries during week 1, as shown above, optimal?

(d) Suppose a tariff is to be levied on goods transported on the route from B to II. Work out the minimum cost solution if the tariff is (i) £5, (ii) £10, (iii) £15 per ton.

17. (a) What do you understand by "game theory"? What relevance has it to decision making in a competitive industry?

(b) Define the following terms as used in game theory:
(i) strategy, (ii) pay-off, (iii) zero-sum games and (iv) saddle-point.

(c) Given the following matrix what is the best strategy for

(i) player A and (ii) player B, to adopt?

		B	
		6	2
A		−1	−4

18. Two companies selling a similar product to the general public are considering their advertising programmes. They have the alternative of advertising either in the press or on television.

The following pay-off matrix shows the gains and losses in £000s of these alternative policies.

Company A	Company B		
	Do nothing	Advert in Press	Advert on TV
Do nothing	0	−50	−250
Advert in Press	50	0	−50
Advert on TV	300	150	100

On the basis of the above data indicate the policy which each company should follow. Expand upon your answer to indicate generally the application of games theory to economic activity.

19. A's pay-off matrix in a two-person zero-sum game is given below.

$$
\begin{array}{cc}
 & \begin{array}{ccc} & \mathbf{B} & \\ \mathrm{I} & \mathrm{II} & \mathrm{III} \end{array} \\
\begin{array}{c} \mathrm{I} \\ \mathrm{A} \ \ \mathrm{II} \\ \mathrm{III} \end{array} &
\begin{array}{|ccc} 2 & 5 & -1 \\ 3 & 6 & 2 \\ 5 & 0 & 3 \end{array}
\end{array}
$$

Determine A's and B's optimum strategies and find the value of the game to A.

20. (a) Maximise $Z = 4x_1 + 3x_2 + 2x_3 + 4x_4$

   subject to the constraints

$$2x_1 + 5x_2 + 4x_3 \leqslant 1000$$
$$6x_2 + 5x_4 \leqslant 2000$$

   (b) If the number on the right-hand side of each linear inequality in (a) is increased by 1 unit to 1001 and 2001 respectively, by how much will Z be increased in the new optimal solution?

   (c) If the contribution of x_3 is increased from 2 to 10 how will the optimal solution of (a) be affected?

21. Annapurna Ltd. is drawing up production plans for the coming year. Four products are available with the following financial characteristics:

Product	A	B	C	D
Amounts per unit:				
Selling price	£55	£53	£97	£86
Cost of materials	£17	£25	£19	£11

Labour hours—Grade A	10	6	—	—
—Grade B	—	—	10	20
—Grade C	—	—	12	6
Variable overheads	£6	£7	£5	£6

Fixed overheads of the firm amount to £35,500 per annum. Each grade of labour is paid £1·50 per hour but skills are specific to a grade so that an employee in one grade cannot be used to undertake the work of another grade. The annual supply of each grade is limited to the following maximum: Grade A, 9000 hours; Grade B, 14,500 hours; Grade C, 12,000 hours. There is no effective limitation of the sales of any product.

(a) Calculate the product mix which will maximise profit for the year and state the amount of the profit.
(b) Calculate the minimum price at which the sale of product A would be worth while.
(c) Calculate the amount by which profit could be increased if the supply of Grade A labour were increased by 1 hour.
(d) Describe shortly the limitations of the technique you have used in answering (a).

CHAPTER 19

Time Discounting

1. The Rate of Interest

Underlying the methods of solving Operational Research problems which have so far been discussed is the assumption that the *timing* of receipts and expenditure is irrelevant. This is equivalent to assuming either that all payments are made simultaneously or that the cost of holding money, that is, the rate of interest, is zero. The second of these assumptions is more appropriate in the context of probabilistic models since these introduce uncertainty which necessarily implies that time is important. A project which takes time entails inflows of cash which are also distributed through time. If the rate of interest is zero then it will not matter when these *cash flows*, as they are called, occur. Cash now will be worth just the same in one year's time and it will not matter when such cash is paid or received. But this is clearly an unrealistic assumption, for a person with cash now is able to invest it at interest so that in one year's time the value of the principal will be greater than it is at present. Hence it cannot be the case, in these circumstances, that a sum of money now has exactly the same value as an *equal* sum in one year's time. In other words, the evaluation of the profitability of a project must be affected by the timing of cash flows, so that timing is not irrelevant as would be the case if it were always assumed that the rate of interest is zero.

In the contemporary world, the timing of cash flows is important from another standpoint, namely that the money units in which calculations are made are not stable through time. Needless to say, this introduces an extra dimension of uncertainty into production planning. But even if the rate at which the value of the unit of account is changing is known with certainty, it is still necessary to allow for this change when making calculations. In other words, when cash flows occur at different points in time it is necessary to adjust their values on the assumption that they occur at a single point in time so that they should be measured in monetary units having the same value. Hence, even if the rate of interest were zero, it would still be necessary to allow for the timing of cash flows if the value of the monetary unit were changing. From the mathematical standpoint, the rate of interest and the rate of inflation are allowed for in a similar manner, though this similarity should not be permitted to obscure the essential difference between the practical significance of these two rates. Provided that all capital is productive, which is a

450

reasonable expectation in a developing free economy, the rate of interest will never be zero. On the other hand, there is nothing self-contradictory in a perfectly stable unit of account. Moreover, a sum of money will accumulate at interest, but will not accumulate simply because prices are rising.

2. Simple and Compound Interest

Simple is distinguished from compound interest by the way in which the interest is applied. If interest on a sum of money placed on deposit is paid to the account holder as it becomes due and is not added to the principal, then interest is simple. If, on the other hand, interest when it becomes due is added to the principal rather than being paid to the account holder, then interest is compound. In each case there is just one *rate* of interest, but the interest earned at this rate is applied differently.

The rate of interest is expressed as a percentage, usually of so much per annum. If the rate of interest is $100i\%$ per annum then, for each £1 invested for one year the amount of interest due is £i, provided that it is due annually. If it is due half-yearly (say), then the sum received in the course of a year will still be £i if interest is simple but will be somewhat greater than £i if interest is compound. It is customary to distinguish between the *nominal* and *effective* rate of interest. The nominal rate is the rate at which interest is earned when it is due annually whilst the effective rate is the rate at which interest actually is earned annually when it is due, possibly, at intervals of time other than one year.

If interest is simple, then the nominal rate is always the same as the effective rate. The simple interest on £P at $100i\%$ p.a. after n years is

$$\text{Simple interest} = in \times £P.$$

If the interest is due half-yearly, then the rate applied each half year is $\frac{1}{2}i$ so, in this case, the simple interest paid in the course of n years is

$$\text{Simple interest} = \tfrac{1}{2}i \times 2n \times £P$$
$$= in \times £P.$$

In other words, when interest is simple, the amount of interest earned in one year is just the same whether the rate is applied yearly or half-yearly or at any other interval. So in this case the effective and nominal rates are identical.

When interest is compound, the effective rate differs from the nominal rate except when the rate is applied annually. The amount of £P after 1 year at compound interest of $100i\%$ p.a. is

$$A_1 = P + iP = P(1 + i).$$

The interest at the end of the second year is calculated on the whole amount A_1 at the beginning of the year, so the amount of £P at the end of two years is

$$A_2 = P(1 + i)(1 + i) = P(1 + i)^2.$$

Similarly, after three years the amount is

$$A_3 = P(1 + i)^2 (1 + i) = P(1 + i)^3.$$

Continuing in this way, the amount of £P after n years at compound interest is

$$A_n = P(1 + i)^{n-1} (1 + i) = P(1 + i)^n.$$

The amount of interest earned in year n is

$$P(1 + i)^n - P(1 + i)^{n-1} = P(1 + i)^{n-1} (1 + i - 1)$$
$$= P(1 + i)^{n-1}i.$$

This is the amount of interest earned in one year on a sum of $P(1 + i)^{n-1}$ so the effective rate of interest in year n (or any other year) is

$$P(1 + i)^{n-1}i/P(1 + i)^{n-1} = i$$

which is the same as the nominal rate.

If interest is due quarterly (say), then the rate applied each quarter is $\frac{1}{4}i$, where i is the nominal rate per annum. In this case, the interest earned in one year on a principal of £P is

$$P(1 + \tfrac{1}{4}i)^4 - P = P\{1 + 4(\tfrac{1}{4}i) + 6(\tfrac{1}{4}i)^2 + 4(\tfrac{1}{4}i)^3 + (\tfrac{1}{4}i)^4 - 1\}$$
$$= P\left(i + \frac{3}{8}i^2 + \frac{1}{16}i^3 + \frac{1}{256}i^4\right) > iP.$$

So, in this case, the effective rate is greater than the nominal rate i.

3. Arithmetical Progressions

Arithmetical progressions are sometimes useful in making calculations involving simple interest. An arithmetical progression is a sequence of numbers every member of which, apart from the first, differs by a constant amount d from its immediate predecessor. Thus if a is the first member of an arithmetic progression, the general form of the progression is

$$a, a + d, a + 2d, a + 3d, \ldots, a + (n - 1)d$$

in which there are n terms. The simplest form of arithmetic progression is that in which $a = 1$ and $d = 1$, in which case the series of the first n natural numbers (positive integers) is obtained:

$$1, 2, 3, \ldots, n.$$

A formula for the sum of this series is easily obtained in the following manner. The sum can be written in two ways:

$$\sum_{r=1}^{n} r = 1 + 2 + 3 + \ldots + n$$

$$\sum_{r=1}^{n} r = n + (n-1) + (n-2) + \ldots + 1$$

Adding the two series term by term,

$$2 \sum_{r=1}^{n} r = (n+1) + (n+1) + (n+1) + \ldots + (n+1)$$
$$= n(n+1).$$

It immediately follows that the sum of the first n natural numbers is

$$\sum_{r=1}^{n} r = \tfrac{1}{2} n(n+1).$$

This formula can be applied to find the sum of the first n terms of any arithmetic progression whose general term is $a + rd$. The sum is

$$\sum_{r=0}^{n-1} (a + rd) = \sum_{r=0}^{n-1} a + \sum_{r=0}^{n-1} dr$$
$$= na + d \{0 + 1 + 2 + \ldots + (n-1)\}$$
$$= na + d \times \tfrac{1}{2}(n-1)n$$
$$= \tfrac{1}{2} n \{2a + d(n-1)\}.$$

EXAMPLE 1

A man sets aside an amount of £3000 at the beginning of each year which earns interest at the rate of 10% p.a. Interest is due half-yearly and is withdrawn immediately it is due. How much interest will be drawn in the course of 12 years.

Amount set aside in the rth year $= r \times$ £3000.
Interest earned in the rth year $= r \times$ £3000i.

Hence the interest earned in 12 years is

$$\sum_{r=1}^{12} (r \times 3000i) = 3000i \times \sum_{r=1}^{12} r$$
$$= 300 \times \tfrac{1}{2} \times 12(12+1) \quad \text{(since } i = 0 \cdot 1\text{)}$$
$$= \text{£23,400.}$$

EXAMPLE 2

On 1st January, John Smith owes £12,000. To reduce the debt he agrees to pay £1200 at the end of each 6 months together with interest at $2\frac{1}{2}\%$ on the opening balance of each period. Find the total interest which he pays.

The amount outstanding at the beginning of the $(r + 1)$th half year $(r = 0, 1, 2 \ldots)$ is

$$£12000 - r \times £1200.$$

Hence when $r = 12000/1200 = 10$, the opening balance is zero. The interest paid at the end of the $(r + 1)$th half year is

$$i(12000 - 1200r).$$

Hence the total interest paid is

$$\sum_{r=0}^{9} i(12000 - 1200r) = 1200i \times \sum_{r=0}^{9} (10 - r)$$
$$= 1200 \times 0\cdot025(10 \times 10 - \tfrac{1}{2} \times 9 \times 10)$$
$$= £1650.$$

Alternatively, the total amount on which interest is paid for 6 months can be found from the general formula for the sum of an arithmetic progression by putting $a = 12000$, $d = -1200$ and $n = 10$.

4. Geometric Progressions

Geometric progressions frequently arise in compound interest problems. Suppose that £P is invested at the beginning of each year at $100i\%$ compound interest. Putting $r = 1 + i$, the amount of the investment at the beginning of the second year (including interest) is

$$Pr + P.$$

At the beginning of the third year it is

$$(Pr + P) r + P = Pr^2 + Pr + P.$$

Continuing in this way, at the beginning of the nth year the amount of the investment is

$$(Pr^{n-2} + Pr^{n-3} + \ldots + P) r + P$$
$$= P + Pr + \ldots + Pr^{n-2} + Pr^{n-1}.$$

The sequence of terms on the right-hand side of this equality is known as a geometric progression. The characteristic feature of such a progression is that each of its terms, apart from the first, is a constant multiple r of its predecessor. A general formula for the sum of the first n terms of a geometric progression may be found as follows:

$$\sum_{t=0}^{n-1} Pr^t = P + Pr + Pr^2 + \ldots + Pr^{n-1} \quad \text{(noting that } r^0 = 1\text{)}.$$

Multiplying this sum by r gives

$$r \sum_{t=0}^{n-1} Pr^t = Pr + Pr^2 + \ldots + Pr^{n-1} + Pr^n$$

Subtracting the second sum from the first then gives

$$(1 - r) \sum_{t=0}^{n-1} Pr^t = P - Pr^n = P(1 - r^n).$$

So the required sum is

$$\sum_{t=0}^{n-1} Pr^t = P \frac{1 - r^n}{1 - r} = P \frac{r^n - 1}{r - 1}.$$

Both forms of the formula are equivalent, though the first is preferable if $|r| < 1$ since it avoids inconvenient negative terms in the numerator and denominator.

The following example illustrates how the formula is applied.

EXAMPLE 3

A small shopkeeper, hoping to expand his business, saves £200 per annum towards the purchase of another shop. If he invests the money at the beginning of each year in a building society paying $7\frac{1}{2}\%$ p.a. tax free, how much will he have accumulated at the end of ten years?

$$\text{Amount accumulated} = Pr^{10} + Pr^9 + \ldots + Pr$$
$$= r(P + Pr + \ldots + Pr^8 + Pr^9)$$

The expression in brackets is a geometric progression whose sum can be found by substituting $P = 200$, $n = 10$ and $r = 1 + 0{\cdot}075 = 1{\cdot}075$ in the formula. Thus

$$\text{Amount accumulated} = 1{\cdot}075 \times 200 \times \frac{(1{\cdot}075)^{10} - 1}{1{\cdot}075 - 1}$$
$$= £3044.$$

The formula, particularly the term r^n, can be readily evaluated using logarithms. It can also be evaluated with the assistance of annuity tables as will be explained later.

Suppose that, in Example 2, John Smith repays the debt of £12,000 on the same terms, except that payment of interest is deferred until the beginning of the sixth year when the final payment of £1200 is made. The amount of the debt outstanding (including interest) at the end of the first half year is £12,000$(1 + i)$ or £12,000r where $r = 1 + i$. Assuming that interest is allowed to accumulate, the amount outstanding at the end of the second half year is

$$(12000r - 1200)r = 12000r^2 - 1200r.$$

Similarly, at the end of the third half year, the amount outstanding is

$$(12000r^2 - 1200r - 1200)r = 12000r^3 - 1200r^2 - 1200r.$$

Continuing in this way, the amount outstanding at the end of the fifth year, before the final payment is made, is

$$12000r^{10} - 1200r^9 - \ldots - 1200r^2 - 1200r$$
$$= 12000r^{10} - 1200r \, (1 + r + \ldots + r^8).$$

The expression in brackets is a geometric progression whose sum can be found by putting $r = 1 + 0.025 = 1.025$, $n = 9$ and $P = 1200r$ in the formula. Hence the amount outstanding at the end of the fifth year is

$$12000(1.025)^{10} - 1200 \times 1.025 \times \frac{(1.025)^9 - 1}{0.025} = £3096.$$

The last payment of the principal is £1200 made at the end of the fifth year, so the total amount of interest which John Smith pays under this arrangement is £$(3096 - 1200) = £1896$ which is, of course, rather more than if interest is paid half-yearly. Curiously enough, there is nothing to choose between the two arrangements because of the timing of the payments. When Smith pays interest half-yearly he relinquishes the use of the money he pays at an earlier point in time than when he pays the whole of the interest due at the end of five years. The mathematical reasons for this will be considered in the following sections.

If r is a number lying in value between -1 and 1, then the sum of the geometric progression

$$1 + r + r^2 + \ldots + r^n$$

is always a finite number however many terms are included in the progression. The sum of such a series is said to be *convergent*. The fact that this sum is finite can be shown as follows. The sum of the first n terms of the series is

$$\frac{1 - r^n}{1 - r} = \frac{1}{1 - r} - \frac{r^n}{1 - r}.$$

Now if the value of r lies between -1 and 1, then r^n approximates more closely to zero as n increases. In fact, whether r is positive or negative, the sum falls short of or exceeds the positive number

$$\frac{1}{1 - r}$$

but approximates more closely to this number as the number of terms included in the progression increases. For example, if $r = \frac{1}{4}$ and $n = 10$, then $r^n = (\frac{1}{4})^{10} = 0 \cdot 000001$, so that the sum of the first ten terms of this progression is very nearly equal to

$$\frac{1}{1 - \frac{1}{4}} = 1\frac{1}{3}.$$

5. Annuities

An annuity is a constant annual payment extending usually over a stated number of years. There are several ways in which such payments may arise. For example, a person may wish to receive a fixed annual income over a term of years in return for a cash payment made in the present. Another possibility is that a person may wish to pay off a debt by means of a series of fixed annual payments. In either case, someone has relinquished the use of money for a term of years and receives it back at regular intervals. It follows that the amounts which he receives must include not only the principal which has been laid out initially, but also interest on whatever amounts of the principal have not been repaid. Hence the annuity or constant annual payment contains both interest and principal. In the early stages of the annuity, when a large amount of the principal is still outstanding, one would expect that a larger proportion of the fixed sum will consist of interest than will be the case at later stages when a good deal of the principal has been repaid.

Suppose that a man borrows £10,000 which he agrees to repay in equal annual instalments, the payments being made at the *end* of each year. Two factors govern the amount of each instalment: first the number of years over which the debt is to be repaid, and secondly the rate of interest to be charged on the amount of the debt outstanding at any instant. If the number of years for repayment is 8 and the rate of interest to be charged is 10% and the amount of each instalment is £X then the size of £X must be such that the creditor would be no worse off if he had invested his £10,000 at 10% for

8 years rather than converting it into a series of annuity payments over the same period of time. Now the principal will amount in 8 years time to

$$£10,000(1 + 0·1)^8 = £21,436.$$

If the creditor invests each instalment of £X at 10% as it becomes due, then in 8 years time this will have accumulated to

$$Xr^7 + Xr^6 + \ldots + Xr + X = X(1 + r + r^2 + \ldots + r^7)$$
$$= X\frac{r^8 - 1}{r - 1} \quad \text{(where } r = 1 + 0·1.\text{)}$$
$$= X\frac{(1·1)^8 - 1}{0·1}$$
$$= 11·44X.$$

This must be equal to the value of £10,000 in 8 years time, that is

$$11·44X = 21436$$

whence

$$X = 21436/11·44 = £1874,$$

and this is the amount of the annual payment. In the first year the amount of interest included in the payment is obviously 10% of £10,000 so that only £874 of this instalment represents repayment of the principal. Throughout the second year the amount of the debt outstanding is £$(10000 - 874) = £9126$ on which the interest is £913 (to the nearest £). So the amount of the principal repaid in the second instalment is £$(1874 - 913) = £961$. In this way one can analyse the components of interest and principal in each instalment of the annuity. The result is shown in the following table.

Year	Amount Outstanding at beginning of Year	Amount of Instalment	Interest at 10% p.a.	Principal Repaid
1	£10000	£1874	£1000	£ 874
2	9126	1874	913	961
3	8165	1874	817	1057
4	7108	1874	711	1163
5	5945	1874	595	1279
6	4666	1874	467	1407
7	3259	1874	326	1548
8	1711	1874	171	1703
		14992	5000	9992

The total principal repaid should, of course, be £10,000 and the total of the final column of the table differs from this due to rounding errors. The total amount of interest paid is approximately £5000 which is considerably less than the amount which would have been paid if the repayment of the principal and interest had been deferred until the end of the eighth year, namely £(21436 − 10000) = £11,436. The reason is that interest is paid only on the outstanding balance at the beginning of each year.

An annuity of the above kind, which is paid at the *end* of each year is known as an *immediate* annuity. The *amount* of an immediate annuity after n years is the sum to which it would accumulate if each instalment were invested at compound interest as it becomes due and allowed to accumulate during the remaining life of the annuity. For example, the amount of an annuity of £1874 after 8 years is £21,436. Annuity calculations using four-figure logarithms will usually result in answers correct only to three significant figures. More accurate calculations are based on specially constructed annuity tables. These show, among other things, the amount of an immediate annuity of £1 after n years at different rates of interest. The amount of an annuity of £1 after n years at $100i\%$ p.a. is denoted by $s_{\overline{n,\,i}|}$ and can be obtained from the following formula which depends on the formula for the sum of a geometric progression:

$$s_{\overline{n,\,i}|} = 1(1 + i)^{n-1} + 1(1 + i)^{n-2} + \ldots + 1(1 + i) + 1$$
$$= \frac{(1 + i)^n - 1}{(1 + i) - 1}$$
$$= \frac{(1 + i)^n - 1}{i}.$$

The amount of an annuity of £X after n years at the same rate of interest is obtained from this by simple proportion, that is,

$$\text{amount} = £X \times s_{\overline{n,\,i}|}.$$

For example, when $n = 8$ and $i = 0.1$, $s_{\overline{n,\,i}|} = £11.44$. So the amount of an annuity of £1874 is

$$£1874 \times s_{\overline{8,\,0.1}|} = £1874 \times 11.44$$
$$= £21,436.$$

Another method of finding the instalment £X of an annuity payable for n years at interest i when the purchase price is £P is to consider the *present value* of the annuity. The present value of £X payable in n years time when the interest rate is i is the sum which, if invested at compound interest now would, in n years amount to

£X. For example, if the annuity consisted of only one payment made at the end of the year, then

$$X = P(1 + i)$$

so that the present value of £X payable at the end of the year is

$$\frac{X}{1 + i} = P.$$

If the single sum £X were payable at the end of the second year, its present value would be

$$\frac{X}{(1 + i)^2} = P \quad \text{because} \quad X = P(1 + i)^2.$$

In other words, to find the present value of any amount £X payable in n years time, £X is divided by the factor $(1 + i)^n$ or, what amounts to the same thing, is multiplied by the factor $(1 + i)^{-n}$. In making present value calculations, it is convenient to replace the expression $(1 + i)^{-n}$ by the more compact symbol v^n, so that

$$v^n = \frac{1}{(1 + i)^n}.$$

v^n is known as a *present value factor* and is the present value of £1 payable in n years time at interest i. A table of present value factors for $n = 1$ to 15 and different rates of interest is given at the end of the book (see Table 7).

It has been seen that, if £P is the purchase price of an immediate annuity of £X payable for n years then £X satisfies the equation

$$P(1 + i)^n = X + X(1 + i) + X(1 + i)^2 + \ldots + X(1 + i)^{n-1}.$$

The present value of the annuity is obtained by dividing both sides of this equation by $(1 + i)^n$, that is,

Present value $= P$

$$= \frac{X}{(1 + i)^n} + \frac{X}{(1 + i)^{n-1}} + \frac{X}{(1 + i)^{n-2}} + \ldots + \frac{X}{1 + i}$$
$$= Xv^n + Xv^{n-1} + Xv^{n-2} + \ldots + Xv$$
$$= Xv(1 + v + \ldots + v^{n-1})$$
$$= Xv\frac{1 - v^n}{1 - v}.$$

Putting $X = 1$, the formula gives the present value of an annuity of £1 payable for n years which is denoted by the symbol $a_{\overline{n},\,i|}$, the rate of interest being $100i\%$ p.a. Thus

Present value of an annuity of £1 $= a_{\overline{n},\,i}$

$$= \frac{v(1-v^n)}{1-v}.$$

Annuity tables also give the values of $a_{\overline{n},\,i}$ so that if these tables are used, the above formula is unnecessary. As an illustration of its use, the value of the annuity of £X can be found by considering its present value. Since

$$P = £X \times a_{\overline{n},\,i} \quad \text{then } £X = P/a_{\overline{n},\,i}$$

where $P = £10{,}000$, $n = 8$ and $i = 0{\cdot}1$. Hence $v = 1/1{\cdot}1 = 0{\cdot}9091$

and

$$a_{\overline{8},\,0\cdot 1} = \frac{0{\cdot}9091(1 - 0{\cdot}9091^8)}{1 - 0{\cdot}9091} = 5{\cdot}3355.$$

(The more accurate value given in annuity tables is $5{\cdot}3349$.)
Hence the value of each instalment is

$$X = 10000/5{\cdot}3355 = £1874 \text{ (as before)}.$$

The value of $a_{\overline{n},\,i}$ can also be computed from Table 7. Since this gives the present value of £1 payable in 1 year's time, 2 years' time, 3 years' time, etc., it follows that

$$a_{\overline{n}} = \sum_{t=1}^{r} v^t$$

so that $a_{\overline{n},\,i}$ is the sum of the entries in column i from $t = 1$ to $t = n$. For example

$$a_{\overline{8},\,0\cdot 1} = 0{\cdot}9091 + 0{\cdot}8264 + \ldots + 0{\cdot}5132 + 0{\cdot}4665$$
$$= 5{\cdot}3349.$$

Having found $a_{\overline{n},\,i}$ one can, if necessary, calculate $s_{\overline{n},\,i}$ also using the data in Table 7. For

$$s_{\overline{n},\,i} = (1 + i)^n \, a_{\overline{n},\,i}$$
$$= v^{-n} \, a_{\overline{n},\,i}.$$

For example, with $n = 8$ and $i = 0{\cdot}1$, $v^n = 0{\cdot}4665$. So

$$s_{\overline{8},\,0\cdot 1} = v^{-8} \, a_{\overline{8},\,0\cdot 1}$$
$$= 5{\cdot}3349/0{\cdot}4665$$
$$= 11{\cdot}44.$$

An annuity may be payable either at the end or at the beginning of each year. The formulae for the amount and present value of an annuity obtained above all refer to an immediate annuity, that is, an annuity payable at the end of each year. An annuity payable at the beginning of each year is called an *annuity due*, and the amount and present value of such an annuity can be obtained from the corresponding formulae for an immediate annuity by a simple adjustment. This can be simply explained in terms of the diagram in Fig. 88.

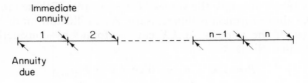

An annuity due which is payable for n years contains the same number of annual payments as an immediate annuity but each payment is made one year earlier. Hence the present value of an annuity due will be greater than that of the corresponding immediate annuity by a factor of $1 + i$. Thus the present value of annuity due of £1 payable for n years is

$$(1 + i)\, a_{\overline{n,\, i}|}$$

where $a_{\overline{n,\, i}|}$ is the present value of the corresponding immediate annuity. Also, since each instalment of an annuity due is available to the recipient for one year longer than that of the corresponding immediate annuity, its amount at the end of n years is greater than that of the corresponding immediate annuity, also by a factor $1 + i$. So the amount of an annuity due of £1 payable for n years is

$$(1 + i)\, s_{\overline{n,\, i}|}$$

where $s_{\overline{n,\, i}|}$ is the amount of the corresponding immediate annuity. The application of these two concepts is illustrated by the following example which also shows the importance of the idea of present values in a decision-making context.

EXAMPLE 4

The lease of certain business premises is due to expire shortly. The owner has offered the occupier, AB, an extended lease for 15 years only at a considerably increased rent. The new rent asked is £600 per quarter payable in advance.

Alternative premises are therefore being considered. The lease of these premises, which provides comparable facilities, can be purchased for £20,000. AB can borrow this sum at 4% per half-year with the loan and interest payable by thirty equal amounts at six-monthly intervals. The first repayment would be due six months after the date of the sale agreement.

(a) *What would be the amount of each half-yearly payment?*

(b) *Would you recommend that the lease of the alternative premises be bought? (Taxation should be ignored.)*

(a) The fact that a half-yearly instead of an annual payment is involved does not affect the annuity principle. The present value of an immediate annuity of £1 payable in thirty instalments when the rate of interest is 4% is

$$a_{\overline{30},\,0.04|} = 17\cdot292.$$

(This can be found either from annuity tables or from the formula.) If the amount of each instalment is £X it follows that the present value of the payments is

$$£X \times 17\cdot292 = £20,000$$

whence

$$X = 20000/17\cdot292 = 1157.$$

So the amount of the half-yearly instalment is £1157.

(b) The rent payable forms an annuity due consisting of sixty payments, the present value of which can be compared with that of the annuity in (a) by taking a comparable rate of interest of 2% per quarter. The present value of an annuity due of £1 payable in sixty instalments at this rate is

$$(1\cdot02)\,a_{\overline{60},\,0.02|} = 1\cdot02 \times 34\cdot761$$
$$= 35\cdot456.$$

Hence the present value of an annuity of £600 on the same terms is

$$£600 \times 35\cdot456 = £21,274.$$

In terms of the present values of the payments made in each case, it is therefore more expensive (by £1274) to continue the lease of the existing premises.

Finding the present value of a series of payments distributed through time is known as *time discounting* which provides a means of comparing streams of payments or cash flows which have different distributions through time. Given a fixed interest rate structure, the present value of an annuity is the sum of money between which and the annuity there is nothing to choose. Hence if two annuities have different present values, then the one with the higher present value is preferable from the viewpoint of its possessor. From the standpoint of the person paying the annuity, as in the above example, the annuity with the lower present value is preferable if it is being purchased on more or less the same terms. This criterion for comparing different income streams is of the greatest importance in what follows.

Before leaving the subject of annuitities, however, it is worth bringing out a further distinction between their different kinds. The annuities so far considered are known as *terminable* annuities since the instalments are payable during a stated term of years. In contrast, a *perpetuity* is annuity which is payable for an indefinitely long period, perhaps during the lifetime of an individual or even longer. Theoretically, the instalments payable under such an annuity would continue for ever and it is relevant to ask whether such an annuity has a present value. Clearly, if £1 payable in perpetuity has a present value, then any other finite sum will also. Writing $v = 1/(1 + i)$, the present value of an immediate annuity of £1 is

$$v + v^2 + \ldots + v^n = v \frac{1 - v^n}{1 - v}$$

$$= \frac{v}{1 - v} - \frac{v^{n+1}}{1 - v}.$$

If the number of years the annuity has to run is very large, the term v^{n+1} will be negligible, particularly if the rate of interest is high. For example, suppose that $i = 0 \cdot 1$ (a rate of 10%), then $v = 1/1 \cdot 1 = 0 \cdot 90909$. Hence when $n = 60$,

$$v^{n+1} = (0 \cdot 90909)^{61} = 0 \cdot 003$$

so that the negative term in the above formula for the present value of the annuity is practically zero and this present value differs very little from

$$\frac{v}{1 - v} = \frac{0 \cdot 90909}{1 - 0 \cdot 90909} = 10.$$

Hence the present value of the annuity of £1 cannot exceed £10 however long it is paid, and the longer it is paid the more closely will the present value approach £10. Another interesting feature of a perpetuity is that the instalments include only interest on the purchase price; they make no contribution to the repayment of the purchase price. For example, if someone borrows £10,000 which he agrees to repay by a series of annual instalments of £1000, the rate of interest being 10%, then each instalment represents only the interest for one year on £10,000 so that none of the capital sum is ever repaid under the arrangement.

The payment of an annuity may begin immediately, that is, either at the beginning or end of the first year, or be *deferred* a number of years. The present value of an immediate annuity which is deferred m years and then runs for n years is equal to the present value of an annuity which runs for $m + n$ years less the present value of an annuity which runs for m years, that is,

Present value of deferred annuity of £1 $= a_{\overline{m+n}|} - a_{\overline{m}|}$.

The reason for this should be obvious. The deferred annuity consists of n payments of £1 each which do not begin until year $m + 1$ and its value discounted to the beginning of year $m + 1$ is $a_{\overline{n}|}$. In order to obtain its present value, this must be discounted a further m years, that is,

$$\text{Present value} = v^m \, a_{\overline{n}|} = v^m \times v \, \frac{1 - v^n}{1 - v}$$

$$= v \, \frac{v^m - v^{n+m}}{1 - v}$$

$$= v \, \frac{(1 - v^{m+n}) - (1 - v^m)}{1 - v}$$

$$= v \, \frac{1 - v^{m+n}}{1 - v} - v \, \frac{1 - v^m}{1 - v}$$

$$= a_{\overline{m+n}|} - a_{\overline{m}|}.$$

For example, the present value of an immediate annuity of £1000 payable for 15 years and deferred 5 years, the rate of interest being 12% is

$$
\begin{array}{ll}
 & £ \\
1000 \, a_{\overline{20,\,0\cdot12}|} & = 7469 \\
1000 \, a_{\overline{5,\,0\cdot12}|} & = 3605 \\
\hline
\text{Present value} & = 3864 \\
\hline
\end{array}
$$

The present value of a deferred perpetuity is found in the same way. Thus the present value of a perpetuity of £1 at 10% is £10 and if payment is deferred for the first five years, the present value will be

$$10 - a_{\overline{5,\,0\cdot1}|} = 10 - 3\cdot7908$$
$$= £6\cdot2092.$$

6. Cash Flows

The value of a capital project depends on the relation between the inflows and outflows of cash connected with the project and the timing of these cash flows throughout the life of the project. In the simplest case, one could regard these cash flows as consisting of a cash outlay on capital equipment at the beginning of the project followed by a series of equal cash inflows, forming an immediate annuity, during the life of the project. Whether the project is worth while, in these circumstances, depends on the rate of discount at which the present value of the positive cash flows (inflows of cash) is equal to the initial cash outlay and the rate which could be earned on the initial outlay if it were invested in some other way, either at the market rate of interest or in some other project. Obviously, if the rate of discount applied is higher than that which could be obtained in any other way, then the project will be worth while.

In normal cases, the cash flows associated with a given project are not equal each year, nor do they appear regularly at the end of each year. It will simplify the analysis if the assumption is made that the cash flows do, in fact, appear at the end of each year, an assumption which is to some extent justified if they are distributed uniformly throughout the year. On the other hand, the fact that the value of cash flows varies from year to year means that one cannot employ the simple annuity method for finding their present value. Instead it is necessary to multiply the cash flow each year by the appropriate discount or present value factor v^n and add the products in order to find the present value of the cash flows. Thus if the life of a project is n years, and the cash flow in year t is A_t, then the discounted value of the cash flow is $A_t v^t$ at some suitable rate of interest, and the present value of the cash flow is

$$\sum_{t=1}^{n} A_t v^t = A_1 v + A_2 v^2 + \ldots + A_n v^n.$$

The cash flows considered for this purpose are *net cash flows*, and the object of the valuation is to determine whether these are sufficient, having regard to their timing, to finance the initial capital outlay and meet the interest charges which it involves. Consequently the net cash flows must include an allowance for depreciation, which is normally included among costs when computing profit. Moreover, profit in the accounting sense is computed net of the taxes due in the year in which the profit was earned. But since the collection of such taxes is often delayed beyond the current year, the cash outflow associated with the payment of taxes in any year will be different from the figure used to calculate the net profit for the year, so that this must be adjusted by adding to net profit the difference between taxes due and taxes actually paid in order to obtain a correct measure of the cash flow for the year in question. Although cash flows include depreciation, it is necessary to deduct from the cash flow in each year any new capital expenditure associated with the project, and it could happen, if such expenditure were heavy, that the cash flows for some years will be negative. Hence the net cash flow for each year consists of the following elements: pre-tax profit, *plus* depreciation, *less* taxes when paid, *less* new capital expenditure.

There is a good deal of controversy about the most suitable method to use in order to obtain a reliable estimate of the profitability of an investment. Two methods are described here, and later something will be said of their relative merits.

(a) Net present value.

The net present value (NPV) of an investment is defined as the difference between the initial capital outlay and the present value of the cash flows to which it gives rise discounted at a rate equal to the cost of borrowing capital. Thus if the initial outlay is A_0 and the cost of capital is $100i\%$, then

$$\text{NPV} = \sum_{t=1}^{n} A_t v^t - A_0 \quad \text{where } v = 1/(1 + i).$$

The investment will be just worth while if its net present value is zero, for in this case the cash flow will be just sufficient to repay the capital outlay A_0 together with interest i on the amount of capital outstanding each year. Consider, for example, the following cash flow:

Year	0	1	2	3	4
Net Cash Flow (£)	−86,133	20,000	30,000	40,000	25,000

Assuming that the cost of capital is 12% p.a., the net present value of the investment is

$$\text{NPV} = 20000 \times 0.8929 + 30000 \times 0.7972 + 40000 \times 0.7118$$
$$+ 25000 \times 0.6355 - 86133$$
$$= £0.$$

The present value factors 0.8929, 0.7972, etc., are obtained from Table 7. The components of interest and capital in the cash flow each year are analysed in the following table.

Had the initial investment been only £80,000, then the NPV of the project would have been £6133, in which case, the cash flows would have been more than sufficient to repay capital and interest on the initial amount. The balance of £6133 plus interest might then have been distributed to shareholders so that the cash flows could still be

Year	Amount Outstanding at beginning of Year	Net Cash Flow	Interest at 12% p.a.	Principal Repaid
1	£86133	£20000	£10336	£ 9664
2	76469	30000	9176	20824
3	55645	40000	6677	33323
4	22322	25000	2678	22322
5	0	—	—	—

regarded as just sufficient to finance an original capital expenditure of £86,133.

If only one capital project is being considered, then it will be acceptable provided that its net present value is positive. If NPV is negative, then it will obviously not be profitable at the existing cost of capital. The cost of capital is determined by the rate at which a company can borrow and will be the same as this rate if taxation is ignored. If taxation is not ignored, then any interest payments can be set off against taxable income, so that the cost of capital, net of tax, will be less than the market rate of interest.

The calculation of NPV provides a means of ranking alternative investments which are mutually exclusive. In certain circumstances, the investment with the highest NPV is the most desirable. However, it is precisely in connection with the ranking of investments that the NPV method has been most criticised and it has sometimes been considered as inferior to the yield method from this viewpoint.

(b) Yield.

The yield, sometimes also called the *internal rate of return*, on an investment is the discount rate at which the present value of the net cash flow is just equal to the initial capital outlay. In other words, the yield is that market rate at which NPV would be zero. If the cash flows consist of equal amounts each year, then the yield can easily be estimated by interpolation in annuity tables. For example, if an initial investment of £20,000 gives rise to an immediate annuity of £6000 over four years, then the yield is the value of i such that

$$6000 \times a_{\overline{4},\,i|} = 20000$$

or

$$a_{\overline{4},\,i|} = 20000/6000 = 3.3333.$$

By reference to annuity tables (or by calculation) one finds that $a_{\overline{4},\,0.07|} = 3.3872$ and $a_{\overline{4},\,0.08|} = 3.3121$ so that the yield in this case lies between 7% and 8% being, in fact, closer to 8%.

When the cash flows are not equal amounts, the usual method of estimating yield is by trial and error. A provisional estimate can be obtained by considering the cash flows as occurring at one point in time determined by the average of the number of years which the project has to run weighted by the cash flow each year. The total cash flow is then discounted over this average time. This is illustrated for the following cash flow.

Year	0	1	2	3	4
Net Cash Flow (£)	−50,000	15,000	35,000	30,000	25,000

$$\text{Weighted average time} = \frac{15 \times 1 + 35 \times 2 + 30 \times 3 + 25 \times 4}{105}$$

$$= 2 \cdot 619.$$

The present value of the cash flows extending over four years is roughly equivalent to the present value of the total cash flow, £105,000 payable in 2·619 years time, discounted at the same rate i. The value of i which equates this present value to the initial outlay of £50,000 can be found directly or from tables of present value factors once the relevant value of v has been calculated. Thus

$$105000 \times v^{2 \cdot 619} = 50000$$

so

$$v = \sqrt[2 \cdot 619]{\left(\frac{50000}{105000}\right)}$$

$$= 0 \cdot 7534.$$

Hence

$$1 + i = \frac{1}{v}$$

$$= 1 \cdot 3273$$

so that

$$i = 0 \cdot 33 \text{ (approximately)}.$$

The yield on this particular investment is therefore about 33%. This estimate should be checked by discounting the cash flows at adjacent interest rates to see whether the estimate can be improved. In the present instance, a better estimate is found to be 35%. This means that if the cash flow is discounted at 35% its present value is £50,000, so that the company could afford to pay 35% on the borrowed capital and still break even. Hence if the cost of capital is less than the yield the investment will be worth while. This is equivalent to the condition that the investment will be worth while if its net present value is positive, and if the decision is simply between making and not making this investment both methods of evaluation produce the same result, that is, if the investment is rejected by one method it will also be rejected by the other so, from this point of view, there is nothing to choose between the two methods. If the decision concerns a choice between alternative investments and only one can be chosen, then both methods provide a means of ranking the alternatives. The optimum choice is the investment with the highest NPV or the investment with the highest yield. However, it can happen that each method produces a different ranking and it is in this connection that one must consider the rival merits of the two methods. This is discussed at the end of the present section.

The validity of the yield calculation depends on the existence of a unique (or single) rate of discount i at which NPV is zero. This rate is found by solving the equation

$$\sum_{t=1}^{n} A_t v^t = A_0$$

and this equation could have as many as n roots, that is, there could be as many as n values of i which would satisfy it. Obviously, if the calculations give rise to several internal rates of return it will be inconclusive. Fortunately, a unique rate of return is guaranteed if all the net cash flows are positive. In this case, the present value (PV) as a function of the rate of discount i can be represented graphically by a curve sloping downwards from left to right, as in Fig. 89. The

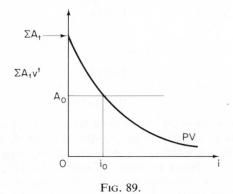

FIG. 89.

present value of the initial capital outlay A_0 is, of course, A_0 so that the yield i_0 is given by the point of intersection of the PV curve with a horizontal line through A_0 and there is only one such point of intersection and therefore only one value of i_0 satisfying the required condition. Negative cash flows may arise due to new capital expenditure, but provided that these negative amounts occur early in the life of the project there will still be a unique yield i_0. However, it could happen that the negative cash flows occur late in the life of the project if, for example, a good deal of replacement of capital equipment becomes necessary then. In this case the project will break even before the negative cash flows occur, at the yield calculated on the total cash flow. For example, the yield for the following cash flow is 30% and the cash flow in year 6, discounted at this rate, is

Year	0	1	2	3	4	5	6
Net cash flow (£)	−400	250	250	250	250	250	−1000
D.C.F. at 30%	−400	192	148	114	88	67	−207
Cumulative NPV	−400	−208	−60	54	142	209	—

negative. Moreover, the cumulative NPV at this rate is positive in Years 3 to 5 so that in Year 6 the project is a liability. Also the cash flow has another yield point at 14%, for at this rate NPV is also zero. If the cost of capital is 10% the project has a net present value which is negative (−£17), so the two methods of evaluation give contradictory decisions. Since the cost of capital is below either yield one would expect the investment to be worth while. However, the net present value of the investment is negative so, according to this criterion, it should be rejected. This possibility has sometimes been urged as a weakness of the yield method, but it has been suggested that it points to the fact that when a contradiction of this kind arises due to the existence of negative cash flows late in the life of a project, it is necessary to modify the yield method so that it gives a meaningful result.

Apart from the foregoing complication, the internal rate of return has certain advantages. Provided that a project has a positive NPV the yield will usually be greater than the cost of capital. This means that cash flows later in the life of the project will be more heavily discounted when computing yield, and since these distant cash flows are liable to greater risk than those earlier in the project life, a high yield will reflect the riskiness of the project more adequately than NPV. In other words, the project having the highest yield is the one in which the greatest allowance has been made for the risk factor, which justifies its ranking first among the alternatives. A second advantage of yield is that it is more readily understood by accountants and others concerned with decision-making than NPV. Finally, in using NPV as a means of evaluating an investment, there may be some difficulty about assessing the cost of capital used for discounting; the computation of yield does not rest on any assumptions about the external rate of interest.

Despite these advantages of yield, the NPV method is generally considered as providing a more reliable measure of profitability. One reason for this is that it is an *absolute* measure which is obtained by reference to objective conditions, particularly the cost of capital. The yield does not indicate how much profit will be obtained; it might be large or small depending on the size of the investment and the time which it has to run. Provided that an accurate estimate of the cost of capital can be obtained, and it is often possible to do this, NPV is a valid indication of profitability, even when there are complications in the cash flow, such as the occurrence of negative flows at a late stage of the project life.

EXAMPLE 5

On 1st January 1969, Pontus Ltd purchased a plot of land for £80,000. The directors are now considering a development of the land. Plans have been prepared, at a cost of £45,000, for building a block of 40 flats. Building could start on 1st January 1976. It is estimated that construction would cost £500,000, £200,000 payable on 1st January 1976 and £300,000 payable on 1st January 1977. The flats would be ready for occupation on 1st January 1978.

The flats would be let on tenancies at an annual rent. The plot of land is expected to have a market value of £100,000 on 1st January 1976. The building would have an expected life of 20 years, i.e. would be let for the last time during the year ending 31st December 1997. It would have to be demolished at that time at an estimated cost £184,000. The estimated market value of the land on 31st December 1997 is £750,000. All costs are expressed in terms of the value of money at 1st January 1976.

Pontus requires a rate of return on investment of $15\frac{1}{2}\%$ p.a. Assume that receipts for rent arise on the last day of the calendar year to which they relate.

Calculate the minimum rental per flat at which it would be worth while for Pontus to undertake the development of the land instead of holding the land in its present condition.

Since the decision concerns whether to go ahead with development, the cost of the plans (£45,000), which occurred at an earlier date and is not recoverable, will not effect the minimum level of rent. Moreover, the value of the land which is applicable is £100,000 on 1st January 1976, since this can be recovered if the plans are not proceeded with. The relevant cash flows are then:

Year	1st Jan. 1976	1st Jan. 1977	1978–1996	1997
			X p.a.	X
Cash	−200,000	−300,000		750,000
flow (£)	−100,000			−184,000

The required rate of return is $i = 0{\cdot}155$ and at this rate the PV of the cash flows apart from rent is

$$-300000 - \frac{300000}{1{\cdot}155} + \frac{750000 - 184000}{(1{\cdot}155)^{22}} = -535{,}980.$$

The present value of the total annual rent of £X can be found by considering the present value of an immediate annuity of £X payable for 20 years and deferred 2 years, that is

$$\text{PV of rent} = £X(a_{\overline{22}|} - a_{\overline{2}|})$$

where

$$a_{\overline{22}|} = \frac{v(1 - v^{22})}{1 - v} \quad (v = 1/1{\cdot}155 = 0{\cdot}8658)$$

$$= \frac{1 - v^{22}}{i}$$

$$= \frac{1 - 0{\cdot}8658^{22}}{0{\cdot}155}$$

$$= 6{\cdot}1813$$

and

$$a_{\overline{2}|} = \frac{1 - 0{\cdot}8658^{2}}{0{\cdot}155}$$

$$= 1{\cdot}6155.$$

Hence

$$\text{PV of rent} = £X(6{\cdot}1813 - 1{\cdot}6155) = 4{\cdot}5658X.$$

So the minimum total rent per annum which would allow the project to break even is

$$X = 535980/4{\cdot}5658 = 117{,}390.$$

The minimum rent per flat is therefore

$$117390/40 = £2935.$$

7. Inflation

There may be considerable uncertainty about the rate of inflation over the life of a capital project, although it may be desirable to estimate cash flows on the assumption that price increases are taking place during this period. It is therefore necessary to make some assumption about the annual inflation rate so that cash flows appearing at different points in time can be expressed in the same money unit, say at current prices. When the values of the cash flows have been adjusted in this way, NPV calculations are performed in just the same way on the adjusted values as that explained in the preceding section.

The nature of the adjustment required when prices are changing can be established by considering that if the rate of inflation is $100d\%$ p.a. then the purchasing power of £1 now will be the same as the purchasing power of $£(1 + d)^n$ in n years time. It follows that the purchasing power of £1 in n years time at this rate of inflation is equivalent to the purchasing power of $£1/(1 + d)^n$ now. Hence $£X$ receivable in n years time, expressed in terms of current prices is

$$\frac{£X}{(1 + d)^n}.$$

If the rate of discount is i, then the present value of $£X$ payable in n years time, expressed in terms of current prices is

$$\frac{£X}{(1 + i)^n (1 + d)^n}.$$

For example, if the rate of interest is 12% and the rate of inflation is 15% p.a. then the present value of £250 payable in 5 years time in terms of present prices is

$$\frac{£250}{(1 \cdot 12)^5 (1 \cdot 15)^5} = £71.$$

In Example 5 the simplifying assumption is made that all cash flows are expressed in terms of current prices. In fact, with a continuing rate of inflation until 1997, it is obviously necessary to adjust the annual rent to allow for this. Suppose that the rate of inflation is expected to be 10% per annum and that the actual rent received at the end of 1978 is $£X$, then the cash flows from 1978 onwards (adjusted for inflation) are

$$£X, £(1 \cdot 1)X, £(1 \cdot 1)^2 X, \ldots, £(1 \cdot 1)^{19} X.$$

Before calculating NPV at 1st January 1976 it is accordingly necessary to deflate this series of payments in order to obtain the cash flows at current (January 1976) prices. The deflated series is

$$£X/(1 \cdot 1)^3, £(1 \cdot 1)X/(1 \cdot 1)^4, £(1 \cdot 1)^2 X/(1 \cdot 1)^5, \text{ etc.}$$

so that the annual cash flow at current prices is $£X/(1 \cdot 1)^3$. Assuming that all other cash flows are at 1976 prices, the total rent required in 1978 is given by

$$\frac{X}{(1 \cdot 1)^3} = \frac{535980}{4 \cdot 5658}$$

so, in this case,

$$X = (1 \cdot 1)^3 \times 117390 = 156,250.$$

The minimum rent per flat required in 1978 is therefore $156250/40 = £3906$ which is, of course, considerably higher than that calculated on the assumption of constant prices.

It is of particular importance to estimate cash flows in terms of money values in the years in which they occur if the prices of inputs and outputs are expected to rise at different rates. For example, it may be expected that the price of imported raw materials will rise at a rate $100d' \%$ p.a. whilst the prices of all other inputs and outputs rise at the general inflation rate $100d\%$ which is reflected by the index of retail prices. If the annual expenditure on imported raw materials, at current prices, is $£Y$ and the annual cash flow from every other source, also at current prices, is $£X$ then the net annual cash flow, before adjusting for inflation, is $£(X - Y)$. However, the expenditure on imported materials in money terms in Year n will be $(1 + d')^n £Y$ whilst the money value of all other cash flows in the same year will be $(1 + d)^n £X$. Hence the net cash flow in Year n at Year n prices will be

$$(1 + d)^n £X - (1 + d')^n £Y.$$

The net cash flows at current prices (in Year 0) are obtained by applying the general inflation rate d to the net cash flow in money terms in Year n, that is, one divides this cash flow by $(1 + d)^n$ to give

$$£ \left\{ X - \frac{(1 + d')^n}{(1 + d)^n} Y \right\}$$

as the net cash flow for Year n at current prices. Since d and d' are unequal, the net cash flow so obtained is obviously different from the unadjusted figure $£(X - Y)$ which will give an under-estimate of NPV if $d' < d$ and an over-estimate if $d' > d$.

8. Uncertainty

The fact that estimates of future cash flows are liable to error suggests the desirability of a decision-theory approach to the evaluation of the profitability of investments. This involves the incorporation of a probability factor into the estimates of future cash flows and, provided the probabilities can be established with reasonable certainty, the utility of NPV calculations will be greatly increased. The following example illustrates how probability factors can be included in an investment appraisal problem.

EXAMPLE 6

A project requires an initial capital investment of £250,000. Raw material is purchased now and costs £1·50 per unit of product produced. The product will be offered for sale at a price of £4·50 two years after the commencement of the project. The probability distribution of demand at this price is:

'000 units sold	Probability
300	0·2
400	0·2
500	0·4

The cost of capital is 25% p.a. and storage costs consist entirely of interest on the initial amount spent on raw materials and are payable at the end of each year. In order that the correct quantity of raw material may be ordered now, a decision must be made about how many units of goods should be produced for sale in two years time. Assuming that the quantity produced will be 300,000 units, 400,000 units or 500,000 units and that unsold stock has no scrap value, calculate the quantity that should be produced in order to maximise expected net present value.

Receipts and storage costs are due in one or two years' time, so these must be discounted to find their present value.

$$\text{Discounted revenue per 1000 units sold} = \frac{4\cdot5 \times 1000}{1\cdot25^2} = \text{£}2880.$$

Discounted cost of storage per £1000 of material cost

$$= \frac{250}{1\cdot25} + \frac{250}{1\cdot25^2} = \text{£}360.$$

If $1000X$ units of goods are produced and $1000Y$ units is the expected number sold, then the expected NPV

$$= \text{£}2880Y - \text{£}(250000 + 1500X + 360 \times 1\cdot5X)$$
$$= \text{£}2880Y - \text{£}(250000 + 2040X).$$

The value of Y depends on the value of X and the probability distribution of demand as follows:

		Probability and no. sold ('000)			
		300	400	500	
X		0·2	0·4	0·4	Y
300		60	120	120	300
400		60	160	160	380
500		60	160	200	420

The expected NPV for each value of X can now be found.

When $X = 300$

Expected NPV (£'000) = $2·88 \times 300 - (250 + 2·04 \times 300)$
                     = 2.

When $X = 400$

Expected NPV (£'000) = $2·88 \times 380 - (250 + 2·04 \times 400)$
                     = 28·4

When $X = 500$

Expected NPV (£'000) = $2·88 \times 420 - (250 + 2·04 \times 500)$
                     = — 60·4

The best policy, therefore, is to produce 400,000 units.

9. Capital Rationing

The criterion of adopting that project, among several competing projects, which gives the highest net present value assumes that the amount of capital required for each project can be readily obtained at the estimated cost of capital. This assumption will not be justified if, for some reason, a company decides that, during a limited period, the amount of cash it has available for new investment is insufficient. This may happen, for example, if the level of profits has been reduced by competition, so that the amount available for re-investment out of net cash flows will be less than what might be required to finance all new projects whilst, at the same time, the company may be unable to obtain new capital externally on acceptable terms. A company in this situation having to decide among a number of investment projects will be forced to eliminate some of them if the total capital required to finance them all exceeds what is available. The problem of choosing the optimal set of investments will still involve the maximisation of the net present value of the investments selected, but maximisation in this case will be subject to the constraints imposed by capital rationing. This suggests that the solution of such a problem could be effected by linear programming techniques. The following example illustrates.

EXAMPLE 7

The following investment projects are available for acceptance by Olympus Ltd. during 1977 and 1978:

Project	1	2	3
Outlay	£'000	£'000	£'000
1st January 1977	40	60	12
1st January 1978	40	40	80
Net receipt at			
31st December 1978	132	168	144

Each investment is expected to yield only one receipt on 31st December 1978. The estimated cost of capital of Olympus is 20% p.a. and it has been decided that, after dividends have been paid, the amount of cash available for reinvestment will be £150,000 on 1st January 1977 and £135,000 on 1st January 1978. It can be assumed that the investment projects available are divisible, i.e. that outlays may be reduced or increased by any proportion and that the receipts will then be reduced or increased in the same proportion. Determine the optimum set of investments.

The coefficients of the objective function are the NPV's of each project. These are calculated as follows.

Project 1

$$\text{NPV} = -40 - \frac{40}{1 \cdot 2} + \frac{132}{1 \cdot 2^2} = 18 \cdot 3$$

Project 2

$$\text{NPV} = -60 - \frac{40}{1 \cdot 2} + \frac{168}{1 \cdot 2^2} = 23 \cdot 3$$

Project 3

$$\text{NPV} = -12 - \frac{80}{1 \cdot 2} + \frac{144}{1 \cdot 2^2} = 21 \cdot 3.$$

Hence if x_1, x_2 and x_3 are the proportions of the investments taken up in Projects 1, 2 and 3 respectively, the objective function is

$$Z = 18 \cdot 3x_1 + 23 \cdot 3x_2 + 21 \cdot 3x_3$$

where Z is the net present value of the investments undertaken and the object is to maximise Z under the capital rationing constraints:

$$40x_1 + 60x_2 + 12x_3 \leqslant 150 \quad \text{(for 1st January 1977)}$$
$$40x_1 + 40x_2 + 80x_3 \leqslant 135 \quad \text{(for 1st January 1978)}.$$

This is an elementary programming problem which can be solved by the Simplex method. The reader should verify that the solution is $x_1 = 0$, $x_2 = 2\cdot4$ and $x_3 = 0\cdot5$ (approximately). The maximum NPV resulting from this choice is £66,600.

10. Depreciation

It has been seen that, in order to compute net cash flows, it is necessary to add annual depreciation to profit. Two important methods of calculating depreciation are the *straight line method* and the *reducing balance method*.

(a) The straight line method.

This consists simply in writing off a fixed amount each year from the book value of assets. For example, if a machine cost £X when new and in n years time will have a resale value of £Y, then the value written off each year will be

$$\frac{£(X - Y)}{n}.$$

Assuming that the project life is n years, this amount must be added annually to profit in order to obtain the net cash flow for the year.

(b) The reducing balance method.

This consists of writing off a fixed percentage $100i$ from the book value of assets each year. If a machine costs £X when new, then its value at the end of its first year of life will be £$(1 - i)X$ so that the amount written off during the first year is £$X - £(1 - i)X = £iX$. Similarly, the value of the machine at the end of the second year is $(1 - i) \times £(1 - i)X = £(1 - i)^2X$ so that the amount of depreciation in the second year is

$$£(1 - i)X - £(1 - i)^2X = (1 - i) \times £iX.$$

Continuing in this way, the value of the machine at the end of the nth year will be £$(1 - i)^nX$ so that the amount of depreciation in the nth year is

$$£(1 - i)^{n-1}X - £(1 - i)^nX = (1 - i)^{n-1} \times £iX.$$

The rate i at which the asset is depreciated is determined by the project life, n years, and the resale or scrap value of the asset. If the resale value is £Y, then the value of i satisfies the equation

$$(1 - i)^n X = Y$$

which can be solved using logarithms. For example, let $X = $ £5000, $n = 6$ years and $Y = $ £450. Then

$$n \log (1 - i) = \log 450 - \log 5000$$
$$= -1 \cdot 0458$$

so

$$\log (1 - i) = -1 \cdot 0458/6 = -0 \cdot 1743$$

and

$$1 - i = \text{antilog} (-0 \cdot 1743) = 0 \cdot 6694.$$

Hence

$$i = 1 - 0 \cdot 6694 = 0 \cdot 33 \text{ or } 33 \%$$

and this is the annual rate to be applied using the reducing balance method. It follows that the amount of depreciation in the fourth year, say, is

$$(1 - 0 \cdot 33)^3 \times £(0 \cdot 33 \times 5000) = £496.$$

This is the amount which must be added back in the fourth year in order to obtain the net cash flow for that year. It is not difficult to see that the reducing balance method results in a larger amount of depreciation earlier in the life of the asset compared to the later life, which tends to raise the present value of the project. The straight line method, on the other hand, leads to a more conservative estimate of NPV. However, this difference is not likely to be very significant if the same method is used consistently when comparing different investments.

A third method of depreciation which is used in the evaluation of certain kinds of investment is the *sinking fund method*. This consists of setting aside annually a fixed sum which will accumulate at interest to the amount of the initial investment. The sum set aside each year is an annuity, the amount of which will be just sufficient to replace the asset at the end of its working life. If $s_{\overline{n}, \overline{i}|}$ is the amount of an immediate annuity of £1 at the end of n years, each instalment being invested at compound interest as it becomes due, then an annuity of

$$\frac{1}{s_{\overline{n}, \overline{i}|}}$$

will amount to £1 at the end of n years. Hence if the value of the asset is £C, the annuity required to replace the asset is

$$\frac{C}{s_{\overline{n},\,i|}} = \frac{Ci}{(1 + i)^n - 1}.$$

In certain large undertakings, the capital required to finance the investment is borrowed at a fixed rate $100i\%$ per annum, and the capital sum is not repaid until the end of the project life. Hence the annual interest charge, which is payable each year, is Ci. The annual sum required to finance the investment, or total annual capital charge, is therefore

$$\frac{Ci}{(1 + i)^n - 1} + Ci = \frac{Ci(1 + i)^n}{(1 + i)^n - 1}.$$

Whether or not the investment is worth while depends on the sufficiency of the net cash flow to meet the annual capital charge. Suppose, for example, that an initial investment of £100,000 generates the following cash flows:

Year	0	1	2	3	4
Net cash flow (£'000)	-100	35	35	35	35
Annual capital charge (£'000) at $i = 0\cdot1$	—	$-31\cdot5$	$-31\cdot5$	$-31\cdot5$	$-31\cdot5$
Surplus (£'000)		$3\cdot5$	$3\cdot5$	$3\cdot5$	$3\cdot5$

The sinking fund accumulates at the cost of capital, which is assumed to be 10%. The total annual capital charge is then

$$\frac{100 \times 0\cdot1 \times (1\cdot1)^4}{(1\cdot1)^4 - 1} = 31\cdot5 \ (\text{£'000}).$$

Since this is less than the annual cash flow, the investment can be financed at the existing cost of capital and so will be worth while. The fact that there is a positive surplus after meeting the annual capital charge means also that the NPV of the project is positive. Moreover, the yield on the investment, that is, the discount rate at which the present value of the cash flows is equal to the initial outlay is 15% which is above the cost of capital. Hence all three methods of investment appraisal here give the same result.

The annual interest charge on the initial investment (at 10%) is 10 (£'000) which, together with the surplus of $3\cdot5$ (£'000) gives the total return per annum on the investment. This amount is expressed as a percentage of the initial outlay 100 (£'000) to give the *sinking fund rate of return* which, in this case is $13\cdot5\%$, rather less than the yield. One could express the criterion for accepting or rejecting the project in an alternative form by saying that the project should be accepted only if the sinking fund rate of return is above the cost of capital. This method of capital appraisal is known as the *annual capital charge method*, and it can be shown that, where both the NPV and Yield methods give the same result, so also will the annual capital charge method. For example, if the cost of capital is equal to the yield so that NPV is zero, then the sinking fund rate of return will also be equal to the cost of capital so that the surplus will be zero.

In private industry where cash flows are irregular, the NPV method is generally easier to apply. It is possible to convert an irregular cash flow into a series of regular cash flows so that the sinking fund rate of return could be calculated in this case; however, this is not quite the same thing as having cash available when it is required. Moreover, the cost of capital in connection with the capital charge method may be a somewhat nebulous concept. It must be the rate at which the sinking fund accumulates, that is, the rate at which the annual instalments are reinvested. It is logical to assume that these instalments are invested in marginal projects, that is, projects which have not yet been taken up but which are just worth while at the existing cost of capital. Another complication which may arise in connection with this method is that the project being evaluated could involve further capital outlays later in its life, and this will clearly have an effect on the sinking fund rate of return which is difficult to assess.

EXERCISES 19

1. A firm retains out of profits, £100 in the first month, £120 in the second month and continues to increase the amount retained by £20 each month for 36 months. Use the formula for the sum of an arithmetic progression to calculate how much the firm will have accumulated at the end of 36 months.

2. A colleague has asked for advice concerning his investments. He has already invested, on a long term basis, the sums at rates as given below:

Investment £	Rate of interest per annum %
2,800	7·4
3,300	7·8
4,120	8·5

He now has an opportunity of investing a lump sum at 10% per annum. How much must he invest at 10% per annum so that his annual income from investments will be 9% per annum on the entire investments?

3. At the beginning of each year a company invests a sum of £1500 at $9\frac{1}{2}$% per annum in order to purchase a new machine at the end of five years. How much will have been accumulated at the end of this time, provided that the interest is not withdrawn? How much interest would be earned if it were withdrawn at the end of each year?

4. It is estimated that a machine costing £5000 will have a saleable value of £2048 after 4 years. Derive a suitable formula for the reducing balance method of depreciation and find the depreciation rate per cent to be applied during the four year life.

5. Calculate the present value of £1 due to be paid in:
   (i) ten years' time at an interest rate of 3%; and
   (ii) five years' time at an interest rate of 6%.

6. What amount would £8500 accumulate to in 12 years if it was invested at a compound interest rate of 10% (gross) per annum?

7. What sum of money is required to purchase an immediate annuity of £1200 per annum (gross, before tax) payable quarterly for a man who is expected to live 12 years, if the rate of interest is $2\frac{1}{2}$% per quarter? The first payment would be made three months after the receipt of the purchase money.

8. Show that the present value of an annuity of £1 payable at the end of each year in perpetuity when the rate of interest is $100i$% p.a. is $\frac{1}{i}$. If the purchase price of a perpetuity is £10,000 and the interest rate is 5% p.a., what will be the amount of the annual payment to be made at the end of each year?

9. A machine costing £13,150 will have no scrap value, and has a useful life of 10 years.
   (a) What is the annual amount of depreciation if the straight line method is used?
   (b) What is the depreciation rate per cent if the reducing balance method is used?

10. Ignoring taxation, at what fixed rate of compound interest must £1000 be invested in order to accumulate to £2261 in ten years?

11. Calculate the present value of £50,000 due to be paid in twenty years from now assuming an interest rate of $7\frac{1}{2}$%.

12. Find the amount of an annuity of £50 payable at the end of each year for 15 years, the rate of interest being 14%.

13. Find the present value of an immediate annuity of £625 payable for 12 years, the rate of interest being 9%.

14. In order to purchase a property for £20,000 a loan of £15,000 is negotiated with a finance company. The balance of £5000 is to be paid out of personal resources.
The terms of the loan are as follows:
    Duration of the loan is for 15 years.
    Rate of interest is fixed at 10% per annum throughout the 15 years.
    The annual interest charge is to be calculated on the balance outstanding at the beginning of each year.
    Repayment is to be in 15 equal annual instalments. Each instalment will include both interest and capital.
    Calculate the amount to be paid each year on the loan of £15,000.

15. If property values were to appreciate at the rate of 7% per annum, what would be the value, in 15 years time, of property purchased now for £30,000?

16. £1250 is invested now at a compound interest rate of $9\frac{1}{2}$% per annum. What will be the amount of the investment in 5 years time? If the annual rate of inflation during that time is 15%, what will be the amount of the investment in 5 years time in terms of present prices?

17. The net cash flows on a new project are estimated to be as follows:

Year	0	1	2	3	4
Net cash flow (£)	−20,000	8000	12,000	9000	7000

    (a) Calculate the yield on the investment.
    (b) If the cost of capital is 14%, calculate the net present value of the investment.
    (c) Estimate the annual inflation rate at which the investment would be only just profitable.

18. Your company has an internal rate of return on its current investments of 17%. Money can be borrowed externally at 14% over a 5 year period.
The following project has been put forward for consideration. There are no competing projects at the moment.
    Project: Alphaspring
    Initial cash outflow £200,000

Cash inflow Year 1 £ 30,000;   Year 2 £80,000;
          Year 3 £120,000;   Year 4 £70,000;
              Total £300,000.

Locate the approximate percentage return on this project and state whether or not the project should be undertaken.

19. A company is considering investing in two projects, project A and project B. However, project B can only be undertaken if there is a positive cash flow from A. The possible cash flows and their probabilities are as follows:

Project A

Cash flow	Probability	Date
—£1200	0·15	31st December 1977
+£2500	0·45	31st December 1977
—£100	0·40	31st December 1977

Cash flow	Probability of B's cash inflow if A returns £2500	Date
+£4000	0·50	31st December 1978
+£500	0·25	31st December 1978
—£2000	0·25	31st December 1978

(i) Calculate the expected cash flow from project A at the 31st December 1977.

(ii) Calculate the NPV of the expected cash flow from project B at the 31st December 1977 using a 10% interest rate.

(iii) What course of action would you recommend and why?

(iv) Draw a tree diagram showing the different outcomes that may result if your recommendation is followed and calculate the total expected NPV of this course of action.

20. A company is considering the following three investment projects for acceptance:

Project	1	2	3
Outlay	£'000	£'000	£'000
1st Jan. 1977	60	50	40
1st Jan. 1978	—	30	90
Net receipt at			
1st Jan. 1979	40	40	90
1st Jan. 1980	70	100	90

It is estimated that only £100,000 will be available for investment at 1st January 1977 and also £100,000 at 1st January 1978.

Investment outlays and receipts are linearly related and can be reduced or increased by any desired proportion. The cost of capital is 15% per annum. Use linear programming methods to determine the optimal set of investments. State the total outlay in each project which this selection involves and the resulting NPV of the investments.

21. Everest Ltd is considering the replacement of a group of machines used exclusively for the manufacture of one of its products, the Yeti. The existing machines have a book value of £65,000 after deducting straight line depreciation from historical cost; however, they could be sold for only £45,000. The new machines would cost £100,000. Everest expects to sell Yetis for four more years. The existing machines could be kept in operation for that period of time if it were economically desirable to do so. After four years, the scrap value of both the existing machines and the new machines would be zero.

The current cost per unit of manufacturing Yetis on the existing machines and the new machines are as follows:

	Existing machines £		New machines £
Materials	22·00		20·00
Labour (32 hours @ £1·25)	40·00	(16 hours @ £1·25)	20·00
Overheads (32 hours @ £0·60)	19·20	(16 hours @ £1·80)	28·80
Total cost	81·20		68·80

Overheads are allocated to products on the labour hour rate method. The hourly rates of 60p and £1·80 comprise 25p and 62·5p for variable overheads and 35p and £1·175 for fixed overheads, including depreciation.

Current sales of Yetis are 1000 units per annum at £90 each; if the new machines are purchased, output would be increased to 1200 units and the selling price would be reduced to £80. Everest requires a minimum rate of return on investment of 20 per cent per annum in money terms. Material costs, overheads and selling prices are expected to increase at the rate of 15 per cent per annum, in step with the index of retail prices. Labour costs are expected to increase at the rate of 20 per cent per annum. Assume that annual receipts and payments would arise annually on the anniversary of the installation of the new machinery.

(a) Give calculations to show whether the purchase of the new machines would be worth while.

(b) Explain shortly your treatment of inflation.

22. The initial outlay on a project is £75,000, the project extending over 4 years. Annual expenditure on raw materials is fixed at a contractual level of £20,000. Other cash flows, valued at present prices, are expected to be £50,000 each year. The cost of capital is 16% p.a. and the annual inflation rate is 12% p.a. Assuming that all cash flows occur at the end of each year after the start of the project, (a) estimate the internal rate of return, and (b) calculate the NPV of the project.

CHAPTER 20

Matrices

1. Definition of a Matrix

A manufacturer produces four kinds of goods: W, X, Y, Z, each of which utilises three raw materials L, M, N. The cost of each raw material needed to make one unit of each product is shown in the following table:

		\multicolumn{4}{c}{Product}			
		W	X	Y	Z	
Raw	L	2	5	4	3	
material	M	3	1	4	5	£'s
	N	1	8	3	5	

The table shows, for example, that in order to produce 1 unit of Y, £4 must be spent on L, £4 on M and £3 on N. Calculations using data in this form are often facilitated if the numbers (or costs) are written down in a rectangular array, omitting the bordering letters:

$$\begin{pmatrix} 2 & 5 & 4 & 3 \\ 3 & 1 & 4 & 5 \\ 1 & 8 & 3 & 5 \end{pmatrix}.$$

Such an array is called a *matrix*. It consists of three rows and four columns and is, accordingly, called a 3×4 matrix. In general, a rectangular array of numbers with m rows and n columns is referred to as an $m \times n$ matrix. The first number in this product (m in the present instance) always refers to the number of *rows*, whilst the second number always refers to the number of *columns*. For example, an $n \times m$ matrix would be a matrix with n rows and m columns.

Two matrices are said to be *equal* if and only if they have the same number of rows and columns and the element in any specified row and column of one is equal to the element in the corresponding row and column of the other. This definition is important, since it is needed to discuss equations between sets of matrices which are combined by addition and multiplication.

It is often convenient, particularly when discussing operations with matrices, to denote a matrix by a capital letter. For example, the above matrix might be denoted by the letter **A**.

2. Addition of Matrices

Two matrices can be added together if they have the same number of rows and columns. Thus if **A** and **B** are both $m \times n$ matrices, their sum **A** + **B** can be found. Suppose, for example, that the costs of raw materials per unit of product referred to in section 1 change at some future date by the amounts shown in the matrix **B** below.

$$\mathbf{B} = \begin{array}{c} \\ L \\ M \\ N \end{array} \begin{array}{cccc} W & X & Y & Z \\ \begin{pmatrix} 1 & 2 & 3 & 1 \\ 0 & 1 & 2 & -2 \\ 1 & -3 & 1 & 0 \end{pmatrix} \end{array}.$$

The numbers show, for example, that in the production of 1 unit of Y, the cost of L has risen by £3, of M by £2, of N by £1. The negative entries indicate that costs have fallen, possibly due to some economy in the use of the materials for certain products. In order to find the revised cost matrix, the original cost matrix **A** is added to **B** to give:

$$\mathbf{A} + \mathbf{B} = \begin{pmatrix} 2 & 5 & 4 & 3 \\ 3 & 1 & 4 & 5 \\ 1 & 8 & 3 & 5 \end{pmatrix} + \begin{pmatrix} 1 & 2 & 3 & 1 \\ 0 & 1 & 2 & -2 \\ 1 & -3 & 1 & 0 \end{pmatrix}$$

$$= \begin{pmatrix} 2+1 & 5+2 & 4+3 & 3+1 \\ 3+0 & 1+1 & 4+2 & 5-2 \\ 1+1 & 8-3 & 3+1 & 5+0 \end{pmatrix}$$

$$= \begin{pmatrix} 3 & 7 & 7 & 4 \\ 3 & 2 & 6 & 3 \\ 2 & 5 & 4 & 5 \end{pmatrix}.$$

The final matrix gives the cost of raw materials after adjusting for price changes. The second line of working clearly shows what is involved in adding matrices. To obtain the element in row i and column j of the final matrix, the elements in row i and column j of each of the matrices **A** and **B** are added—that is why two matrices cannot be added unless they have the same number of rows and columns. If a negative number is added to a positive number, the result is the difference between the two numbers, just as in ordinary arithmetic. In fact the whole process of addition between the *elements* of the two matrices is the same as that of ordinary arithmetic. This means that the same matrix sum should be obtained whether the matrices are added in the order **A** + **B** or in the order **B** + **A**. Matrix addition, like the addition of ordinary numbers, is *commutative*, that is

$$\mathbf{A} + \mathbf{B} = \mathbf{B} + \mathbf{A}.$$

The sum of two $m \times n$ matrices is also an $m \times n$ matrix.

In order to find the difference between two matrices **A** and **B** (say $\mathbf{A} - \mathbf{B}$), subtract the element of any row and column of **B** from the element in the same row and column of **A**. The difference between two $m \times n$ matrices is also an $m \times n$ matrix. However, subtraction is *not* commutative, that is, $\mathbf{A} - \mathbf{B} \neq \mathbf{B} - \mathbf{A}$ in general. In fact, it is not difficult to see that if

$$\mathbf{A} - \mathbf{B} = \mathbf{B} - \mathbf{A}$$

then

$$\mathbf{A} + \mathbf{A} = \mathbf{B} + \mathbf{B} \quad \text{or} \quad \mathbf{A} = \mathbf{B}$$

from which it follows that subtraction is commutative only when **A** and **B** are identical matrices element for element.

3. Multiplication of Matrices

Associated with the cost matrix in section 1 there is a quantity matrix which shows the quantities of W, X, Y and Z produced in a given time interval. These quantities can be written as a 4×1 column matrix:

$$\mathbf{Q} = \begin{matrix} W \\ X \\ Y \\ Z \end{matrix} \begin{pmatrix} 2 \\ 4 \\ 3 \\ 5 \end{pmatrix}.$$

The elements of this matrix show the number of units of each product produced. To find the total cost of raw material L at the original prices shown in the matrix **A**, it is necessary to multiply each element in the L row of **A** by the corresponding quantity of each product produced. That is,

Total cost of raw material L

$$= (2 \times 2) + (5 \times 4) + (4 \times 3) + (3 \times 5)$$
$$= £51.$$

The total cost of materials M and N are found in a similar way. A more compact way of finding the total costs of the three materials is to evaluate the *product* of the matrices **A** and **Q**. This product is written as:

$$\mathbf{AQ} = \begin{pmatrix} 2 & 5 & 4 & 3 \\ 3 & 1 & 4 & 5 \\ 1 & 8 & 3 & 5 \end{pmatrix} \begin{pmatrix} 2 \\ 4 \\ 3 \\ 5 \end{pmatrix} = \begin{pmatrix} 51 \\ 47 \\ 68 \end{pmatrix}.$$

The product is another column matrix, in order to obtain which the elements of each column of a given row of **A** are multiplied by the corresponding elements in the rows of **Q** and the products added. For example, to find the cost of M, each element in the second row of **A** is multiplied by the corresponding element in **Q**, so that the element in the jth column of **A** is multiplied by the element in the jth row of **Q**:

$$(3 \times 2) + (1 \times 4) + (4 \times 3) + (5 \times 5) = £47.$$

This is done for each of the three rows of **A** in turn and the final column matrix shows that £51 is spent on L, £47 is spent on M and £68 is spent on N.

In this example of matrix multiplication, the product matrix is easy to find because one of the matrices, **Q**, consists of only one column. Suppose that the elements of **Q** give the outputs of W, X, etc., in one week and that information is also available about output in each of the two following weeks, given in the matrix **R**:

$$\mathbf{R} = \begin{array}{c} \\ W \\ X \\ Y \\ Z \end{array} \begin{array}{ccc} \text{1st} & \text{2nd} & \text{3rd} \\ \text{week} & \text{week} & \text{week} \\ \left(\begin{array}{ccc} 2 & 2 & 1 \\ 4 & 5 & 0 \\ 3 & 5 & 7 \\ 5 & 3 & 5 \end{array} \right). \end{array}$$

The total cost of materials used in each of the three weeks is found by evaluating the product matrix **AR** in a similar way to that in which the matrix **AQ** was evaluated, namely:

$$\mathbf{AR} = \begin{pmatrix} 2 & 5 & 4 & 3 \\ 3 & 1 & 4 & 5 \\ 1 & 8 & 3 & 5 \end{pmatrix} \begin{pmatrix} 2 & 2 & 1 \\ 4 & 5 & 0 \\ 3 & 5 & 7 \\ 5 & 3 & 5 \end{pmatrix}$$

$$= \begin{pmatrix} 51 & 58 & 45 \\ 47 & 46 & 56 \\ 68 & 72 & 47 \end{pmatrix}.$$

The first column of the final matrix, in this case, shows exactly the same information as the column matrix **AQ**, that is, the total cost of L, M, and N in the first week. The second and third columns give these total costs for the second and third weeks respectively. To obtain the element in the ith row and jth column of the product matrix, the elements of the ith row of **A** are multiplied by the corresponding elements of the jth column of **R**. For example, to

obtain the element in the third row and second column of the final
matrix (72), the elements of the third row of **A** are multiplied by the
elements of the second column of **R** and the products added:

$$(1 \times 2) + (8 \times 5) + (3 \times 5) + (5 \times 3) = \pounds72.$$

The matrix **AR** gives the total costs of materials and it is worth
enquiring whether any meaning attaches to the product matrix
obtained when the order of multiplication is reversed, that is, the
product **RA**. If the first row of **R** is multiplied by the first column of
A, the cost incurred in producing W is obtained of L in the first
week, M in the second week and N in the third week—which is not
particularly significant. In fact none of the elements of the product
matrix in this case have any important significance. However, the
product matrix is given for reference, and the reader should check
that it is correct:

$$\mathbf{RA} = \begin{pmatrix} 11 & 20 & 19 & 21 \\ 23 & 25 & 36 & 37 \\ 28 & 76 & 53 & 69 \\ 24 & 68 & 47 & 55 \end{pmatrix}.$$

One striking feature of the matrix **AR** compared to the matrix **RA**
is that the number of rows and columns in each are not the same.
Thus **AR** is a 3×3 matrix and **RA** is a 4×4 matrix. This shows at
once that the result of multiplying the matrix **A** by **R** is different from
the result of multiplying the matrix **R** by **A**, since a necessary
condition for two matrices to be equal is that they have the same
number of rows and columns. In any case, in the example just given,
it is easy to see that the matrices **AR** and **RA** have a completely
different significance. This illustrates an important property of
matrix multiplication, namely that it is *not* commutative, that is, in
general

$$\mathbf{AB} \neq \mathbf{BA}$$

where **A** and **B** are any two matrices. Compare this with multiplication of ordinary numbers, which is commutative, e.g.
$15 \times 23 = 23 \times 15$.

Thus the order in which matrices are multiplied is important. In
the product **AR**, **R** is said to be *pre-multiplied* by **A** and **A** is said to
be *post-multiplied* by **R**. To find the product **AB** of any two matrices
A and **B**, the ith row of **A** is multiplied by each column of **B** in turn
and the resulting numbers are the elements in the ith row of the final
matrix. Clearly this matrix will have the same number of rows as **A**
and the same number of columns as **B**. Moreover, in order that the

product **AB** should exist, it is necessary that **A** has the same number of columns as **B** has rows, otherwise it will be impossible to match up all the elements of each matrix in order to find the product. Thus in order that the product **AB** should exist, if **A** is an $m \times n$ matrix, **B** must be an $n \times p$ matrix. Conversely, if **A** is an $m \times n$ matrix and **B** is a $k \times p$ matrix and **AB** exists, then $n = k$. The resulting product is then an $m \times p$ matrix, that is, it has the same number of rows as **A** and the same number of columns as **B** as already indicated. This can be verified for the products **AR** and **RA** found above. Thus **A** is a 3×4 matrix and **R** is a 4×3 matrix so **AR** exists and is a 3×3 matrix. Also **A** has the same number of rows as **R** has columns, so that **RA** exists and is a 4×4 matrix.

To summarise, if **A** is an $m \times n$ matrix and **B** is a $k \times p$ matrix, then

   (i) in general $\mathbf{AB} \neq \mathbf{BA}$.
   (ii) **AB** exists if and only if $n = k$.
   (iii) **BA** exists if and only if $p = m$.
   (iv) If **AB** and **BA** both exist, then **AB** is an $m \times p$ matrix and **BA** is a $k \times n$ matrix.

From these conditions it follows that, unless m, n, k and p are all equal to each other, the product matrices will be unequal, since the number of rows and columns of each will differ. Hence one can certainly say, in this case, that **A** and **B** do not commute under multiplication. If a matrix **A** has m rows and n columns, it is sometimes convenient to refer to $m \times n$ as the *order* of **A**.

4. Square Matrices

A matrix which has the same number of rows as it has columns is called a *square matrix*. The products of any two square matrices of the same order always exist, whatever the order in which they are multiplied together. This does not mean, however, that all square matrices of the same order commute under multiplication, although some do. Consider, for example, the following 2×2 matrices:

$$\mathbf{A} = \begin{pmatrix} 1 & 4 \\ 3 & 2 \end{pmatrix} \qquad \mathbf{B} = \begin{pmatrix} 2 & 1 \\ 5 & 3 \end{pmatrix}.$$

By the rules of matrix multiplication,

$$\mathbf{AB} = \begin{pmatrix} (1 \times 2) + (4 \times 5) & (1 \times 1) + (4 \times 3) \\ (3 \times 2) + (2 \times 5) & (3 \times 1) + (2 \times 3) \end{pmatrix}$$
$$= \begin{pmatrix} 22 & 13 \\ 16 & 9 \end{pmatrix}$$

and
$$\mathbf{BA} = \begin{pmatrix} 2 & 1 \\ 5 & 3 \end{pmatrix}\begin{pmatrix} 1 & 4 \\ 3 & 2 \end{pmatrix}$$
$$= \begin{pmatrix} 5 & 10 \\ 14 & 26 \end{pmatrix}.$$

Hence in this case it is not true that $\mathbf{AB}$ and $\mathbf{BA}$ are equal, although they are of the same order (2×2). However, let

$$\mathbf{C} = \begin{pmatrix} 4 & 12 \\ 9 & 7 \end{pmatrix}.$$

Then $\mathbf{AC}$ and $\mathbf{CA}$ are both equal to the same 2×2 matrix:

$$\begin{pmatrix} 40 & 40 \\ 30 & 50 \end{pmatrix}.$$

Hence some square matrices of the same order do commute under multiplication, though this is not true in general. Of course, every square matrix commutes with itself under multiplication.

5. Associative and Distributive Laws

It has been seen that addition of matrices is commutative, but that multiplication is not. Two other laws of arithmetic also hold for matrices. First, *the associative law:*

$$(\mathbf{A} + \mathbf{B}) + \mathbf{C} = \mathbf{A} + (\mathbf{B} + \mathbf{C}) \quad \text{(Addition)}$$
$$(\mathbf{AB})\mathbf{C} = \mathbf{A}(\mathbf{BC}) \quad \text{(Multiplication)}$$

This law states that if several matrices have to be added together, it is immaterial how the additions are grouped, the same answer will be obtained. Similarly, if several matrices are multiplied together, the grouping of the matrices for multiplication will not affect the result—although changing the order of multiplication may do so since matrices are non-commutative under multiplication.

Second, *the distributive law:*

$$\mathbf{A}(\mathbf{B} + \mathbf{C}) = \mathbf{AB} + \mathbf{AC}.$$

This states that matrix multiplication is distributive over matrix addition. Note, however, that in general

$$\mathbf{A}(\mathbf{B} + \mathbf{C}) \neq (\mathbf{B} + \mathbf{C})\mathbf{A}$$

since matrix multiplication is non-commutative.

6. The Transpose of a Matrix

The *transpose* of any matrix $\mathbf{A}$ is formed by interchanging its rows and columns, and is denoted by $\mathbf{A}'$. Thus the ith row of $\mathbf{A}$ becomes the ith column of $\mathbf{A}'$ and the jth column of $\mathbf{A}$ becomes the jth row of $\mathbf{A}'$. It follows that if $\mathbf{A}$ is of order $m \times n$ then $\mathbf{A}'$ is of order $n \times m$. For example, let

$$\mathbf{A} = \begin{pmatrix} 1 & 3 \\ 2 & 0 \\ 5 & 8 \end{pmatrix} \quad \text{then} \quad \mathbf{A}' = \begin{pmatrix} 1 & 2 & 5 \\ 3 & 0 & 8 \end{pmatrix}.$$

There are two laws for the transposition of the sums or products of matrices:

For sums $(\mathbf{A} + \mathbf{B})' = \mathbf{A}' + \mathbf{B}'.$

For example, if

$$\mathbf{A} = \begin{pmatrix} 2 & 5 \\ 1 & 4 \end{pmatrix}, \quad \mathbf{B} = \begin{pmatrix} 7 & -1 \\ 2 & 6 \end{pmatrix}$$

then

$$\mathbf{A} + \mathbf{B} = \begin{pmatrix} 9 & 4 \\ 3 & 10 \end{pmatrix} \quad \text{and} \quad (\mathbf{A} + \mathbf{B})' = \begin{pmatrix} 9 & 3 \\ 4 & 10 \end{pmatrix}.$$

Also

$$\mathbf{A}' + \mathbf{B}' = \begin{pmatrix} 2 & 1 \\ 5 & 4 \end{pmatrix} + \begin{pmatrix} 7 & 2 \\ -1 & 6 \end{pmatrix} = \begin{pmatrix} 9 & 3 \\ 4 & 10 \end{pmatrix}.$$

So in this case $(\mathbf{A} + \mathbf{B})' = \mathbf{A}' + \mathbf{B}'$ and this is true of all pairs of matrices $\mathbf{A}$ and $\mathbf{B}$ of the same order.

For products $(\mathbf{AB})' = \mathbf{B}'\mathbf{A}'.$

Thus if $\mathbf{A}$ and $\mathbf{B}$ are the same matrices as above, then

$$\mathbf{AB} = \begin{pmatrix} 24 & 28 \\ 15 & 23 \end{pmatrix} \quad \text{and} \quad (\mathbf{AB})' = \begin{pmatrix} 24 & 15 \\ 28 & 23 \end{pmatrix}.$$

Also

$$\mathbf{B}'\mathbf{A}' = \begin{pmatrix} 7 & 2 \\ -1 & 6 \end{pmatrix}\begin{pmatrix} 2 & 1 \\ 5 & 4 \end{pmatrix} = \begin{pmatrix} 24 & 15 \\ 28 & 23 \end{pmatrix} = (\mathbf{AB})'.$$

In particular, if $\mathbf{C}$ is an $n \times 1$ column matrix, then $\mathbf{C}'$ is a $1 \times n$ row matrix. Hence if $\mathbf{A}$ is any $m \times n$ matrix, $\mathbf{AC}$ is an $m \times 1$ column matrix and

$$(\mathbf{AC})' = \mathbf{C}'\mathbf{A}'$$

is a $1 \times m$ row matrix. In section 3, the cost of materials was found from the matrix product $\mathbf{AQ}$ so that, by interchanging the rows and columns of $\mathbf{A}$ and $\mathbf{Q}$ respectively, the costs could also be obtained from the row matrix $\mathbf{Q}'\mathbf{A}'$.

7. The Zero and Unit Matrices

If a square matrix of order $n \times n$ is multiplied by another $n \times n$ square matrix all of whose elements are zero, the resulting matrix is also an $n \times n$ matrix with all its elements zero. It is called the *zero matrix* of order $n \times n$. Thus

$$\mathbf{O} = \begin{pmatrix} 0 & 0 \\ 0 & 0 \end{pmatrix}$$

is the zero matrix of order 2×2. If any other zero matrix of order 2×2 is multiplied by this matrix, the result is the zero matrix, whatever the order of multiplication, i.e. $\mathbf{AO} = \mathbf{OA} = \mathbf{O}$. In general, any matrix having all its elements equal to zero is a zero matrix, so that one can always write

$$\mathbf{A} - \mathbf{A} = \mathbf{O}.$$

A square matrix of order $n \times n$ in which all the elements of the diagonal descending from the top left-hand corner to the bottom right-hand corner (the leading diagonal) are 1's and the remaining elements are zeros is known as the *unit matrix* of order $n \times n$ which is always denoted by the letter $\mathbf{I}$. Thus

$$\mathbf{I} = \begin{pmatrix} 1 & 0 \\ 0 & 1 \end{pmatrix}$$

is the unit 2×2 matrix. If any other 2×2 matrix is multiplied by $\mathbf{I}$ in either order, then the product is equal to that matrix, that is, $\mathbf{AI} = \mathbf{IA} = \mathbf{A}$. For example,

$$\begin{pmatrix} 2 & 5 \\ 6 & 3 \end{pmatrix}\begin{pmatrix} 1 & 0 \\ 0 & 1 \end{pmatrix} = \begin{pmatrix} (2 \times 1) + (5 \times 0) & (2 \times 0) + (5 \times 1) \\ (6 \times 1) + (3 \times 0) & (6 \times 0) + (3 \times 1) \end{pmatrix}$$

$$= \begin{pmatrix} 2 & 5 \\ 6 & 3 \end{pmatrix}$$

$$= \begin{pmatrix} 1 & 0 \\ 0 & 1 \end{pmatrix}\begin{pmatrix} 2 & 5 \\ 6 & 3 \end{pmatrix}.$$

In ordinary algebra, if the product of two numbers is equal to zero, then either one or both of the numbers must be equal to zero. This is not necessarily true in matrix algebra. Thus if $\mathbf{A}$ and $\mathbf{B}$ are any two matrices such that the product $\mathbf{AB}$ exists and is zero, it does not follow that $\mathbf{A} = \mathbf{O}$ or $\mathbf{B} = \mathbf{O}$. For example

$$\begin{pmatrix} 2 & -1 \\ 2 & -1 \end{pmatrix}\begin{pmatrix} 2 & 3 \\ 4 & 6 \end{pmatrix} = \begin{pmatrix} 0 & 0 \\ 0 & 0 \end{pmatrix}.$$

8. Matrix Equations

Operational research problems often require the solution of sets of simultaneous equations. These equations embody information about the production process which can be concisely summarised in matrix form. Suppose that a manufacturer is producing two products X and Y which use materials L and M. In order to produce 1 unit of X, 4 units of L are required whilst in order to produce 1 unit of Y, 9 units of L are required, the total availability of L being 800 units. At the same time, 2 units and 5 units of M are required in the production of 1 unit of X and Y respectively, the total availability of M being 424 units. The problem is to determine how much of X and Y can be produced. The information can be set forth in three matrices:

$$\begin{array}{cc} & X \quad Y \\ \begin{array}{c} \text{Material} \\ \text{requirements} \end{array} & \begin{array}{c} L \\ M \end{array} \begin{pmatrix} 4 & 9 \\ 2 & 5 \end{pmatrix} = \mathbf{A}. \end{array}$$

$$\begin{array}{c} \text{Quantities} \\ \text{produced} \end{array} \begin{array}{c} X \\ Y \end{array} \begin{pmatrix} x \\ y \end{pmatrix} = \mathbf{B}.$$

$$\begin{array}{c} \text{Material} \\ \text{available} \end{array} \begin{array}{c} L \\ M \end{array} \begin{pmatrix} 800 \\ 424 \end{pmatrix} = \mathbf{C}.$$

The product of the matrices $\mathbf{A}$ and $\mathbf{B}$ will obviously give the total quantities of L and M used. The output must therefore be such that the elements of the product matrix $\mathbf{AB}$ are the same as the elements of the matrix $\mathbf{C}$, which show how much material is available. Hence the quantities of X and Y produced must satisfy the matrix equation

$$\mathbf{AB} = \mathbf{C}$$

or, writing it out in full:

$$\begin{pmatrix} 4 & 9 \\ 2 & 5 \end{pmatrix} \begin{pmatrix} x \\ y \end{pmatrix} = \begin{pmatrix} 800 \\ 424 \end{pmatrix}.$$

Multiplying the two matrices on the left hand side of this equation gives:

$$\begin{pmatrix} 4x + 9y \\ 2x + 5y \end{pmatrix} = \begin{pmatrix} 800 \\ 424 \end{pmatrix}.$$

Since these two matrices are equal it follows that corresponding elements are equal, so that

$$4x + 9y = 800$$
$$2x + 5y = 424.$$

The solution of the problem is the values of x and y which satisfy this pair of simultaneous equations. Solving the equations by the ordinary method of elimination, the values are

$$x = 92 \quad \text{and} \quad y = 48.$$

Although it is easy enough, when there are only two unknowns, to find the solution of simultaneous equations by elimination, it is not so easy when there is a large number of unknowns. Fortunately, matrices provide a means of solving simultaneous equations which can be readily programmed for solution by a computer. The problem in two unknowns which has just been solved by other means will be used to illustrate the method.

9. The Inverse Matrix

The problem was expressed in the form of the matrix equation

$$\mathbf{AB} = \mathbf{C}.$$

The column matrix $\mathbf{B}$ contains the unknowns of the problem, so the solution consists of finding the matrix $\mathbf{B}$. In other words, the equation must be transformed so that the matrix $\mathbf{B}$ stands alone on the left-hand side, whilst on the right-hand side a matrix is obtained all of whose elements are known numbers. It will have to be a 2×1 column matrix since $\mathbf{B}$ is a 2×1 column matrix. Suppose that there exists a matrix $\mathbf{D}$ such that the product of $\mathbf{D}$ and $\mathbf{A}$ is the unit matrix, that is,

$$\mathbf{DA} = \mathbf{I}.$$

Pre-multiplying both sides of the equation $\mathbf{AB} = \mathbf{C}$ by $\mathbf{D}$ gives

$$\mathbf{DAB} = \mathbf{DC}$$

or

$$\mathbf{IB} = \mathbf{DC}$$

or

$$\mathbf{B} = \mathbf{DC} \quad (\text{since } \mathbf{IB} = \mathbf{B}).$$

The product $\mathbf{DC}$ is a 2×1 column matrix containing known numbers, so this is clearly the solution of the problem. The essential step is finding the matrix $\mathbf{D}$ such that $\mathbf{DA} = \mathbf{I}$. The matrix $\mathbf{D}$ is called the *inverse* of $\mathbf{A}$. The product of any matrix with its inverse is the unit matrix. To find the matrix $\mathbf{D}$ for the problem in section 8, let

$$\mathbf{D} = \begin{pmatrix} a & b \\ c & d \end{pmatrix}$$

where a, b, c, d are numbers to be evaluated. Then

$$\mathbf{DA} = \begin{pmatrix} a & b \\ c & d \end{pmatrix}\begin{pmatrix} 4 & 9 \\ 2 & 5 \end{pmatrix} = \begin{pmatrix} 1 & 0 \\ 0 & 1 \end{pmatrix} = \mathbf{I}.$$

This results in four equations from which the values of the elements of $\mathbf{D}$ can be determined:

$$4a + 2b = 1$$
$$9a + 5b = 0$$
$$4c + 2d = 0$$
$$9c + 5d = 1$$

These are easily solved by elimination to give:

$$a = 5/2, \, b = -9/2, \, c = -1, \, d = 2.$$

Each of these numbers has a factor $\frac{1}{2}$, so that the matrix $\mathbf{D}$ can be written as

$$\mathbf{D} = \tfrac{1}{2}\begin{pmatrix} 5 & -9 \\ -2 & 4 \end{pmatrix}$$

where it is understood that the factor $\frac{1}{2}$ outside the matrix multiplies each of the four elements within the matrix. Then

$$\mathbf{DA} = \tfrac{1}{2}\begin{pmatrix} 5 & -9 \\ -2 & 4 \end{pmatrix}\begin{pmatrix} 4 & 9 \\ 2 & 5 \end{pmatrix}$$
$$= \tfrac{1}{2}\begin{pmatrix} (20 - 18) & (45 - 45) \\ (-8 + 8) & (-18 + 20) \end{pmatrix}$$
$$= \begin{pmatrix} 1 & 0 \\ 0 & 1 \end{pmatrix} = \mathbf{I}.$$

So $\mathbf{D}$ is the inverse of $\mathbf{A}$. It is usual to write the inverse of a square matrix $\mathbf{A}$ as $\mathbf{A}^{-1}$, the negative index -1 having much the same meaning it has when used in ordinary algebra as, for example, x^{-1} is the reciprocal of x, namely $1/x$, so that $x^{-1} \times x = 1$ provided that x is not zero.

The solution of the matrix equation $\mathbf{AB} = \mathbf{C}$ is thus

$$\mathbf{B} = \mathbf{A}^{-1}\mathbf{C}$$

where $\mathbf{A}^{-1}$ is the inverse matrix of $\mathbf{A}$. Hence in the example which has been discussed,

$$\mathbf{B} = \begin{pmatrix} x \\ y \end{pmatrix} = \tfrac{1}{2}\begin{pmatrix} 5 & -9 \\ -2 & 4 \end{pmatrix}\begin{pmatrix} 800 \\ 424 \end{pmatrix}$$
$$= \tfrac{1}{2}\begin{pmatrix} (4000 - 3816) \\ (-1600 + 1696) \end{pmatrix}$$
$$= \tfrac{1}{2}\begin{pmatrix} 184 \\ 96 \end{pmatrix} = \begin{pmatrix} 92 \\ 48 \end{pmatrix}.$$

Hence by solving the matrix equation, the same result is obtained as by the ordinary method of solving simultaneous equations by eliminating unknowns, namely, $x = 92$ and $y = 48$.

The method of obtaining the inverse matrix outlined above is rather tedious, although it will work for a square matrix of any order—for example, it can be used to obtain the inverse of a 3×3 matrix. Fortunately, there is a much simpler way of obtaining the inverse of a 2×2 matrix. Comparing the matrix **A** and its inverse **A**$^{-1}$ obtained above:

$$\mathbf{A} = \begin{pmatrix} 4 & 9 \\ 2 & 5 \end{pmatrix} \qquad \mathbf{A}^{-1} = \tfrac{1}{2}\begin{pmatrix} 5 & -9 \\ -2 & 4 \end{pmatrix},$$

it will be seen that the elements within the brackets of the inverse matrix are the same as those of the matrix **A** itself except that the positions of the elements 4 and 5 have been interchanged, whilst the positions of the elements 2 and 9 are the same but have been given opposite signs from what they have in the matrix **A**. This change of position and signs follows the same pattern when finding the inverse of any 2×2 matrix. Secondly, the fraction outside the brackets of the inverse matrix is obtained in the same way for all 2×2 matrices, namely by multiplying the pairs of numbers on each diagonal and subtracting from the product of the leading diagonal pair the product of the pair on the other diagonal:

$$(4 \times 5) - (2 \times 9) = 2.$$

The factor of the inverse matrix is then found by taking the reciprocal of this number, namely, $\tfrac{1}{2}$. Thus for any 2×2 matrix

$$\mathbf{A} = \begin{pmatrix} p & q \\ r & s \end{pmatrix}$$

the inverse is

$$\mathbf{A}^{-1} = \frac{1}{ps - qr}\begin{pmatrix} s & -q \\ -r & p \end{pmatrix}.$$

For instance, the inverse of the matrix

$$\begin{pmatrix} 5 & -1 \\ 1 & 2 \end{pmatrix} \quad \text{is} \quad \frac{1}{11}\begin{pmatrix} 2 & 1 \\ -1 & 5 \end{pmatrix}$$

as the reader should verify by multiplying these two matrices together to obtain the unit matrix **I**.

The product of any square matrix with its inverse is commutative. This can be proved as follows. Suppose that

$$A^{-1}A = I \quad \text{and} \quad AA^{-1} \neq I.$$

Post-multiplying both sides of the inequality by A gives

$$A(A^{-1}A) \neq IA \quad \text{or} \quad A \neq A.$$

Hence the hypothesis that $AA^{-1} \neq I$ leads to a contradiction and is therefore false. So

$$A^{-1}A = AA^{-1} = I.$$

It is also easy to show that if a matrix has an inverse, then it has one and only one inverse. Thus let

$$BA = I \quad \text{and} \quad AC = I.$$

Post-multiplying both sides of the first equation by C and pre-multiplying both sides of the second equation by B gives

$$(BA)C = IC = C \quad \text{and} \quad B(AC) = BI = B.$$

Since multiplication of matrices is associative it follows that

$$(BA)C = B(AC) \quad \text{and so} \quad B = C = A^{-1}.$$

Only square matrices have inverses, but not all square matrices have inverses. A square matrix which has an inverse is called *non-singular*, whilst if it has no inverse it is called *singular*. This can be remembered by thinking of a matrix without an inverse as somehow standing by itself, that is, being single. The condition for a 2×2 matrix to have an inverse is that the product of the two diagonal pairs of numbers should be unequal. If they were equal, then the factor of the inverse matrix would be $1/0$ which is, of course, one way of writing infinity, and is not a number. That is why a singular matrix has no inverse. For example

$$\begin{pmatrix} 25 & 125 \\ 9 & 45 \end{pmatrix}$$

is a singular matrix because $(25 \times 45) - (9 \times 125) = 0$.

There is a systematic way of finding the inverse of any square matrix, though this becomes complicated for matrices of higher order. Writing the general 3×3 matrix as

$$\begin{pmatrix} p & q & r \\ s & t & u \\ v & w & x \end{pmatrix}$$

the inverse matrix is

$$\frac{1}{k}\begin{pmatrix} tx - uw & rw - qx & qu - rt \\ uv - sx & px - rv & rs - pu \\ sw - tv & qv - pw & pt - qs \end{pmatrix}$$

where $k = p(tx - uw) - q(sx - uv) + r(sw - tv)$.
For example, let

$$\mathbf{A} = \begin{pmatrix} 2 & -3 & 2 \\ 4 & 4 & -3 \\ 3 & 2 & -3 \end{pmatrix}$$

then

$$\mathbf{A}^{-1} = \frac{1}{k}\begin{pmatrix} (-12 + 6) & (4 - 9) & (9 - 8) \\ (-9 + 12) & (-6 - 6) & (8 + 6) \\ (8 - 12) & (-9 - 4) & (8 + 12) \end{pmatrix}$$

$$= \frac{1}{k}\begin{pmatrix} -6 & -5 & 1 \\ 3 & -12 & 14 \\ -4 & -13 & 20 \end{pmatrix}$$

where $k = 2(-12 + 6) - (-3)(-12 + 9) + 2(8 - 12) = -29$.

This should be verified by actual multiplication, showing that $\mathbf{AA}^{-1} = \mathbf{A}^{-1}\mathbf{A} = \mathbf{I}$.

A matrix equation which includes a 3×3 matrix occurs in the solution of a set of simultaneous equations in which there are three unknowns. Consider, for example, the following set of simultaneous equations:

$$2x - 3y + 2z = 14$$
$$4x + 4y - 3z = 6$$
$$3x + 2y - 3z = -2.$$

These equations can be expressed as a single matrix equation $\mathbf{AB} = \mathbf{C}$ where $\mathbf{A}$ is the matrix shown above, and

$$\mathbf{B} = \begin{pmatrix} x \\ y \\ z \end{pmatrix} \qquad \mathbf{C} = \begin{pmatrix} 14 \\ 6 \\ -2 \end{pmatrix}.$$

The elements of $\mathbf{A}$ are the coefficients of the unknowns x, y, z in just the same way as the elements of a 2×2 matrix consist of the coefficients of the unknowns in a set of equations with two unknowns. The solution of the equations is $\mathbf{B} = \mathbf{A}^{-1}\mathbf{C}$, that is

$$\mathbf{B} = \begin{pmatrix} x \\ y \\ z \end{pmatrix} = -\frac{1}{29}\begin{pmatrix} -6 & -5 & 1 \\ 3 & -12 & 14 \\ -4 & -13 & 20 \end{pmatrix}\begin{pmatrix} 14 \\ 6 \\ -2 \end{pmatrix}$$

$$= -\frac{1}{29}\begin{pmatrix} -116 \\ -58 \\ -174 \end{pmatrix} = \begin{pmatrix} 4 \\ 2 \\ 6 \end{pmatrix}.$$

This system of equations is therefore satisfied by $x = 4$, $y = 2$ and $z = 6$.

10. Insoluble Simultaneous Equations

In the study of ordinary algebra one finds that a set of linear simultaneous equations either (a) has a unique solution, that is, only one set of values of the unknowns satisfies the equations, or (b) has no solution, in which case the equations are inconsistent, or (c) has an infinite number of solutions. These different possibilities can be expressed in terms of a condition on the matrix containing the coefficients of the unknowns. Thus (a) if this matrix is non-singular, the system has a unique solution; (b) and (c) if the matrix is singular, then the system either has no solution or an infinite number of solutions.

The matrix equation $\mathbf{AB} = \mathbf{C}$ has no solution if $\mathbf{B} = \mathbf{A^{-1}C} = \mathbf{K}/0$, where $\mathbf{K}$ is a non-zero matrix. The equation has an infinite number of solutions if $\mathbf{B} = \mathbf{A^{-1}C} = \mathbf{O}/0$ where $\mathbf{O}$ is the zero matrix. For example, the equations

$$5x + 10y = 3$$
$$2x + 4y = 5$$

have no solution. The matrix

$$\begin{pmatrix} 5 & 10 \\ 2 & 4 \end{pmatrix}$$

is singular, and

$$\frac{1}{0}\begin{pmatrix} 4 & -10 \\ -2 & 5 \end{pmatrix}\begin{pmatrix} 3 \\ 5 \end{pmatrix} = \frac{1}{0}\begin{pmatrix} -38 \\ 19 \end{pmatrix} = \mathbf{K}/0.$$

On the other hand, the set of equations

$$5x + 10y = 15$$
$$2x + 4y = 6$$

has an infinite number of solutions, for in this case

$$\frac{1}{0}\begin{pmatrix} 4 & -10 \\ -2 & 5 \end{pmatrix}\begin{pmatrix} 15 \\ 6 \end{pmatrix} = \frac{1}{0}\begin{pmatrix} 0 \\ 0 \end{pmatrix} = \mathbf{O}/0.$$

One can therefore give a practical interpretation to the significance of a singular matrix. If the coefficients of the unknowns of a system of simultaneous equations form a singular matrix, then the system has no unique solution.

11. Input-Output Analysis

The determination of optimum output or product mix by methods previously explained in this book has always implicitly assumed that whatever quantity is produced will reach the final consumer. However, it is not unusual for some part of a product to be re-absorbed in a productive process, so that net output, that is output coming onto the market, is less than the total output of the product in question. An oil company, for example, will consume some part of the oil it produces in order to fuel tankers or provide a source of energy in the productive process. It follows that if optimum output is net, then the true output necessary in order to achieve the target will have to be greater than this optimum. There is obviously no difficulty in making the appropriate adjustment to target figures in the case of a single-product firm, since this involves only the solution of a single equation with one unknown, namely the quantity of the product to be produced. The coefficients of the equation are given by the target figure for net output and the proportion of total output which is reabsorbed by the firm.

Where a multi-product firm is in question, the fixing of total output for all the products involved requires the solution of several linear simultaneous equations which can be put into matrix form. Thus if a firm produces three products X, Y and Z, each of which are partly reabsorbed in production, one requires first the proportions of the outputs of these products which are used also as inputs. An analysis of these proportions might be as shown in the following table:

		Input		
		X	Y	Z
	X	0·1	0·2	0·1
Output	Y	0·3	0·1	0·2
	Z	0·1	0·1	0·1

The first row of the table shows, for example, that the production of 1 unit of X, Y and Z require 0·1, 0·2 and 0·1 units of X respectively. As the products are not homogeneous, their quantities must be measured in a common unit, the obvious choice being that of money. The production targets for the optimum quantities to be placed on the market are, perhaps, £100,000 of X, £150,000 of Y and £125,000 of Z. In order to meet these targets, the total outputs of X, Y and Z must be £x ('000), £y ('000), £z ('000). To determine the values of these three unknowns, three equations are needed embodying the target figures and the quantities of outputs which are reabsorbed as inputs:

$$x = 0.1x + 0.2y + 0.1z + 100$$
$$y = 0.3x + 0.1y + 0.2z + 150$$
$$z = 0.1x + 0.1y + 0.1z + 125.$$

In each of these equations, x, y, and z can be regarded as the total money costs of production which include other costs apart from those incurred in the reabsorption of the products themselves. However, the costs of these other inputs are not relevant to the problem since the amount employed of an input such as labour does not affect the quantities of each of the products to be produced once the target figures have been set. The solutions of these equations therefore give the required quantities. The terms of the equations can be rearranged in the form:

$$0.9x - 0.2y - 0.1z = 100$$
$$-0.3x + 0.9y - 0.2z = 150$$
$$-0.1x - 0.1y + 0.9z = 125.$$

The corresponding matrix equation is:

$$\begin{pmatrix} 0.9 & -0.2 & -0.1 \\ -0.3 & 0.9 & -0.2 \\ -0.1 & -0.1 & 0.9 \end{pmatrix} \begin{pmatrix} x \\ y \\ z \end{pmatrix} = \begin{pmatrix} 100 \\ 150 \\ 125 \end{pmatrix}.$$

The solution is obtained by finding the inverse of the matrix containing the proportions of outputs which are reabsorbed as inputs on the left of this equation. Thus

$$\begin{pmatrix} x \\ y \\ z \end{pmatrix} = \frac{1}{0.641} \begin{pmatrix} 0.79 & 0.19 & 0.13 \\ 0.29 & 0.80 & 0.21 \\ 0.12 & 0.11 & 0.75 \end{pmatrix} \begin{pmatrix} 100 \\ 150 \\ 125 \end{pmatrix} = \begin{pmatrix} 193.05 \\ 273.40 \\ 190.71 \end{pmatrix}.$$

In order to meet output targets, therefore, the amounts of each product which should be produced are X(£193,050), Y(£273,400) and Z(£190,710). A useful method of checking the accuracy of this result is to add the coefficients of both sides of the original set of simultaneous equations to obtain the single equation:

$$0.5x + 0.6y + 0.6z = 375.$$

The values of x, y, and z found above should then satisfy this equation, that is,

$$0.5(193.05) + 0.6(273.40) + 0.6(190.71) = 375.$$

The principles underlying input-output analysis, which are illustrated here for the individual firm, are also applicable in the wider context of the economy as a whole. So long as the outputs of industries are determined by competitive conditions, as in a market economy, decisions about how much to produce are taken within individual firms without reference to the decisions about the sizes of outputs in other industries. However, industries are inter-dependent in the sense that they are consumers of each other's products.In a planned economy, this is obviously relevant when deciding on the outputs of the inter-related industries belonging to the public sector. In other words, a planned economy would be highly inefficient if decisions about the output of each industry were taken without reference to the decisions and requirements of the other industries. The public sector of an economy might, for example, be composed of three industries: Steel, Electricity and Oil. Clearly, each of these industries will be substantial users of their own and each other's products. One can therefore use input-output analysis on a universal scale to determine the total outputs of individual industries when the production targets consist of the amount of the product of each industry which it is desired shall reach the final consumer. The principles involved in solving such a problem are precisely the same as for the individual firm, except that the private firm is not concerned in any direct way with the decisions of his competitors. In other words, the data of the individual firm for this kind of decision is internal. On the other hand, the publicly owned industries must be regulated by an overall plan if they are to function successfully, and so the data for decision-making within any publicly owned industry must take account of the specific targets of other industries in the public sector. What is needed here is a unified decision about the outputs, not of one, but of several industries.

12. Stochastic Matrices

In earlier chapters, several examples involving probabilities have been solved with the aid of matrices. Usually, these examples could be solved by other methods, using, for example, a tree diagram. However, it should be evident that matrices provide a very compact way of solving such problems and in certain cases a solution by any other method would be impossible. For example, in Chapter 16, section 3, *long-run* expected profit was calculated and although it was possible to find expected profit in Years 1, 2, 3, etc., by means of a tree diagram, in order to find the long-run expected profit it was necessary to solve a set of simultaneous equations to obtain the long-run probability distribution of the different profit levels. This method of solution was possible since the probability distribution of outcomes in each year was independent of all but the outcomes in the immediately preceding year, in other words, the sequence of probability distributions had a Markov chain structure. The initial distribution of probabilities in a Markov chain can be expressed in a $1 \times n$ row matrix, n being the number of different outcomes at each stage. The conditional probability that the system is in state j in period $t + 1$ when it is in state i in period t is known as a *transition probability* which can be denoted by p_{ij}. The different states of the system are mutually exclusive and collectively exhaustive, so that for each state i in period t,

$$\sum_{j=1}^{n} p_{ij} = 1.$$

The transition probabilities from state i to state j in consecutive periods are written in a transition probability matrix $\mathbf{P}$ as shown below.

$$\mathbf{P} = \begin{array}{c} \\ 1 \\ 2 \\ \vdots \\ n \end{array} \begin{pmatrix} p_{11} & p_{12} & \cdots & p_{1n} \\ p_{21} & p_{22} & \cdots & p_{2n} \\ & & & \\ p_{n1} & p_{n2} & \cdots & p_{nn} \end{pmatrix}.$$

A matrix of this kind, whose elements are all probabilities, is known as a *stochastic matrix*. An important property of a stochastic matrix is that the elements in each row of the matrix sum to 1. Of course, one could take the transpose of the matrix, in which case, the elements in each column would sum to 1.

EXAMPLE 1

A firm has 100 similar items of equipment, each subject to failure. An item which fails in period t is automatically replaced with a new item at the start of period (t + 1). The probability p_{ij} that an item which is in its ith period of operation in period t is in its jth period of operation in period (t + 1), is given by the entries in the matrix $\mathbf{P}$ below.

$$\mathbf{P} = \begin{array}{c} 1 \\ 2 \\ 3 \\ 4 \end{array} \begin{pmatrix} 0{\cdot}1 & 0{\cdot}9 & 0 & 0 \\ 0{\cdot}2 & 0 & 0{\cdot}8 & 0 \\ 0{\cdot}5 & 0 & 0 & 0{\cdot}5 \\ 1{\cdot}0 & 0 & 0 & 0 \end{pmatrix}.$$

In the long run, what is the average number of failures per period which can be expected? An alternative replacement policy is proposed, in which any item which survives through 3 periods of life is preventatively replaced by a new item at the end of its third period. What change will this make in the long-run average demand for new items as replacements? If replacement of a failed item costs £15, whilst preventative replacement of an item costs £10, what choice should be made between the two policies?

Let $(p_1 \quad p_2 \quad p_3 \quad p_4)$ be the long-run distribution of probabilities at the end of period t so that, for example, p_3 is the long-run probability that an item chosen at random will be in the third period of its operation. Then this row matrix satisfies the matrix equation

$$(p_1 \quad p_2 \quad p_3 \quad p_4) = (p_1 \quad p_2 \quad p_3 \quad p_4)\mathbf{P}.$$

The matrix product on the right is another 1×4 row matrix the elements of which are

$$p_1, p_2 = 0{\cdot}9p_1, p_3 = 0{\cdot}8p_2, p_4 = 0{\cdot}5p_3.$$

But

$$p_1 + p_2 + p_3 + p_4 = p_1 + 0{\cdot}9p_1 + 0{\cdot}72p_1 + 0{\cdot}36p_1.$$
$$= 1.$$

Hence

$$p_1 = 1/(1 + 0{\cdot}9 + 0{\cdot}72 + 0{\cdot}36)$$
$$= 100/298.$$

The probability that, in any period $(t + 1)$ an item has been replaced is clearly the probability that it is in the first period of its operation, that is, p_1. So the long-run expected number of replacements per period is

$$\frac{100}{298} \times 100 = 33{\cdot}56.$$

If all items reaching their third period are replaced at the end of that period, then $p_4 = 0$, and the transition probability matrix becomes:

$$\mathbf{Q} = \begin{array}{c} \\ 1 \\ 2 \\ 3 \end{array}\begin{pmatrix} 0{\cdot}1 & 0{\cdot}9 & 0 \\ 0{\cdot}2 & 0 & 0{\cdot}8 \\ 1{\cdot}0 & 0 & 0 \end{pmatrix}.$$

with column headings $j = 1, 2, 3$ and row index i.

In this case, the long-run probabilities satisfy the equation

$$(p_1 \quad p_2 \quad p_3) = (p_1 \quad p_2 \quad p_3)\mathbf{Q}.$$

Hence
$$p_1 + p_2 + p_3 = p_1 + 0{\cdot}9p_1 + 0{\cdot}8p_2$$
$$= p_1 + 0{\cdot}9p_1 + 0{\cdot}72p_1$$
$$\text{(since } p_3 = 0{\cdot}8p_2 = 0{\cdot}72p_1\text{)}$$
$$= 1.$$

So
$$p_1 = 1/(1 + 0{\cdot}9 + 0{\cdot}72) = 100/262.$$
$$p_2 = 0{\cdot}9p_1 = 90/262.$$
$$p_3 = 0{\cdot}8p_2 = 72/262.$$

It follows that under the new arrangement, the long-run average demand for replacements per period is

$$100p_1 = 100 \times \frac{100}{262}$$
$$= 38{\cdot}16$$

which is somewhat higher than under the old policy since no item is now allowed to pass into its fourth period. However, not all of this number of items have to be replaced at the full cost (£15). On the average, the number which are preventatively replaced in any period is

$$100p_3 = 100 \times \frac{72}{262}$$
$$= 27{\cdot}48$$

since p_3 is the probability that, at any time, an item is in the third period of its operation and so will have to be replaced in the next period. Hence

Preventative cost $\qquad = 27{\cdot}48 \times £10 = £274{\cdot}80$
Full cost $\qquad\qquad = (38{\cdot}16 - 27{\cdot}48) \times £15 = £160{\cdot}20$
Total cost of new policy $= £435{\cdot}00.$
Total cost of old policy $= 33{\cdot}56 \times £15 = £503{\cdot}40.$

So preventative replacement is cheaper.

A Markov chain, such as that in Example 1, which tends in the long run to a stable state is said to be *convergent*. If the initial distribution of probabilities is given by the row matrix $\mathbf{A}_0$ and the transition probability matrix is $\mathbf{P}$, then the probability that the system is in a given state at the end of the first period is given by the row matrix

$$\mathbf{A}_1 = \mathbf{A}_0\mathbf{P}.$$

Similarly, the probability distribution of the states of the system at the end of the second period is

$$A_2 = A_1P$$
$$= (A_0P)P$$
$$= A_0P^2.$$

Continuing in this way, the probability distribution of the states of the system at the end of the nth period is

$$A_n = A_0P^n.$$

This formula provides an alternative means of finding the probability distribution at any stage instead of the tree diagram, which is obviously very convenient when there are so many stages that the tree diagram is impossible to draw. If the system tends to a stable state in the long run, then for sufficiently large values of n,

$$A_n = A_{n+1}$$
$$= (A_0P^n)P$$
$$= A_nP.$$

This means that after a certain stage, the probability distribution of the states of the system is always the same no matter what the initial distribution A_0 was. In fact the stable state probabilities depend only on the transitional probabilities P.

Some Markov chains are not convergent. For example, the transition probability matrix

$$P = \begin{matrix} & j & 1 & 2 \\ i & & & \\ & 1 & \begin{pmatrix} 0 & 1 \\ 2 & 1 & 0 \end{pmatrix} \end{matrix}$$

is the matrix of a two-state system which oscillates from one state to the other in successive periods. Hence if it was in state 1 initially, then at the end of an even number of periods it will again be in state 1, whilst at the end of an odd number of periods it will be in state 2. So the probability distribution of the states of the system at the end of any period never becomes independent of the initial state of the system, however many periods there are.

EXERCISES 20

1. Let

$$A = \begin{pmatrix} 2 & 5 \\ 4 & 8 \end{pmatrix} \qquad B = \begin{pmatrix} 1 & 1 \\ 0 & 2 \end{pmatrix} \qquad C = \begin{pmatrix} 3 & 3 & 1 \\ 2 & 3 & 4 \end{pmatrix}$$

(a) Find $\mathbf{A} + \mathbf{B}$;
(b) find $\mathbf{AB}$, $\mathbf{AC}$ and $\mathbf{BC}$;
(c) show that $(\mathbf{AB})\mathbf{C} = \mathbf{A}(\mathbf{BC})$;
(d) explain why the product $\mathbf{CA}$ does not exist.

2. $\mathbf{A}$ and $\mathbf{B}$ are two matrices such that their sum $\mathbf{A} + \mathbf{B}$ and their product $\mathbf{AB}$ both exist. Show that the product $\mathbf{BA}$ also exists. What kind of matrices are $\mathbf{A}$ and $\mathbf{B}$?

3. Let $\mathbf{A}$ be a 2×3 matrix, $\mathbf{B}$ a 3×2 matrix and $\mathbf{C}$ a 2×4 matrix. Write down (a) the order of $\mathbf{BA}$, (b) the order of $\mathbf{BC}$, and (c) the order of $\mathbf{ABC}$.

4. Given that $\mathbf{A}$, $\mathbf{B}$, $\mathbf{C}$ are 2×2 matrices and that $\mathbf{AB} = \mathbf{AC}$, construct an example to show that it is not necessarily true that $\mathbf{A} = 0$ or $\mathbf{B} = \mathbf{C}$.
If $\mathbf{B} \neq \mathbf{C}$ what can you say about $\mathbf{A}$?

5. Find the inverses of the following matrices (where they exist):

(a) $\begin{pmatrix} 2 & 6 \\ 7 & 23 \end{pmatrix}$ $\qquad$ (b) $\begin{pmatrix} 2 & 2 \\ 1 & 2 \end{pmatrix}$

(c) $\begin{pmatrix} -3 & 2 \\ 6 & -4 \end{pmatrix}$ $\qquad$ (d) $\begin{pmatrix} \frac{1}{2} & -\frac{3}{4} \\ 2 & 1 \end{pmatrix}$

6. Solve the following sets of simultaneous equations by matrix methods:

(a) $3x + 5y = 11$ $\qquad\qquad$ (b) $2x + 3y = 10$
$\quad\ \ 4x + 6y = 14$ $\qquad\qquad\qquad$ $4x - 7y = -6$
(c) $\quad x + \ \ y = 0$ $\qquad\qquad$ (d) $9x - 2y = 0$
$\quad\ \ 2x + 4y = 1$ $\qquad\qquad\qquad$ $4x - 3y = 0$

7. The equations $2x + 5y = 7$ and $ax + 2y = 8$ have no solution. What is the value of a?

8. Find the inverse of the 3×3 matrix

$$\begin{pmatrix} 1 & 2 & 1 \\ -2 & 1 & 2 \\ 1 & 1 & 1 \end{pmatrix}$$

Hence solve the equations

$$\begin{aligned} x + 2y + \ \ z &= 12 \\ -2x + \ \ y + 2z &= 15 \\ x + \ \ y + \ \ z &= 9. \end{aligned}$$

9.

$$A = (1 \quad 4 \quad 5), \qquad B = \begin{pmatrix} 1 & 0 & 3 \\ 2 & 5 & 1 \\ 6 & 0 & 4 \end{pmatrix}, \qquad C = \begin{pmatrix} 3 & 2 & 1 \\ -1 & 2 & 1 \\ 4 & 1 & 3 \end{pmatrix}.$$

(a) Find the products **AB** and **ABC**.
(b) Explain why the product **BA** does not exist.
(c) Evaluate **B** − **C**.
(d) Let **(ABC)′** be the transpose of **ABC**. Show that **(ABC)′** = **C′B′A′**.

10. The normal equations for finding the coefficients a and b of the least squares regression line are

$$an + b \, \Sigma \, x = \Sigma y$$
$$a \, \Sigma \, x + b \, \Sigma \, x^2 = \Sigma xy.$$

Express these as a single matrix equation and hence find the values of a and b.

11. The following table shows the fixed cost (F) and the variable cost (V) of producing 1 unit of X or 1 unit of Y:

		Product		
		X	Y	
Cost	F	5	8	(£'000)
	V	4	12	

When x units of X and y units of Y are produced, the total fixed cost is £640,000 and total variable cost is £820,000. Express this information as a matrix equation and hence find the quantities of X and Y produced.

12. X, Y and Z are three products produced in two processes. The process time in hours per unit of product for the three products are as follows:

		Product		
		X	Y	Z
Process	I	3	5	4
	II	2	1	5

The process times available are 1700 hours in Process I and 900 hours in Process II. It is decided that 100 units of X must be produced. Use matrix methods to determine how much of Y and Z should be produced if the process time is fully utilised.

13. A pharmaceutical company produces three products X, Y and Z which are partially used in the manufacture of these products. However, none of the products is used in its own manufacture. The quantities of the outputs of each product which are used as inputs in the manufacture of one unit of each of the other products are:

		Input		
		X	Y	Z
	X	0	0·3	0·4
Output	Y	0·2	0	0·3
	Z	0·1	0·5	0

The production targets for each product are £150,000 for X, £200,000 for Y and £100,000 for Z, these being the amounts of the three products which are to reach the final consumer. Use input-ouput analysis to determine how much of each of the products should be produced.

14. An engineering firm has capacity for producing each year either 75, or 100 or 125 or 150 machines but no intermediate number. No machines are held in stock. The probability distribution of demand for machines is:

No. sold	Probability
75	0·1
100	0·3
125	0·5
150	0·1
	1·0

Form a stochastic matrix $\mathbf{P}$, showing the probability of selling j machines when i machines are produced ($i, j = 75, 100, 125, 150$).

The profit on each machine sold is £50, whilst the loss on each machine not sold is £60. Form the pay-off matrix $\mathbf{Q}$ showing the loss or profit when i machines are produced and j machines are sold.

By considering the matrix product $\mathbf{PQ}$ or otherwise, find the optimum production policy and state the profit in this case.

What will be the expected annual profit if it is known exactly how many machines will be sold each year?

15. Glass bottles are manufactured in sequence; the probability that the $(i + 1)$th bottle is defective is 0·1 if the ith bottle is defective

and 0·01 if the ith bottle is good. If the first bottle is defective, find the probabilities (a) that the third bottle is defective, (b) that the fourth bottle is defective.

Assuming that the system reaches a stable state in the long run, find the probability that the Nth bottle is defective when N is a very large number.

Illustrate the sequence as far as the fourth bottle by means of a tree diagram.

16. The matrix $\begin{pmatrix} p & q \\ r & s \end{pmatrix}$ commutes under multiplication with the matrix $\begin{pmatrix} a & b \\ c & d \end{pmatrix}$.

If k is a constant, show that $q = kb$, $r = kc$ and $p - s = k(a - d)$. Hence form a matrix which commutes under multiplication with the matrix $\begin{pmatrix} 2 & -9 \\ 4 & 1 \end{pmatrix}$.

17. Show that, for the data in Example 3 of Chapter 16, section 6, the transition probability p_{ij} that a unit of electrical equipment which is in the ith week of its operation in week t is in the jth week of its operation in week $(t + 1)$ is given by the entries in the matrix:

j	1	2	3	4	5
i					
1	0	1	0	0	0
2	0·2	0	0·8	0	0
3	0·5	0	0	0·5	0
4	0·75	0	0	0	0·25
5	1	0	0	0	0

By considering that all items of equipment are in their first week of operation in week 1, use matrix methods to solve Example 3 (a) and (b).

STATISTICAL TABLES

TABLE 1

The Distribution Function, $F(X)$, of the Normal Probability Function, $P(X)$

X	0·00	0·01	0·02	0·03	0·04	0·05	0·06	0·07	0·08	0·09
0·0	0·5000	0·5040	0·5080	0·5120	0·5160	0·5199	0·5239	0·5279	0·5319	0·5359
0·1	0·5398	0·5438	0·5478	0·5517	0·5557	0·5596	0·5636	0·5675	0·5714	0·5753
0·2	0·5793	0·5832	0·5871	0·5910	0·5948	0·5987	0·6026	0·6064	0·6103	0·6141
0·3	0·6179	0·6217	0·6255	0·6293	0·6331	0·6368	0·6406	0·6443	0·6480	0·6517
0·4	0·6554	0·6591	0·6628	0·6664	0·6700	0·6736	0·6772	0·6808	0·6844	0·6879
0·5	0·6915	0·6950	0·6985	0·7019	0·7054	0·7088	0·7123	0·7517	0·7190	0·7224
0·6	0·7257	0·7291	0·7324	0·7357	0·7389	0·7422	0·7454	0·7486	0·7517	0·7549
0·7	0·7580	0·7611	0·7642	0·7673	0·7704	0·7734	0·7764	0·7794	0·7823	0·7852
0·8	0·7881	0·7910	0·7939	0·7967	0·7995	0·8023	0·8051	0·8078	0·8106	0·8133
0·9	0·8159	0·8186	0·8212	0·8238	0·8264	0·8289	0·8315	0·8340	0·8365	0·8389
1·0	0·8413	0·8438	0·8461	0·8485	0·8508	0·8531	0·8554	0·8577	0·8599	0·8621
1·1	0·8643	0·8665	0·8686	0·8708	0·8729	0·8749	0·8770	0·8790	0·8810	0·8830
1·2	0·8849	0·8869	0·8888	0·8907	0·8925	0·8944	0·8962	0·8980	0·8997	0·9015
1·3	0·9032	0·9049	0·9066	0·9082	0·9099	0·9115	0·9131	0·9147	0·9162	0·9177
1·4	0·9192	0·9207	0·9222	0·9236	0·9251	0·9265	0·9279	0·9292	0·9306	0·9319
1·5	0·9332	0·9345	0·9357	0·9370	0·9382	0·9394	0·9406	0·9418	0·9429	0·9441
1·6	0·9452	0·9463	0·9474	0·9484	0·9495	0·9505	0·9515	0·9525	0·9535	0·9545
1·7	0·9554	0·9564	0·9573	0·9582	0·9591	0·9599	0·9608	0·9616	0·9625	0·9633
1·8	0·9641	0·9649	0·9656	0·9664	0·9671	0·9678	0·9686	0·9693	0·9699	0·9706
1·9	0·9713	0·9719	0·9726	0·9732	0·9738	0·9744	0·9750	0·9756	0·9761	0·9767
2·0	0·97725	0·97778	0·97831	0·97882	0·97932	0·97982	0·98030	0·98077	0·98124	0·98169
2·1	0·98214	0·98257	0·98300	0·98341	0·98382	0·98422	0·98461	0·98500	0·98537	0·98574
2·2	0·98610	0·98645	0·98679	0·98713	0·98745	0·98778	0·98809	0·98840	0·98870	0·98899
2·3	0·98928	0·98956	0·98983	0·99010	0·99036	0·99061	0·99086	0·99111	0·99134	0·99158
2·4	0·99180	0·99202	0·99224	0·99245	0·99266	0·99286	0·99305	0·99324	0·99343	0·99361
2·5	0·99379	0·99396	0·99413	0·99430	0·99446	0·99461	0·99477	0·99492	0·99506	0·99520
2·6	0·99534	0·99547	0·99560	0·99573	0·99585	0·99598	0·99609	0·99621	0·99632	0·99643
2·7	0·99653	0·99664	0·99674	0·99683	0·99693	0·99702	0·99711	0·99720	0·99728	0·99736
2·8	0·99744	0·99752	0·99760	0·99767	0·99774	0·99781	0·99788	0·99795	0·99801	0·99807
2·9	0·99813	0·99819	0·99825	0·99831	0·99836	0·99841	0·99846	0·99851	0·99856	0·99861
3·0	0·99865	0·99869	0·99874	0·99878	0·99882	0·99886	0·99889	0·99893	0·99896	0·99900

X	3·1	3·2	3·3	3·4	3·5	3·6	3·7	3·8	3·9	4·0
F	0·99903	0·99931	0·99952	0·99966	0·99977	0·99984	0·99989	0·99993	0·99995	0·99997

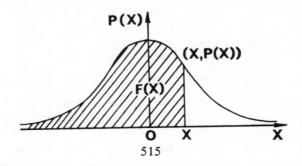

TABLE 2

Percentage Points of the *t*-Distribution

	One tail $P = 0.10$	0.05	0.025	0.01	0.005	0.001	0.0005
	Two tail $P = 0.20$	0.10	0.05	0.02	0.01	0.002	0.001
$v = 1$	3.08	6.31	12.7	31.8	63.7	318	637
2	1.89	2.92	4.30	6.96	9.92	22.3	31.6
3	1.64	2.35	3.18	4.54	5.84	10.2	12.9
4	1.53	2.13	2.78	3.75	4.60	7.17	8.61
5	1.48	2.02	2.57	3.36	4.03	5.89	6.87
6	1.44	1.94	2.45	3.14	3.71	5.21	5.96
7	1.42	1.89	2.36	3.00	3.50	4.79	5.41
8	1.40	1.86	2.31	2.90	3.36	4.50	5.04
9	1.38	1.83	2.26	2.82	3.25	4.30	4.78
10	1.37	1.81	2.23	2.76	3.17	4.14	4.59
11	1.36	1.80	2.20	2.72	3.12	4.02	4.44
12	1.36	1.78	2.18	2.68	3.05	3.93	4.32
13	1.35	1.77	2.16	2.65	3.01	3.85	4.22
14	1.35	1.76	2.14	2.62	2.98	3.79	4.14
15	1.34	1.75	2.13	2.60	2.95	3.73	4.07
16	1.34	1.75	2.12	2.58	2.92	3.69	4.02
17	1.33	1.74	2.11	2.57	2.90	3.65	3.97
18	1.33	1.73	2.10	2.55	2.88	3.61	3.92
19	1.33	1.73	2.09	2.54	2.86	3.58	3.88
20	1.33	1.72	2.09	2.53	2.85	3.55	3.85
21	1.32	1.72	2.08	2.52	2.83	3.53	3.82
22	1.32	1.72	2.07	2.51	2.82	3.50	3.79
23	1.32	1.71	2.07	2.50	2.81	3.48	3.77
24	1.32	1.71	2.06	2.49	2.80	3.47	3.75
25	1.32	1.71	2.06	2.49	2.79	3.45	3.74
26	1.32	1.71	2.06	2.48	2.78	3.44	3.71
27	1.31	1.70	2.05	2.47	2.77	3.42	3.69
28	1.31	1.70	2.05	2.47	2.76	3.41	3.67
29	1.31	1.70	2.05	2.46	2.76	3.40	3.66
30	1.31	1.70	2.04	2.46	2.75	3.39	3.65
40	1.30	1.68	2.02	2.42	2.70	3.31	3.55
60	1.30	1.67	2.00	2.39	2.66	3.23	3.46
120	1.29	1.66	1.98	2.36	2.62	3.16	3.37
∞	1.28	1.64	1.96	2.33	2.58	3.09	3.29

TABLE 3

Table of Probabilities associated with Σd^2 in Spearman's Rank Correlation Coefficient, ρ (r_{rank}).
Probability that Σd^2 exceeds, or is less than, certain values, for $4 < n < 10$

n = 4, MAX. $\Sigma d^2 = 20$

Σd^2 <	Σd^2 >	P
8	12	·458
6	14	·375
4	16	·208
2	18	·167
0	20	·0417

n = 5, MAX. $\Sigma d^2 = 40$

Σd^2 <	Σd^2 >	P
18	22	·475
16	24	·392
14	26	·342
12	28	·258
10	30	·225
8	32	·175
6	34	·117
4	36	·0667
2	38	·0417
0	40	·0083

n = 6, MAX. $\Sigma d^2 = 70$

Σd^2 <	Σd^2 >	P
28	42	·357
26	44	·329
24	46	·282
22	48	·249
20	50	·210
18	52	·178
16	54	·149
14	56	·121
12	58	·0875
10	60	·0681
8	62	·0514
6	64	·0292
4	66	·0167
2	68	·0083
0	70	·0014

n = 7, MAX. $\Sigma d^2 = 112$

Σd^2 <	Σd^2 >	P
54	58	·482
52	60	·453
50	62	·420
48	64	·391
46	66	·356
44	68	·331
42	70	·297
40	72	·278
38	74	·249
36	76	·222
34	78	·198
32	80	·177
30	82	·151
28	84	·133
26	86	·118
24	88	·100
22	90	·0833
20	92	·0694
18	94	·0548
16	96	·0440
14	98	·0331
12	100	·0240
10	102	·0171
8	104	·0119
6	106	·0062
4	108	·0034
2	110	·0014

n = 8, MAX. $\Sigma d^2 = 168$

Σd^2 <	Σd^2 >	P
78	90	·441
74	94	·397
68	100	·332
64	104	·291
60	108	·250
56	112	·214
54	114	·195
52	116	·180
48	120	·150
46	122	·134
44	124	·122
42	126	·108
40	128	·0983
38	130	·0855
36	132	·0756
34	134	·0661
32	136	·0575
30	138	·0481
28	140	·0415
24	144	·0288
20	148	·0184
16	152	·0109
14	154	·0077
12	156	·0054
10	158	·0036
6	162	·0011
4	164	·0006

n = 9, MAX. $\Sigma d^2 = 240$

Σd^2 <	Σd^2 >	P
112	128	·440
108	132	·405
104	136	·371
100	140	·339
96	144	·307
92	148	·276
88	152	·247
84	156	·218
80	160	·193
76	164	·168
72	168	·146
68	172	·125
64	176	·106
62	178	·0969
56	184	·0738
50	190	·0540
48	192	·0484
40	200	·0294
34	206	·0184
28	212	·0107
26	214	·0086
22	218	·0054
20	220	·0041
16	224	·0023
14	226	·0015
12	228	·0010
10	230	·0007

n = 10, MAX. $\Sigma d^2 = 330$

Σd^2 <	Σd^2 >	P
160	170	·473
154	176	·433
148	182	·393
140	190	·341
132	198	·292
124	206	·246
116	214	·204
114	216	·194
108	222	·165
100	230	·132
92	238	·102
90	240	·0956
84	246	·0774
78	252	·0616
74	256	·0524
72	258	·0481
68	262	·0403
62	268	·0302
56	274	·0219
50	280	·0153
44	286	·0101
42	288	·0087
36	294	·0053
30	300	·0029
22	308	·0011
16	314	·0004
10	320	·0001

MAX. $\Sigma d^2 = n(n^2 - 1)/3$.
For $10 < n < 20$: $\rho\sqrt{(n-2)/(1-\rho^2)}$ is distributed t_{n-2}.
For $20 < n$: $\rho\sqrt{n-1}$ is distributed $N(0,1)$.

TABLE 4

The χ^2 Distribution

v \ p	0·20	0·10	0·05	0·01
1	1·642	2·706	3·841	6·635
2	3·219	4·605	5·991	9·210
3	4·642	6·251	7·815	11·341
4	5·989	7·779	9·488	13·277
5	7·289	9·236	11·070	15·086
6	8·558	10·645	12·592	16·812
7	9·803	12·017	14·067	18·475
8	11·030	13·362	15·507	20·090
9	12·242	14·684	16·919	21·666
10	13·442	15·987	18·307	23·209

The table shows the probability p that a selected value of χ^2 is exceeded due to random sampling errors when the number of degrees of freedom is v.

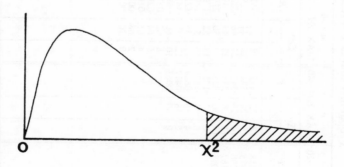

TABLE 5

Random Sampling Numbers

```
23 15    75 48    59 01    83 72    59 93    76 24    97 08    86 95    23 03    67 44
05 54    55 50    43 10    53 74    35 08    90 61    18 37    44 10    96 22    13 43
14 87    16 03    50 32    40 43    62 23    50 05    10 03    22 11    54 38    08 34
38 97    67 49    51 94    05 17    58 53    78 80    59 01    94 32    42 87    16 95
97 31    26 17    18 99    75 53    08 70    94 25    12 58    41 54    88 21    05 13

11 74    26 93    81 44    33 93    08 72    32 79    73 31    18 22    64 70    68 50
43 36    12 88    59 11    01 64    56 23    93 00    90 04    99 43    64 07    40 36
93 80    62 04    78 38    26 80    44 91    55 75    11 89    32 58    47 55    25 71
49 54    01 31    81 08    42 98    41 87    69 53    82 96    61 77    73 80    95 27
36 76    87 26    33 37    94 82    15 69    41 95    96 86    70 45    27 48    38 80

07 09    25 23    92 24    62 71    26 07    06 55    84 53    44 67    33 84    53 20
43 31    00 10    81 44    86 38    03 07    52 55    51 61    48 89    74 29    46 47
61 57    00 63    60 06    17 36    37 75    63 14    89 51    23 35    01 74    69 93
31 35    28 37    99 10    77 91    89 41    31 57    97 64    48 62    58 48    69 19
57 04    88 65    26 27    79 59    36 82    90 52    95 65    46 35    06 53    22 54

09 24    34 42    00 68    72 10    71 37    30 72    97 57    56 09    29 82    76 50
97 95    53 50    18 40    89 48    83 29    52 23    08 25    21 22    53 26    15 87
93 73    25 95    70 43    78 19    88 85    56 67    16 68    26 95    99 64    45 69
72 62    11 12    25 00    92 26    82 64    35 66    65 94    34 71    68 75    18 67
61 02    07 44    18 45    37 12    07 94    95 91    73 78    66 99    53 61    93 78

97 83    98 54    74 33    05 59    17 18    45 47    35 41    44 22    03 42    30 00
89 16    09 71    92 22    23 29    06 37    35 05    54 54    89 88    43 81    63 61
25 96    68 82    20 62    87 17    92 65    02 82    35 28    62 84    91 95    48 83
81 44    33 17    19 05    04 95    48 06    74 69    00 75    67 65    01 71    65 45
11 32    25 49    31 42    36 23    43 86    08 62    49 76    67 42    24 52    32 45
```

TABLE 6

The Exponential Function e^x

x	0·0	0·1	0·2	0·3	0·4	0·5	0·6	0·7	0·8	0·9
0	1·00	1·105	1·221	1·350	1·492	1·649	1·822	2·014	2·226	2·460
1	2·718	3·004	3·320	3·669	4·055	4·482	4·953	5·474	6·050	6·686
2	7·39	8·17	9·03	9·97	11·02	12·18	13·46	14·88	16·44	18·17
3	20·09	22·20	24·53	27·11	29·96	33·12	36·60	40·45	44·70	49·40
4	54·60	60·3	66·7	73·7	81·5	90·0	99·5	109·9	121·5	134·3
5	148·4									

Present Value Factors

TABLE 7

n	1%	2%	3%	4%	5%	6%	7%	8%	9%	10%	11%
1	0·9901	0·9804	0·9709	0·9615	0·9524	0·9434	0·9346	0·9259	0·9174	0·9091	0·9009
2	0·9803	0·9612	0·9426	0·9246	0·9070	0·8900	0·8734	0·8573	0·8417	0·8264	0·8116
3	0·9706	0·9423	0·9151	0·8890	0·8638	0·8396	0·8163	0·7938	0·7722	0·7513	0·7312
4	0·9610	0·9238	0·8885	0·8548	0·8227	0·7921	0·7629	0·7350	0·7084	0·6830	0·6587
5	0·9515	0·9057	0·8626	0·8219	0·7835	0·7473	0·7130	0·6806	0·6499	0·6209	0·5935
6	0·9420	0·8880	0·8375	0·7903	0·7462	0·7050	0·6663	0·6302	0·5963	0·5645	0·5346
7	0·9327	0·8706	0·8131	0·7599	0·7107	0·6651	0·6227	0·5835	0·5470	0·5132	0·4817
8	0·9235	0·8535	0·7894	0·7307	0·6768	0·6274	0·5820	0·5403	0·5019	0·4665	0·4339
9	0·9143	0·8368	0·7664	0·7026	0·6446	0·5919	0·5439	0·5002	0·4604	0·4241	0·3909
10	0·9053	0·8203	0·7441	0·6756	0·6139	0·5584	0·5083	0·4632	0·4224	0·3855	0·3522
11	0·8963	0·8043	0·7224	0·6496	0·5847	0·5268	0·4751	0·4289	0·3875	0·3505	0·3173
12	0·8874	0·7885	0·7014	0·6246	0·5568	0·4970	0·4440	0·3971	0·3555	0·3186	0·2858
13	0·8787	0·7730	0·6810	0·6006	0·5303	0·4688	0·4150	0·3677	0·3262	0·2897	0·2575
14	0·8700	0·7579	0·6611	0·5775	0·5051	0·4423	0·3878	0·3405	0·2992	0·2633	0·2320
15	0·8613	0·7430	0·6419	0·5553	0·4810	0·4173	0·3624	0·3152	0·2745	0·2394	0·2090

The table shows the present value of £1 to be received or paid at the end of n years when the rate of interest is $100i\%$ p.a., that is, $v^n = (1 + i)^{-n}$.

The present value of an immediate annuity of £1 payable for n years is

$$a_{\overline{n}|} = \sum_{t=1}^{n} v^t.$$

The amount of £1 after n years at compound interest of $100i\%$ is $(1 + i)^n = v^{-n}$.

TABLE 7 (continued)

100i \ n	12%	13%	14%	15%	16%	17%	18%	19%	20%	21%	22%	n
1	0·8929	0·8850	0·8772	0·8696	0·8621	0·8547	0·8475	0·8403	0·8333	0·8264	0·8197	1
2	0·7972	0·7831	0·7695	0·7561	0·7432	0·7305	0·7182	0·7062	0·6944	0·6830	0·6719	2
3	0·7118	0·6931	0·6750	0·6575	0·6407	0·6244	0·6086	0·5934	0·5787	0·5645	0·5507	3
4	0·6355	0·6133	0·5921	0·5718	0·5523	0·5337	0·5158	0·4987	0·4823	0·4665	0·4514	4
5	0·5674	0·5428	0·5194	0·4972	0·4761	0·4561	0·4371	0·4190	0·4019	0·3855	0·3700	5
6	0·5066	0·4803	0·4556	0·4323	0·4104	0·3898	0·3704	0·3521	0·3349	0·3186	0·3033	6
7	0·4523	0·4251	0·3996	0·3759	0·3538	0·3332	0·3139	0·2959	0·2791	0·2633	0·2486	7
8	0·4039	0·3762	0·3506	0·3269	0·3050	0·2848	0·2660	0·2487	0·2326	0·2176	0·2038	8
9	0·3606	0·3329	0·3075	0·2843	0·2630	0·2434	0·2255	0·2090	0·1938	0·1799	0·1670	9
10	0·3220	0·2946	0·2697	0·2472	0·2267	0·2080	0·1911	0·1756	0·1615	0·1486	0·1369	10
11	0·2875	0·2607	0·2366	0·2149	0·1954	0·1778	0·1619	0·1476	0·1346	0·1228	0·1122	11
12	0·2567	0·2307	0·2076	0·1869	0·1685	0·1520	0·1372	0·1240	0·1122	0·1015	0·0920	12
13	0·2292	0·2042	0·1821	0·1625	0·1452	0·1299	0·1163	0·1042	0·0935	0·0839	0·0754	13
14	0·2046	0·1807	0·1597	0·1413	0·1252	0·1110	0·0985	0·0876	0·0779	0·0693	0·0618	14
15	0·1827	0·1599	0·1401	0·1229	0·1079	0·0949	0·0835	0·0736	0·0649	0·0573	0·0507	15

TABLE 7 (*continued*)

100i / n	23%	24%	25%	26%	27%	28%	29%	30%	31%	32%
1	0·8130	0·8065	0·8000	0·7937	0·7874	0·7813	0·7752	0·7692	0·7634	0·7576
2	0·6610	0·6504	0·6400	0·6299	0·6200	0·6104	0·6009	0·5917	0·5827	0·5739
3	0·5374	0·5245	0·5120	0·4999	0·4882	0·4768	0·4658	0·4552	0·4448	0·4348
4	0·4369	0·4230	0·4096	0·3968	0·3844	0·3725	0·3611	0·3501	0·3396	0·3294
5	0·3552	0·3411	0·3277	0·3149	0·3027	0·2910	0·2799	0·2693	0·2592	0·2495
6	0·2888	0·2751	0·2621	0·2499	0·2383	0·2274	0·2170	0·2072	0·1979	0·1890
7	0·2348	0·2218	0·2097	0·1983	0·1877	0·1776	0·1682	0·1594	0·1510	0·1432
8	0·1909	0·1789	0·1678	0·1574	0·1478	0·1388	0·1304	0·1226	0·1153	0·1085
9	0·1552	0·1443	0·1342	0·1249	0·1164	0·1084	0·1011	0·0943	0·0880	0·0822
10	0·1262	0·1164	0·1074	0·0992	0·0916	0·0847	0·0784	0·0725	0·0672	0·0623
11	0·1026	0·0938	0·0859	0·0787	0·0721	0·0662	0·0607	0·0558	0·0513	0·0472
12	0·0834	0·0757	0·0687	0·0625	0·0568	0·0517	0·0471	0·0429	0·0392	0·0357
13	0·0678	0·0610	0·0550	0·0496	0·0447	0·0404	0·0365	0·0330	0·0299	0·0271
14	0·0551	0·0492	0·0440	0·0393	0·0352	0·0316	0·0283	0·0253	0·0228	0·0205
15	0·0448	0·0397	0·0352	0·0312	0·0277	0·0247	0·0219	0·0195	0·0174	0·0155

ANSWERS TO EXERCISES

EXERCISES 1

6. Spurious accuracy gives the impression that data is more reliable than it really is. For example, an estimate given as $10\frac{1}{2}\%$ is naturally assumed to be correct to the nearest $\frac{1}{4}\%$. **7.** (ii). **8.** Both expressions $= [1, 8]$. **9.** (i) and (iv). (ii) is always false and (iii) is false if b is negative. **10.** 20 (correct to 1 significant figure), when $B = [5, 7]$, $A/B = [17\cdot8, 28]$ and the limits do not agree even correct to 1 significant figure. **11.** $A \times (B + C) = [2, 12]$, $A \times B + A \times C = [-2, 14]$. **14.** 0·81 sq. cm., 5%. **15.** (a) £5600, £6400, (b) £6975, £9095, (c) £575, £3495, (d) 62p, £3·27. **16.** (b) 2 million units, (c) 20·61, 19·41. **17.** Between 12·9 cm and 13·8 cm.

EXERCISES 2

1. For example, age or sex. **3.** (a) (i), (iii), (b) (i), (ii), (iii). **4.** (a) Number of matches in a matchbox, Number of children in a family, (b) temperature, rainfall, (c) nationality, occupation. **5.** Title, explanatory notes if needed, clear indication of units, logic·l consistency. **9.** 45 degrees. **10.** 12 cm. **11.** The data can be represented by a Pie Chart or a Bar Chart. The former gives the best indication of the relation of components to total, the latter of relation between components. **14.** Greater positive skewness for Year 1 shows that income distribution has become more symmetrical between the two years. **16.** Neither measure is very satisfactory. Physical product is not homogeneous, whilst value of sales, though measured in homogeneous units, depends on several other factors apart from labour productivity. Of the two, the latter is preferable. **17.** (i) A bar chart, with rectangles of different heights, can be used for the data as it stands. If only percentages are given, then a percentage component bar chart should be used.

18.

Interval (mm)	247–248	248–249	249–250	250–251
Frequency	3	4	12	14
Interval (mm)	251–252	252–253	253–254	254–255
Frequency	11	2	1	3

19. 1%. **21.** Pictograms and Strata Charts, for example.

22. (b)

Year	1971	1972	1973	1974
	%	%	%	%
Wheat	43	53	50	49
Barley	23	17	19	14
Oats	34	30	31	37

EXERCISES 3

1. $(n + 1)/2$. **2.** 15. **3.** £145,200. **5.** £19·70. **6.** 7 cm. **7.** Between 49·0 km/h and 51·0 km/h. **8.** 0–1, 1–2, 2–4, 4–10. **9.** $Q_1 = 2225l$, $Q_2 = 2669l$, $Q_3 = 3069l$. **10.** £22. **11.** May be true: (c), (d); Must be false: (a), (b). **12.** (i) 585, (ii) 47%, (iii) 10. **13.** $Q_1 = £20·42$, $Q_2 = £24·77$, $Q_3 = £31·80$, $D_9 = £38·10$, $Z = £21·42$, Mean $= £26·38$. The histogram shows that the distribution is positively skewed. The mode is less than the median which is less than the mean. The earnings of considerably more than 50% of the clerks are below the average. **14.** (a) $Q_1 = 16·9$, $Q_2 = 34$, $Q_3 = 51·2$, (b) 12%, 14%, 14%. **15.** (a) 12, (b) 16·2. **16.** 10·5%. **17.** To estimate the aggregate income for each range, multiply each frequency (no. of incomes) by the central value of the corresponding range. For example, for the range 2000–4000, the estimated aggregate is 3000×178 (thousands) or £534 m. A histogram of the data will indicate its skewness. In drawing the histogram, care must be taken to make the area of each rectangle proportional to frequency, since income ranges are not equal. **18.** (a) 45, (b) 285. **19.** 25, 5. **20.** $\Sigma (X - \bar{X})^2 = 68$, $\Sigma X^2 - n\bar{X}^2 = 644 - 576 = 68$. **21.** $\Sigma (X - \bar{X})(Y - \bar{Y}) = 37$, $\Sigma XY - n\bar{X}\bar{Y} = 187 - 150 = 37$. **23.** 34·96. **24.** (a)

Distance (miles)	0–	10–	20–	30–	40–	50–60
Frequency	1	1	25	29	2	2

Mean = 31 miles.

(b) $Q_2 = 31·2$ miles. The distribution is slightly negatively skewed.

EXERCISES 4

1. 2·8. **2.** 8. **3.** 48. **4.** $3\frac{1}{3}$. **5.** The mode. **6.** 0·81, 0·99. **7.** 40. **8.** $\bar{X} = 3224$ hours, $\sigma = 732$ hours, 22·7%, $\frac{1}{2}(Q_3 - Q_1) = 485$ hours, sk. $= -0·029$. **9.** 0·15. **10.** (a) 74, (b) 7·2, (c) 8·67, Range $= 24$. **11.** (a) 8, (b) 2·25. **12.** (a) 54, (b) 12·4, (c) 14·44, 7. **14.** $\bar{X} = 1·71$ m, M.D. $= 0·12$ m, $\sigma = 0·13$ m. **15.** (a) $\frac{1}{100} \times 3 + 4$, $\frac{1}{100} \times 7 + 4$, etc., (b) $\bar{X} = 6·5$, $\bar{Y} = 4·065$, Var. $(X) = 9·65$, Var. $(Y) = 9·65 \times 10^{-4}$ or 0·000965, (c) $Z = 0·8Y + 5·9$. **16.** (a) 96, (b) 10·5, (c) 12. (d) 10·9%. **17.** (a) £1343, (b) £200. **18.** (a) 8870.
19. (a)

Goals	0	1	2	3	4	5
No. of teams	14	26	12	6	0	2

Mean $= 1·3$, $\sigma = 1·13$, M.D. $= 0·87$.
 (b) 5 teams.

EXERCISES 5

1. (i) 1/8, (ii) 1/8, (iii) 3/4. **2.** (i) 0·36, (ii) 0·52. **3.** 2/3.
4. $\frac{30}{365} \times \frac{10}{30} = 2/73$. **5.** (i) 1/4, (ii) 4/13. **6.** 3/4. **7.** (a) false, (b) true, (c) false. **8.** 18. **9.** (i) 15/406, (ii) 1/27.
10. $P(A \text{ or } B) = P(A) + P(B) - P(A)P(B|A)$, 98/663. **11.** (a) only.
12. 24; **13.** (a) 120, (b) 5040, (c) 720. **14.** $(41 \times 2^9 \times 3^9)/5^{18} = 0·011\%$ (app.). **15.** (a) 128/625, (b) 821/3125. **16.** (i) $4! = 24$, (a) $\frac{1}{4}$, (b) 7/24, (ii) 3360, $\frac{1}{4}$. **17.** $2^4 = 16$, 375/1024. **18.** (i) 64·96, (ii) 0·064.
19. (a) 2·29, (b) 1·43. **20.** (a) 21 ways, 1/6, (b) 5/6. **21.** 24/115.
22. (a) 0·1587, (b) 0·02275, (c) 0·1587. **23.** $P(0 \leqslant X \leqslant 1·65) = 0·4505$,

0·3346. **24.** $\sum_{r=0}^{n} \binom{n}{r}$ is the number of different outcomes from n bi-

nomial trials. At each trial there are 2 outcomes; so in n trials there are 2^n outcomes. **25.** 9/64.

26. $\bar{X} = \{(n - a) \times 0 + a \times 1\}/n = a/n$. $\bar{X}$ is the expected proportion of successes in n independent binomial trials when the probability of success in any trial is $\bar{X}$.

$$\begin{aligned} \text{Var. } (X) &= \{(n - a)(0 - \bar{X})^2 + a(1 - \bar{X})^2\}/n \\ &= (n\bar{X}^2 - a\bar{X}^2 + a - 2a\bar{X} + a\bar{X}^2)/n \\ &= \bar{X}^2 + \frac{a}{n} - \frac{2a\bar{X}}{n} \\ &= \bar{X}^2 + \bar{X} - 2\bar{X}^2 \\ &= \bar{X}(1 - \bar{X}). \end{aligned}$$

27. $\binom{12}{3} = \binom{12}{9} = 220$. **28.** 3. **29.** (a) 1, 10, 45, 120, 210, 252, 210, 120, 45, 10, 1. (b) Probability of success $= \frac{1}{2}$, mean $= 5$, S.D. $= 1\cdot58$. **30.** (a) $6\cdot04$, (b) $4\cdot54$, (c) $20\cdot38$, (d) $2\cdot41$. **31.** (a) $0\cdot3830$, (b) $0\cdot1173$, (c) $0\cdot8490$, (d) $0\cdot1360$, (e) $0\cdot9181$, (f) $0\cdot4823$.

EXERCISES 6

1. (a) $\mu = 9$, $\sigma/\sqrt{n} = \sqrt{7}$, (b) 6, $\sqrt{3}$, (c) 9, $2\sqrt{5}$, (d) 6, $\frac{1}{3}\sqrt{26}$.
2. (a) $1 - 0\cdot8413 = 0\cdot1587$, (b) $0\cdot1587$, (c) $1 - 2 \times 0\cdot1587 = 0\cdot6826$.
3. Only (c) is true. **4.** (a) $(0\cdot3707)^2 = 0\cdot1375$, (b) $2! \times 0\cdot3707 \times 0\cdot6293 = 0\cdot4666$. **5.** (a) $X = 0\cdot77$, $1 - 0\cdot7794 = 0\cdot2206$, (b) $X = -3\cdot6$, $1 - 0\cdot99984 = 0\cdot00016$, (c) $X = 1\cdot18$, $2(1 - 0\cdot8810) = 0\cdot238$.
6. Sample values will differ in the majority of samples so that their mean lies between extreme items. Hence these means have less variability than the population values. **7.** $X = 1\cdot65$, Yes. **9.** $5 \pm 0\cdot588$.
10. $X = 1\cdot39$, (a) Null Hypothesis that the coin is fair is not rejected by a two-tail test, (b) Null Hypothesis that the coin is biased in favour of heads is rejected by a one-tailed test. **11.** (a) Since there is 1 way of guessing correctly and there are 3 ways of guessing wrongly, probability $= \frac{1}{4}$, (b) 125, (c) $X = (0\cdot3 - 0\cdot25)/\sqrt{(\frac{1}{4} \times \frac{3}{4}/500)} = 2\cdot58$. Null Hypothesis rejected at the 1% level. If a one-tailed test is used, the Null Hypothesis is that the sample proportion is not greater than $0\cdot25$. **12.** (b) (i) 3413, (ii) $95\cdot45\%$. **13.** (a) 294, (b) 6, (c) 32. **14.** (b) £45. **15.** (a) 5000, (b) 1360, (c) 3413, (d) 1587.
16. (b) $0\cdot1 \pm 0\cdot026$. **17.** $X = (35 - 30)/\sqrt{(60 \times \frac{1}{2} \times \frac{1}{2})} = 1\cdot29$. The probability that X lies outside the limits $[-1\cdot29, 1\cdot29]$ is almost 20% when the proportion possessing attribute A is 50%. The sample could easily have come from such a population. **18.** Solve the equations: $(\mu - 90)/\sigma = 1\cdot64$, $(90\cdot6 - \mu)/\sigma = 1\cdot41$, $2\cdot118\%$. **19.** $\mu = 1\cdot68$ metres, $\sigma = 0\cdot09$ metres, $Q_1 = 1\cdot62$ metres, $Q_3 = 1\cdot74$ metres, $Q_3 - Q_1 = 0\cdot12$ metres. **20.** (ii) $0\cdot6826$, $0\cdot9545$, $0\cdot9973$, (iii) (a) 74, (b) 10. **21.** $11/512$ or $2\cdot15\%$. Probability of obtaining at least 8 heads or at most 2 heads is $7/64$ or 11%. The Null Hypothesis that the coin is fair is not rejected on this evidence.
22. $X = (0\cdot25 - 0\cdot17)/\sqrt{(\frac{1}{6} \times \frac{5}{6}/100)} = 2\cdot14$. The Null Hypothesis is rejected at the 5% level but not at the 1% level. **23.** If the hypothesis is not rejected at the 5% level, then the smallest value of $X = (5\cdot1 - 5)/(2/\sqrt{n})$ is $1\cdot96$. Hence the smallest value of n is $\{(2 \times 1\cdot96)/0\cdot1\}^2 = 1537$. **24.** (a) $X = 0\cdot03/\sqrt{(0\cdot6 \times 0\cdot4/n)}$, $n = 1024$, (b) If 60% is rejected, assume 50% of employees prefer the protective clothing. Then $n = 1067$. **25.** $n = 9590$. **26.** $\mu = 4\cdot5$, $\sigma = 2\cdot87$, $X = 2\cdot09$, the hypothesis that the numbers are randomly

selected is rejected at the 5% level. **27.** $X = 0.10$, $2 \times 0.5398 - 1$ $= 0.0796$ or 8% (approx.), $X = 3.06$, $1 - 0.99903 = 0.00097$ or 0.1% (approx.).

EXERCISES 7

1. (a) 0.97, (b) 0.97, (c) 0.97. **4.** The causal connection is mainly indirect, both increases being due to the rising standard of living. The correlation coefficient indicates only a numerical relationship between two variables, and its interpretation requires a background knowledge of their real relationship. **5.** (a) $y = 1.27x + 0.13$, $r = 0.93$, (b) $y = 6x + 0.6$, $r = 0.995$, (c) $y = 39x - 313$, $r = 0.994$. The value of r is close to unity in each case so that there is justification for using the linear regression equations here. **6.** $y = 1.01x + 1.08$, $x = 0.8y$. **8.** $y = 19.8 - 0.02x$. Estimated cinema attendances in 1971: 170 m. **9.** Fit a trend line visually, passing through the point $\bar{P} = 4.5$, $\bar{Q} = 4.53$. A close fit is possible. **10.** $y = 11.8 - 1.1x$, $r = -0.95$. **11.** $r = 0.72$. **12.** (a) $r_{rank} = 0.85$, $\Sigma d^2 = 24$ could have occurred by chance with only 0.1% probability when $n = 10$. **13.** (ii) $r_{rank} = 0.75$, this is significant at the 1% level. $r_{rank} = +1$ indicates complete agreement. (The value -1 would show complete disagreement.) **14.** $r_{rank} = 0.39$. There is almost a 20% chance of obtaining $\Sigma d^2 = 34$ through sampling errors when $n = 7$, so this result is not significant. The competitor's arrangement could be a random ordering in relation to the adjudicator's. **15.** (i) 0.79, (ii) -0.62, (iii) 0.86. The closest correlation is between goal average and position. **16.** 10. **17.** (i) $r_{rank} = 0$, (ii) B's ranks: 3 1 4 2. **18.** The rate at which one variable changes as another changes. **19.** (i) $r_{rank} = 0.53$, (ii) $r = 0.45$. Paper Y was more difficult since the marks were, in general, much lower than in Paper X. Paper X discriminated between good and bad candidates much more effectively and so produced a wider spread of results. **20.** (a) $r = 0.97$, (b) $Y = 1.98X - 97$. **22.** (a) $r = 0.96$, (b) $Y = 2.41X + 8.9$.

EXERCISES 8

1. 107.1. **2.** 1966 = 100, 1967 = 97, 1968 = 96, 1969 = 104. **3.** The price relatives for each item on 1970 = 100 are 105, 108, 114, 107, 105. Index of service costs for 1971 = 109.7. **4.** (a) 12.6 mn., (b) 1970. **5.** 165. **6.** 8. **7.** 116. **8.** 22,100. Both human and animal populations tend to increase at a compound rate, so that the semi-logarithmic graph of such data is usually a straight line. Predictions made with such a graph are therefore likely to be more reliable than if a natural scale graph were used. 30% per decade.

9.   PERSONAL SAVINGS AS A PERCENTAGE OF
                      PERSONAL DISPOSABLE INCOME

| | (Seasonally corrected) | | |
	1968	1969	1970
1st Qr.	5·9	8·4	7·7
2nd Qr.	8·6	7·6	8·7
3rd Qr.	8·1	7·7	8·4
4th Qr.	7·9	8·3	9·3

Forecast percentage personal disposable income 1st Qr. 1971 = 13%
10. There is evidence of seasonal variation. Approx. value for 1st Qr.
1969 is 16 mn. pairs.

12.

	Real Personal Saving (£th. m.)	Real Personal Income (£th. m.)
1959	0·9	21·6
1960	1·3	23·2
1961	1·8	24·4
1962	1·6	24·6
1963	1·6	25·6
1964	1·7	26·8
1965	1·8	27·8
1966	2·0	28·6
1967	1·8	29·4
1968	1·7	30·0

The proportion of money income saved rose in one decade by
1·4%. Assuming the same rate of increase, the predicted value for
1978 is 6·9%. However, there is evidence of considerable irregularity
in saving compared to income.
13. The regression equation is $y = 15·5 - 0·047u$, where $u =$
Year $- 1964\frac{1}{2}$. Predicted daily circulation for 1972 is about 15·1 mn.
A graph shows that there is very little, if any, linear correlation here, however, and circulation could be as low as 13 mn.
in 1972. **14.** The regression equation is $y = 414 - 6·5u$, where
$u =$ Year $- 1965$. Production for 1975 predicted by this equation
is 349. The exact figure is, however, difficult to forecast since there

is some evidence of a cyclical movement in aircraft production. **15.** Currency circulation rose at an average rate of 4% per annum, whilst wholesale prices rose at only 2% per annum. **18.** 40, 39, 39, 40, 41, 41·4, 42·32. **19.** 415. **20.** $Y = 13\ e^{0·02682(x-1921)}$, (a) 22,200, (b) The correlation coefficient for log Y on X is almost exactly 1, so the fit is a very good one.

EXERCISES 9

5. (i) Measurement of industrial output, (ii) Distribution of employed persons between industries, (iii) Recording basic weekly wage rates in different industries.

18. (i) Males: Crude death rate $= 15·9$ per thousand
Standardised death rate $= 14·5$ per thousand
(ii) Females: Crude death rate $= 16·1$ per thousand
Standardised death rate $= 13·8$ per thousand.

The lower standardised rate for women indicates that fewer of them die each year than men. So women, on the whole, live longer than men on the evidence of this town. Since sex is the main difference, after eliminating age distribution, it is reasonable to infer that this is true of the general population.

20. For Town X: Crude death rate $= 14·8$ per thousand
Standardised death rate $= 20·1$ per thousand
For Town Y: Crude death rate $= 11$ per thousand
Standardised death rate $= 20·9$ per thousand.

EXERCISES 11

1. Gradient of $PQ = -1/3$, Gradient of $QR = 1$, Gradient of $RP = -1$. **2.** $(\frac{1}{3}, 3\frac{2}{3})$. **3.** $\frac{1}{4}$. **4.** 1 and 3. **5.** (b) $(2, 4)$ and $(-2, 12)$. **6.** (a) $E = 0·278W + 1·76$, (b) 87%. **7.** $dy/dx = 2x - 2$, 1, $y_{min} = 3$. **8.** Break even points at $x = 2$ and $x = 4$, $R(x) = 750x - 125x^2 - 1000$. $R(x)$ is maximum when $x = 3$, $\bar{S}(x) = £380$, $\bar{C}(x) = £338·33$. **9.** $R(0) = -15$, $R(3) = 18$, $R(5) = -20$, 2. **10.** $x = 2$ or 5, $y_{min} = 24\frac{15}{16}$, $y_{max} = 58·8$. **11.** (a) $1/5! = 1/120$, (b) $2^5/5! = 4/15$.

12.
$$y = e^{\lambda x} = 1 + \frac{\lambda x}{1!} + \frac{\lambda^2 x^2}{2!} + \frac{\lambda^3 x^3}{3!} + \text{etc.}$$

$$dy/dx = 0 + \lambda + \frac{\lambda^2 x}{1!} + \frac{\lambda^3 x^2}{2!} + \text{etc.}$$

$$= \lambda\left(1 + \frac{\lambda x}{1!} + \frac{\lambda^2 x^2}{2!} + \text{etc.}\right) = \lambda\ e^{\lambda x}.$$

13. (a) 16, (b) 25, (c) 132, (d) $50\frac{2}{3}$. **14.** (a) 1·72, (b) 6·39. **15.** 0·8.
17. 7,400 copies per month. If fixed cost were £437 per month, break
even distribution is 8,600 copies. **18.** (b) $66\frac{2}{3}$ units, £90, (c) 84 units
and 36 units (to nearest whole number). **19.** (a) 2·5218, (b) −0·8301,
(c) 6·2935, (d) 1·7786, (e) 5·6750, (f) 6·8574. **20.** (a) 2 and 3, (b) −14
and 9, (c) −1 and 1·5, (d) 5 (repeated), (e) 0·382 and 2·618, (f) no
solution. **21.** (a) 6, (b) 64. **22.** (a) 6, (b) 2070,

(c) $d^2y/dx^2 = \dfrac{20000}{x^3} + e^x > 0$ provided $x > 0$.

EXERCISES 12

1. $\{a\}$, $\{b\}$, $\{c\}$, $\{a, b\}$, $\{a, c\}$, $\{b, c\}$, U, ø. **2.** $\{2\}$, $\{2, 1\}$, $\{2, 3\}$, $\{2, 4\}$,
$\{2, 1, 3\}$, $\{2, 1, 4\}$, $\{2, 3, 4\}$. **3.** $\{a\}$, $\{b\}$, U, ø. Complements are $\{a\}$
and $\{b\}$, U and ø. **5.** $\{1, 2, 4\}$, $\{1, 2, 8\}$, $\{1, 4, 8\}$, $\{2, 4, 8\}$, (i) $\frac{3}{4}$, (ii) $\frac{1}{2}$.
6. 5 and 9. **7.** $A \cup B$. **8.** (i) A, (ii) Some dogs are not fat. **9.** 8. **10.** (i)
$x = 4$, (ii) 3/8, (iii) 2/9. **11.** 34. The total number of customers can
be found if the number of those in the retail trade who are neither
in the North of England nor late in paying is known. **12.** (i) 8/15,
(ii) 8/9. **13.** 56·5%. **14.** (ii) 0·156, (iii) 35/422, (iv) 0·86.

15. Initial matrix: $\begin{matrix} P & L \\ (1 & 0) \end{matrix}$

Transition probability matrix: $\begin{matrix} & P & L \\ P & \\ L \end{matrix} \begin{pmatrix} 9/10 & 1/10 \\ 5/10 & 5/10 \end{pmatrix}$

Probability of profit in Year 4 = 0·8376.

16. $k = 1, 0·6$. **17.** $\bar{x} = 3$, Var. $(x) = 1/3$. **18.** $k = \frac{3}{4}, \bar{x} = 1, Q_2 = 1$.
19. (b) 38/51. **20.** (a) 8/15, (b) $\frac{1}{4}$, (c) 13/25.

EXERCISES 13

1. $t = 2$ with 9 degrees of freedom. Sample mean does not differ significantly from 2 lb. True mean lies in the interval $2·1 \pm 2·26 \times 0·05$
or between 1·99 lb. and 2·21 lb. with 95% probability. There is some
dispersion, but a significant proportion of bags will not be underweight. **2.** $t = 2·67$ with 16 degrees of freedom. Significant at the 5%
but not at the 1% level. **3.** $\bar{x} = 1·12$ cm. Using 6 d.f., the mean lies
in the interval $1·12 \pm 2·45 \times 0·0082$ with 95% confidence, i.e.,
between 1·10 cm. and 1·14 cm. Number of additional measurements
needed = 23, i.e. $n = 30$. **4.** $X = 16/\sqrt{152} = 1·30$. Not significant.
If the standard error of the difference between the means is 8 lb.

then $X = 2$ which is significant at the 5% level. **5.** $X = 3.26$. Highly significant. **6.** Proportion of errors in 1970 $= 0.09$. Estimated proportion in 1971 $= 0.05$. Standard error of proportion $= \sqrt{(0.09 \times 0.91/365)}$. $X = 2.67$. Significant. **7.** $X = 2.54$. Almost significant at the 1% level of a two-tailed test. It is highly probable that A is superior to B. **8.** $X = 6$. Highly significant provided that each sample is random and the sampling frames cover all employees in each company. **9.** $X = 2.58$. Significant at both the 5% and 1% level. **10.** $t = 1.98$ with 19 d.f. Not significant at the 5% level. Using a Normal distribution, $X = 2.03$ and this would be significant at the 5% level. **11.** (a) $\bar{x} = 24.0$ cm., $s_x = 0.15$ cm., $\bar{y} = 24.1$ cm., $s_y = 0.12$ cm., (b) $\hat{\sigma} = 0.15$ cm., $t = 1.03$ with 8 d.f. Not significant. **12.** $X = 1.83$. Not significant. **13.** $t = 1.01$ with 4 d.f. Not significant. This is a further indication that Papers X and Y were significantly different in standard. **14.** (a) $t = 3.58$ with 2 d.f., $r = 0.93$ not significantly different from zero. (b) $t = 17.2$ with 3 d.f. Highly significant. $y \pm 3.18 \times 1.32 = y \pm 4.2$. (c) $t = 17.2$ (approximately). Highly significant. $y \pm 135$. **15.** $X = 0.145/\{1/\sqrt{(10 - 3)}\} = 0.38$. Not significant. Population correlation coefficient could be 0.5. **16.** Exports to Britain have dropped by 4.7% from 1965 to 1969. $t = 2.71$ with 13 d.f. Significant at the 5% level. Imports from Britain have dropped by 1.8% from 1965 to 1969. $t = 2.22$ with 13 d.f. Just significant at the 5% level. Commonwealth exports and imports to and from Britain have significantly declined, particularly exports sold to this country. **17.** Size of Type I error $= 0.05$. Size of Type II error $= 0.09$. **18.** Critical region: reject H_0 if $x < -1.16$. Size of Type II error $= 0.86$. **19.** (a) For a given size of Type I error, the critical region should be the tail of the distribution which maximises the power (i.e. minimises the probability of Type II error). For example, if $H_0 : \bar{x} = \mu_1$ and $H_1 : \bar{x} = \mu_2$ and $\mu_2 < \mu_1$, choose the left tail to test H_0. (b) Testing decline in absenteeism rates when a new bonus scheme is introduced. Testing increase in efficiency rating when a new incentive scheme is put in operation. Here H_0 is the appropriate rate before the change and H_1 is the desired rate necessary to make either scheme worthwhile.

20.

No. of successes, x	0	1	2	3	4	5	Total
Frequency	243	405	270	90	15	1	1024

$$P(x > 2) = 53/512.$$

21. (i) (b) $\sqrt{(npq)} = 14.5$, (ii) 0.42. **22.** (a) $821/3125$, (b) 0.006, (c) 0.63. **23.** $P(0) = 0.37$, $P(1) = 0.37$, $P(2) = 0.18$, $P(3) = 0.06$, $P(4) = 0.015$, $P(x > 0) = 1 - P(0) = 0.63$, 60 ± 15.2. **24.** (a) Poisson distribution, (b) $P(k) = \dfrac{m^k}{k!} e^{-m}$ where m is both mean and variance

of k, (c) Normal distribution, (d) $X = (16 - 9)/\sqrt{(16 + 9)} = 1\cdot4$.
Not significant. **25.** $0\cdot35$. **26.** $\hat{\sigma} = 3\cdot35$; using the range $\hat{\sigma} = 3\cdot25$
(assuming the population is normally distributed). **27.** $t = 0\cdot94$
with 18 d.f. Not significant. It is assumed that the samples are
unpaired, that the two variances are the same, and that the times are
normally distributed. **28.** $0\cdot4422$. The number absent per day has a
Poisson distribution—each man in the shift has an equal chance of
being absent.

EXERCISES 14

1. (a) $0\cdot05$, (b) $0\cdot01$, (c) not significant, (d) $0\cdot05$.
2. $X = (50 - 32)/\sqrt{(100 \times \frac{1}{2} \times \frac{1}{2})} = 3\cdot6$. $\chi^2 = 12\cdot96$ with 1 d.f.
The probability is only $0\cdot016\%$ of obtaining this number of heads
or less by chance. The hypothesis that the coin is fair is rejected.
4.

	Smokers	Non-smokers	Total
Died	40	10	50
Living	260	190	450
Total	300	200	500

$\chi^2 = 9\cdot23$ with 1 d.f. Highly significant.
5. $\chi^2 = 2\cdot36$ with 1 d.f. Not significant. **6.** $\chi^2 = 3\cdot89$ with $(3-1)(2-1)$
$= 2$ d.f. Not significant. **7.** $\chi^2 = 9\cdot57$ with $(3 - 1)(3 - 1) = 4$ d.f.
Significant at the 5% level. **8.** $\chi^2 = 4\cdot79$ with 2 d.f. Not significant.
9. The first two and last two cells should be combined. $\chi^2 = 32\cdot26$
with 4 d.f. Highly significant. **10.** $\chi^2 = 4\cdot08$ with 4 d.f. Not significant. The distribution of the number of strikes per week could
follow a Poisson distribution. **11.** Mean $= 3$, S.D. $= 1\cdot64$. The
distribution could be Poisson with $m = 3$.

Failures/ week	0	1	2	3	4	5	6	7	8 (or more)
0	4	16	21	23	17	11	6	2	0
							\multicolumn 8		
E	5·0	14·9	22·4	22·4	16·8	10·1	5·0	2·2	1·2
							8·4		

$\chi^2 = 0\cdot49$ with 6 d.f. The observed frequencies agree well with
the Poisson frequencies.

12. Binomial with $n = 4$, $np = 0.6837$, $p = 0.171$.

Variable	0	1	2	3	4
0	227	42	26	15	22
				37	
E	156.8	129.4	40.0	5.5	0.3
				5.8	

$\chi^2 = 263.2$ with 4 d.f. The chance of each tooth being lost is not the same.

13. $P(0) + P(1) = (\frac{1}{2})^{10} + 10(\frac{1}{2})^{10} = 0.01$. The mean is unlikely to be as high as 10.

14. $X = \dfrac{12.5 - 4}{\frac{1}{2}\sqrt{25}} = 3.4$. Significant at the 1% level. The new agreement is very likely to lead to a wage increase of more than 20%.

15.

	Sample A	Sample B
Above median	6	11
Below median	9	6

$\chi^2 = 2.02$ with 1 d.f. Not significant.

16. Rank sum Sample A $(R_1) = 341.5$, $n_1 = 16$, $n_2 = 20$, $U = 114.5$;
$X = \dfrac{160 - 114.5}{31.4} = 1.45$. Not significant.

17.

x	0	1	2	3	4	5	6	7	8
bin. freq.	5.76	19.77	29.65	25.41	13.61	4.67	1.00	0.12	0
normal freq.	7.21	17.30	28.68	27.04	14.51	4.39	0.79	0.08	0

$\chi^2 = 0.92$ with 6 d.f. A very good fit.

EXERCISES 15

1. 136 ± 14.8. **4.** 4%, 1.25%. **6.** Mean $= 102.5$, S.D. $= 2$. 10% of packets have fewer than 100 sheets, so the manufacturer's specification is not being met. **7.** There is a consumer's risk of 13.5% of accepting a lot containing 20% defectives. **8.** (a) S.D. $= 3.33$; (b) $1/40$ limits: 49.54 ± 3.27, $1/1000$ limits: 49.54 ± 5.15; (c) The probability is 0.6% that an individual lies outside the required limits. But the sample mean 58.1 suggests further investigation.

EXERCISES 16

1. Player's expected gain = £0·75. The game is not fair. In order to make it fair, the player should lose £2 if 1 tail occurs. **2.** A's expected gain = £1·50. **3.** £20. **4.** $X = (60 - 50)/\sqrt{(100 \times \frac{1}{2} \times \frac{1}{2})} = 2$. Player's expected loss = $25\frac{1}{2}$p. **5.** £2. **6.** Choose second location yielding an expected profit of £2500. **7.** (a) The Pay-off and expected profits matrices (in £'s) are:

			Made		
Sold	48	49	50	51	52
48	2·40	2·30	2·20	2·10	2·00
49	2·40	2·45	2·35	2·25	2·15
50	2·40	2·45	2·50	2·40	2·30
51	2·40	2·45	2·50	2·55	2·45
52	2·40	2·45	2·50	2·55	2·60

Probability	Sold	48	49	Made 50	51	52	
0·1	48	·24	·23	·22	·21	·20	
0·3	49	·72	·735	·705	·675	·645	
0·4	50	·96	·98	1·00	·96	·92	
0·1	51	·24	·245	·25	·255	·245	
0·1	52	·24	·245	·25	·255	·26	
Expected profit		2·40	2·435	2·425	2·355	2·27	2·49

Expected profit is greatest when 49 loaves are made. (b) £2·49. **8.** (a) Expected profit from purchasing 100, 200, 300, 400 bunches: £13·75, £22·50, £21·25, £13·75, (b) £10, (c) £9·75. **9.** (a) Plan B at a cost of £0·25 per unit, (b) No inspection might be recommended if the proportion of defectives actually found was small, provided that the goodwill of customers would not be impaired if a very few items are faulty and have to be returned to the maker. **10.** (b) £4000. **11.** If drilling is undertaken without an initial study, expected profit = 0·064 × £20 mn. − £2 mn. = −£720,000. If an initial study is made and drilling is undertaken only if positive results are shown, expected profit = 0·05 × 0·9 × £20 mn. − 0·05 × £2 mn. − £100,000 = £700,000. This gives a good rate of return. **12.** £6150, £6150. **13.** (b) 24 minutes. **15.** Graph t (in minutes) against ρ for the equation $t = \rho/(1 - \rho)(0 \leqslant \rho < 1)$. **16.** 0·22.

17. Expected cost for $A = 1 \times £2 + £1$
$= £3$ per hour.
Expected cost for $B = 2 \times £2 + £0·75$
$= £4·75$ per hour.

A is more economical.

18. (a) 1·5, (b) 3, giving a least expected cost of £7000, (c) On the assumption that the probabilities of failure are all equal, it is indifferent whether 3 or 4 spares are held. Prudence suggests holding 4 spares. **19.** (b) The net saving resulting from sending the operator is £60. **20.** Cost of: (a) £15,000, (b) £12,050, (c) £14,660, (d) £12,941. Plan (b) is best.

21. (a) £4·75, (b) 9000 units, £14,124·50. **22.** (a) 1/6, (b) 20 min., (c) 2 hours 20 min., (d) 1·17. If there are only two machines queue length cannot exceed 1. The length of a simple queue could be infinite. **23.** (a) 0·36, (b) (10/19 6/19 3/19), (c) 3·79. **24.** (a) 1, (b) £5 per hour, (c) 1 hour 4 min. (d) £5·60 per hour. **25.** $\mu = 30$, 4 min. **26.** Replace all motors after 20 weeks at a cost of £17·63 each per week.

EXERCISES 17

1. (a) 1–4, 4–5, 5–7, (b) 12 hours, (c) A total float time of 1 hour is available on activities 1–2 and 2–5, 4–6 and 6–7, and also on activities 1–3, 3–6 and 6–7. **3.** Critical path activities: 0–1, 1–3, 3–4, 4–7, 7–8, 8–9. Critical path time = 41 days. Sub-critical activities: 0–2, 2–4, 3–6, 6–8, 3–5, 5–8. **4.** For the sub-critical activities, float times are as follows: Prepare architect's drawings: 5 days; Obtain planning permission: 11 days; Complete purchase of land: 8 days; Arrange services: 8 days; Prepare foundations: 1 day; Lay drains: 1 day; Obtain tiles: 3 days (free float); Construct roofing: 6 days; Fit wiring: 2 days; Lay paths: 15 days; Landscaping: 15 days; Plastering: 1 day; Fit doors: 1 day. Unless otherwise indicated, the float times shown are interfering floats. The float times show that little spare time exists either for laying drains or fitting wiring, so that if the duration of these activities is prolonged, the project time will almost certainly be increased. There is more spare time in the construction of roofing, however, so that delay here will be less serious. **5.** (a) 17 days, £2300 (including £400 penalty for lateness), (b) £2040, (c) The duration of the project can be reduced from 15 days to 11 days by crashing activity 6–7 by 4 days at a cost of $4 \times £90 = £360$ but with a gain of £400 in bonus for early completion. The optimum plan would then cost £2000. (d) Duration of the project can be reduced to 15 days by crashing activity 4–6 by 2 days, 5–6 by 1 day and 6–7 by 4 days at a cost of £2470. **6.** (b) 33 days, (c) Float time for activity: 0–1 (1 day), 0–2 (0 days), 1–3 (5 days), 1–4 (1 day), 2–4 (0 days), 3–5 (5 days), 4–5 (0 days), 5–6 (0 days), (d) £1130, (e) 28 days, £1230. **7.** 28, £21·21. **8.** 7300 (approximately), £548. **9.** (a) 26,000, (b) The new policy produces a saving of £9600 — (9760 − 1800) = £1640. **10.** 800 tons. **11.** 9. **12.** When buffer stock is zero, average excess demand $= 1 \times (0.5 - 0.37) + 2 \times (0.37 - 0.25) + 3 \times (0.25 - 0.16) + 4 \times (0.16 - 0.09) + 5 \times (0.09 - 0.05) + 6 \times (0.05 - 0.02) + 7 \times (0.02 - 0.01) + 8 \times (0.01 - 0.00) = 0.5 + 0.37 + 0.25 + 0.16 + 0.09 + 0.05 + 0.02 + 0.01 = 1.45$. The average excess demand with other sizes of buffer stock are obtained in a similar way. Buffer stock should be 5 or 6 at a minimum cost of £6·60. **13.** Standard Normal variable = 79 and 56 for the old and new policies respectively. There is virtually no chance of running out of stock in either case. **14.** Replace after 5 years when average cost is minimum at £1350. **15.** A—B—D—E—H—J—K—L—N. Least time = 70 days. If H becomes shorter, least time would be shortened and F could become critical. There are 7 paths through the network (including the critical path). Of these A—B—D—E—F—K—L—N (time 68 days) is certainly sub-critical and possibly also A—B—D—E—M—N (time 63 days). **16.** Obtain 57 units of Product 1 and 40 units of Product 3 from Supplier 4. Obtain 20 units of Product 2 and 31 units of Product 4 from Supplier 3. **17.** (a) 620, (b) 400. **18.** (b) 20,000, (c) £503,750, £4·03, (d) 3750. **19.** 1400 units. The production rate is irrelevant.

20. $\sqrt{\left(\dfrac{IC(P - Y)YCs}{50P}\right)}$ or $\sqrt{\left(\dfrac{2H(P - Y)YCs}{P}\right)}$.

EXERCISES 18

1. (a) (1, 1), (2, 1), (b) (1, 4), (3, 1), (c) (4, 2). **2.** (a) and (c). **3.** 3.
4. $x \leqslant 20$, $y \leqslant 30$, $x + y \leqslant 36$. Establishment runs at a loss if
$4x + 3y < 72$. **5.** (b) $x = 12$, $y = 6$. **6.** $2x + 3y \geqslant 15$, $x + 5y \geqslant 10$,
(a) $Z = x + y$ is minimum when $x = 3$, $y = 4$, (b) $Z = x + 2y$ is
minimum when $x = 7$, $y = 1$. **7.** $X = 66\frac{2}{3}$, $Y = 33\frac{1}{3}$, $Z_{\min} = £2667$.
8. $x_1 = 0$, $x_2 = 0$, $x_3 = 1000$, $Z_{\max} = 10,000$. The second constraint can be expressed as $x_1 + x_2 + x_3 \leqslant 3000$, and therefore
includes the first constraint and so is redundant. Hence two variables
in the objective function at most can be basic variables in the final
solution. The problem could be solved graphically as a two-variable
one, setting each variable in turn equal to zero. **10.** $x_1 = 3$, $x_2 = 0$,
$x_3 = 4$, $Z_{\max} = 15$. **11.** (a) $Z = 20x_1 + 20x_2 + 31x_3 + 11x_4 + 12x_5$,
$x_i \geqslant 0$ for all i. Z is to be minimised. (b) Foods 1 and 3 can be
eliminated whatever the quantity of calories and vitamins required.
12. Minimum cost = £7250. **13.** Minimum ton–mileage = 3,320,000
ton–miles, Cost of plan = £166,000. **14.** Minimum cost = 459.
15. (a) Maximum profit = £3850. **16.** (a) By eliminating the route
(B, I) and sending 10 units by (A, I) the reduction in cost is £20. In
order to maintain the total availabilities and requirements constant,
10 units could be transferred from (A, III) to (B, III) with an increased cost of £10. So a net saving of £10 would be effected.
(b) £860. The solution is not unique. (c) Cost of route (A, III) must
be reduced by £1. (d) (i) £910, (ii) £960, (iii) £1010. **17.** (c) The game
has a saddle-point. A should play strategy I and B strategy II as
pure strategies. **18.** The game has a saddle-point. Both companies
should advertise on TV, the gain to one being £100,000 and to the
other −£100,000. **19.** A should play strategies II and III for 3/7 and
4/7 of the time respectively. B should play strategies II and III for
1/7 and 6/7 of the time respectively. Value of the game to A = $2\frac{4}{7}$.
20. (a) $x_1 = 500$, $x_4 = 400$, $x_2 = x_3 = 0$, $Z = 3600$; (b) 2·8;
(c) $x_3 = 250$, $x_4 = 400$, $x_1 = x_2 = 0$, $Z = 4100$. **21.** (a) $a = 0$,
$b = 1500$, $c = 850$, $d = 300$, $Z = £61,000$, Profit = £25,500;
(b) £58; (c) £2.

EXERCISES 19

1. £16,200. **2.** £10,500. **3.** £9924, £2137·50. **4.** 20% p.a. **5.** (a) £8·79,
(b) £4·47. **6.** £26,680. **7.** £8332. **8.** £500. **9.** (a) £1315, (b) Literally
100%; but at $75\frac{1}{2}$% p.a. the scrap value will be 1p after 10 years.
10. $8\frac{1}{2}$% p.a. **11.** £11,760. **12.** £2192. **13.** £4475. **14.** £1972.
15. £82,770. **16.** £1968, £978. **17.** (a) 29%, (b) £6472, (c) 13%.

18. Yield $= 16\%$, NPV $=$ £1033. The investment would be worth while provided that there is no prospect of investing the £200,000 in existing projects at the higher rate of return of 17%. **19.** (i) £905, (ii) £1477 (given a positive cash flow from A), (ii) Invest in A as NPV is positive. Invest in B if A shows a positive return. (iv) £1570. **20.** Invest only in Project 2. Total outlay $=$ £160,000, NPV $=$ £39,800. **21.** (a) For existing machines, NPV $=$ £54,193. For the new machines, NPV $=$ £38,120. The purchase of the new machines would not be profitable, (b) The net cash flow for each year consists of (1) receipts *plus* depreciation *less* materials *less* overheads, and (2) *less* labour costs. The values of these are recalculated for Years 1, 2, 3 and 4 using an inflation rate of 15% for (1) and 20% for (2). The net cash flow is then calculated for each year and deflated at the retail price index rate of 15%. The deflated cash flows are then discounted at 20% to give NPV. Note that the resale value of the old machines (£45,000) occurs as a positive cash flow in the present (Year 0), among the cash flows for the new machines. **22.** (a) 29%, (b) £21,529.

EXERCISES 20

1. (a) $\begin{pmatrix} 3 & 6 \\ 4 & 10 \end{pmatrix}$; (b) $\begin{pmatrix} 2 & 12 \\ 4 & 20 \end{pmatrix}$, $\begin{pmatrix} 16 & 21 & 22 \\ 28 & 36 & 36 \end{pmatrix}$, $\begin{pmatrix} 5 & 6 & 5 \\ 4 & 6 & 8 \end{pmatrix}$.

2. Since $\mathbf{A} + \mathbf{B}$ exists, $\mathbf{A}$ and $\mathbf{B}$ are $m \times n$ matrices. Since $\mathbf{AB}$ exists $m = n$. $\mathbf{A}$ and $\mathbf{B}$ are both square matrices so $\mathbf{BA}$ also exists.

3. (a) 3×3, (b) 3×4, (c) 2×4.

4. For example,

$$\mathbf{A} = \begin{pmatrix} 1 & 0 \\ 2 & 0 \end{pmatrix}, \qquad \mathbf{B} = \begin{pmatrix} 3 & 3 \\ 0 & 0 \end{pmatrix}, \qquad \mathbf{C} = \begin{pmatrix} 3 & 3 \\ 2 & 2 \end{pmatrix}.$$

If $\mathbf{B} \neq \mathbf{C}$, $\mathbf{A}$ must be singular.

5. (a) $\frac{1}{4}\begin{pmatrix} 23 & -6 \\ -7 & 2 \end{pmatrix}$, (b) $\frac{1}{2}\begin{pmatrix} 2 & -2 \\ -1 & 2 \end{pmatrix}$, (c) is singular,

(d) $\frac{1}{2}\begin{pmatrix} 1 & \frac{3}{4} \\ -2 & \frac{1}{2} \end{pmatrix}$.

6. (a) $x = 2$, $y = 1$; (b) $x = y = 2$; (c) $x = -\frac{1}{2}$, $y = \frac{1}{2}$; (d) $x = y = 0$.

7. $a = 0{\cdot}8$.

8. $\frac{1}{4}\begin{pmatrix} -1 & -1 & 3 \\ 4 & 0 & -4 \\ -3 & 1 & 5 \end{pmatrix}$; $x = 0$, $y = 3$, $z = 6$.

9. (a) (39 20 27), (205 145 140); (c) $\begin{pmatrix} -2 & -2 & 2 \\ 3 & 3 & 0 \\ 2 & -1 & 1 \end{pmatrix}$.

10. $\begin{pmatrix} n & \Sigma x \\ \Sigma x & \Sigma x^2 \end{pmatrix}\begin{pmatrix} a \\ b \end{pmatrix} = \begin{pmatrix} \Sigma y \\ \Sigma xy \end{pmatrix}$.

11. $x = 40$, $y = 55$. **12.** $y = 200$, $z = 100$. **13.** X(£394,430), Y(£377,310), Z(£328,100).

14.

$$\mathbf{P} = \begin{array}{c|cccc} i \backslash j \text{ (sold)} & 75 & 100 & 125 & 150 \\ \hline 75 & 1 & 0 & 0 & 0 \\ 100 & 0{\cdot}1 & 0{\cdot}9 & 0 & 0 \\ 125 & 0{\cdot}1 & 0{\cdot}3 & 0{\cdot}6 & 0 \\ 150 & 0{\cdot}1 & 0{\cdot}3 & 0{\cdot}5 & 0{\cdot}1 \end{array},$$

$$\mathbf{Q} = \begin{array}{c|cccc} j \backslash i \text{ (produced)} & 75 & 100 & 125 & 150 \\ \hline 75 & 3750 & 2250 & 750 & -750 \\ 100 & — & 5000 & 3500 & 2000 \\ 125 & — & — & 6250 & 4750 \\ 150 & — & — & — & 7500 \end{array}.$$

The elements on the leading diagonal of the product **PQ** are the expected profits from each policy. The optimum policy is to produce 125 giving an expected profit of £4875. If the exact number of machines demanded is produced each year, expected profit = £5750.

15. (a) 0·019, (b) 0·01171. If N is large, probability that the Nth bottle is defective is 1/91.

INDEX